METHODS
IN ANALYSIS

A series of advanced mathematics
texts under the editorship of
CARL B. ALLENDOERFER

METHODS
IN ANALYSIS

Jack Indritz *Department of Mathematics*
Institute of Technology, University of Minnesota

The Macmillan Company, New York
Collier-Macmillan Limited, London

First Printing

Designed by Andrew Roberts

Library of Congress catalog card number: 63-8428

The Macmillan Company, New York
Collier-Macmillan Canada Ltd, Toronto

Printed in the United States of America

Preface

Methods in Analysis is a textbook for a year course whose prerequisite is Advanced Calculus, the subject normally taken in the junior year. The purpose of this text is to bridge the gap between Advanced Calculus and graduate analysis courses, supplying the motivation needed for their study and increasing the mathematical maturity of the student. At the same time, a treatment is provided of the mathematics needed by science students in their theoretical studies at the corresponding level in the physical sciences. This is especially desirable since science students do not have the necessary time to acquire the relevant background needed in the detailed studies at the graduate level of the topics of interest to them.

The level of the text is definitely above that of Advanced Calculus, where formal manipulations are stressed. However, the important ideas introduced in earlier courses are reviewed and the student's knowledge is consolidated. The text is essentially self-contained. In a unified treatment, the reader is introduced to a number of disciplines treated in graduate courses, none of which this book attempts to replace. Each of the topics is dealt with rigorously, but not at the most general level, the purpose being to acquaint the student with fundamental ideas. For the same reason, the technical vocabulary is kept to a minimum. For clearer insight, a particular topic is often analyzed by different methods. Applications are not neglected. An effort is made to alternate the concrete and the abstract.

The subject matter is centered about eigenvalue theory. The content is divided into three parts, the pattern of thought developed in the first being repeated in the later parts.

The first third of the book (Chapters 1 and 2) is devoted to eigenvalues of a linear transformation on a finite-dimensional vector space with emphasis on the extremal properties. For brevity, Section 2.3 on determinants may be passed over rapidly, and Section 2.10 may be omitted.

The second part (Chapters 3, 4, and 5), dealing with the Hilbert-Schmidt theory and orthonormal sequences, may be handled in various ways, depending on the background of the students. For an advanced class, only the highlights of Chapter 3 need be discussed. For the average class, it would be better to omit Sections 5.4, 5.5, and parts of 5.7. Consideration of Riemann integrable functions as the elements of a vector space is probably the student's first breakaway from the class of continuous functions.

The third part (Chapters 6 and 7) considers a Sturm-Liouville problem with separated boundary conditions and concludes with an introduction to the Fourier transform.

The instructor may desire to restrict the year's work to the first six chapters.

To encourage the student to read mathematics independently, Sections 2.10, 5.4, 5.5, 5.7, 6.1 may be assigned as extra reading.

The exercises are an integral part of the text and are chosen to fit the content and level of the course.

At this stage of mathematical maturity, the theorem-proof method is pedagogically effective. A star is used to indicate the end of a proof.

The development of some topics in the text has been influenced by unpublished notes of Professor I. I. Hirschman who very generously made them available to me when I taught a preliminary version of this course at Washington University, St. Louis. I would like to express my appreciation for his interest in this project.

I am grateful to Professor Fulton Koehler of the University of Minnesota who read the manuscript carefully and suggested several improvements in form and content.

JACK INDRITZ

Contents

METHODS
IN ANALYSIS

CHAPTER
1

Euclidean Vector Spaces and Linear Transformations

1.1

VECTOR

SPACES

Certain quantities used frequently in describing the physical world, such as velocities and accelerations, may be represented as directed line segments, also called geometrical vectors. We assume the reader is familiar with their use. The following comments are merely intended to recall some elementary properties of geometrical vectors.

For simplicity, we shall consider only vectors which emanate from a fixed point called the origin. It is useful to adjoin to the class of directed line segments a so-called zero vector, represented by the origin. When $c \neq 0$ is any real number, and α is any vector, the vector $c\alpha$ is defined as that vector whose length is $|c|$ times the length of α and which extends in the same direction as α if $c > 0$ and in the opposite direction if $c < 0$. 0α is defined to be the zero vector. By the sum $\alpha + \beta$ of two vectors we mean that vector from the origin to the vertex opposite the origin of the parallelogram having α and β as adjacent sides.

It is easily verified that these operations have the following properties:

1. $\alpha + \beta = \beta + \alpha$.

2. $\alpha + (\beta + \mu) = (\alpha + \beta) + \mu$.

If c, d are real numbers:

3. $c(\alpha + \beta) = c\alpha + c\beta$ and $(c + d)\alpha = c\alpha + d\alpha$.

4. $c(d\alpha) = (cd)\alpha$ and $1\alpha = \alpha$.

5. There is a zero vector (denoted by θ) such that for every α, $0\alpha = \theta$.

It has been discovered that many different sets of objects may have operations defined on their elements so as to satisfy the above five properties. For this reason it is useful to consider the subject from an abstract point of view.

Let us agree that by the set of **scalars** $\mathscr{S}$ we will mean either the set of real numbers or the set of complex numbers. (Scalars will be denoted by small letters such as a, b, c, ...) A **vector space** $\mathscr{V}$ is then defined to be a set of elements called **vectors** (denoted by Greek letters such as α, β, σ, μ) such that

3

any two vectors α and β in $\mathscr{V}$ determine a unique vector $\alpha + \beta$ in $\mathscr{V}$ and such that any vector α in $\mathscr{V}$ and any scalar c in $\mathscr{S}$ determine a unique vector $c\alpha$ in $\mathscr{V}$, and these operations satisfy the axioms 1–5 above.

In case the set $\mathscr{S}$ of scalars consists of the real numbers, $\mathscr{V}$ is called a **real vector space**. In case $\mathscr{S}$ consists of the complex numbers $\mathscr{V}$ is called a **complex vector space**.

One may manipulate vectors, as far as addition is concerned, very much as one manipulates real numbers. The following theorem gives a representative list of common properties. In the sequel we shall use the properties listed below without further comment.

THEOREM 1.1A

1. For every α in $\mathscr{V}$, $\alpha + \theta = \theta + \alpha = \alpha$.
2. For every scalar c, $c\theta = \theta$.
3. If $-\alpha$ is defined as $(-1)\alpha$, then $\alpha + (-\alpha) = -\alpha + \alpha = \theta$.
4. If $\alpha + \beta = \alpha + \mu$, then $\beta = \mu$.
5. If $a\alpha = b\alpha$ and $\alpha \neq \theta$, then $a = b$.
6. If $\alpha - \beta$ is defined as $\alpha + (-\beta)$, then the unique solution of the equation $\mu + \beta = \alpha$ is $\mu = \alpha - \beta$.

Proof The reader must remember that the fact that a property is intuitively obvious (which means that it clearly holds for two- or three-dimensional geometrical vectors) does not prove that it holds for a general vector space $\mathscr{V}$. A *proof* is a step by step deduction of the desired result using the vector space axioms and also known properties of scalars. We begin with property **1**; we have

$$\begin{aligned} \alpha &= 1\alpha && \text{by axiom 4,} \\ &= (1 + 0)\alpha && \text{because } 1 + 0 = 1, \\ &= 1\alpha + 0\alpha && \text{by axiom 3,} \\ &= \alpha + \theta && \text{by axioms 4 and 5,} \\ &= \theta + \alpha && \text{by axiom 1.} \end{aligned}$$

Property **2** is Exercise 1.1–1. We will establish property **3**; we have

$$\begin{aligned} \alpha + (-\alpha) &= \alpha + (-1)\alpha && \text{by definition of } -\alpha, \\ &= 1\alpha + (-1)\alpha && \text{by axiom 4,} \\ &= (1 + (-1))\alpha && \text{by axiom 3,} \\ &= 0\alpha && \text{because } 1 + (-1) = 0, \\ &= \theta && \text{by axiom 5.} \end{aligned}$$

Finally

$$\begin{aligned} -\alpha + \alpha &= \alpha + (-\alpha) && \text{by axiom 1,} \\ &= \theta && \text{by the above.} \end{aligned}$$

To establish property **4** we proceed as follows: We have

$$\alpha + \beta = \alpha + \mu \qquad \text{by assumption,}$$
$$-\alpha + (\alpha + \beta) = -\alpha + (\alpha + \mu) \qquad \text{adding } -\alpha \text{ to both sides,}$$
$$(-\alpha + \alpha) + \beta = (-\alpha + \alpha) + \mu \qquad \text{by axiom 2,}$$
$$\theta + \beta = \theta + \mu \qquad \text{by property 3,}$$
$$\beta = \mu \qquad \text{by property 1.}$$

Properties **5** and **6** are left to the reader as Exercises 1.1–2 and 1.1–3. ★

Two- and three-dimensional geometrical vectors possess another operation. The scalar product or inner product or dot product (α, β) of two geometrical vectors (in either two or three dimensions) is the product of their lengths and the cosine of the angle between them. Note that the inner product of two geometrical vectors is a real number and not a vector. It is a familiar fact that this inner product has the properties:

1$_r$. $\qquad (\alpha, \beta) = (\beta, \alpha) \qquad$ (symmetry);

2. $\quad (\alpha + \beta, \mu) = (\alpha, \mu) + (\beta, \mu) \qquad$ (linearity),

$\qquad\qquad (c\alpha, \beta) = c(\alpha, \beta) \qquad$ (homogeneity);

3. $\qquad (\alpha, \alpha) > 0 \qquad$ unless $\alpha = \theta$ (positivity).

Definition

A **real Euclidean vector space** is a real vector space with a **real inner product** (α, β) such that the properties **1$_r$**, **2**, and **3** above hold as axioms.

In general we shall deal with real vector spaces. However, it sometimes becomes necessary to use complex vector spaces. In this case the first inner product axiom will be slightly revised:

$$\textbf{1}_c. \ (\alpha, \beta) = \overline{(\beta, \alpha)} \text{ where } \overline{a + ib} = a - ib.$$

The desirability of such a revision will become apparent after further study.

Definition

A **complex Euclidean vector space** is a complex vector space with a complex valued product (α, β) such that the properties **1$_c$**, **2**, **3** above hold.

In both real and complex vector spaces we define the **norm** of α, written $\|\alpha\|$, to be $(\alpha, \alpha)^{1/2}$. If α is a geometrical vector, $\|\alpha\|$ is its length.

THEOREM 1.1B   In any Euclidean vector space $\mathscr{E}$ the norm has the following properties:

1. $\|c\alpha\| = |c| \, \|\alpha\|$;
2. $\|\alpha\| > 0$ unless $\alpha = \theta$;
3. $|(\alpha, \beta)| \leq \|\alpha\| \, \|\beta\|$ (Schwarz's inequality);
4. $\|\alpha + \beta\| \leq \|\alpha\| + \|\beta\|$ (Triangle inequality).

We shall assume that $\mathscr{E}$ is a real Euclidean vector space and assign the proof for the complex case as an exercise. Since $(c\alpha, c\alpha) = |c|^2(\alpha, \alpha)$, we have property **1**. Property **2** is a corollary of the positivity property of the inner product. To prove **3**, let x be an arbitrary real number. Then

$$0 \leq (x\alpha + \beta, \, x\alpha + \beta) = x^2(\alpha, \alpha) + 2x(\alpha, \beta) + (\beta, \beta).$$

If the quadratic function $ax^2 + bx + c$ is always nonnegative, we must have $b^2 - 4ac \leq 0$ as otherwise the equation $ax^2 + bx + c = 0$ would have two unequal real roots and the parabola $y = ax^2 + bx + c$ would cross the x axis. It follows that

$$4(\alpha, \beta)^2 - 4(\alpha, \alpha)(\beta, \beta) \leq 0$$

proving statement **3**. Finally, note that

$$\|\alpha + \beta\|^2 = (\alpha + \beta, \, \alpha + \beta) = \|\alpha\|^2 + 2(\alpha, \beta) + \|\beta\|^2$$
$$\leq \|\alpha\|^2 + 2\|\alpha\| \, \|\beta\| + \|\beta\|^2 = (\|\alpha\| + \|\beta\|)^2. \quad \star$$

Important examples of Euclidean vector spaces will now be considered.

EXAMPLE 1   Let $\mathscr{E}_n$ be the set of n-tuples of real numbers $(a_1, \ldots, a_n)$. If $\alpha = (a_1, \ldots, a_n)$, $\beta = (b_1, \ldots, b_n)$, define

$$\alpha = \beta \quad \text{if and only if} \quad a_i = b_i, \quad i = 1 \ldots n,$$
$$\alpha + \beta = (a_1 + b_1, a_2 + b_2, \ldots, a_n + b_n),$$
$$c\alpha = (ca_1, \ldots, ca_n),$$
$$(\alpha, \beta) = \sum_{i=1}^{n} a_i b_i.$$

Then $\mathscr{E}_n$ is a real Euclidean vector space. In this space the Schwarz inequality states

$$\left| \sum_{i=1}^{n} a_i b_i \right|^2 \leq \sum_{i=1}^{n} a_i^2 \sum_{i=1}^{n} b_i^2$$

and the triangle inequality states

$$\left(\sum_{i=1}^{n}\left\{a_i + b_i\right\}^2\right)^{1/2} \le \left(\sum_{i=1}^{n} a_i^2\right)^{1/2} + \left(\sum_{i=1}^{n} b_i^2\right)^{1/2}.$$

EXAMPLE 2 Let $\mathscr{C} = \mathscr{C}\{a, b\}$ be the set of real continuous functions α on $a \le x \le b$. Define

$$\alpha = \beta \quad \text{if and only if} \quad \alpha(x) = \beta(x) \quad \text{for every } x \text{ on } a \le x \le b$$

and define $\alpha + \beta$, $c\alpha$, and (α, β) by

$$(\alpha + \beta)(x) = \alpha(x) + \beta(x),$$
$$(c\alpha)(x) = c\alpha(x),$$
$$(\alpha, \beta) = \int_a^b \alpha(x)\beta(x)\, dx.$$

Then $\mathscr{C}$ is a real Euclidean vector space. In this space the Schwarz inequality states

$$\left|\int_a^b a(x)\beta(x)\, dx\right|^2 \le \int_a^b a(x)^2\, dx \int_a^b \beta(x)^2\, dx$$

and the triangle inequality states

$$\left(\int_a^b (\alpha + \beta)^2 dx\right)^{1/2} \le \left(\int_a^b a^2 dx\right)^{1/2} + \left(\int_a^b \beta^2 dx\right)^{1/2}.$$

EXAMPLE 3 Let $\mathscr{E}_\infty$ be the set of all real sequences $(x_1, x_2, \ldots)$ having the property that $\sum_{i=1}^{\infty} x_i^2 < \infty$. If $\alpha = (x_1, x_2, \ldots)$ and $\beta = (y_1, y_2, \ldots)$ are in $\mathscr{E}_\infty$, define

$$\alpha = \beta \quad \text{if and only if} \quad x_i = y_i \quad \text{for } i = 1, 2, \ldots$$

and define $\alpha + \beta$, $c\alpha$, (α, β) by

$$\alpha + \beta = (x_1 + y_1, x_2 + y_2, \ldots),$$
$$c\alpha = (cx_1, cx_2, \ldots),$$
$$(\alpha, \beta) = \sum_{i=1}^{\infty} x_i y_i.$$

The reader should note that it is not obvious that $\alpha + \beta$ is defined for every α and β in $\mathscr{E}_\infty$. This is because $\mathscr{E}_\infty$ does not consist of all the elements $(a_1, a_2, \ldots)$ but only of those for which $\sum_1^\infty a_i^2$ is finite. Thus to prove one can add any two vectors in $\mathscr{E}_\infty$ one must show that if $\sum_1^\infty x_i^2 < \infty$ and $\sum_1^\infty y_i^2 < \infty$ then $\sum_1^\infty (x_i + y_i)^2 < \infty$. This follows immediately from the inequality $(x + y)^2 \leq 2x^2 + 2y^2$. This is the only difficult point in verifying that $\mathscr{E}_\infty$ is a real vector space. For example, to verify $\alpha + \beta = \beta + \alpha$, note that $\alpha + \beta = (x_1 + y_1,\ x_2 + y_2,\ \ldots)$ while $\beta + \alpha = (y_1 + x_1,\ y_2 + x_2,\ \ldots)$. Since $x_i + y_i = y_i + x_i$ for real numbers, we have $\alpha + \beta = \beta + \alpha$.

To show that $\mathscr{E}_\infty$ is Euclidean, it is necessary to prove $\sum_{i=1}^\infty x_i y_i$ is finite. This is true in view of the inequality $|2xy| \leq x^2 + y^2$. The axioms for inner product are then readily verified.

EXAMPLE 4 A real function $\alpha(x)$ defined on the finite interval $a \leq x \leq b$ is said to be **piecewise continuous** if there is a finite number of points $a = t_0,\ t_1,\ t_2,\ \ldots,\ t_n = b$ such that $\alpha(x)$ is continuous for each x within an interval $t_{i-1} < x < t_i$, $i = 1, \ldots, n$, and $\alpha(x)$ has right and left limits as x approaches t_i, $i = 1, 2, \ldots, n - 1$, and $\alpha(x)$ has a right hand limit at $t_0 = a$ and a left hand limit at $t_n = b$.

Let $\mathscr{P} = \mathscr{P}\{a, b\}$ be the set of real-valued piecewise continuous functions α on $a \leq x \leq b$. Let addition and multiplication be defined in the usual way as in Example 2. For the scalar product we take

$$(\alpha, \beta) = \int_a^b \alpha(x)\beta(x)\, dx.$$

$\mathscr{P}\{a, b\}$ satisfies all the axioms for a Euclidean vector space except positivity of the inner product. To see that positivity is not satisfied note that θ, the zero element in $\mathscr{P}$, is the function which vanishes identically. Consider a function α which vanishes for all x except for one value $x = c$. Then $(\alpha, \alpha) = 0$ although $\alpha \neq \theta$.

In order to overcome this difficulty, we generalize the concept of equality for vectors which, up to now, we have used in the sense of logical identity.

Let us list the properties which are attributed to logical identity, denoted by " $=$ ", and interpreted as "is". They are

1. $\alpha = \alpha$.   (Reflexivity)
2. If $\alpha = \beta$, then $\beta = \alpha$.   (Symmetry)
3. If $\alpha = \beta$, $\beta = \mu$, then $\alpha = \mu$.   (Transitivity)
4. The result of an operation on α is unchanged whenever α is replaced by σ, if $\sigma = \alpha$.

If, instead of the relation " $=$ " for vectors, we use a relation " $\cong$ ", which has the properties listed above, we develop a theory different only in that " $=$ " is replaced by " $\cong$ ".

For our vector space $\mathscr{P}$, let us say $\alpha \cong \beta$ if $\alpha(x)$ and $\beta(x)$ are equal at each point x where α and β are both continuous. (We may note that then $\alpha \cong \beta$ if and only if $\int_a^b (\alpha - \beta)^2 \, dx = 0$.) It is easily checked that $\alpha \cong \alpha$; if $\alpha \cong \beta$ then $\beta \cong \alpha$; if $\alpha \cong \beta$, $\beta \cong \mu$ then $\alpha \cong \mu$. Further $\alpha \cong \beta$ implies $\alpha + \mu \cong \beta + \mu$ for every vector μ, $c\alpha \cong c\beta$ for every scalar c, and $(\alpha, \mu) = (\beta, \mu)$ for every vector μ. Moreover $(\alpha, \alpha) = 0$ if and only if $\alpha \cong \theta$. Thus $\mathscr{P}$ is a Euclidean vector space in a slightly generalized sense. Since it will cause no confusion we shall in the future replace " $\cong$ " by " $=$ ". However, it must then be remembered that " $=$ " has for $\mathscr{P}$ a special meaning.

Exercise 1.1

1. Prove property **2** of Theorem 1.1.A.
2. Prove property **5** of Theorem 1.1.A. *Hint:* It is sufficient to show that $a\alpha = b\alpha$ and $a \neq b$ implies $\alpha = \theta$.
3. Prove property **6** of Theorem 1.1.A.
4. Solve the vector equations $2\sigma + \mu = \alpha$, $\sigma + 2\mu = \beta$ assuming α and β are known and σ and μ are to be determined.
5. Show that two dimensional geometric vectors do satisfy axioms $\mathbf{1}_r$, **2**, **3** for inner products. To verify axiom **2** is satisfied show that if (x_1, x_2) are the co-ordinates of α and (y_1, y_2) are the coordinates of β, then $(\alpha, \beta) = x_1 y_1 + x_2 y_2$.
6. Show that a complex inner product has the properties $(\alpha, c\beta) = \bar{c}(\alpha, \beta)$ and $(\alpha, \beta + \mu) = (\alpha, \beta) + (\alpha, \mu)$.
7. Show that $(\alpha, \beta) = 0$ whenever $\alpha = \theta$.
8. Prove Theorem 1.1.B. for complex Euclidean vector spaces. *Hint:* For the Schwarz inequality, choose x real, choose t so that $e^{it}(\alpha, \beta)$ is real, and consider $(x\alpha + e^{-it}\beta, x\alpha + e^{-it}\beta)$. Use the result of Exercise 6.
9. Let $\mathscr{E}_n{}^*$ be the set of n-tuples $(a_1, \ldots, a_n)$ of complex numbers. If $\alpha = (a_1, \ldots, a_n)$, $\beta = (b_1, \ldots, b_n)$ define $\alpha + \beta$, $c\alpha$ for complex c as in Example 1 of the text and $(\alpha, \beta) = \sum_{i=1}^{n} a_i \bar{b}_i$. Verify that $\mathscr{E}_n{}^*$ is a complex Euclidean vector space. What are the Schwarz and triangle inequalities?
10. (a) Let $\mathscr{C}^*$ be the set of complex continuous functions of a real variable x on $a \leq x \leq b$. Form a complex Euclidean vector space with these functions as elements.

(b)   A complex valued function is called piecewise continuous if its real and imaginary parts are piecewise continuous. Let $\mathscr{P}^*$ be the set of complex valued piecewise continuous functions α on $a \le x \le b$. Form a complex Euclidean vector space with these functions as elements.

(c)   Let $\mathscr{E}_\infty{}^*$ be the set of all sequences $(x_1, x_2, \ldots)$ of complex numbers with $\sum\limits_{i=1}^{\infty} |x_i|^2 < \infty$. Form a complex Euclidean vector space with these sequences as elements.

11.   Show that $|\, \|\alpha\| - \|\beta\| \,| \le \|\alpha - \beta\|$.

12.   Let $p(x)$ be a continuous function on $a \le x \le b$ with $p(x) > 0$ on $a < x < b$. Consider the space $\mathscr{C}\{a, b; p\}$ of real continuous functions α on $a \le x \le b$. Define
$$(\alpha + \beta)(x) = \alpha(x) + \beta(x),$$
$$(c\alpha)(x) = c\alpha(x) \quad\quad \text{for real scalars } c,$$
$$(\alpha, \beta) = \int_a^b p\alpha\beta \, dx.$$
Show that this is a real Euclidean vector space.

13.   Consider the following classes of real functions on $0 \le x \le 1$ where addition and multiplication by real scalars are defined as in Example 2 of the text. State which classes are vector spaces. In case a class is not a vector space, indicate the vector space axioms which are violated.

(a)   All functions with two continuous derivatives.

(b)   All polynomials which vanish at $x = 0$.

(c)   All polynomials which assume the value 1 at $x = 0$.

(d)   All polynomials of degree 7.

(e)   All solutions of the differential equation
$$a\frac{d^2\alpha}{dx^2} + b\frac{d\alpha}{dx} + c\alpha = 0$$
where a, b, c are real scalars.

(f)   The solutions of the differential equation
$$\frac{d^2\alpha}{dx^2} + x^2\alpha = 0.$$

(g)   The solutions of the differential equation
$$\frac{d^3\alpha}{dx^3} + a\alpha^2 = 0 \quad\quad \text{for scalar } a.$$

14.   Consider the vector space of real polynomials α on $0 \le x \le 1$, where addition and multiplication by scalars are defined as usual (see Example 2 of the text). Under which of the following definitions of inner product do we obtain a Euclidean vector space?

(a) $(\alpha, \beta) = \displaystyle\int_0^1 \alpha(x)\beta(x) \, dx.$

(b) $(\alpha, \beta) = \displaystyle\int_0^1 a'(x)\beta'(x) \, dx$ where the prime denotes differentiation.

(c) $(\alpha, \beta) = \displaystyle\int_0^1 \alpha'(x)\beta'(x) \, dx + \alpha(0)\beta(0).$

(d) $(\alpha, \beta) = \displaystyle\int_0^1 a'(x)\beta'(x) \, dx + |\,\alpha(0)\beta(0)\,|.$

In case the space is not Euclidean indicate which inner product axioms are violated.

15.   Show that $|(\alpha, \beta)| = \|\alpha\| \, \|\beta\|$ if and only if $\alpha = c\beta$ for some scalar c.

1.2

LINEARLY
INDEPENDENT VECTORS

A subset of a vector space $\mathscr{V}$ may be itself a vector space with respect to the operations of addition and multiplication by scalars. In this case the subset is called a **linear manifold** of $\mathscr{V}$. If $\mathscr{W}$ is a subset of $\mathscr{V}$ then it is a linear manifold if α and β in $\mathscr{W}$ imply $\alpha + \beta$ and $c\alpha$ in $\mathscr{W}$ for any scalar c. For the other laws defining a vector space must certainly be valid in $\mathscr{W}$ if they are valid in $\mathscr{V}$.

In any vector space $\mathscr{V}$, the set $\mathscr{V}$ itself is a linear manifold. So is the set consisting of the single element θ.

In the space of three dimensional geometrical vectors (originating at the origin) the set of all vectors lying on a given line (or in a given plane) through the origin is a linear manifold.

Consider the set $\mathscr{W}$ of all linear combinations

$$c_1\alpha_1 + \cdots + c_n\alpha_n$$

obtained from a fixed set $\alpha_1, \ldots, \alpha_n$ of vectors in $\mathscr{V}$ and arbitrary scalars c_i in $\mathscr{S}$. If

$$\sigma = c_1\alpha_1 + \cdots + c_n\alpha_n, \ \mu = d_1\alpha_1 + \cdots + d_n\alpha_n$$

then

$$\sigma + \mu = (c_1 + d_1)\alpha_1 + \cdots + (c_n + d_n)\alpha_n$$

and

$$c\sigma = cc_1\alpha_1 + \cdots + cc_n\alpha_n$$

are also in $\mathscr{W}$. Thus $\mathscr{W}$ is a linear manifold. In fact, $\mathscr{W}$ is the smallest linear manifold containing the vectors $\alpha_1, \ldots, \alpha_n$ and is therefore called the linear manifold **generated** or **spanned** by $\alpha_1, \ldots, \alpha_n$.

This raises the question as to whether or not $\mathscr{W}$ is spanned by fewer than the n vectors $\alpha_1, \ldots, \alpha_n$. It will soon be seen that $\mathscr{W}$ is spanned by what is called a linearly independent subset of the vectors $\alpha_1, \ldots, \alpha_n$. The vectors $\alpha_1, \ldots, \alpha_k$ in $\mathscr{V}$ are called **linearly independent** if and only if the condition

$$c_1\alpha_1 + \cdots + c_k\alpha_k = \theta$$

for scalars c_i implies that all c_i are 0. Vectors which are not linearly independent are called **linearly dependent.**

It is clear from the definition that the set consisting of just the zero vector θ is linearly dependent. Any subset of a linearly independent set is linearly independent and any superset of a linearly dependent set is linearly dependent.

THEOREM 1.2A   The nonzero vectors $\alpha_1, \ldots, \alpha_n$ are linearly dependent if and only if some one of the vectors α_k is a linear combination of the preceding ones.

Proof   When

$$\alpha_k = c_1\alpha_1 + \cdots + c_{k-1}\alpha_{k-1}$$

we have

$$c_1\alpha_1 + \cdots + c_{k-1}\alpha_{k-1} + (-1)\alpha_k = \theta$$

with at least one coefficient (-1) not zero so that $\alpha_1, \ldots, \alpha_k$ and hence $\alpha_1, \ldots, \alpha_n$ are linearly dependent. Conversely, if the vectors are dependent so that

$$d_1\alpha_1 + \cdots + d_n\alpha_n = \theta, \qquad \text{(not all } d_i = 0)$$

and k is the last subscript for which $d_k \neq 0$, one can solve for α_k, if $k \neq 1$, as a combination of the preceding

$$\alpha_k = \frac{-d_1}{d_k}\alpha_1 + \cdots + \frac{-d_{k-1}}{d_k}\alpha_{k-1}.$$

In case $k = 1$, we have $d_1\alpha_1 = \theta$ with $d_1 \neq 0$ so $\alpha_1 = \theta$, contrary to the hypothesis that none of the given vectors is the zero vector.   ★

Corollary

A finite set of vectors, not all zero, contains a linearly independent subset which spans the same linear manifold.

This corollary contains the answer to our question as to the possibility of obtaining a smaller subset spanning a linear manifold $\mathscr{W}$ generated by a finite number of vectors. Every vector in $\mathscr{W}$ can be expressed as a linear combination of the elements of a linearly independent subset. We call a linearly independent subset which spans a linear manifold $\mathscr{W}$ a **basis** for $\mathscr{W}$. We note that if $\alpha_1, \ldots, \alpha_n$ is a basis for $\mathscr{W}$ then each vector can be expressed as a linear combination of $\alpha_1, \ldots, \alpha_n$ in one and only one way. Indeed suppose that

$$\sigma = x_1\alpha_1 + \cdots + x_n\alpha_n = y_1\alpha_1 + \cdots + y_n\alpha_n.$$

Subtracting, we have

$$(x_1 - y_1)\alpha_1 + \cdots + (x_n - y_n)\alpha_n = \theta.$$

Since the α's are linearly independent, $x_i = y_i$ for each i.

Not every linear manifold has a finite basis, but if it does then the number of elements in the basis is independent of the basis chosen. This is the content of the next theorem.

THEOREM 1.2B If $\mathscr{W}$ has a finite basis then every basis of $\mathscr{W}$ consists of the same number of elements.

Proof Let $\beta_1, \ldots, \beta_s$ be a basis for $\mathscr{W}$ and let $\alpha_1, \ldots, \alpha_r$ be a set of linearly independent elements of $\mathscr{W}$. We assert that $r \leq s$. To show this we shall suppose $r > s$ and obtain a contradiction. Since $\beta_1, \beta_2, \ldots, \beta_s$ is a basis, α_1 is expressible as a linear combination of the β's, and there exist constants $d_1, \ldots, d_s$ such that

$$\alpha_1 = d_1\beta_1 + \ldots + d_s\beta_s.$$

Not all the d's are zero, since α_1 is a member of a linearly independent set and thus cannot be the zero vector. Renumbering the β's if necessary, we may assume $d_1 \neq 0$ and hence can solve for β_1 in terms of $\alpha_1, \beta_2, \ldots, \beta_s$. It follows that $\alpha_1, \beta_2, \ldots, \beta_s$ span $\mathscr{W}$. Thus α_2 is expressible as a linear combination of $\alpha_1, \beta_2, \ldots, \beta_s$ and there exist constants $c_1, g_2, \ldots, g_s$ such that

$$\alpha_2 = c_1\alpha_1 + g_2\beta_2 + \ldots + g_s\beta_s.$$

Not all the g's are zero, for then α_1 and α_2 would be linearly dependent. Renumbering the β's if necessary, we may assume $g_2 \neq 0$ and hence can solve for β_2 in terms of $\alpha_1, \alpha_2, \beta_3, \ldots, \beta_s$. It follows that $\alpha_1, \alpha_2, \beta_3, \ldots, \beta_s$ span $\mathscr{W}$. Continuing in this fashion we finally find that $\alpha_1, \alpha_2, \ldots, \alpha_s$ span $\mathscr{W}$. This is a contradiction since $\alpha_{s+1}, \ldots, \alpha_r$ cannot be expressed in terms of $\alpha_1, \ldots, \alpha_s$. The result we have proved clearly implies our theorem. ★

A linear manifold which has a basis of n elements (which by Theorem 1.2B implies that every basis has n elements) is said to be of **dimension** n. If a linear manifold has more than n independent elements for every n it is said to be **infinite dimensional.**

THEOREM 1.2C Any independent set of vectors in a finite dimensional space $\mathscr{V}$ is part of a basis.

Proof Let the independent set be $\beta_1, \ldots, \beta_r$ and let $\alpha_1, \ldots, \alpha_n$ be a basis for $\mathscr{V}$. From the set $\beta_1, \ldots, \beta_r, \alpha_1, \ldots, \alpha_n$ we can extract an independent subset which also spans $\mathscr{V}$ by deleting one-by-one vectors which are linear combinations of their predecessors. Since the β_i are independent no β_i will be deleted, and so the resulting basis will include every β_i. ★

Corollary 1
If dim $\mathscr{V} = n$, then any n independent vectors form a basis for $\mathscr{V}$.

Corollary 2

If dim $\mathscr{V} = n$ every $n + 1$ vectors are linearly dependent.

The statement "dim $\mathscr{V} = n$" in the corollaries indicates $\mathscr{V}$ has dimension n.

Exercise 1.2

1. Prove the validity of the following statements given in the text:
   (a) Any subset of a linearly independent set is a linearly independent set.
   (b) Any superset of a linearly dependent set is linearly dependent.

2. Consider the vector space $\mathscr{C}$ of continuous functions α on $a \leq x \leq b$ as defined in Example 2 of Section 1.1. Which of the following subsets are linear manifolds?
   (a) All functions with two continuous derivatives.
   (b) All functions with two continuous derivatives which satisfy the equation

$$e(x)\frac{d^2\alpha}{dx^2} + m(x)\frac{d\alpha}{dx} + n(x)\alpha = 0.$$

   (c) All functions with two continuous derivatives which satisfy

$$e(x)\frac{d^2\alpha}{dx^2} + m(x)\frac{d\alpha}{dx} + n(x)\alpha = r(x).$$

   (d) All continuous functions α satisfying

$$\int_a^b \alpha(x) \sin 3x\, dx = 0.$$

3. Show that the space $\mathscr{E}_n$ of Example 1, Section 1.1. has dimension n. *Hint:* First show that the n vectors

$$(1, 0, \ldots 0), (0, 1, 0, \ldots 0), \ldots (0, 0, \ldots 0, 1)$$

   form a basis.

4. Show that the space $\mathscr{E}_\infty$ of Example 3, Section 1.1, does not have a finite basis.

5. (a) Show that the vector space of polynomials on $a \leq x \leq b$ is infinite dimensional.
   (b) Deduce that the space $\mathscr{C}$ of continuous functions on $a \leq x \leq b$ is infinite dimensional.

6. Find constants c_1, c_2, c_3 such that the vectors $\alpha_1 = (1, 5)$, $\alpha_2 = (3, 7)$, $\alpha_3 = (2, 9)$, in $\mathscr{E}_2$ satisfy $c_1\alpha_1 + c_2\alpha_2 + c_3\alpha_3 = \theta$. Express α_3 in terms of α_1 and α_2.

7. Given that the sets $[\alpha, \beta]$, $[\alpha, \mu]$, $[\beta, \mu]$, are each linearly independent, does it necessarily follow that the set $[\alpha, \beta, \mu]$ is linearly independent?

8. (a) If $\mathscr{W}_1$ and $\mathscr{W}_2$ are linear manifolds in a vector space $\mathscr{V}$ and if $\mathscr{W}_1\mathscr{W}_2$ is the set of vectors belonging to both $\mathscr{W}_1$ and $\mathscr{W}_2$, show that $\mathscr{W}_1\mathscr{W}_2$ is a linear manifold.
   (b) Let $\mathscr{W}_1 + \mathscr{W}_2$ be the smallest linear manifold containing $\mathscr{W}_1$ and $\mathscr{W}_2$. Show that

$$\dim \mathscr{W}_1 + \mathscr{W}_2 + \dim \mathscr{W}_1\mathscr{W}_2 = \dim \mathscr{W}_1 + \dim \mathscr{W}_2.$$

1.3

ORTHONORMAL
VECTORS

In a Euclidean vector space $\mathscr{E}$ we can define the concept of orthogonality. Two vectors α and β are called **orthogonal** if $(\alpha, \beta) = 0$. We then write $\alpha \perp \beta$. For two or three dimensional geometrical vectors orthogonality is equivalent to perpendicularity. A set of vectors $\alpha_1, \ldots, \alpha_n$ is called **orthonormal** if

1. $\alpha_i \perp \alpha_j$ $i \neq j$,
2. $\|\alpha_i\| = 1$ all i.

We often use the symbol δ_{ij} with the following meaning: $\delta_{ij} = 0$ if $i \neq j$, $\delta_{ii} = 1$. Using this symbol, called the **Kronecker delta**, we may say the α_i are orthonormal if and only if $(\alpha_i, \alpha_j) = \delta_{ij}$. Note that although δ_{ij} is denoted by a Greek letter it is not a vector.

An example of an orthonormal set of vectors is the set of vectors $(1, 0, 0)$, $(0, 1, 0)$, and $(0, 0, 1)$ in $\mathscr{E}_3$.

The theorems of this section are stated for Euclidean vector spaces without specifying whether they are real or complex since the statements and proofs are valid for both cases.

THEOREM 1.3A   Nonzero orthogonal vectors $\alpha_1, \ldots, \alpha_n$ of a Euclidean vector space are linearly independent.

Proof   If $x_1 \alpha_1 + \ldots + x_n \alpha_n = \theta$ then orthogonality yields

$$x_k(\alpha_k, \alpha_k) = (x_1 \alpha_1 + \ldots + x_n \alpha_n, \alpha_k) = (\theta, \alpha_k) = 0.$$

Now $\alpha_k \neq \theta$ so that $(\alpha_k, \alpha_k) \neq 0$ and $x_k = 0$.   ★

THEOREM 1.3B   For any set of linearly independent vectors $\beta_1, \ldots, \beta_n$ in $\mathscr{E}$ there exists an orthonormal set $\alpha_1, \ldots, \alpha_n$ spanning the same linear manifold.

Proof   If $\alpha_1 = \beta_1 / \|\beta_1\|$ then $\|\alpha_1\| = 1$.

The vector $\mu_2 = \beta_2 - (\beta_2, \alpha_1) \alpha_1$ is orthogonal to α_1. It is not the zero vector since otherwise

$$\beta_2 = (\beta_2, \alpha_1)\alpha_1 = (\beta_2, \alpha_1)\beta_1 / \|\beta_1\|$$

implying that β_1 and β_2 are linearly dependent. Thus if we define $\alpha_2 = \mu_2 / \|\mu_2\|$, we obtain $\|\alpha_2\| = 1$ and $\alpha_2 \perp \alpha_1$.

The vector $\mu_3 = \beta_3 - (\beta_3, \alpha_1)\alpha_1 - (\beta_3, \alpha_2)\alpha_2$ is orthogonal to α_1 and α_2. It is not the zero vector since otherwise β_3 would be dependent on β_1 and β_2. Thus if we define $\alpha_3 = \mu_3/\|\mu_3\|$, we obtain $\|\alpha_3\| = 1$ and $\alpha_3 \perp \alpha_1$, $\alpha_3 \perp \alpha_2$. After n such steps we will have obtained an orthonormal set $\alpha_1, \ldots, \alpha_n$ contained in the linear manifold spanned by $\beta_1, \ldots, \beta_n$. Applying Corollary 1 of Theorem 1.2C we see that $\alpha_1, \ldots, \alpha_n$ is a basis for the linear manifold.   ★

The above method of computing $\alpha_1, \ldots, \alpha_n$ is called the **Gram – Schmidt process**.

THEOREM 1.3C   Let $\mathscr{E}$ have dimension n. If $\alpha_1, \ldots, \alpha_r, r < n$, is an orthonormal subset of $\mathscr{E}$, then vectors $\alpha_{r+1}, \ldots, \alpha_n$ can be found such that $\alpha_1, \ldots, \alpha_n$ is an orthonormal basis for $\mathscr{E}$.

Proof   By Theorem 1.2C there exist vectors $\mu_{r+1}, \ldots, \mu_n$ such that $\alpha_1, \ldots, \alpha_r, \mu_{r+1}, \ldots, \mu_n$ is a basis for $\mathscr{E}$. When we apply the Gram-Schmidt process to obtain an orthonormal basis, the first r vectors will be exactly $\alpha_1, \ldots, \alpha_r$.   ★

THEOREM 1.3D   Let $\alpha_1, \ldots, \alpha_n$ be an orthonormal basis for the Euclidean vector space $\mathscr{E}$. If β is a vector in $\mathscr{E}$ then we have

(1)
$$\beta = \sum_{i=1}^{n} (\beta, \alpha_i)\alpha_i.$$

Proof   Since $\alpha_1, \ldots, \alpha_n$ is a basis for $\mathscr{E}$ we have

$$\beta = \sum_{i=1}^{n} c_i\alpha_i$$

for suitable c_i. Taking the scalar product of both sides with α_j we obtain

$$(\beta, \alpha_j) = \sum_{i=1}^{n} c_i(\alpha_i, \alpha_j) = c_j$$

and our proof is complete.   ★

Taking the scalar product of both sides of (1) with an arbitrary vector μ of $\mathscr{E}$ we obtain

Corollary 1
$$(\beta, \mu) = \sum_{i=1}^{n} (\beta, \alpha_i)(\alpha_i, \mu).$$

Putting $\mu = \beta$ we have

Corollary 2

$$\|\beta\|^2 = \sum_{i=1}^{n} |(\beta,\, \alpha_i)|^2.$$

Suppose now that $\alpha_1, \ldots, \alpha_r$ is an orthonormal set of vectors in $\mathscr{E}$ but not necessarily a basis. Then we assert that

(2) $$\sum_{i=1}^{r} |(\beta,\, \alpha_i)|^2 \leq \|\beta\|^2.$$

To see this, note that with an evident notation Theorems 1.3C and Corollary 2 of Theorem 1.3D imply that

$$\sum_{i=1}^{n} |(\beta,\, \alpha_i)|^2 = \|\beta\|^2.$$

If the terms $i = r + 1, \ldots, n$ on the left are omitted, this equality becomes the inequality (2). This result, known as **Bessel's inequality**, is of great importance. We have not stated it as a theorem because, as we shall now show, we can by a slight rearrangement of our argument, prove it without assuming $\mathscr{E}$ is finite dimensional.

Let $\mathscr{W}$ be a subset of $\mathscr{E}$. A vector β in $\mathscr{E}$ is said to be orthogonal to $\mathscr{W}$ if it is orthogonal to every vector in $\mathscr{W}$. We write $\beta \perp \mathscr{W}$. If every element of the set $\mathscr{T}$ is orthogonal to $\mathscr{W}$, we write $\mathscr{T} \perp \mathscr{W}$.

THEOREM 1.3E   Let $\mathscr{E}$ be a Euclidean vector space and $\mathscr{W}$ a finite dimensional linear manifold in $\mathscr{E}$. Each vector β in $\mathscr{E}$ can be uniquely decomposed into the sum $\beta = \beta_1 + \beta_2$ of a vector β_1 in $\mathscr{W}$ and a vector β_2 orthogonal to $\mathscr{W}$.

Proof   We will first show that such a decomposition is unique. Suppose that

$$\beta = \beta_1 + \beta_2 = \mu_1 + \mu_2$$

where β_1 and μ_1 are in $\mathscr{W}$ and β_2 and μ_2 are perpendicular to $\mathscr{W}$. Then $\beta_1 - \mu_1 = \mu_2 - \beta_2$. Since μ_2 and β_2 are orthogonal to β_1 and μ_1 we have

$$\|\beta_1 - \mu_1\|^2 = (\beta_1 - \mu_1,\, \beta_1 - \mu_1) = (\beta_1 - \mu_1,\, \mu_2 - \beta_2) = 0,$$

and thus $\beta_1 = \mu_1$ and $\beta_2 = \beta - \beta_1 = \beta - \mu_1 = \mu_2$.

To prove that any vector β can be so decomposed let $\alpha_1, \ldots, \alpha_r$ be an orthonormal basis for $\mathscr{W}$. We set

$$(3) \qquad \beta_1 = \sum_{i=1}^{r} (\beta, \alpha_i)\alpha_i, \quad \beta_2 = \beta - \beta_1.$$

Clearly β_1 is in $\mathscr{W}$. We assert that β_2 is orthogonal to $\mathscr{W}$. We have

$$(\beta_2, \alpha_j) = (\beta, \alpha_j) - (\beta_1, \alpha_j) = (\beta, \alpha_j) - (\beta, \alpha_j), \qquad j = 1, \ldots, r.$$

Thus β_2 is orthogonal to $\alpha_1, \ldots, \alpha_r$; but then it is orthogonal to any linear combination of $\alpha_1, \ldots, \alpha_r$ and thus to any vector in $\mathscr{W}$. The formula (3), which affords a method of computing β_1 is of some interest.   ★

Corollary 1

If $\alpha_1, \ldots, \alpha_r$ is an orthonormal set in $\mathscr{E}$ then, for any vector β in $\mathscr{E}$,

$$\sum_{i=1}^{r} |(\beta, \alpha_i)|^2 \leq \|\beta\|^2.$$

Proof Let $\mathscr{W}$ be the linear manifold spanned by $\alpha_1, \ldots, \alpha_r$. We have

$$\|\beta\|^2 = (\beta, \beta) = (\beta_1 + \beta_2, \beta_1 + \beta_2) = (\beta_1, \beta_1) + (\beta_2, \beta_2),$$

$$\geq (\beta_1, \beta_1) = \sum_{i=1}^{r} |(\beta, \alpha_i)|^2. \quad ★$$

Corollary 2

If $\alpha_1, \alpha_2, \ldots$ is an infinite orthonormal set in $\mathscr{E}$ then, for any vector β in $\mathscr{E}$,

$$\sum_{i=1}^{\infty} |(\beta, \alpha_i)|^2 \leq \|\beta\|^2.$$

Proof By Corollary 1 the inequality is valid if the summation instead of extending from $i = 1$ to ∞ extends from $i = 1$ to $i = r$. Let $r \to \infty$.   ★

The vector β_1 in Theorem 1.3E is called the **projection of** β **on** $\mathscr{W}$. β_1 possesses the interesting extremal property of being of all vectors in $\mathscr{W}$ the nearest to β.

THEOREM 1.3F Let $\mathscr{E}$ be a Euclidean vector space and $\mathscr{W}$ a finite dimensional linear manifold of $\mathscr{E}$. Let β be any vector in $\mathscr{E}$ and β_1 its projection on $\mathscr{W}$. Then, if μ is in $\mathscr{W}$,

$$\|\beta - \mu\| \geq \|\beta - \beta_1\|,$$

and there is equality if and only if $\mu = \beta_1$.

Proof $\|\beta - \mu\|^2 = (\beta - \mu, \beta - \mu) = (\beta_1 + \beta_2 - \mu, \beta_1 + \beta_2 - \mu)$
$$= (\beta_1 - \mu, \beta_1 - \mu) + (\beta_2, \beta_2),$$

the other terms dropping out since β_2 is orthogonal to β_1 and μ. Now $(\beta_2, \beta_2) = \|\beta - \beta_1\|^2$ and thus

$$\|\beta - \mu\|^2 \geq \|\beta - \beta_1\|^2$$

with equality only if $(\beta_1 - \mu, \beta_1 - \mu) = 0$, that is if $\mu = \beta_1$. ★

Corollary 1

Let $\alpha_1, \alpha_2, \ldots, \alpha_r$ be an orthonormal set of vectors in a Euclidean vector space $\mathscr{E}$. Then, if β is any vector in $\mathscr{E}$,

$$\left\|\beta - \sum_{i=1}^{r} c_i \alpha_i\right\| \geq \left\|\beta - \sum_{i=1}^{r} (\beta, \alpha_i)\alpha_i\right\|,$$

with equality holding only if $c_i = (\beta, \alpha_i)$, $i = 1, 2, \ldots, r$.
This follows from Theorem 1.3F and formula (3).

Exercise 1.3

1. Show that if $\beta_1, \ldots, \beta_r$ is any set of vectors in $\mathscr{E}$ and if $\mathscr{V}$ is the set of μ in $\mathscr{E}$ which are orthogonal to $\beta_1, \ldots, \beta_r$ then $\mathscr{V}$ is a linear manifold. If $\mathscr{W}$ is the linear manifold spanned by $\beta_1, \ldots, \beta_r$ then $\mathscr{V} \perp \mathscr{W}$. Finally prove dim $\mathscr{V}$ + dim $\mathscr{W}$ = dim $\mathscr{E}$.

2. Apply the Gram-Schmidt process to the vectors $(1, 3, 5)$, $(0, 2, 4)$, $(2, 4, 3)$ in $\mathscr{E}_3$ to obtain an orthonormal basis for $\mathscr{E}_3$.

3. (a) Find an orthonormal basis in $\mathscr{E}_3$ for all vectors orthogonal to $(3, 4, -1)$.
   (b) Find an orthonormal basis in $\mathscr{E}_4$ for all vectors orthogonal to $(1, 1, 0, 0)$ and $(1, 0, 2, 1)$.

4. Find the projection of the vector t^2 on the linear subspace of $\mathscr{C}\{0, 1\}$ spanned by 1 and t.

5. (a) Write $\left\|\beta - \sum_{i=1}^{r} c_i \alpha_i\right\|^2 = \|\beta\|^2 - \sum_{i=1}^{r} |(\beta, \alpha_i)|^2 + \sum_{i=1}^{r} |c_i - (\beta, \alpha_i)|^2$

   for the orthonormal set $\alpha_1, \ldots, \alpha_r$ and thus deduce again the corollary to Theorem 1.3F.
   (b) The left side of the equality in (a) is nonnegative. Obtain Bessel's inequality using this fact.

1.4

LINEAR

TRANSFORMATIONS

A **transformation** or **operator** L on a vector space $\mathscr{V}$ to a vector space $\mathscr{W}$ is an operation on a subset $\mathscr{D}(L)$ of $\mathscr{V}$, called the **domain** of L, which assigns to each vector α in $\mathscr{D}(L)$ another vector $L\alpha$ in $\mathscr{W}$, called the **image** of α under L. Transformations will be denoted by capital letters such as L, T, U, etc.

Two transformations L_1 and L_2 on $\mathscr{V}$ to $\mathscr{W}$ will be called equal if

$$\mathscr{D}(L_1) = \mathscr{D}(L_2) \text{ and } L_1\alpha = L_2\alpha$$

for all α in $\mathscr{D}(L_1) = \mathscr{D}(L_2)$.

The **range** $\mathscr{R}(L)$ of a transformation L is the set of all vectors β of the form $\beta = L\alpha$ for α in $\mathscr{D}(L)$.

A transformation L is said to be **linear** if $\mathscr{D}(L)$ is a linear manifold in $\mathscr{V}$ and if

(1) $$L(a\alpha_1 + b\alpha_2) = aL\alpha_1 + bL\alpha_2$$

for α_1 and α_2 in $\mathscr{D}(L)$ and all scalars a, b. In this book we shall consider only linear transformations. When L is linear, the range is necessarily a linear manifold, since formula (1) implies $aL\alpha_1 + bL\alpha_2$ is in $\mathscr{R}(L)$ whenever $L\alpha_1$ and $L\alpha_2$ are in $\mathscr{R}(L)$.

Every linear transformation carries the zero vector in $\mathscr{V}$ into the zero vector in $\mathscr{W}$. Indeed, if θ is the zero vector in $\mathscr{V}$, then

$$L\theta = L(2\theta) = L(\theta + \theta) = L\theta + L\theta$$

so that $L\theta$ must be the zero vector in $\mathscr{W}$. To distinguish between the zero vectors in $\mathscr{V}$ and $\mathscr{W}$, we might use the notation $\theta(\mathscr{V})$ and $\theta(\mathscr{W})$, but we shall not do so because it will be clear from the context to which θ reference is made. Moreover, in this book we shall deal mainly with the case when $\mathscr{V} = \mathscr{W}$, so that L is a transformation on $\mathscr{V}$ to itself.

The transformation I defined by $I\alpha = \alpha$ for every α in $\mathscr{V}$ is called the **identity transformation**. The transformation 0 defined by $0\alpha = \theta$ for every α in $\mathscr{V}$ is called the **zero transformation**. Both I and 0 are linear transformations whose domain is the whole space $\mathscr{V}$.

For another example, let $\mathscr{V}$ be a finite dimensional linear manifold in a Euclidean vector space $\mathscr{E}$. By Theorem 1.3E, each α in $\mathscr{E}$ may be written uniquely as $\alpha = \alpha_1 + \alpha_2$ where α_1 is in $\mathscr{V}$ and $\alpha_2 \perp \mathscr{V}$. If we define $L\alpha = \alpha_1$, we can readily verify that L is a linear transformation whose domain is $\mathscr{E}$ and range is $\mathscr{V}$.

Examples of linear transformations on the space of two dimensional geometric vectors are

(a)   The rotation of every vector through the same angle about the origin,
(b)   The multiplication of every vector by a real number c,
(c)   The reflection of every vector with respect to a fixed line l through the origin,
(d)   The projection of every vector on a fixed line l through the origin.

The accompanying figure shows the position of the image of α corresponding to each of the above operations.

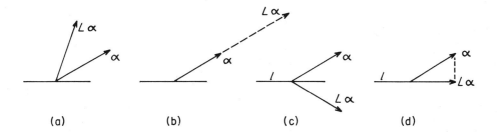

      (a)   (b)   (c)   (d)

It will be shown that the dimension of the range of a linear transformation L is never greater than the dimension of the domain. For a more complete statement we make use of the following definition: The set of vectors α in $\mathscr{V}$ such that $L\alpha = \theta$ is called the **null space** of L. One can verify that the null space is a linear manifold in $\mathscr{D}(L)$.

THEOREM 1.4A   The dimension of the domain is equal to the dimension of the null space plus the dimension of the range.

Proof   If $\mathscr{D}(L)$ has infinite dimension, we must show that the null space and range cannot both have finite dimension. Assuming the contrary, let $\alpha_1, \ldots, \alpha_r$ be a basis for the null space and let $\alpha_1, \ldots, \alpha_r, \alpha_{r+1}, \ldots, \alpha_{r+n}$ be a linearly independent set in $\mathscr{D}(L)$, where n is larger than the dimension of the range. $L\alpha_{r+1}, \ldots, L\alpha_{r+n}$ then forms a dependent set and there exist scalars $c_{r+1}, \ldots, c_{r+n}$, not all zero, such that

$$L\left(\sum_{i=r+1}^{r+n} c_i \alpha_i\right) = \sum_{i=r+1}^{r+n} c_i L\alpha_i = \theta.$$

It follows that $\sum\limits_{i=r+1}^{r+n} c_i\alpha_i$ is in the null space of L and may be written as a linear combination of $\alpha_1, \ldots, \alpha_r$. The linear independence of $\alpha_1, \ldots, \alpha_{r+n}$ indicates $c_{r+1}, \ldots, c_{r+n}$ are all zero, a contradiction.

We consider next the case where $\mathscr{D}(L)$ has finite dimension. If L transforms every vector into the zero vector, the theorem is trivial. Otherwise, let $\alpha_1, \ldots, \alpha_r$ be a basis for the null space and $\alpha_1, \ldots, \alpha_r, \alpha_{r+1}, \ldots, \alpha_{r+n}$ be a basis for $\mathscr{D}(L)$. We shall show $L\alpha_{r+1}, \ldots, L\alpha_{r+n}$ is a basis for the range, proving the theorem. If β is in the range, $\beta = L\alpha$ for some α in $\mathscr{D}(L)$. Writing $\alpha = \sum\limits_{i=1}^{r+n} c_i\alpha_i$, we have

$$\beta = L\left(\sum_{i=1}^{r+n} c_i\alpha_i\right) = \sum_{i=r+1}^{r+n} c_i L\alpha_i,$$

indicating that $L\alpha_{r+1}, \ldots, L\alpha_{r+n}$ span the range. Moreover these vectors are linearly independent, since the contrary assumption has already been seen to lead to the existence of $c_{r+1}, \ldots, c_{r+n}$, not all zero, such that $\sum\limits_{i=r+1}^{r+n} c_i\alpha_i$ lies in the null space, a contradiction. ★

An important concept in the theory of linear transformations is that of inverse transformation. Suppose that $L\alpha_1 = L\alpha_2$ implies $\alpha_1 = \alpha_2$, that is, L transforms distinct vectors into distinct vectors. Then every vector β in the range $\mathscr{R}(L)$ is associated by $\beta = L\alpha$ with a unique α in $\mathscr{D}(L)$ and we may define a transformation L^{-1}, called the **inverse transformation**, by $\alpha = L^{-1}\beta$. The domain of L^{-1} is $\mathscr{R}(L)$ and the range of L^{-1} is $\mathscr{D}(L)$. L^{-1} is a linear transformation for if $\beta_1 = L\alpha_1$ and $\beta_2 = L\alpha_2$ are in $\mathscr{D}(L^{-1})$, then $L(a\alpha_1 + b\alpha_2) = a\beta_1 + b\beta_2$ is in $\mathscr{R}(L)$ and $L^{-1}(a\beta_1 + b\beta_2) = a\alpha_1 + b\alpha_2 = aL^{-1}\beta_1 + bL^{-1}\beta_2$. It is apparent that if L^{-1} exists, then there exists $(L^{-1})^{-1} = L$.

THEOREM 1.4B   The inverse of a linear transformation L exists if and only if $L\alpha = \theta$ implies $\alpha = \theta$.

Proof L^{-1} exists if and only if $L\alpha_1 = L\alpha_2$ implies $\alpha_1 = \alpha_2$. Thus if L^{-1} exists and $L\alpha = \theta$, the relation $L\theta = \theta$ indicates $\alpha = \theta$. Conversely, if $L\alpha = \theta$ implies $\alpha = \theta$, and $L\alpha_1 = L\alpha_2$, we obtain $L(\alpha_1 - \alpha_2) = \theta$, $\alpha_1 - \alpha_2 = \theta$, $\alpha_1 = \alpha_2$, and L^{-1} exists. ★

Corollary 1

An inverse for a linear transformation whose domain is finite dimensional exists if and only if the range has the same dimension as the domain.

Proof   Theorem 1.4B states that L^{-1} exists if and only if the only element of the null space is the zero vector. The desired result now follows from Theorem 1.4A.   ★

One may consider all the linear transformations on $\mathscr{V}$ to $\mathscr{V}$ whose domain is the whole space $\mathscr{V}$ as objects to be studied. Let $\mathscr{T}$ denote the class of all such transformations. If L and M are in $\mathscr{T}$, define $L + M$ and cM for scalar c, by

$$(L + M)\alpha = L\alpha + M\alpha, \qquad (cM)\alpha = cM\alpha.$$

It is left to the reader to verify that $L + M$ and cM are linear and that $\mathscr{T}$ is a vector space, with 0 as the zero vector.

For $\mathscr{T}$ we may even define the product LM of two linear transformations L and M by

$$(LM)\alpha = L(M\alpha).$$

Since the domain of L is $\mathscr{V}$, the vector $L(M\alpha)$ is well defined. The linearity of LM is shown by

$$(LM)(a\alpha_1 + b\alpha_2) = L[M(a\alpha_1 + b\alpha_2)] = L(aM\alpha_1 + bM\alpha_2)$$
$$= aL(M\alpha_1) + bL(M\alpha_2) = a(LM)\alpha_1 + b(LM)\alpha_2.$$

The product notation is justified by

THEOREM 1.4C   Let L, M, N be linear transformations on $\mathscr{V}$ to $\mathscr{V}$ with domain $\mathscr{V}$. Then

1. $L(MN) \quad = (LM)N \quad$ (Associative law).
2. $L(M + N) = LM + LN$
    $(M + N)L = ML + NL$ $\Big\}$ (Distributive law).
3. $L0 = 0L = 0, \qquad LI = IL = L.$

Proof   We shall prove statement **1** only. For α in $\mathscr{V}$,

$$[L(MN)]\alpha = L[(MN)\alpha] = L[M(N\alpha)]$$

and also

$$[L(MN)]\alpha = (LM)N\alpha = L[M(N\alpha)].$$

This proves that $L(MN) = (LM)N$.   ★

The **commutative law** $LM = ML$ need not be valid. In fact, if $\mathscr{V}$ is the space of two dimensional geometric vectors, L is the operation of rotation counterclockwise about the origin through an angle of $\pi/2$ radians, M is the operation of projection on a given line through the origin, then a simple picture illustrates that LM need not equal ML.

When L^{-1} exists, we have $L^{-1}(L\alpha) = \alpha$ for α in $\mathscr{D}(L)$ and $L(L^{-1}\beta) = \beta$ for β in $\mathscr{R}(L)$. If both L and L^{-1} are defined over $\mathscr{V}$, we may write $L^{-1}L = I$, $LL^{-1} = I$. Such conditions may be used to characterize the existence of L^{-1} with domain $\mathscr{V}$.

THEOREM 1.4D   Let L be a linear transformation on $\mathscr{V}$ to $\mathscr{V}$ with domain $\mathscr{V}$. Then L^{-1} exists as a linear transformation with domain $\mathscr{V}$ if and only if there exist transformations M and N with domain $\mathscr{V}$ such that $ML = I$ and $LN = I$. Moreover $M = N = L^{-1}$.

Proof   Assuming $ML = I$, we shall show that L^{-1} exists. If $L\alpha_1 = L\alpha_2$ then $\alpha_1 - \alpha_2 = ML(\alpha_1 - \alpha_2) = M(L\alpha_1 - L\alpha_2) = M\theta = \theta$. Thus $\alpha_1 = \alpha_2$ and L^{-1} exists. If $\beta = L\alpha$, then $\alpha = I\alpha = ML\alpha = M\beta$ so that L^{-1} is equal to M considered as a transformation with domain restricted to $\mathscr{R}(L)$. The hypothesis $LN = I$ will be used to show that $\mathscr{R}(L) = \mathscr{V}$ thus insuring $L^{-1} = M$. In fact, if α is in $\mathscr{V}$, let $\beta = N\alpha$ so that $L\beta = LN\alpha = I\alpha = \alpha$ and α is in the range of L. Finally,

$$N = (L^{-1}L)N = L^{-1}(LN) = L^{-1}I = L^{-1}. \quad \star$$

If the domain has finite dimension, a simpler result is valid.

THEOREM 1.4E   Let $\mathscr{V}$ have finite dimension and L on $\mathscr{V}$ to $\mathscr{V}$ have $\mathscr{D}(L) = \mathscr{V}$. Then L^{-1} exists with domain $\mathscr{V}$ if either $ML = I$ or $LN = I$ for linear transformations M, N with domain $\mathscr{V}$.

Proof   We have seen that $ML = I$ insures the existence of L^{-1}. By the corollary to Theorem 1.4B, the dimension of $\mathscr{R}(L)$, the domain of L^{-1}, is that of $\mathscr{V}$, from which we conclude $\mathscr{R}(L) = \mathscr{V}$ and $M = L^{-1}$.

If $LN = I$, the above reasoning indicates that $L = N^{-1}$. Hence there exists $L^{-1} = (N^{-1})^{-1} = N$. $\quad \star$

To see what may happen in a concrete case, let $\mathscr{V}$ be the class of all polynomials α defined over $a \leq x \leq b$. Define $\alpha + \beta$ by $(\alpha + \beta)(x) = \alpha(x) + \beta(x)$ and $c\alpha$ by $(c\alpha)(x) = c\alpha(x)$. Then $\mathscr{V}$ is a vector space. Define the operator L by $L\alpha = \alpha'$, where prime denotes differentiation, and the operator N by $N\alpha = \int_0^x \alpha(t)dt$. Then L and N are linear operators on $\mathscr{V}$. We have $LN = I$. However, $NL\alpha = \alpha(x) - \alpha(0)$ so that $NL \neq LN$. The operator L has no inverse defined over $\mathscr{V}$. From the statement $L\alpha_1 = L\alpha_2$ we cannot conclude $\alpha_1 = \alpha_2$. The operator N has an inverse, but the domain of the inverse is not $\mathscr{V}$. The inverse of N is the operator L restricted so that the domain of L is the range of N.

Exercise 1.4
1. Verify the following statements made in the text regarding a linear operator L:
   (a) The null space is a linear manifold.
   (b) $(L^{-1})^{-1} = L$ when L^{-1} exists.
2. If the domain of L on $\mathscr{V}$ to $\mathscr{V}$ is the whole space $\mathscr{V}$, define the operator L^n by $L^n\alpha = L\{L[\ldots(L\alpha)\ldots]\}$, the operation L being repeated n times. Show that $L^{m+n} = L^mL^n$. If L has an inverse, show L^n has an inverse and $(L^n)^{-1} = (L^{-1})^n$.
3. If L and M have domain $\mathscr{V}$ and L^{-1}, M^{-1} exist with domain $\mathscr{V}$, then $(LM)^{-1} = M^{-1}L^{-1}$.
4. Prove statements **2** and **3** of Theorem 1.4C.
5. Show that the range of the operator N in the example following Theorem 1.4E is not $\mathscr{V}$.
6. Which of the examples (a), (b), (c), (d) given in the text preceding Theorem 1.4A have inverses?
7. Let T defined on $\mathscr{E}_2$ carry (x_1, x_2) into $(x_1 - x_2, x_1 + x_2)$. Show that T is linear, T^{-1} exists, and find T^{-1}.
8. Let $\mathscr{V}$ be the space of sequences $\alpha = (a_1, a_2, \ldots)$ with $\lim_{i\to\infty} a_i$ existing. Show that $\mathscr{V}$ is a vector space. Define $T\alpha = \beta$ by

$$\beta = (b_1, b_2, \ldots) = \left(a_1, \frac{a_1 + a_2}{2}, \frac{a_1 + a_2 + a_3}{3}, \ldots\right).$$

   Show that T is a linear transformation on $\mathscr{V}$ to $\mathscr{V}$ (you must show that $T\alpha$ is in $\mathscr{V}$. In fact, $\lim_{i\to\infty} a_i = L$ implies $\lim_{i\to\infty} b_i = L$). Show that $T\alpha_1 = T\alpha_2$ implies $\alpha_1 = \alpha_2$ and hence T^{-1} exists. Show that the range of T is not all of $\mathscr{V}$. *Hint:* $(1, 0, 1/3, 0, 1/5, 0, 1/7, 0, \ldots)$ is in $\mathscr{V}$.
9. Let $\mathscr{V}$ the space of polynomials of degree two or less. Define T by $T\alpha(x) = \alpha(x + 1)$. Show that T is linear, T^{-1} exists, and find T^{-1}.
10. Define the operation $*$ for linear transformations on $\mathscr{V}$ to $\mathscr{V}$ with domain $\mathscr{V}$ by $L * M = LM - ML$. Show that $k(L * M) = kL * M = L * kM$ for scalar k, $L * M = -M * L$, $L * L = 0$, $L * I = I * L = 0$, $L * (M + N) = L * M + L * N$, $L * (M * N) + M * (N * L) + N * (L * M) = 0$. Show also that $*$ is not an associative operation.
11. If T has an inverse, then T transforms linearly independent vectors into linearly independent vectors.
12. (a) For $\alpha = (x_1, x_2, x_3)$ in $\mathscr{E}_3$, define $T\alpha = (x_1, 0, x_2)$. Show that T is linear. Find the range and null space of T. What are their dimensions?
    (b) If T is restricted so that its domain is the linear manifold of vectors with $x_3 = 0$, does T^{-1} exist?

Matrix
Operators

2.1

MATRICES

It will be shown in this section that corresponding to a fixed basis in a finite dimensional vector space $\mathscr{V}$ every linear transformation on $\mathscr{V}$ to $\mathscr{V}$ with domain $\mathscr{V}$ has a representation as an array of numbers called a matrix. Moreover, if appropriate definitions of addition, multiplication by scalars, and multiplication are assigned to these matrices, there will exist a one-to-one correspondence between the transformations and the matrices preserving these operations. Thus, if a basis is determined, one can study the linear transformations by studying their matrix representations. However, this is not the sole reason for studying matrices. In fact, the matrix of a linear transformation depends on the basis chosen and any study of linear transformations would be an attempt to find those properties which are independent of the basis. But linear transformations often arise in applications as matrices and the representations as matrices are helpful in solving specific problems.

Let $\mathscr{V}$ be a vector space of dimension n with $\sigma_1, \ldots, \sigma_n$ as a basis. If α is in $\mathscr{V}$, it can be represented uniquely as

$$\alpha = x_1\sigma_1 + \ldots + x_n\sigma_n.$$

Thus α is completely determined by the array

$$\begin{bmatrix} x_1 \\ \cdot \\ \cdot \\ \cdot \\ x_n \end{bmatrix}.$$

This array is called an $n \times 1$ **matrix** since it has n rows and one column. It is also called the **coordinate representation** of α in the σ system. The numbers x_i are the **coordinates**. We shall write

$$(1) \qquad \alpha \overset{\sigma}{\leftrightarrow} \begin{bmatrix} x_1 \\ \cdot \\ \cdot \\ \cdot \\ x_n \end{bmatrix} = [x_i]_n$$

to indicate the relation between α and its matrix. The σ recalls the fact that the matrix has been computed relative to the basis $\sigma_1, \ldots, \sigma_n$. When there is no ambiguity as to which basis is being employed the σ may be dropped. Similarly the subscript n in $[x_i]_n$ may be omitted. If also

$$\beta = y_1\sigma_1 + \ldots + y_n\sigma_n$$

so that

$$\beta \overset{\sigma}{\leftrightarrow} \begin{bmatrix} y_1 \\ \cdot \\ \cdot \\ \cdot \\ y_n \end{bmatrix},$$

then

$$c\alpha = cx_1\sigma_1 + \ldots + cx_n\sigma_n,$$

$$\alpha + \beta = (x_1 + y_1)\sigma_1 + \ldots + (x_n + y_n)\sigma_n,$$

indicate that

$$c\alpha \overset{\sigma}{\leftrightarrow} \begin{bmatrix} cx_1, \\ \cdot \\ \cdot \\ \cdot \\ cx_n \end{bmatrix}, \quad \alpha + \beta \overset{\sigma}{\leftrightarrow} \begin{bmatrix} x_1 + y_1 \\ \cdot \\ \cdot \\ \cdot \\ x_n + y_n \end{bmatrix}.$$

The $n \times 1$ matrices with real elements may be considered as the vectors of $\mathscr{E}_n$ (see 1.1) where addition and scalar multiplication were defined by

$$c\begin{bmatrix} x_1 \\ \cdot \\ \cdot \\ \cdot \\ x_n \end{bmatrix} = \begin{bmatrix} cx_1 \\ \cdot \\ \cdot \\ \cdot \\ cx_n \end{bmatrix}, \quad \begin{bmatrix} x_1 \\ \cdot \\ \cdot \\ \cdot \\ x_n \end{bmatrix} + \begin{bmatrix} y_1 \\ \cdot \\ \cdot \\ \cdot \\ y_n \end{bmatrix} = \begin{bmatrix} x_1 + y_1 \\ \cdot \\ \cdot \\ \cdot \\ x_n + y_n \end{bmatrix}.$$

We have therefore proved

THEOREM 2.1A The representation (1) sets up a one-to-one correspondence between a real vector space $\mathscr{V}$ and the vector space $\mathscr{E}_n$ of all $n \times 1$ real matrices which preserves the operations of addition and multiplication by scalars.

The statement about preservation of addition merely means that we obtain the same matrix representation for $\alpha + \beta$ whether we use the representation for $\alpha + \beta$ given by (1) or whether we add the $n \times 1$ matrices corresponding to α and β.

It is not true that the inner product operation is preserved when $\mathscr{V}$ is a real Euclidean vector space. If

$$\alpha = x_1\sigma_1 + \ldots + x_n\sigma_n, \quad \beta = y_1\sigma_1 + \ldots + y_n\sigma_n$$

then $(\alpha, \beta) = \sum\limits_{i=1}^{n}\sum\limits_{j=1}^{n} x_i y_j (\sigma_i, \sigma_j)$, whereas the inner product in $\mathscr{E}_n$ of the $n \times 1$ matrices corresponding to α and β is $\sum\limits_{i=1}^{n} x_i y_i$. If, however, $\sigma_1, \ldots, \sigma_n$ is an orthonormal basis, it will be true that the inner product is preserved.

If $\mathscr{V}$ were a complex vector space, we would obtain a theorem analogous to Theorem 2.1A by replacing $\mathscr{E}_n$ by $\mathscr{E}_n{}^*$ (see Exercise 1.1–9).

Now let T be a linear transformation on $\mathscr{V}$ to $\mathscr{V}$ with domain $\mathscr{V}$. T is completely determined by knowledge of the vectors $T\sigma_1, \ldots, T\sigma_n$. More specifically, given

$$(2) \qquad \begin{cases} T\sigma_1 = t_{11}\sigma_1 + \ldots + t_{n1}\sigma_n \\ \quad \cdot \\ \quad \cdot \\ \quad \cdot \\ T\sigma_n = t_{1n}\sigma_1 + \ldots + t_{nn}\sigma_n \end{cases}$$

one can find $T\alpha$ for any α in $\mathscr{V}$. For, if

$$\alpha = x_1\sigma_1 + \ldots + x_n\sigma_n$$

then

$$T\alpha = x_1 T\sigma_1 + \ldots + x_n T\sigma_n,$$

so that, by (2),

$$T\alpha = x_1\{t_{11}\sigma_1 + \ldots + t_{n1}\sigma_n\} + \ldots$$
$$+ x_n\{t_{1n}\sigma_1 + \ldots + t_{nn}\sigma_n\},$$

or

$$(3) \qquad T\alpha = \{t_{11}x_1 + \ldots + t_{1n}x_n\}\sigma_1$$
$$+ \cdots +$$
$$+ \{t_{n1}x_1 + \ldots + t_{nn}x_n\}\sigma_n.$$

Thus the transformation T is completely determined by the array

$$
\begin{bmatrix}
t_{11} \cdots t_{1n} \\
t_{21} \cdots t_{2n} \\
\cdots \cdots \cdots \\
t_{n1} \cdots t_{nn}
\end{bmatrix},
$$

which is called an **$n \times n$ matrix**.

We shall write

$$
T \overset{\sigma}{\leftrightarrow}
\begin{bmatrix}
t_{11} \cdots t_{1n} \\
\cdot \\
\cdot \\
\cdot \\
t_{n1} \cdots t_{nn}
\end{bmatrix}
$$

or more briefly, $T \overset{\sigma}{\leftrightarrow} [t_{ij}], \quad i, j = 1, \ldots, n.$

Thus, to say T has the representation $[t_{ij}]$ in the σ basis means $T\sigma_i = \sum_{j=1}^{n} t_{ji}\sigma_j, \quad i = 1, \ldots, n,$ or its equivalent, $T\alpha = \sum_{i=1}^{n} \sum_{j=1}^{n} t_{ij}x_j\sigma_i$ whenever $\alpha = \sum_{j=1}^{n} x_j\sigma_j.$

Conversely, every array $[t_{ij}]$ determines by means of (3) a linear operator T whose domain is $\mathscr{V}$.

Our next objective is to introduce a calculus of matrices by means of which we can make the computations associated with linear transformations.

An array of real or complex numbers

$$
\begin{bmatrix}
a_{11} \cdots a_{1n} \\
a_{21} \cdots a_{2n} \\
\cdot \\
\cdot \\
\cdot \\
a_{m1} \cdots a_{mn}
\end{bmatrix}
= [a_{ij}]_{m,n} = [A]
$$

is called an **$m \times n$ matrix**. The first number "m" counts the rows, the second number "n" counts the columns. Note that in a_{ij} the first index prescribes the row and the second the column. If the dimensions m and n are obvious from the context they may be dropped. If $n = m$, we say the matrix is of **order** n and that the matrix is a **square matrix.** The quantities a_{ij} are called the **elements** of the matrix.

Consider a second $m \times n$ matrix

$$\begin{bmatrix} b_{11} \cdots b_{1n} \\ \cdot \\ \cdot \\ \cdot \\ b_{m1} \cdots b_{mn} \end{bmatrix} = [b_{ij}]_{m,n} = [B].$$

We define addition and multiplication by scalars simultaneously by

$$r[a_{ij}]_{m,n} + s[b_{ij}]_{m,n} = [ra_{ij} + sb_{ij}]_{m,n}.$$

For example,

$$2\begin{bmatrix} 2 & 0 \\ -1 & 4 \\ 3 & 1 \end{bmatrix} + 5\begin{bmatrix} 0 & 1 \\ -1 & 2 \\ 0 & 3 \end{bmatrix} = \begin{bmatrix} 4 & 5 \\ -7 & 18 \\ 6 & 17 \end{bmatrix}.$$

It is then evident that the set of all $m \times n$ matrices forms a vector space of dimension nm. The zero vector in this space is the matrix $[0] = [0]_{m,n}$ all of whose entries are 0.

We now define multiplication of matrices by

$$[a_{ij}]_{m,n}[b_{ij}]_{n,p} = [c_{ij}]_{m,p}$$

where $c_{ij} = \sum\limits_{k=1}^{n} a_{ik}b_{kj}.$

Multiplication of matrices is defined only when the number of columns of the matrix on the left is equal to the number of rows of the matrix on the right. We obtain the element in the ith row, j^{th} column of the product as the sum of the term by term products of the entries in the ith row of $[a_{ij}]$ with the entries in the jth column of $[b_{ij}]$.

For example,

$$\begin{bmatrix} 1 & 0 & 4 \\ 2 & -3 & 2 \end{bmatrix}\begin{bmatrix} 0 & 1 \\ 0 & 4 \\ 6 & -7 \end{bmatrix} = \begin{bmatrix} 24 & -27 \\ 12 & -24 \end{bmatrix}.$$

The example

$$\begin{bmatrix} 1 & 2 \\ -1 & 1 \end{bmatrix}\begin{bmatrix} 3 & 4 \\ 5 & 2 \end{bmatrix} = \begin{bmatrix} 13 & 8 \\ 2 & -2 \end{bmatrix}$$

$$\begin{bmatrix} 3 & 4 \\ 5 & 2 \end{bmatrix}\begin{bmatrix} 1 & 2 \\ -1 & 1 \end{bmatrix} = \begin{bmatrix} -1 & 10 \\ 3 & 12 \end{bmatrix}$$

shows that the operation of multiplication is not in general commutative.

It is possible for $[b_{ij}][a_{ij}]$ to be meaningless even though $[a_{ij}][b_{ij}]$ is defined. For example,

$$\begin{bmatrix} 2 \\ 0 \\ 4 \end{bmatrix} \begin{bmatrix} 1 & 3 \end{bmatrix} = \begin{bmatrix} 2 & 6 \\ 0 & 0 \\ 4 & 12 \end{bmatrix}$$

whereas

$$\begin{bmatrix} 1 & 3 \end{bmatrix} \begin{bmatrix} 2 \\ 0 \\ 4 \end{bmatrix}$$

is undefined.

The $n \times n$ identity matrix is defined by

$$\begin{bmatrix} 1 & 0 & 0 \ldots 0 \\ 0 & 1 & 0 \ldots 0 \\ & & \cdot \\ & & \cdot \\ & & 0 \\ 0 & 0 & 0 \ldots 1 \end{bmatrix} = [\delta_{ij}]_{n,n} = [I]$$

where every element is zero except those along the diagonal, which are equal to 1.

Consider now a vector space $\mathscr{V}$ with basis $\sigma_1, \ldots, \sigma_n$ and let T be a linear transformation on $\mathscr{V}$ to $\mathscr{V}$ with domain $\mathscr{V}$. If α is in $\mathscr{V}$ and

$$\alpha \overset{\sigma}{\longleftrightarrow} [x_i], \quad T \overset{\sigma}{\longleftrightarrow} [t_{ij}],$$

then $T\alpha$ is given by (3) as

$$T\alpha = \sum_{i=1}^{n} \left(\sum_{j=1}^{n} t_{ij} x_j \right) \sigma_i.$$

In view of our definition of matrix multiplication, this is equivalent to

(4) $$T\alpha \overset{\sigma}{\longleftrightarrow} [t_{ij}][x_i].$$

In other words, the matrix representation of the vector obtained by operating on α by T is the matrix obtained by multiplying (operating on) the matrix representation of α by the matrix representation of T. Indeed, this is the motivation for our definition of matrix multiplication.

In particular, let $\mathscr{V}$ be the vector space $\mathscr{E}_n$ and

$$\sigma_1 = \begin{bmatrix} 1 \\ 0 \\ \cdot \\ \cdot \\ \cdot \\ 0 \\ 0 \end{bmatrix}, \ \sigma_2 = \begin{bmatrix} 0 \\ 1 \\ 0 \\ \cdot \\ \cdot \\ \cdot \\ 0 \end{bmatrix}, \dots, \sigma_n = \begin{bmatrix} 0 \\ 0 \\ \cdot \\ \cdot \\ \cdot \\ 0 \\ 1 \end{bmatrix}.$$

If T is a linear transformation with domain $\mathscr{E}_n$, $T \overset{\sigma}{\leftrightarrow} [t_{ij}]$, and $\alpha = [x_i]$ is in $\mathscr{E}_n$, then by (3),

$$T[x_i] = \left(\sum_{j=1}^{n} t_{1j}x_j \right) \begin{bmatrix} 1 \\ 0 \\ \cdot \\ \cdot \\ \cdot \\ 0 \end{bmatrix} + \cdots + \left(\sum_{j} t_{nj}x_j \right) \begin{bmatrix} 0 \\ \cdot \\ \cdot \\ \cdot \\ 0 \\ 1 \end{bmatrix}$$

$$= \begin{bmatrix} \sum_{j=1}^{n} t_{1j}x_j \\ \cdot \\ \cdot \\ \cdot \\ \sum_{j=1}^{n} t_{nj}x_j \end{bmatrix} = [t_{ij}][x_i].$$

Thus for a linear transformation on $\mathscr{E}_n$ to $\mathscr{E}_n$, $\overset{\sigma}{\leftrightarrow}$ in (4) is replaced by $=$, and the operation $T\alpha$ is multiplication of α by a matrix. Conversely, every real matrix $[t_{ij}]$ may be considered as a linear transformation with domain $\mathscr{E}_n$ be defining $T[x_i] = [t_{ij}][x_i]$. Similarly every matrix with complex elements is a linear transformation on $\mathscr{E}_n{}^*$ to $\mathscr{E}_n{}^*$ with domain $\mathscr{E}_n{}^*$ and conversely.

The next theorem indicates that we can study a linear operator over a vector space $\mathscr{V}$ by its matrix representation.

THEOREM 2.1B Let $\mathscr{V}$ be an n dimensional real (complex) vector space. Then the relation 2.1(3) yields a one-to-one correspondence between the space of linear transformations on $\mathscr{V}$ to $\mathscr{V}$ with domain $\mathscr{V}$ and $n \times n$ real (complex) matrices which preserves the operations of addition, multiplication, and multiplication by scalars.

Proof We have seen that the coefficients t_{ij} determine by (3) a unique transformation T which the reader can show to be linear. Conversely, a transformation T with domain $\mathscr{V}$ determines $T\sigma_i$ uniquely and hence the coefficients t_{ji} of $T\sigma_i$ in terms of the basis $\sigma_1, \ldots, \sigma_n$. If

$$T \overset{\sigma}{\leftrightarrow} [t_{ij}], \qquad U \overset{\sigma}{\leftrightarrow} [u_{ij}],$$

then

$$T\sigma_i = \sum_{j=1}^{n} t_{ji}\sigma_j, \qquad U\sigma_i = \sum_{j=1}^{n} u_{ji}\sigma_j,$$

so that

$$(T + U)\sigma_i = \sum_{j=1}^{n}(t_{ji} + u_{ji})\sigma_j,$$

$$(cT)\sigma_i = \sum_{j=1}^{n} ct_{ji}\sigma_j,$$

$$(TU)\sigma_i = T(U\sigma_i) = T\left(\sum_{j=1}^{n} u_{ji}\sigma_j\right) = \sum_{j=1}^{n} u_{ji}T\sigma_j$$

$$= \sum_{j=1}^{n} u_{ji} \sum_{k=1}^{n} t_{kj}\sigma_k = \sum_{k=1}^{n}\left(\sum_{j=1}^{n} t_{kj}u_{ji}\right)\sigma_k.$$

These results imply that

$$T + U \overset{\sigma}{\leftrightarrow} [t_{ij} + u_{ij}] = [t_{ij}] + [u_{ij}],$$

$$cT \overset{\sigma}{\leftrightarrow} [ct_{ij}] = c[t_{ij}],$$

$$TU \overset{\sigma}{\leftrightarrow} [t_{ij}][u_{ij}]. \quad \star$$

Since matrices may be regarded as linear transformations over $\mathscr{E}_n{}^*$, it is clear that the results obtained in Theorem 1.4C are valid for $n \times n$ matrices. Actually the results of that theorem are often valid when the matrices are rectangular and not necessarily square.

THEOREM 2.1C When the operations are possible, the following statements are valid for matrices:

1. $[A]([B] + [C]) = [A][B] + [A][C]$.
2. $([B] + [C])[A] = [B][A] + [C][A]$.
3. $[A]([B][C]) = ([A][B])[C]$.
4. $[A][0] = [0], \qquad [0][B] = [0]$.
5. $[A][I] = [A], \qquad [I][B] = [B]$.

Proof We shall prove only the associative law **3**.
If $[A] = [a_{ij}]_{n,p}$, $[B] = [b_{ij}]_{p,m}$, $[C] = [c_{ij}]_{m,q}$, then $[A][B]$ is an $n \times m$ matrix and $([A][B])[C]$ is an $n \times q$ matrix. Also $[B][C]$ is a $p \times q$ matrix and $[A]([B][C])$ is an $n \times q$ matrix. Consequently $([A][B])[C]$ and $[A]([B][C])$ have the same structure. The element in the ith row and j^{th} column of $([A][B])[C]$ is $\sum_{k=1}^{m}(\sum_{r=1}^{p}a_{ir}b_{rk})c_{kj}$ while the element in the ith row and j^{th} column of $[A]([B][C])$ is $\sum_{r=1}^{p}a_{ir}(\sum_{k=1}^{m}b_{rk}c_{kj})$. These elements are thus the same.   ★

Just as the results of Theorem 1.4C can be validated for $n \times n$ matrices by considering the latter as transformations on $\mathcal{V}$ to $\mathcal{V}$, so the results of Theorem 2.1C can be validated for $m \times n$ rectangular matrices by considering them as transformations with domain in a vector space of dimension n and range in a vector space of dimension m. (See Exercise 2.1–17.)

The theory of inverses developed in 1.4 is applicable to $n \times n$ matrices considered as transformations. Suppose $[A][B] = [I]$. Then Theorem 1.4E indicates $[A] = [B]^{-1}$, $[B] = [A]^{-1}$. Moreover the dimension of the range of both $[A]$ and $[B]$ is n. We shall consider in a later section the determination of the inverse of an $n \times n$ matrix.

Exercise 2.1

1. Compute

$$\begin{bmatrix} 1 & 0 & 2 \\ 2 & 0 & -1 \\ 3 & 1 & 2 \end{bmatrix} \begin{bmatrix} 4 & 6 \\ 2 & 1 \\ 1 & 0 \end{bmatrix} \begin{bmatrix} 1 & 1 & 1 & 1 \\ 2 & 3 & 2 & 3 \end{bmatrix}.$$

2. Find the most general matrix $[A]$ such that

$$\begin{bmatrix} 0 & 1 & 0 & 0 \\ 0 & 0 & 1 & 0 \\ 0 & 0 & 0 & 0 \\ 1 & 0 & 0 & 0 \end{bmatrix} [A] = [A] \begin{bmatrix} 0 & 1 & 0 \\ 0 & 0 & 0 \\ 0 & 0 & 1 \end{bmatrix}.$$

3. (a) In multiplying $[A][B][C]$ one can find the element in the ith row and j^{th} column of the product by multiplying $_i[A][B][C]_j$ where $_i[A]$ denotes the matrix consisting of the ith row of $[A]$ and $[C]_j$ denotes the matrix consisting of the jth column of $[C]$. Prove this.

(b) Find the diagonal elements of the product in problem 1 by use of problem 3(a).

4. What conditions must x, y, z satisfy if $[A] = \begin{bmatrix} x & y \\ z & -x \end{bmatrix}$ has the property $[A]^2 = [I]$? Hence show the equation $[A]^2 = [I]$ has an infinity of solutions.

5. With respect to a given basis σ_1, σ_2, σ_3 the linear transformation L has the matrix representation

$$\begin{bmatrix} 1 & 0 & 2 \\ 3 & 1 & 1 \\ -1 & 4 & 3 \end{bmatrix}.$$

Find the matrix representation of L^3.

6. If matrices $[A]$ and $[B]$ are given by

$$[A] = \begin{bmatrix} 1 & 2 & 1 \\ 3 & 2 & 4 \\ 1 & 2 & -1 \end{bmatrix}, \qquad [B] = \begin{bmatrix} 3 & -1 & 2 \\ 2 & 1 & 3 \\ 0 & 2 & 1 \end{bmatrix},$$

find $[A]^2 - [B]^2$. Is this result also equal to $([A] - [B])([A] + [B])$?

7. Give an example of matrices $[A]$ and $[B]$ such that $[B][A] \neq [0]$, yet $[A][B] = [0]$.

8. If $\mathscr{V}$ has a basis $\sigma_1, \ldots, \sigma_n$, $T \overset{\sigma}{\leftrightarrow} [t_{ij}]$, and T^{-1} exists, then $T^{-1} \overset{\sigma}{\leftrightarrow} [t_{ij}]^{-1}$.

9. Any matrix which commutes with every other matrix must be of the form $c[I]$ where c is a scalar.

10. Find a basis for the nm dimensional vector space of all $m \times n$ matrices.

11. As a check on the arithmetic when obtaining the matrix product $[A][B]$, place an additional column α to the right of $[B]$, the element in the ith row of this column being the sum of the elements in the ith row of $[B]$. Then the element in the ith row of $[A]\alpha$ should equal the sum of the elements in the ith row of $[A][B]$. Justify this.

12. Consider the space of geometric vectors in the plane which emanate from the origin. Set up a Cartesian coordinate system and let σ_1 be the vector from the origin to the point $(1, 0)$ while σ_2 is the vector from the origin to the point $(0, 1)$. Show that σ_1, σ_2 form a basis. Then find the matrix representations in that basis for the following linear transformations:
   (a) The rotation of every vector $45°$ counterclockwise about the origin.
   (b) The multiplication of every vector by a real number c.
   (c) The reflection of every vector with respect to the x axis.
   (d) The reflection of every vector with respect to the line $y = x$.
   (e) The projection of every vector on the x axis.
   (f) The projection of every vector on the line $y = x$.

13. Prove statements 1, 2, 4, 5 of Theorem 2.1C.

14. Let $\mathscr{W}$ be a linear manifold in $\mathscr{V}$. Let $\sigma_1, \ldots, \sigma_r$, be a basis for $\mathscr{W}$ and $\sigma_1, \ldots, \sigma_n$ be a basis for $\mathscr{V}$. Suppose a linear transformation T carries every element of $\mathscr{W}$ into another element of $\mathscr{W}$. Show that the matrix representation of T is of the form $\begin{bmatrix} [A_1] & [A_2] \\ [0] & [A_3] \end{bmatrix}$, where $[A_1]$ is of order r and $[A_3]$ is of order $n - r$.

15. Consider the set of all 2×2 matrices of the form $\begin{bmatrix} x & y \\ -y & x \end{bmatrix}$ where x and y are real numbers.
   (a) Show that if x and y are not both zero, then the inverse of $\begin{bmatrix} x & y \\ -y & x \end{bmatrix}$ is

$$\frac{1}{x^2 + y^2} \begin{bmatrix} x & -y \\ y & x \end{bmatrix}.$$

Hence we may define the "quotient" of $\begin{bmatrix} x & y \\ -y & x \end{bmatrix}$ by $\begin{bmatrix} p & q \\ -q & p \end{bmatrix}$ as

$\begin{bmatrix} x & y \\ -y & x \end{bmatrix} \begin{bmatrix} p & q \\ -q & p \end{bmatrix}^{-1}$ whenever $p^2 + q^2 \neq 0$.

(b) Set up the correspondence $\begin{bmatrix} x & y \\ -y & x \end{bmatrix} \leftrightarrow x + iy$, where $i^2 = -1$. Show that this is a one-to-one correspondence preserving the operations of addition, subtraction, multiplication, and division.

16. Let 1, x, x^2, x^3 be a basis for the space of all polynomials of degree at most 3. Let D be the differentiation operator, X the operator which sends $\alpha = \sum_{i=0}^{3} a_i x^i$ into $x\alpha$. Find the matrix representation in the above basis for the operators D, $XD - DX$ and $X^2 D^2 - D^2 X^2$.

17. We have defined a linear transformation T on a real vector space $\mathscr{V}$ to a real vector space $\mathscr{W}$ as an operation assigning to each α in $\mathscr{V}$ a vector $T\alpha$ in $\mathscr{W}$ such that $T(a\alpha + b\beta) = aT\alpha + bT\beta$. Let $\sigma_1, \ldots, \sigma_n$ be a basis for $\mathscr{V}$ and $\mu_1, \ldots, \mu_m$ a basis for $\mathscr{W}$. If $T\sigma_i = \sum_{j=1}^{m} t_{ji}\mu_j$, $i = 1, \ldots, n$, show that the correspondence

$$T \overset{\sigma,\mu}{\leftrightarrow} [t_{ij}]_{m,n}$$

is a one-to-one correspondence between linear transformations on $\mathscr{V}$ to $\mathscr{W}$ and $m \times n$ real matrices preserving addition and multiplication by scalars. If α is in $\mathscr{V}$, find a matrix representation for $T\alpha$ in the μ basis. (Note that the same procedure applies if the word "real" is everywhere replaced by "complex".)

18. If the sum of the elements in each row of a square matrix having an inverse is k, then the sum of the elements in each row of the inverse matrix is $1/k$.

19. (a) Consider the set $\mathscr{Q}$ of all 2×2 matrices of the form

$$Q = \begin{bmatrix} a & b \\ -\bar{b} & \bar{a} \end{bmatrix}$$

where a and b are complex numbers. Show that $\mathscr{Q}$ is a *real* vector space, and that the matrix product of two elements of $\mathscr{Q}$ is in $\mathscr{Q}$. (The elements of $\mathscr{Q}$ are called quaternions.)

(b) If $a = x_1 + ix_2$, $b = x_3 + ix_4$ where x_i are real, show that

$$Q = x_1 I + x_2 U + x_3 V + x_4 W$$

where

$$I = \begin{bmatrix} 1 & 0 \\ 0 & 1 \end{bmatrix}, \ U = \begin{bmatrix} i & 0 \\ 0 & -i \end{bmatrix}, \ V = \begin{bmatrix} 0 & 1 \\ -1 & 0 \end{bmatrix}, \ W = \begin{bmatrix} 0 & i \\ i & 0 \end{bmatrix},$$

so that I, U, V, W form a basis for $\mathscr{Q}$.

(c) Show that $U^2 = V^2 = W^2 = -I$, $UV = W = -VU$, $VW = U = -WV$, $WU = V = -UW$.

(d) If $Q \neq 0$, then $Q^{-1} = \begin{bmatrix} \bar{a} & -b \\ \bar{b} & a \end{bmatrix}$ $(|a|^2 + |b|^2)^{-1} = (x_1 I - x_2 U - x_3 V - x_4 W)(x_1^2 + x_2^2 + x_3^2 + x_4^2)^{-1}$.

2.2

CHANGE OF BASIS

Let $\mathscr{V}$ be a vector space of dimension n and suppose $\sigma_1, \ldots, \sigma_n$ and $\sigma'_1, \ldots, \sigma'_n$ are bases for $\mathscr{V}$. If α is in $\mathscr{V}$, then α has a representation $[x_i]$ in the σ basis and $[x'_i]$ in the σ' basis. What is the relationship between the two representations? If T is a linear transformation on $\mathscr{V}$ to $\mathscr{V}$ with domain $\mathscr{V}$, then T has a representation $[t_{ij}]$ in the σ basis and $[t'_{ij}]$ in the σ' basis. What is the relationship between these two representations?

Express each σ'_i in the σ basis and each σ_i in the σ' basis by

(1) $$\sigma'_i = \sum_{j=1}^{n} p_{ji}\sigma_j, \qquad \sigma_i = \sum_{j=1}^{n} q_{ji}\sigma'_j.$$

Then $[P] = [p_{ij}]$ is the matrix whose k^{th} column is the representation of σ'_k in the σ system, while $[q_{ij}] = [Q]$ is the matrix whose k^{th} column is the representation of σ_k in the σ' system. We shall show that $[p_{ij}]$ and $[q_{ij}]$ are inverse matrices. In fact, from (1),

$$\sigma_i = \sum_{j=1}^{n} q_{ji} \sum_{k=1}^{n} p_{kj}\sigma_k = \sum_{k=1}^{n} \left(\sum_{j=1}^{n} p_{kj}q_{ji} \right)\sigma_k,$$

whence

$$\sum_{j=1}^{n} p_{kj}q_{ji} = \delta_{ki}$$

or

$$[P][Q] = [I].$$

It is instructive to consider this relationship from a different point of view. Consider the linear transformation P defined by

$$P\sigma_i = \sum_{j=1}^{n} p_{ji}\sigma_j$$

so that $[p_{ij}]$ is the representation of P in the σ system. By (1) and the linearity of P, $P\sigma_i = \sigma'_i$ and

$$P\sigma'_i = \sum_{j=1}^{n} p_{ji}P\sigma_j = \sum_{j=1}^{n} p_{ji}\sigma'_j,$$

indicating that $[p_{ij}]$ is also the representation of P in the σ' system. Similarly the linear transformation Q carrying σ_i' into σ_i is represented by $[q_{ij}]$ in both systems. Since P and Q are inverse transformations, it follows that $[p_{ij}]$ and $[q_{ij}]$ are inverse matrices (Exercise 2.1–8).

Now let $\alpha = \displaystyle\sum_{i=1}^{n} x_i \sigma_i = \sum_{i=1}^{n} x_i' \sigma_i'.$

Then

$$\alpha = \sum_{i=1}^{n} x_i \sum_{j=1}^{n} q_{ji} \sigma_j' = \sum_{j=1}^{n} \left(\sum_{i=1}^{n} q_{ji} x_i \right) \sigma_j$$

and

$$\alpha = \sum_{i=1}^{n} x_i' \sum_{j=1}^{n} p_{ji} \sigma_j = \sum_{j=1}^{n} \left(\sum_{i=1}^{n} p_{ji} x_i' \right) \sigma_j.$$

This proves

THEOREM 2.2A   If $\alpha \overset{\sigma}{\leftrightarrow} [x_i]$, $\alpha \overset{\sigma'}{\leftrightarrow} [x_i']$,   then $[x_i'] = [Q][x_i]$, $[x_i] = [P][x_i']$.

The theorem states that we can obtain the representation of α in the σ' basis from that in the σ basis by multiplying the latter on the left by that matrix $[Q]$ whose k^{th} column contains the coordinates of σ_k in the σ' basis. Moreover the coordinates of α in the σ system can be obtained from those in the σ' system by multiplying $[x_i']$ on the left by $[Q]^{-1} = [P]$, the matrix whose k^{th} column contains the coordinates of σ_k' in the σ system.

EXAMPLE 1   Consider the geometric vectors in the plane emanating from the origin. Place a rectangular coordinate system at the origin and let σ_1, σ_2 be the vectors to $(1, 0)$ and $(0, 1)$ respectively. Let σ_1' and σ_2' be obtained from σ_1 and σ_2 by a counterclockwise rotation of angle t.

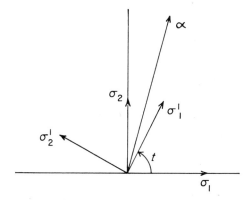

Then the coordinates of σ_1' with respect to the σ basis are $(\cos t, \sin t)$ and those of σ_2' are $(-\sin t, \cos t)$. It follows that

$$
\begin{bmatrix} x_1 \\ x_2 \end{bmatrix} = \begin{bmatrix} \cos t & -\sin t \\ \sin t & \cos t \end{bmatrix} \begin{bmatrix} x_1' \\ x_2' \end{bmatrix}
$$

whenever $\alpha \overset{\sigma}{\leftrightarrow} [x_i]$, $\alpha \overset{\sigma'}{\leftrightarrow} [x_i']$. This is a well-known result of analytic geometry.

The next theorem states that the matrix representation $[t_{ij}']$ of the linear transformation T in the σ' system can be obtained from the matrix representation $[t_{ij}]$ in the σ system.

THEOREM 2.2B If $T \overset{\sigma}{\leftrightarrow} [t_{ij}]$ and $T \overset{\sigma'}{\leftrightarrow} [t_{ij}']$ then

(2) $[t_{ij}'] = [P]^{-1}[t_{ij}][P],$

(3) $[t_{ij}] = [Q]^{-1}[t_{ij}'][Q].$

Proof If α is any vector in $\mathscr{V}$ and $\alpha \overset{\sigma}{\leftrightarrow} [x_i]$, then $T\alpha \overset{\sigma}{\leftrightarrow} [t_{ij}][x_i]$ and by the previous theorem

$$
T\alpha \overset{\sigma'}{\leftrightarrow} [Q][t_{ij}][x_i] = [Q][t_{ij}][P][x_i'].
$$

Comparing this with

$$
T\alpha \overset{\sigma'}{\leftrightarrow} [t_{ij}'][x_i'],
$$

we obtain (2) from which (3) may be obtained by multiplying both sides by $[Q]^{-1}$ on the left and $[Q]$ on the right.   ★

We have just seen that for any two representations $[t_{ij}']$ and $[t_{ij}]$ of a transformation T there is a matrix $[P]$ such that (2) holds. Conversely, if there is a matrix $[P]$ relating two matrices $[t_{ij}]$ and $[t_{ij}']$ in this fashion, then $[t_{ij}]$ and $[t_{ij}']$ may be thought of as different representations of a linear transformation T on $\mathscr{V}$. In fact, for a given σ basis we may define a σ' basis by (1) and T by $T \overset{\sigma}{\leftrightarrow} [t_{ij}]$. Then the representation of T in the σ' system is $[P]^{-1}[t_{ij}][P]$ and hence is $[t_{ij}']$.

Matrix $[t_{ij}']$ is said to be **similar** to $[t_{ij}]$ when (2) is satisfied. It is easy to verify that $[A]$ is similar to itself, that if $[A]$ is similar to $[B]$ then $[B]$ is similar to $[A]$, and that if $[A]$ is similar to $[B]$ and $[B]$ is similar to $[C]$, then $[A]$ is similar to $[C]$. Similar matrices are representations in different bases of the same linear transformation.

For orthonormal bases in a Euclidean vector space $\mathcal{E}$ one may say more about the relationship between the matrices $[P]$ and $[Q]$.

Corresponding to any $m \times n$ matrix $[A] = [a_{ij}]$ one may form an $n \times m$ matrix $[b_{ij}]$, called the **transpose** of $[a_{ij}]$, and denoted by $[A]^T$, by defining $b_{ij} = a_{ji}$. In other words, the transpose of $[A]$ is the matrix whose rows are the columns of $[A]$. For example,

$$\begin{bmatrix} 1 & 2 \\ -1 & 0 \\ 4 & 5 \end{bmatrix}^T = \begin{bmatrix} 1 & -1 & 4 \\ 2 & 0 & 5 \end{bmatrix}.$$

It is clear that $[A]^{TT} = [A]$.

An $n \times n$ matrix $[A]$ will be called **orthogonal** if

(4) $$\sum_{i=1}^{n} a_{ij} a_{ik} = \delta_{jk}, \qquad j, k = 1, 2, \ldots, n,$$

that is, if

$$[A]^T[A] = [I].$$

The last equation implies $[A]^T = [A]^{-1}$ so that we may also write $[A][A]^T = [I]$. Rewriting this as $[A]^{TT}[A]^T = [I]$ we see that $[A]$ is orthogonal if and only if its transpose is orthogonal.

If the elements a_{ij} are real, then the statement that $[a_{ij}]$ is orthogonal is equivalent to the statement that its columns, considered as vectors in the real Euclidean vector space $\mathcal{E}_n$, form an orthonormal set.

THEOREM 2.2C   Let $\mathcal{E}$ be a real Euclidean vector space with bases $\sigma_1, \ldots, \sigma_n$ and $\sigma'_1, \ldots, \sigma'_n$ related by (1). If the bases are orthonormal then $[p_{ij}]$ and $[q_{ij}]$ are orthogonal.

Proof $\delta_{jk} = (\sigma_j, \sigma_k) = \left(\sum_{r=1}^{n} q_{rj} \sigma'_r, \sum_{s=1}^{n} q_{sk} \sigma'_s \right) = \sum_{r=1}^{n} q_{rj} q_{rk}.$

Thus $[q_{ij}]$ and also its inverse $[p_{ij}]$ are orthogonal.   ★

A similar proof justifies

THEOREM 2.2D   Let $\mathcal{E}$ be a real Euclidean vector space with bases $\sigma_1, \ldots, \sigma_n$ and $\sigma'_1, \ldots, \sigma'_n$ related by (1). If $\sigma'_1, \ldots, \sigma'_n$ is an orthonormal basis and $[q_{ij}]$ is orthogonal then $\sigma_1, \ldots, \sigma_n$ is also an orthonormal basis.

EXAMPLE 2 An orthogonal matrix with real elements is the representation of a transformation carrying one orthonormal basis into another. Let us seek the values of a, b, c, d such that $[P] = \begin{bmatrix} a & b \\ c & d \end{bmatrix}$ is a real orthogonal matrix. We have

$$[P]^T[P] = \begin{bmatrix} a & c \\ b & d \end{bmatrix} \begin{bmatrix} a & b \\ c & d \end{bmatrix} = \begin{bmatrix} 1 & 0 \\ 0 & 1 \end{bmatrix}.$$

From the relations $a^2 + c^2 = 1$, $b^2 + d^2 = 1$, we see that there exist real angles t and u with $0 \le t < 2\pi$, $0 \le u < 2\pi$ such that

$$a = \cos t, \qquad c = \sin t,$$
$$b = \sin u, \qquad d = \cos u,$$

while the relation $ab + cd = 0$ leads to

$$\sin(t + u) = \sin t \cos u + \cos t \sin u = cd + ab = 0,$$

yielding 0, π, 2π, 3π as the possible values of $t + u$. Suppose, for example, that $t + u = \pi$. Then $d = \cos u = \cos \pi - t = -\cos t$ while $b = \sin u = \sin \pi - t = \sin t$. Considering the other possibilities in a similar fashion we find that $[P]$ can have two forms:

$$[P_1] = \begin{bmatrix} \cos t & -\sin t \\ \sin t & \cos t \end{bmatrix} \text{ or } [P_2] = \begin{bmatrix} \cos t & \sin t \\ \sin t & -\cos t \end{bmatrix}.$$

If σ_1, σ_2 is an orthonormal basis then $[P_1]$ carries σ_1, σ_2 into an orthonormal basis σ_1', σ_2' obtained from σ_1, σ_2 by a counterclockwise rotation of angle t, while $[P_2]$ carries σ_1, σ_2 into an orthonormal basis σ_1', σ_2' obtained from σ_1, σ_2 by a reflection in the line $x \sin \frac{t}{2} - y \cos \frac{t}{2} = 0$.

EXAMPLE 3 In the study of the motion of a rigid body fixed at one point 0, it is useful to consider a coordinate system fixed to the body at 0. Let σ_1, σ_2, σ_3 be a basis of orthonormal geometric vectors emanating from 0 and σ_1', σ_2', σ_3' an orthonormal basis attached to the body at 0. If

$$\sigma_i' = \sum_{j=1}^{3} p_{ji}\sigma_j, \qquad i = 1, 2, 3,$$

then $p_{ki} = (\sigma_i', \sigma_k)$, $k = 1, 2, 3$, are called the **direction cosines** of σ_i' with respect to the σ basis. By Theorem 2.2C the matrix $[p_{ij}]$ is orthogonal. As the rigid body moves, the direction cosines vary and hence may be considered as parameters specifying the motion. These parameters are not independent in view of the six conditions on $[p_{ij}]$ given by (4), indicating that only three independent parameters are needed to specify the motion. When the equations of motion are written in so-called Lagrangian form, it is advantageous to have the independence of the parameters. An often used set of independent parameters are the **Eulerian angles** which will now be described.

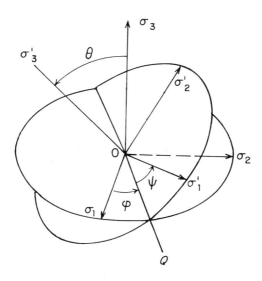

It is customary to suppose σ_1, σ_2, σ_3 form a right handed system in the sense that a rotation of σ_1 into σ_2 is a counterclockwise rotation for an observer standing at 0 with head in direction of σ_3. Similarly let σ'_1, σ'_2, σ'_3 be a right handed system. The plane formed by σ'_1, σ'_2 intersects the plane formed by σ_1, σ_2 in a line $0Q$ called the line of nodes. Let θ be the angle from σ_3 to σ'_3, ϕ be the angle from σ_1 to the line of nodes, ψ be the angle from the line of nodes to σ'_1. Then θ, ϕ, ψ are the Eulerian angles. The transformation P carrying σ_1, σ_2, σ_3 into σ'_1, σ'_2, σ'_3 can be thought of as the product of three transformations $P = RST$, where T is a counterclockwise rotation of angle ϕ about σ_3 carrying σ_1, σ_2, σ_3 into σ''_1, σ''_2, σ''_3 where σ''_1 is a unit vector in the line of nodes and $\sigma''_3 = \sigma_3$; S is a counterclockwise rotation of angle θ about σ''_1 carrying the σ'' basis into a σ''' basis with $\sigma'''_1 = \sigma''_1$ and $\sigma'''_3 = \sigma'_3$; R is a counterclockwise rotation of angle ψ about σ'''_3 carrying σ'''_1 into σ'_1. If

$$\sigma''_i = \sum_{j=1}^{3} t_{ji}\sigma_j, \qquad \sigma'''_i = \sum_{j-1}^{3} s_{ji}\sigma''_j, \qquad \sigma'_i = \sum_{j=1}^{3} r_{ji}\sigma'''_j,$$

then

$$\sigma_i' = \sum_{mkj} r_{mi} s_{km} t_{jk} \sigma_j,$$

indicating

$$p_{ji} = \sum_{mk} t_{jk} s_{km} r_{mi},$$

that is,

$$[P] = [T][S][R].$$

In view of Example 1,

$$[T] = \begin{bmatrix} \cos\phi & -\sin\phi & 0 \\ \sin\phi & \cos\phi & 0 \\ 0 & 0 & 1 \end{bmatrix}, \qquad [S] = \begin{bmatrix} 1 & 0 & 0 \\ 0 & \cos\theta & -\sin\theta \\ 0 & \sin\theta & \cos\theta \end{bmatrix},$$

$$[R] = \begin{bmatrix} \cos\psi & -\sin\psi & 0 \\ \sin\psi & \cos\psi & 0 \\ 0 & 0 & 1 \end{bmatrix},$$

and $[P] =$

$$\begin{bmatrix} \cos\phi\cos\psi -\sin\phi\cos\theta\sin\psi & -\cos\phi\sin\psi -\sin\phi\cos\theta\cos\psi & \sin\phi\sin\theta \\ \sin\phi\cos\psi +\cos\phi\cos\theta\sin\psi & -\sin\phi\sin\psi +\cos\phi\cos\theta\cos\psi & -\cos\phi\sin\theta \\ \sin\theta\sin\psi & \sin\theta\cos\psi & \cos\theta \end{bmatrix}$$

In this way, the direction cosines p_{ij} are expressed in terms of the Eulerian angles.

Analogous theorems may be obtained for complex Euclidean Vector Spaces. For any $m \times n$ matrix $[a_{ij}]$ we may form an $n \times m$ matrix $[b_{ij}]$, called the **adjoint** or **conjugate transpose** of $[a_{ij}]$, and denoted by $[a_{ij}]^*$, by defining $b_{ij} = \overline{a_{ji}}$.
For example,

$$\begin{bmatrix} 2+i & i \\ 3 & 1-i \end{bmatrix}^* = \begin{bmatrix} 2-i & 3 \\ -i & 1+i \end{bmatrix}.$$

We have $[a_{ij}]^{**} = [a_{ij}]$.

An $n \times n$ matrix $[a_{ij}]$ is called **unitary** if

$$[a_{ij}]^*[a_{ij}] = [\delta_{ij}].$$

This means that the columns of $[a_{ij}]$ considered as vectors in the complex Euclidean Vector space $\mathscr{E}_n^*$ form an orthonormal set. Theorems analogous to 2.2C and 2.2D may be obtained by replacing the word "orthogonal" by "unitary", and "real" by "complex".

Exercise 2.2

1. Let σ_1, σ_2 be orthonormal vectors in $\mathscr{E}_2$. Let $[p_{ij}] = \begin{bmatrix} \sqrt{3}/2 & 1/2 \\ -1/2 & \sqrt{3}/2 \end{bmatrix}$ and define the transformation P by $P \overset{\sigma}{\leftrightarrow} [p_{ij}]$.
   (a) Make a sketch to indicate what happens to σ_1 and σ_2 under this transformation.
   (b) If $\sigma_1' = P\sigma_1$ and $\sigma_2' = P\sigma_2$, are σ_1' and σ_2' orthonormal?
   (c) If $\alpha = 2\sigma_1 + 3\sigma_2$, express α in terms of σ_1' and σ_2'.

2. Show that the matrix

$$\frac{1}{2} \begin{bmatrix} -1 & 1 & 1 & 1 \\ 1 & -1 & 1 & 1 \\ 1 & 1 & -1 & 1 \\ 1 & 1 & 1 & -1 \end{bmatrix}$$

   is an orthogonal matrix.

3. If $[A_1]$ is a $p \times p$ matrix, $[A_2]$ is an $(n-p) \times (n-p)$ matrix, $[M]$ is a $p \times (n-p)$ matrix and

$$[A] = \begin{bmatrix} [A_1] & [M] \\ [0] & [A_2] \end{bmatrix}$$

   is a real orthogonal matrix, then $[A_1]$ and $[A_2]$ are orthogonal and $[M] = [0]$.

4. If $[P] = \begin{bmatrix} \cos t & -\sin t \\ \sin t & \cos t \end{bmatrix}$, show $[P^n] = \begin{bmatrix} \cos nt & -\sin nt \\ \sin nt & \cos nt \end{bmatrix}$.

   What is the geometrical interpretation?

5. Consider the matrices $[a_{ij}]_{n,m}$ and $[b_{ij}]_{m,p}$.
   (a) Show that $\{[a_{ij}][b_{ij}]\}^T = [b_{ij}]^T[a_{ij}]^T$.
   (b) Show that $\{[a_{ij}][b_{ij}]\}^* = [b_{ij}]^*[a_{ij}]^*$.

6. If $[a_{ij}]$ and $[b_{ij}]$ are $m \times n$, then
   (a) $[a_{ij}]^T + [b_{ij}]^T = [a_{ij} + b_{ij}]^T$,
   (b) $[a_{ij}]^* + [b_{ij}]^* = [a_{ij} + b_{ij}]^*$,
   (c) $[ca_{ij}]^* = \bar{c}[a_{ij}]^*$.

7. Show that the product of two orthogonal matrices is orthogonal and the product of two unitary matrices is unitary.

8. If $[A]^{-1}$ exists, then $([A]^T)^{-1} = ([A]^{-1})^T$. *Hint:* apply the result of problem 5 to the product $([A]^{-1})^T[A]^T$.

9. (a) Let $\sigma_1, \ldots, \sigma_n$ be an orthonormal basis in a real n dimensional Euclidean vector space $\mathscr{E}$. Let $[p_{ij}]_{n,n}$ be orthogonal and define $P \overset{\sigma}{\leftrightarrow} [p_{ij}]$. Show that $(P\alpha, P\beta) = (\alpha, \beta)$ for α, β in $\mathscr{E}$.
   (b) Let L be a linear transformation on a real n dimensional Euclidean vector space $\mathscr{E}$ to $\mathscr{E}$. Suppose $(L\alpha, L\alpha) = (\alpha, \alpha)$ for every α in $\mathscr{E}$. Show that $(L\alpha, L\beta) = (\alpha, \beta)$ for α and β in $\mathscr{E}$ and that the representation of L in an orthonormal basis is an orthogonal matrix. L is then called an **orthogonal transformation**.

10. (a) Let $\sigma_1, \ldots, \sigma_n$ be an orthonormal basis in a complex n dimensional Euclidean vector space $\mathscr{E}$. Let $[p_{ij}]$ be unitary and define $P \overset{\sigma}{\leftrightarrow} [p_{ij}]$. Show that $(P\alpha, P\beta) = (\alpha, \beta)$ for α, β in $\mathscr{E}$.

(b) Let L be a linear transformation on an n dimensional complex Euclidean vector space $\mathscr{E}$ to $\mathscr{E}$, satisfying $(L\alpha, L\alpha) = (\alpha, \alpha)$ for every α in $\mathscr{E}$. Show that $(L\alpha, L\beta) = (\alpha, \beta)$ for α and β in $\mathscr{E}$ and that the representation of L in an orthonormal basis is a unitary matrix. L is then called a **unitary transformation**.

11. The following transformation from (x, y, z, t) space to (x', y', z', t') space occurs in the study of special relativity:

$$x' = \frac{x - vt}{(1 - \beta^2)^{1/2}}, \qquad y' = y, \qquad z' = z, \qquad t' = \frac{t - (vx/c^2)}{(1 - \beta^2)^{1/2}}$$

where $\beta = v/c$. It is one of the Lorentz transformations which leave invariant the form $x^2 + y^2 + z^2 - (ct)^2$. For mathematical convenience, let $x_1 = x$, $x_2 = y$, $x_3 = z$, $x_4 = ict$. Then the transformation may be written

$$\begin{bmatrix} x_1' \\ x_2' \\ x_3' \\ x_4' \end{bmatrix} = \begin{bmatrix} b & 0 & 0 & ib\beta \\ 0 & 1 & 0 & 0 \\ 0 & 0 & 1 & 0 \\ -ib\beta & 0 & 0 & b \end{bmatrix} \begin{bmatrix} x_1 \\ x_2 \\ x_3 \\ x_4 \end{bmatrix}$$

where $b = \dfrac{1}{(1 - \beta^2)^{1/2}}$. Show that the matrix is orthogonal but not unitary.

12. (a) Show that the matrix

$$\begin{bmatrix} \dfrac{1}{\sqrt{3}} & \dfrac{i}{\sqrt{4}} & \dfrac{-1 + 2i}{\sqrt{12}} \\[2ex] \dfrac{i}{\sqrt{3}} & \dfrac{1 + i}{\sqrt{4}} & \dfrac{1 - i}{\sqrt{12}} \\[2ex] \dfrac{1}{\sqrt{3}} & \dfrac{-1}{\sqrt{4}} & \dfrac{2 - i}{\sqrt{12}} \end{bmatrix}$$

is unitary.

(b) Find a, b, c so that the following matrix is unitary:

$$\begin{bmatrix} \dfrac{1}{\sqrt{3}} & \dfrac{i}{\sqrt{6}} & a \\[2ex] \dfrac{i}{\sqrt{3}} & \dfrac{-1}{\sqrt{6}} & b \\[2ex] \dfrac{1}{\sqrt{3}} & \dfrac{-2i}{\sqrt{6}} & c \end{bmatrix}.$$

2.3

DETERMINANTS

To each $n \times n$ matrix $[a_{ij}]$ we shall assign a number called the determinant of the matrix and denoted by det $[a_{ij}]$. If L is a linear transformation whose domain is an n dimensional vector space, then L may have different matrix representations for each basis chosen, but we shall see that the determinants of these matrices will all be equal. We may therefore designate the determinant of L as the determinant of any of its representations.

Before giving a precise definition of the determinant of an $n \times n$ matrix, it will be convenient to introduce some notation. Let $(i_1, i_2, \ldots, i_n)$ be a permutation of the integers $(1, 2, \ldots, n)$. An interchange of any two elements i_j and i_k in the expression $(i_1, i_2, \ldots, i_n)$ will be called a **transposition**. We may change $(i_1, \ldots, i_n)$ into $(1, 2, \ldots, n)$ by a finite number of transpositions and we may do this in various ways. It is also true that the number of transpositions needed to do this is either always even or always odd. To show that this is so, consider the function

$$P(x_1, x_2, \ldots, x_n) = \prod_{i<j} \{x_i - x_j\} = \{x_1 - x_2\}\{x_1 - x_3\} \ldots \{x_1 - x_n\}$$

$$\cdot \{x_2 - x_3\} \ldots \{x_2 - x_n\}$$

$$\cdot \cdot \cdot \cdot \cdot \cdot \cdot \cdot \cdot \cdot \cdot \cdot$$

$$\cdot \{x_{n-1} - x_n\}$$

We shall prove that the effect on P of interchanging any two distinct integers i and j, is to change the sign of P. The factors of P involving neither i nor j are unchanged by the interchange of i and j. The factor $x_i - x_j$ is changed in sign. The remaining factors may be paired as products $\pm (x_i - x_k)(x_j - x_k)$ where $k \neq i$, $k \neq j$ and such a product is also unchanged by the interchange of i and j. It follows that $P(x_1, \ldots, x_n)$ is transformed into $Q(x_1, \ldots, x_n)$ $= (-1)P(x_1, \ldots, x_n)$. Performing an interchange of two distinct integers in Q involves another interchange of integers in P and carries Q into $(-1)^2 P(x_1, \ldots, x_n)$.

Suppose $(1, 2, \ldots, n)$ is carried into $(i_1, i_2, \ldots, i_n)$ by r transpositions. Performing these interchanges in order on P and the functions obtained from it we obtain $(-1)^r P(x_1, \ldots, x_n)$. The resulting function however is also $P(x_{i_1}, \ldots, x_{i_n})$. Similarly if $(1, 2, \ldots, n)$ is carried into $(i_1, i_2, \ldots, i_n)$ by s interchanges we obtain $(-1)^s P(x_1, \ldots, x_n) = P(x_{i_1}, \ldots, x_{i_n})$. It follows that r and s are both even or both odd.

Define $(i_1, i_2, \ldots, i_n)$ to be an **even permutation** of $(1, 2, \ldots, n)$ if

$(i_1, i_2, \ldots, i_n)$ can be carried into $(1, 2, \ldots, n)$ by an even number of transpositions. Otherwise $(i_1, i_2, \ldots, i_n)$ is an **odd permutation.**

We are now in a position to make a precise definition of a determinant. Permit the integers $i_1, \ldots, i_n$ to assume all values from 1 to n and define

$$\varepsilon(i_1, \ldots, i_n) = \begin{cases} 1 & \text{if } (i_1, \ldots, i_n) \text{ is an even permutation,} \\ -1 & \text{if } (i_1, \ldots, i_n) \text{ is an odd permutation,} \\ 0 & \text{if } i_1, \ldots, i_n \text{ are not all distinct.} \end{cases}$$

Then the **determinant** of the $n \times n$ matrix $[a_{ij}]$, denoted by

$$\det [a_{ij}] \quad \text{or} \quad \begin{vmatrix} a_{11} \ldots a_{1n} \\ \cdot \\ \cdot \\ \cdot \\ a_{n1} \ldots a_{nn} \end{vmatrix}$$

is defined by

$$\det [a_{ij}] = \sum_{i_1=1}^{n} \cdots \sum_{i_n=1}^{n} \epsilon(i_1, \ldots, i_n) a_{i_1 1} \ldots a_{i_n n}.$$

Since $\epsilon(i_1, \ldots, i_n) = 0$ when any two indices are equal, the sum above consists of $n!$ terms, the number of permutations of the integers $1, 2, \ldots, n$. We see that each term is a product containing one and only one element from each row and each column of the matrix $[a_{ij}]$ and that each term is prefixed by a $+$ sign or a $-$ sign according as the row indices form an even or odd permutation of $(1, 2, \ldots, n)$ after the column indices are arranged in the natural order $1, 2, \ldots, n$. We see, moreover, that the determinant of $[a_{ij}]$ may be defined as the sum of all possible terms consisting of one and only one element from each row and each column and prefixed by a $+$ or $-$ sign according as the row indices are transformed into the column indices by an even or odd number of transpositions. In fact, if a term $a_{k_1 j_1} a_{k_2 j_2} \ldots a_{k_n j_n}$, containing one and only one element from each row and each column of $[a_{ij}]$, is carried into $a_{i_1 1} \ldots a_{i_n n}$ by s transpositions which carry $(j_1, \ldots, j_n)$ into $(1, 2, \ldots, n)$ and $(k_1, \ldots, k_n)$ into $(i_1, \ldots, i_n)$, then we can show that the number of transpositions needed to carry $(i_1, \ldots, i_n)$ into $(1, \ldots, n)$ is even or odd according as the number r of transpositions carrying $(k_1, \ldots, k_n)$ into $(j_1, \ldots, j_n)$ is even or odd. This follows immediately upon noticing that a number of transpositions needed to carry $(i_1, \ldots, i_n)$ into $(1, \ldots, n)$ may be calculated as the number of transpositions carrying $(i_1, \ldots, i_n)$ into $(k_1, \ldots, k_n)$ plus the number of transpositions carrying

$(k_1, \ldots, k_n)$ into $(j_1, \ldots, j_n)$ plus the number of transpositions carrying $(j_1, \ldots, j_n)$ into $(1, 2, \ldots, n)$, the total sum being $2s + r$.

In view of this last interpretation of determinant we also have

$$\det [a_{ij}] = \sum_{i_1=1}^{n} \cdots \sum_{i_n=1}^{n} \epsilon(i_1, \ldots, i_n)a_{1i_1} \cdots a_{ni_n}.$$

In the rest of this section, unless stated otherwise, we shall use the so-called **summation convention** which states that a summation from 1 to n is always to be performed for any index which appears twice. With this convention we write

(1) $$\det [a_{ij}] = \epsilon(i_1, \ldots, i_n)a_{i_1 1} \cdots a_{i_n n}$$

$$= \epsilon(i_1, \ldots, i_n)a_{1i_1} \cdots a_{ni_n}.$$

THEOREM 2.3A The determinant of a square matrix is the determinant of its transpose.

Proof If $[b_{ij}] = [a_{ij}]^T$ so that $b_{ij} = a_{ji}$ we have

$$\det [b_{ij}] = \epsilon(i_1, \ldots, i_n)b_{i_1 1} \cdots b_{i_n n}$$

$$= \epsilon(i_1, \ldots, i_n)a_{1i_1} \cdots a_{ni_n}$$

$$= \det [a_{ij}]. \quad \star$$

This result implies the following conclusion: If any theorem regarding the determinant of a matrix involves a statement about the columns then there exists a corresponding theorem with the word "column" replaced by the word "row".

The evaluation of the determinant may often be simplified by the use of the next few theorems.

THEOREM 2.3B Interchanging two columns of a square matrix changes the sign of its determinant.

Proof We may restrict our attention to the first two columns. Since i_1 and i_2 are merely indices, we may write

$$\det [a_{ij}] = \epsilon(i_2, i_1, i_3, \ldots, i_n)a_{i_2 1}a_{i_1 2}a_{i_3 3} \cdots a_{i_n n}$$

$$= \epsilon(i_2, i_1, i_3, \ldots, i_n)a_{i_1 2} a_{i_2 1}a_{i_3 3} \cdots a_{i_n n}$$

$$= -\epsilon(i_1, i_2, \ldots, i_n)a_{i_1 2}a_{i_2 1}a_{i_3 3} \cdots a_{i_n n}.$$

The last equation is a consequence of the fact that an interchange of two indices of $\epsilon(i_2, i_1, i_3, \ldots, i_n)$ changes its sign. The desired result now follows when we note that the determinant of the matrix formed from $[a_{ij}]$ by interchanging the first two columns is exactly

$$\epsilon(i_1, i_2, \ldots, i_n)a_{i_12}a_{i_21}a_{i_33} \ldots a_{i_nn}. \quad \star$$

Corollary 1

If two columns of a square matrix are equal, the value of its determinant is zero.

THEOREM 2.3C Multiplying all the elements of a column of a square matrix by a constant k multiplies the value of the determinant of the matrix by k.

Proof The value of the determinant obtained by multiplying the $j + 1^{\text{st}}$ column by k is

$$\epsilon(i_1, \ldots, i_n)a_{i_11} \ldots a_{i_jj}ka_{i_{j+1}j+1} \ldots a_{i_nn} = k \det [a_{ij}]. \quad \star$$

Corollary 1

If all the elements of a column of a square matrix are zero, the determinant is zero.

THEOREM 2.3D Suppose that the elements of the $n \times n$ matrices $[a_{ij}]$, $[b_{ij}]$, $[c_{ij}]$ are identical except for the elements in the kth column, while the kth column of $[c_{ij}]$ is the sum of the kth columns of $[a_{ij}]$ and $[b_{ij}]$. Then

$$\det [c_{ij}] = \det [a_{ij}] + \det [b_{ij}].$$

In determinant notation, this may be written

$$\begin{vmatrix} a_{11} & \cdots & a_{1k} & \cdots & a_{1n} \\ & & \cdot & & \\ & & \cdot & & \\ & & \cdot & & \\ a_{n1} & \cdots & a_{nk} & \cdots & a_{nn} \end{vmatrix} + \begin{vmatrix} a_{11} & \cdots & b_{1k} & \cdots & a_{1n} \\ & & \cdot & & \\ & & \cdot & & \\ & & \cdot & & \\ a_{n1} & \cdots & b_{nk} & \cdots & a_{nn} \end{vmatrix}$$

$$= \begin{vmatrix} a_{11} & \cdots & a_{1k} + b_{1k} & \cdots & a_{1n} \\ & & \cdot & & \\ & & \cdot & & \\ & & \cdot & & \\ a_{n1} & \cdots & a_{nk} + b_{nk} & \cdots & a_{nn} \end{vmatrix}.$$

Proof $\det [c_{ij}] = \epsilon(i_1, \ldots, i_n)a_{i_11} \ldots \{a_{i_kk} + b_{i_kk}\} \ldots a_{i_nn}$

$\qquad\qquad = \epsilon(i_1, \ldots, i_n)a_{i_11} \ldots a_{i_nn} + \epsilon(i_1, \ldots, i_n)b_{i_11} \ldots b_{i_nn}$

$\qquad\qquad = \det [a_{ij}] + \det [b_{ij}].$ ★

Both of the next two corollaries are obtained from the theorem with the aid of Theorem 2.3C and the corollary to Theorem 2.3B.

Corollary 1
The determinant is left unaltered if a multiple of any column of a square matrix is added to a different column.

Corollary 2
If any column of a square matrix is a linear combination of other columns, the determinant is zero.

EXAMPLE 1

$$\begin{vmatrix} b+c & a & 1 \\ c+a & b & 1 \\ a+b & c & 1 \end{vmatrix} = \begin{vmatrix} b+c+a & a & 1 \\ c+a+b & b & 1 \\ a+b+c & c & 1 \end{vmatrix} = (a+b+c)\begin{vmatrix} 1 & a & 1 \\ 1 & b & 1 \\ 1 & c & 1 \end{vmatrix} = 0.$$

EXAMPLE 2   Let $a_{ij} = 0$ when $i > j$.

Then
$$\begin{vmatrix} a_{11} & a_{12} & \ldots \ldots & a_{1n} \\ 0 & a_{22} & & \cdot \\ \cdot & 0 & & \cdot \\ \cdot & \cdot & & \cdot \\ \cdot & \cdot & & \cdot \\ 0 & 0 & \ldots \ldots & a_{nn} \end{vmatrix} = a_{11}a_{22} \ldots a_{nn}.$$

Indeed, the right side represents the only possible nonzero term containing one and only one element from each row and each column.

EXAMPLE 3   A convenient rule for the evaluation of the determinant
of a 2×2 matrix is given by the diagram

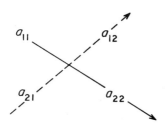

Here the two elements connected by a full line form a positive term and the two elements connected by a dotted line form a negative term. The diagram yields

$$a_{11}a_{22} - a_{21}a_{12}$$

which agrees with the definition.

Thus

$$\begin{vmatrix} -3 & 4 \\ -6 & 2 \end{vmatrix} = (-3)(2) - (4)(-6) = 18.$$

Similarly the determinant of a 3×3 matrix may be evaluated by the diagram

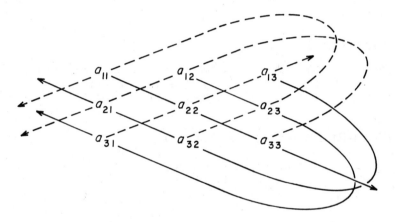

where the full lines and dotted lines have the same significance as described above.

EXAMPLE 4

$$\begin{vmatrix} 13 & 17 & 12 \\ 11 & 14 & 5 \\ 9 & 8 & 6 \end{vmatrix} = \begin{vmatrix} -5 & 1 & 0 \\ 2 & 6 & -1 \\ 9 & 8 & 6 \end{vmatrix} = \begin{vmatrix} -5 & 1 & 0 \\ 2 & 6 & -1 \\ 7 & 2 & 7 \end{vmatrix} = \begin{vmatrix} -5 & 1 & 0 \\ 3 & 6 & -1 \\ 0 & 2 & 7 \end{vmatrix}$$

$$= (-5)(6)(7) - (2)(-1)(-5) - (7)(1)(3) = -241.$$

Begin by subtracting the third row from the second and twice the third from the first. Next subtract the second row from the third row and then subtract the third column from the first. The aim is to obtain small numbers and zeros. Finally use the method of Example 3.

THEOREM 2.3E   The determinant of a product of two square matrices is the product of their determinants.

Proof   First note that the following relations are true:

$$\epsilon(i_1, \ldots, i_n)a_{j_1 i_1} \ldots a_{j_n i_n} = \det [a_{ij}]\epsilon(j_1, \ldots, j_n),$$

$$\epsilon(i_1, \ldots, i_n)a_{i_1 j_1} \ldots a_{i_n j_n} = \det [a_{ij}]\epsilon(j_1, \ldots, j_n).$$

We shall prove the first relation. If $(j_1, \ldots, j_n)$ is not a permutation of $(1, 2, \ldots, n)$, that is, some indices are equal, then the right side is zero by definition of $\epsilon(j_1, \ldots, j_n)$ while the left side is zero because it is the determinant of a matrix with at least two rows alike. If $(j_1, \ldots, j_n)$ is the set $(1, 2, \ldots, n)$ then the first relation is just the definition of the determinant. If $(j_1, \ldots, j_n)$ is a permutation of $(1, 2, \ldots, n)$, the left side is the determinant formed by an interchange of the rows of the matrix and hence, by Theorem 2.3B, is either $\det [a_{ij}]$ or $-\det [a_{ij}]$ according as $(j_1, \ldots, j_n)$ is an even or odd permutation. This, however, is exactly what the right side states.

To prove the theorem, write

$$\det [a_{ij}] \det [b_{ij}] = \det [a_{ij}]\epsilon(i_1, \ldots, i_n)b_{i_1 1} \ldots b_{i_n n}$$

$$= \epsilon(j_1, \ldots, j_n)a_{j_1 i_1} \ldots a_{j_n i_n}b_{i_1 1} \ldots b_{i_n n}$$

$$= \epsilon(j_1, \ldots, j_n)\{a_{j_1 i_1}b_{i_1 1}\} \ldots \{a_{j_n i_n}b_{i_n n}\}$$

$$= \epsilon(j_1, \ldots, j_n)c_{j_1 1} \ldots c_{j_n n} = \det [c_{ij}],$$

where $c_{rs} = \sum_{i=1}^{n} a_{ri}b_{is}$, so that $[c_{ij}] = [a_{ij}][b_{ij}]$.

We have therefore proved

$$\det [a_{ij}] \det [b_{ij}] = \det \{[a_{ij}][b_{ij}]\}. \quad \star$$

The next theorem permits the evaluation of the determinant of an $n \times n$ matrix by the calculation of n determinants of $(n - 1) \times (n - 1)$ matrices. The method used in the evaluation is called **expansion by minors**. Consider the $n \times n$ matrix $[a_{ij}]$. If we omit the ith row and j^{th} column, we obtain an $(n - 1) \times (n - 1)$ matrix whose determinant is called the **minor** of the element a_{ij}. If, for fixed i and j, we replace all the elements in the jth column of $[a_{ij}]$ except a_{ij} by zero and replace a_{ij} by 1, we obtain an $n \times n$ matrix whose determinant is called the **co-factor** A_{ji} of the element a_{ij}.

For example, the minor of the element 2 in the matrix

$$
\begin{bmatrix} 1 & 3 & 4 \\ 2 & 6 & 8 \\ 3 & 5 & 9 \end{bmatrix} \quad \text{is} \quad \begin{vmatrix} 3 & 4 \\ 5 & 9 \end{vmatrix}, \quad \text{while the co-factor is}
$$

$$
\begin{vmatrix} 0 & 3 & 4 \\ 1 & 6 & 8 \\ 0 & 5 & 9 \end{vmatrix} = - \begin{vmatrix} 1 & 6 & 8 \\ 0 & 3 & 4 \\ 0 & 5 & 9 \end{vmatrix} = - \begin{vmatrix} 3 & 4 \\ 5 & 9 \end{vmatrix}.
$$

The first equality is obtained by an interchange of the first two rows, and the second by a consideration of the possible terms in the definition of the 3×3 matrix. The fact illustrated for the particular case above, that the co-factor is related to the minor, may be stated as follows: "The co-factor A_{ji} of the element a_{ij} is equal to the minor of a_{ij} multiplied by $(-1)^{i+j}$." To prove this, recollect that $\delta_{i_j i}$ means zero unless i_j is equal to i, in which case it is equal to one. Thus the definition of co-factor yields

$$
A_{ji} = \epsilon(i_1, \ldots, i_n) a_{i_1 1} \cdots a_{i_{j-1} j-1} \delta_{i_j i} a_{i_{j+1} j+1} \cdots a_{i_n n}.
$$

Since

$$
\epsilon(i_1, \ldots, i_n)\delta_{i_j i} = (-1)^{j-1}\epsilon(i_j, i_i, \ldots, i_{j-1}, i_{j+1}, \ldots, i_n)\delta_{i_j i}
$$
$$
= (-1)^{j-1}(-1)^{i-1}\epsilon(i_1, \ldots, i_{i-1}, i, i_i, \ldots, i_{j-1}, i_{j+1}, \ldots, i_n),
$$

we see that $(-1)^{i+j}A_{ji}$ is equal to

$$
\epsilon(i_1, \ldots, i_{i-1}, i, i_i, \ldots, i_{j-1}, i_{j+1}, \ldots, i_n) a_{i_1 1} \cdots a_{i_{j-1} j-1} a_{i_{j+1} j+1} \cdots a_{i_n n}.
$$

The last expression is exactly the minor of a_{ij} since it is equal to the sum of all terms containing one and only one element from each row and each column of the minor prefixed by a $+$ or $-$ sign according as the row indices can be carried into natural order by an even or odd number of transpositions after the column indices are put in natural order.

In view of this result, we may state that the co-factor A_{ji} of a_{ij} is the minor of a_{ij} prefixed by a $+$ or $-$ sign associated with the element a_{ij} by the following pattern superimposed on the matrix:

$$
\begin{bmatrix} + & - & + & - & & \\ - & + & - & + & & \\ + & - & + & - & & \\ & & & \cdot & & \\ & & & & \cdot & \\ & & & & & + \end{bmatrix}.
$$

THEOREM 2.3F   (Expansion by Minors). For fixed k,

$$\det [a_{ij}] = \sum_{r=1}^{n} A_{kr}a_{rk},$$

$$\det [a_{ij}] = \sum_{r=1}^{n} a_{kr}A_{rk}.$$

Proof   For fixed k, we have $\displaystyle\sum_{r=1}^{n} a_{rk}\delta_{i_k r} = a_{i_k k}.$

Hence

$$\det [a_{ij}] = \varepsilon(i_1, \ldots, i_n)a_{i_1 1} \ldots a_{i_n n}$$

$$= a_{rk}\varepsilon(i_1, \ldots, i_n)a_{i_1 1} \ldots a_{i_{k-1}k-1}\delta_{i_k r}a_{i_{k+1}k+1} \ldots a_{i_n n}$$

$$= a_{rk}A_{kr}.$$

The second formula is obtained by considering the transpose.   ★

The proof is nothing more than an application of Theorem 2.3D. It is merely a condensed version of the fact that

$$\begin{vmatrix} a_{11} \ldots a_{1k} \ldots a_{1n} \\ \cdot \\ \cdot \\ \cdot \\ a_{n1} \ldots a_{nk} \ldots a_{nn} \end{vmatrix} = \begin{vmatrix} a_{11} \ldots a_{1k} \ldots a_{1n} \\ 0 \\ \cdot \\ \cdot \\ \cdot \\ a_{n1} \quad 0 \quad a_{nn} \end{vmatrix} + \ldots + \begin{vmatrix} a_{11} \ldots \quad 0 \ldots a_{1n} \\ \cdot \\ \cdot \\ \cdot \\ 0 \\ a_{n1} \quad a_{nk} \quad a_{nn} \end{vmatrix}.$$

The first formula of the theorem is called an **expansion by elements of the** k^{th} **column.** An expansion by elements of the 2nd column is exhibited by

$$\begin{vmatrix} 1 & 4 & 2 & 3 \\ 2 & 8 & 3 & 5 \\ 4 & 9 & 3 & 2 \\ 5 & 7 & 0 & 6 \end{vmatrix} = -4\begin{vmatrix} 2 & 3 & 5 \\ 4 & 3 & 2 \\ 5 & 0 & 6 \end{vmatrix} + 8\begin{vmatrix} 1 & 2 & 3 \\ 4 & 3 & 2 \\ 5 & 0 & 6 \end{vmatrix} - 9\begin{vmatrix} 1 & 2 & 3 \\ 2 & 3 & 5 \\ 5 & 0 & 6 \end{vmatrix} + 7\begin{vmatrix} 1 & 2 & 3 \\ 2 & 3 & 5 \\ 4 & 3 & 2 \end{vmatrix}.$$

There is a good reason for using the notation A_{ji} for the co-factor of the element a_{ij}. It is customary to call that matrix whose element in the ith row and j^{th} column is A_{ji} the **adjoint** of the matrix $[a_{ij}]$, and denote it by adj $[a_{ij}]$.

(The reader will recall that the word adjoint is also used, as in Section 2.2, for the conjugate transpose $[a_{ij}]^*$.) For example,

$$\text{adj} \begin{bmatrix} 1 & 2 & 3 \\ 2 & 3 & 2 \\ 4 & 1 & 5 \end{bmatrix} = \begin{bmatrix} 13 & -7 & -5 \\ -2 & -7 & 4 \\ -10 & 7 & -1 \end{bmatrix}.$$

THEOREM 2.3G

$$[a_{ij}] \cdot \text{adj} [a_{ij}] = \det [a_{ij}] \cdot [I],$$
$$\text{adj} [a_{ij}] \cdot [a_{ij}] = \det [a_{ij}] \cdot [I].$$

Proof We shall prove the first equality, which states that

(2)
$$\sum_{r=1}^{n} a_{kr} A_{re} = \det [a_{ij}] \cdot \delta_{ke}.$$

When $e = k$, (2) is valid in virtue of Theorem 2.3F. When $e \neq k$, the right side of (2) is zero. The left side is also zero since it is the expansion by minors of the determinant of the matrix formed from $[a_{ij}]$ by replacing the eth row by the kth thus making two rows equal. ★

Corollary
If $\det [a_{ij}] \neq 0$, then $[a_{ij}]$ has an inverse given by

$$[a_{ij}]^{-1} = \frac{\text{adj} [a_{ij}]}{\det [a_{ij}]}.$$

An $n \times n$ matrix is called **singular** or **nonsingular** according as its determinant is or is not equal to zero. The corollary states that a nonsingular matrix has an inverse. The converse is also true, for if

$$[a_{ij}][a_{ij}]^{-1} = [\delta_{ij}]$$

then

$$\det [a_{ij}] \det [a_{ij}]^{-1} = \det [\delta_{ij}] = 1,$$

so that $\det [a_{ij}]$ must be different from zero.

Exercise 2.3

1. Evaluate det $\begin{bmatrix} 1 & 2 & 3 & 4 \\ 2 & 3 & 4 & 1 \\ 3 & 4 & 1 & 2 \\ 4 & 1 & 2 & 3 \end{bmatrix}$

by an expansion by elements of the 2nd row, and also by elements of the 4th column.

2. Let $[a_{ij}]$ be a matrix of odd order, with $a_{ij} = 0$ if $i + j$ is even. Show that det $[a_{ij}] = 0$ by use of the definition of determinant.

3. Show that the determinant of a real orthogonal matrix is 1 or -1. Use Theorem 2.3E.

4. Show that the determinant of a unitary matrix has absolute value 1.

5. Prove that the equation of a straight line in the plane which passes through the points (a, b) and (c, d) is given by

$$\begin{vmatrix} x & y & 1 \\ a & b & 1 \\ c & d & 1 \end{vmatrix} = 0.$$

6. If $[a_{ij}]^{-1}$ exists, then det $[a_{ij}]^{-1} = \dfrac{1}{\det [a_{ij}]}.$

7. Let $[a_{ij}]$ be a matrix of odd order with $a_{ji} = -a_{ij}$. Show that det $[a_{ij}] = 0$.

8. Prove that

$$\begin{vmatrix} 1 & \ldots\ldots & 1 \\ x_1 & \ldots\ldots & x_n \\ x_1^2 & \ldots\ldots & x_n^2 \\ x_1^{n-1} & \ldots\ldots & x_n^{n-1} \end{vmatrix} = \prod_{i<j}\{x_j - x_i\}$$

9. For the matrix of Exercise 1, calculate the adjoint and the inverse. Verify Theorem 2.3G for this matrix.

10. Find the inverses (if they exist) of

$$\text{(a)} \begin{bmatrix} 1 & 3 & 5 \\ 0 & 7 & 9 \\ 2 & 1 & 4 \end{bmatrix} \quad \text{(b)} \begin{bmatrix} 1 & 4 & 2 \\ 2 & 3 & 6 \\ 8 & 17 & 22 \end{bmatrix}.$$

11. (a) If

$$[A] = \begin{bmatrix} 1 & 0 & 0 & 0 \\ 0 & 1 & 0 & 0 \\ e & f & g & h \\ i & j & k & m \end{bmatrix},$$

show that det $[A]$ = det $\begin{bmatrix} g & h \\ k & m \end{bmatrix}$.

(b) If

$$[B] = \begin{bmatrix} a & b & 0 & 0 \\ c & d & 0 & 0 \\ e & f & g & h \\ i & j & k & m \end{bmatrix}$$

write it as

$$\begin{bmatrix} a & b & 0 & 0 \\ c & d & 0 & 0 \\ e & f & 1 & 0 \\ i & j & 0 & 1 \end{bmatrix} \begin{bmatrix} 1 & 0 & 0 & 0 \\ 0 & 1 & 0 & 0 \\ 0 & 0 & g & h \\ 0 & 0 & k & m \end{bmatrix}$$

and show that

$$\det [B] = \det \begin{bmatrix} a & b \\ c & d \end{bmatrix} \cdot \det \begin{bmatrix} g & h \\ k & m \end{bmatrix}.$$

(c) Generalize the result to the case

$$\begin{bmatrix} [L] & [O] \\ [M] & [N] \end{bmatrix}$$

where $[L]$, $[N]$ are square matrices and $[O]$ indicates a matrix of zeros.

12. Express as a single determinant

$$\begin{vmatrix} a + bi & -c + di \\ c + di & a - bi \end{vmatrix} \cdot \begin{vmatrix} e + fi & -g + hi \\ g + hi & e - fi \end{vmatrix}$$

where $i^2 = -1$, and thus prove that the product of two sums of four squares is also expressible as a sum of four squares.

13. If $[a_{ij}]$ is a real orthogonal matrix with determinant equal to one, then every element a_{ij} is equal to its own co-factor.

14. Let $[A_1], \ldots [A_n]$ be square matrices and

$$[A] = \begin{bmatrix} [A_1] & [0] \ldots & \\ [0] & [A_2] & \\ & \cdot & \\ & \cdot & [A_n] \end{bmatrix}$$

where all elements in $[A]$ are 0 if they do not lie in one of $[A_j]$. Prove det $[A]$ = det $[A_1]$ det $[A_2] \ldots$ det $[A_n]$. Use the method suggested in Exercise 11.

2.4

NUMERICAL METHODS

We turn our attention to simple numerical methods of calculating the inverse of a matrix and of determining linear independence of vectors.

For a given $n \times n$ matrix $[A] = [a_{ij}]$, the nth degree polynomial det $[x\delta_{ij} - a_{ij}] = \sum\limits_{i=0}^{n} d_i x^i$ is called the **characteristic function** of $[A]$. The equation in x given by

$$\det [x\delta_{ij} - a_{ij}] = \sum_{i=0}^{n} d_i x^i = 0$$

is called the **characteristic equation** of $[A]$. The next theorem, known as the

Hamilton–Cayley Theorem, states that every matrix satisfies its characteristic equation in the sense that $\sum_{i=0}^{n} d_i[A]^i = [0]$. Thus the $n + 1$ matrices

$$[I] = [A]^0, [A] = [A]^1, [A]^2, \ldots, [A]^n$$

are linearly dependent when considered as elements in the vector space of all $n \times n$ matrices. Some such result might have been expected since the vector space of $n \times n$ matrices has dimension n^2 so that the first $n^2 + 1$ powers of $[A]$ are linearly dependent.

The matrix $[x\delta_{ij} - a_{ij}]$ is an example of a matrix whose elements are polynomials in x. Every such matrix can be written uniquely as a polynomial in x with coefficients which are matrices with scalar elements. For example,

$$\begin{bmatrix} 2x + 3 & x \\ 3 & 3x^2 + 1 \end{bmatrix} = \begin{bmatrix} 0 & 0 \\ 0 & 3 \end{bmatrix} x^2 + \begin{bmatrix} 2 & 1 \\ 0 & 0 \end{bmatrix} x + \begin{bmatrix} 3 & 0 \\ 3 & 1 \end{bmatrix}.$$

The $(i, j)^{th}$ element of the matrix which is the coefficient of x^p on the right side of the equality is exactly the coefficient of x^p in the $(i, j)^{th}$ element of the matrix on the left side.

THEOREM 2.4A   Let the characteristic function of $[A] = [a_{ij}]_{n,n}$ be $\det [x\delta_{ij} - a_{ij}] = \sum_{i=0}^{n} d_i x^i$. Then

$$\sum_{i=0}^{n} d_i[A]^i = [0].$$

Proof   If $[C_i]$, $[D_i]$ are $n \times n$ matrices, the polynomial identity

(1) $$\left\{ \sum_{i=0}^{p-1} [C_i]x^i \right\} \left\{ x[I] - [A] \right\} = \sum_{i=0}^{p} [D_i]x^i$$

means that the coefficients $[D_i]$ on the right side are given by

$$[D_0] = -[C_0][A]$$
$$[D_1] = [C_0] - [C_1][A]$$
$$\cdot$$
$$\cdot$$
$$\cdot$$
$$[D_{p-1}] = [C_{p-2}] - [C_{p-1}][A]$$
$$[D_p] = [C_{p-1}].$$

From (1) we obtain an identity by substituting formally for x any matrix $[M]$ which commutes with $[A]$. For computation yields

$$\left\{ \sum_{i=0}^{p-1} [C_i][M]^i \right\} \left\{ [M][I] - [A] \right\} = \sum_{i=0}^{p-1} [C_i][M]^{i+1} - \sum_{i=0}^{p-1} [C_i][A][M]^i$$

$$= \sum_{i=0}^{p} [D_i][M]^i.$$

In particular, if $[M] = [A]$, then $\displaystyle\sum_{i=0}^{p} [D_i][A]^i = [0]$.

Apply this reasoning to the polynomial identity

$$\{\mathrm{adj}\,[x\delta_{ij} - a_{ij}]\}[x\delta_{ij} - a_{ij}] = \{\det\,[x\delta_{ij} - a_{ij}]\}[I]$$

$$= \left\{ \sum_{i=0}^{n} d_i x^i \right\}[I] = \sum_{i=0}^{n} [D_i]x^i,$$

where $[D_i] = d_i[I]$, to get

$$\sum_{i=0}^{n} [D_i][A]^i = [0].$$

This shows that $\displaystyle\sum_{i=0}^{n} d_i[A]^i = [0]$. ★

This theorem can be used to obtain the inverse of a nonsingular matrix $[A]$. If $\sum_{i=0}^{n} d_i x^i$ is the characteristic function, then

$$d_n[A]^n + d_{n-1}[A]^{n-1} + \cdots + d_1[A] + d_0[I] = [0],$$

from which one gets

$$\{d_n[A]^{n-1} + d_{n-1}[A]^{n-2} + \cdots + d_1[I]\}[A] = -d_0[I].$$

The number d_0 is not zero if $\det [A] \neq 0$, since the identity

$$\det [x\delta_{ij} - a_{ij}] = \sum_{i=0}^{n} d_i x^i$$

indicates $(-1)^n \det [a_{ij}] = d_0$. Hence

(2) $$[A]^{-1} = \frac{-1}{d_0} \left\{ d_n[A]^{n-1} + \ldots + d_1[I] \right\}.$$

Another technique for the calculation of inverses is obtained from an interpretation of the statement

$$[B][A] = [I] \text{ implies } [B] = [A]^{-1}.$$

If we rewrite this as

$$[B][A] = [I] \text{ implies } [B][I] = [A]^{-1},$$

we can interpret it as follows: That operator $[B]$ which yields $[I]$ when acting on $[A]$ will also yield $[A]^{-1}$ when acting on $[I]$. This suggests we study methods of carrying $[A]$ into $[I]$. We shall show that this can be done, when $[A]$ is nonsingular, by a sequence of operations of the following three types, called **elementary row transformations**:

    (i)   Interchange of two rows.
    (ii) Multiplication of a row by a nonzero scalar c.
   (iii) Addition of a multiple k of any row to another row.

If $\det [A] \neq 0$, not all the elements of the first column are zero. By an interchange of rows, we may suppose $a_{11} \neq 0$. Divide the first row by a_{11} and subtract appropriate multiples of the new first row from the other rows to make all elements of the first column, except the first element, equal to zero. Denote by b_{ij} the element in the ith row and j^{th} column of the resulting matrix. We have $b_{k1} = 0$ for $k \neq 1$, $b_{11} = 1$. By an interchange of the last $n - 1$ rows we may assume $b_{22} \neq 0$. Divide the second row by b_{22} and subtract appropriate multiples of the new second row from the other rows to make all elements of the second column, except the second element, equal to zero. The operations performed on the elements b_{ij} will not affect the first column. Continuing in this fashion we obtain $[I]$.

EXAMPLE 1   Let

(3)
$$[A] = \begin{bmatrix} 2 & -2 & 1 \\ 0 & 1 & \frac{1}{2} \\ 1 & 5 & 0 \end{bmatrix}.$$

Multiplying the first row by $\frac{1}{2}$ and subtracting the new first row from the third, we get

$$\begin{bmatrix} 1 & -1 & \frac{1}{2} \\ 0 & 1 & \frac{1}{2} \\ 0 & 6 & -\frac{1}{2} \end{bmatrix}.$$

The element in the second row, second column is already 1. Add the second row to the first and subtract six times the second row from the third to form

$$\begin{bmatrix} 1 & 0 & 1 \\ 0 & 1 & \frac{1}{2} \\ 0 & 0 & -\frac{7}{2} \end{bmatrix}.$$

Multiply the third row by $-\frac{2}{7}$, add $-\frac{1}{2}$ the new third row to the second and -1 times the new third row to the first to obtain the identity matrix.

Now each of the three elementary row transformations can be effected by multiplication on the left by a matrix obtained from the identity matrix by applying the corresponding row transformation to $[I]$. Thus to interchange the ith and j^{th} rows of an $m \times n$ matrix $[D]$, premultiply $[D]$ by that $m \times m$ matrix obtained from the $m \times m$ identity matrix by interchanging the ith and j^{th} rows. To multiply the ith row of $[D]$ by the scalar c, premultiply $[D]$ by that matrix obtained from the $m \times m$ identity matrix by replacing 1 by c in the ith row and i^{th} column. To add k times the ith row of $[D]$ to the jth row, premultiply $[D]$ by that matrix obtained from the $m \times m$ identity matrix by replacing 0 by k in the jth row and i^{th} column. The three types of matrices obtained by performing elementary row transformations on the identity matrix are called **elementary matrices.**

It follows that the matrix $[B]$ such that $[B][A] = [I]$ is a product of matrices corresponding to elementary row transformations. We have seen that premultiplication of $[I]$ by $[B]$, that is, application of these elementary row transformations to $[I]$, will produce $[A]^{-1}$.

EXAMPLE 2   Using the matrix $[A]$ of Example 1, apply the transformations used to carry $[A]$ into $[I]$ to the identity matrix

$$[I] = \begin{bmatrix} 1 & 0 & 0 \\ 0 & 1 & 0 \\ 0 & 0 & 1 \end{bmatrix}$$

to obtain in turn

$$\begin{bmatrix} \frac{1}{2} & 0 & 0 \\ 0 & 1 & 0 \\ -\frac{1}{2} & 0 & 1 \end{bmatrix}, \quad \begin{bmatrix} \frac{1}{2} & 1 & 0 \\ 0 & 1 & 0 \\ -\frac{1}{2} & -6 & 1 \end{bmatrix}, \quad \begin{bmatrix} \frac{5}{14} & -\frac{5}{7} & \frac{2}{7} \\ -\frac{1}{14} & \frac{1}{7} & \frac{1}{7} \\ \frac{1}{7} & \frac{12}{7} & -\frac{2}{7} \end{bmatrix} = [A]^{-1}.$$

Both matrices may be transformed simultaneously by applying the elementary row transformations to

$$\begin{bmatrix} 2 & -2 & 1 & 1 & 0 & 0 \\ 0 & 1 & \frac{1}{2} & 0 & 1 & 0 \\ 1 & 5 & 0 & 0 & 0 & 1 \end{bmatrix}.$$

For further details regarding matrix inversion, the reader may consult the article *Methods of Matrix Inversion* by D. Greenspan in the *American Mathematical Monthly*, Vol. 62, Number 5, May 1955.

The following application of matrix inversion to integration illustrates some of the concepts already discussed. Let $\mathscr{V}$ be the vector space of continuously differentiable functions on $-\infty < x < \infty$ with addition and scalar multiplication defined as usual. Let $\sigma_1, \ldots, \sigma_n$ be a basis for a linear manifold $\mathscr{M}$ having the property that the derivatives of $\sigma_1, \ldots, \sigma_n$ lie in $\mathscr{M}$. Then the operation D of differentiation is a linear transformation on $\mathscr{M}$ to $\mathscr{M}$. Let $D \overset{\sigma}{\leftrightarrow} [D]$. If $[D]^{-1}$ exists and the vector α in $\mathscr{M}$ has the representation $\alpha \overset{\sigma}{\leftrightarrow} [x_i]$ then $D^{-1}\alpha \overset{\sigma}{\leftrightarrow} [D]^{-1}[x_i]$. In this way we can obtain antiderivatives for elements of $\mathscr{M}$.

EXAMPLE 3 If $\sigma_1 = e^{at} \sin bt$, $\sigma_2 = e^{at} \cos bt$, then

$$D\sigma_1 = ae^{at} \sin bt + be^{at} \cos bt = a\sigma_1 + b\sigma_2,$$

$$D\sigma_2 = -be^{at} \sin bt + ae^{at} \cos bt = -b\sigma_1 + a\sigma_2,$$

so that

$$D \overset{\sigma}{\leftrightarrow} \begin{bmatrix} a & -b \\ b & a \end{bmatrix},$$

from which we obtain

$$D^{-1} \overset{\sigma}{\leftrightarrow} \frac{1}{a^2 + b^2} \begin{bmatrix} a & b \\ -b & a \end{bmatrix}.$$

If we take $\alpha = e^{at} \sin bt = 1\sigma_1 + 0\sigma_2$, then

$$D^{-1}\alpha = \int e^{at} \sin bt \, dt \overset{\sigma}{\leftrightarrow} \frac{1}{a^2 + b^2} \begin{bmatrix} a & b \\ -b & a \end{bmatrix} \begin{bmatrix} 1 \\ 0 \end{bmatrix} = \frac{1}{a^2 + b^2} \begin{bmatrix} a \\ -b \end{bmatrix}$$

and

$$\int e^{at} \sin bt \, dt = \frac{1}{a^2 + b^2} (ae^{at} \sin bt - be^{at} \cos bt).$$

It will be convenient to introduce the concept of rank. The **rank** of an $m \times n$ matrix is defined to be the order of the largest nonsingular square submatrix. By a **submatrix** we mean the matrix or a matrix obtained from the given matrix by the deletion of rows and columns. It is clear from the definition that the rank of a matrix is equal to the rank of its transpose.

The following theorem is fundamental.

THEOREM 2.4B The rank of an $m \times n$ matrix is equal to the number of linearly independent column vectors and is also equal to the number of linearly independent row vectors.

Proof It is only necessary to show that the rank r of the $m \times n$ matrix $[a_{ij}]$ is equal to the number s of linearly independent column vectors

$$\alpha_i = \begin{bmatrix} a_{1i} \\ \cdot \\ \cdot \\ \cdot \\ \cdot \\ a_{mi} \end{bmatrix}, \qquad i = 1, \ldots, n,$$

in $\mathscr{E}_m$ (or $\mathscr{E}_m{}^*$) as the statement regarding rows will then follow by considering $[a_{ij}]^T$. We note that $r \le n$, $r \le m$, $s \le n$. For notational simplicity, suppose

$$[b_{ij}]_{rr} = \begin{bmatrix} a_{11} \ldots \ldots a_{1r} \\ \cdot \qquad \cdot \\ \cdot \qquad \cdot \\ \cdot \qquad \cdot \\ a_{r1} \ldots \ldots a_{rr} \end{bmatrix}$$

has det $[b_{ij}] \ne 0$. We shall show that $\alpha_1, \ldots, \alpha_r$ are linearly independent. None of $\alpha_1, \ldots, \alpha_r$ is the zero vector, since det $[b_{ij}] \ne 0$. If $\sum_{i=1}^{r} c_i \alpha_i = \theta$ for scalar c_i not all zero, then one of $\alpha_1, \ldots, \alpha_r$ is a linear combination of the preceding, say $\alpha_j = \sum_{i=1}^{j-1} d_i \alpha_i$. If we define α_i' to be the r-rowed vector obtained from α_i by using only the first r elements, we have $\alpha_i' = \sum_{i=1}^{j-1} d_i \alpha_i'$. By Corollary 2 of Theorem 2.3D, det $[b_{ij}] = 0$. This contradiction shows that $s \ge r$.

If $r = n$, then $s \le n = r$ so that $s = r$ and the theorem is proved.

If $r < n$, the matrix

(4)
$$\begin{bmatrix} a_{11} \ldots \ldots a_{1r}\ a_{1j} \\ \cdot \\ \cdot \\ \cdot \\ a_{r1} \ldots \ldots a_{rr}\ a_{rj} \\ a_{k1} \ldots \ldots a_{kr}\ a_{kj} \end{bmatrix}$$

has zero determinant for every j and k, $j = r + 1, \ldots, n$, $k = 1, \ldots, m$. Expanding the determinant of (4) by elements of the last row, we see that

$$a_{k1} A_{1k} + a_{k2} A_{2k} + \ldots a_{kr} A_{rk} + a_{kj} A_{jk} = 0,$$

where A_{pk} is the co-factor of a_{kp}. This relation is valid for each fixed k, $k = 1, \ldots, m$ and each fixed $j, j = r + 1, \ldots, n$. For fixed j, the numbers $y_i = A_{ik}$ are independent of k, since they are co-factors of a_{ki} and thus are calculated from the first r rows of (4). Hence for fixed j, we obtain

(5)
$$y_1 \alpha_1 + \cdots + y_r \alpha_r + y_j \alpha_j = \theta.$$

The coefficient $y_j = A_{jk} = \det [b_{ij}] \neq 0$, indicating that $\alpha_j, j = r + 1, \ldots, n$, is a linear combination of $\alpha_1, \ldots, \alpha_r$. It follows that $s \leq r$.

The inequalities $s \geq r, s \leq r$ yield $s = r$, proving the theorem. ★

The theorem yields an algorithm for obtaining the number of linearly independent vectors in a set. Let $\sigma_1, \ldots, \sigma_m$ be a basis in a vector space $\mathscr{V}$ and let

$$\alpha_1 = a_{11} \sigma_1 + \ldots + a_{m1} \sigma_m$$
$$\cdots \cdots \cdots \cdots \cdots$$
$$\alpha_n = a_{1n} \sigma_1 + \ldots + a_{mn} \sigma_m.$$

be n vectors in $\mathscr{V}$. Form the matrix $[a_{ij}]$ whose k^{th} column is the $m \times 1$ matrix representation of α_k. Then the number of linearly independent α_i is the rank r of the matrix.

Suppose that $\alpha_1, \ldots, \alpha_r$ are linearly independent and that

$$\mu = b_1 \sigma_1 + \ldots + b_m \sigma_m$$

lies in the linear manifold spanned by $\alpha_1, \ldots, \alpha_r$. Then there are constants $c_1, \ldots, c_r$ such that

$$\mu = c_1 \alpha_1 + \ldots + c_r \alpha_r.$$

We seek to determine the constants c_i. By interchanging σ_i if necessary, we may suppose

$$\Delta = \begin{bmatrix} a_{11} \cdots \cdots a_{1r} \\ \cdot \\ \cdot \\ \cdot \\ a_{r1} \cdots \cdots a_{rr} \end{bmatrix} \neq 0.$$

Use equation (5) with α_j replaced by $\begin{bmatrix} b_1 \\ \cdot \\ \cdot \\ \cdot \\ b_m \end{bmatrix} \overset{\sigma}{\leftrightarrow} \mu$ to determine μ in terms of

$\alpha_1, \ldots, \alpha_r$. Since μ is represented uniquely in terms of $\alpha_1, \ldots, \alpha_r$, we must have $c_i = -y_i/y_j$, $i = 1, \ldots, r$. We leave it to the reader to verify

$$c_1 = \frac{1}{\Delta} \begin{vmatrix} b_1, a_{12} \ldots a_{1r} \\ \cdot \\ \cdot \\ \cdot \\ b_r, a_{r2} \ldots a_{rr} \end{vmatrix}, \qquad c_2 = \frac{1}{\Delta} \begin{vmatrix} a_{11}, b_1, a_{13} \ldots a_{1r} \\ \cdot \\ \cdot \\ \cdot \\ a_{r1}, b_r, a_{r3} \ldots a_{rr} \end{vmatrix}, \qquad \text{etc.}$$

Elementary transformations may be used to advantage in the calculation of rank. We leave to the reader as Exercise 2.4–4 the proof of the fact that elementary matrices are not singular. From this it follows at once that elementary row transformations on an $m \times n$ matrix $[A]$ cannot change the rank of $[A]$. Indeed, an elementary row transformation changes $[A]$ into $[E][A] = [B]$ and since each row of $[B]$ is a linear combination of the rows of $[A]$, the rank of $[B]$ cannot exceed that of $[A]$. Moreover, the nonsingularity of the elementary matrix $[E]$ permits us to write $[A] = [E]^{-1}[B]$ showing, in the same way, that the rank of $[A]$ cannot exceed the rank of $[B]$. By elementary row transformations one may reduce $[A]$ to a matrix with numerous zeros and thus simplify the calculation of rank.

In a similar fashion one may define and deal with elementary column transformations.

EXAMPLE 4   Consider the matrix

$$(6) \qquad \begin{bmatrix} 2 & 1 & 3 & 4 & 2 \\ -1 & 5 & 0 & 3 & 8 \\ 4 & 1 & 4 & 2 & 2 \\ 9 & -2 & 10 & 7 & -2 \end{bmatrix}.$$

Denote the columns by $\alpha_1, \ldots, \alpha_5$. By elementary row transformations we can reduce the matrix to

$$(7) \qquad \begin{bmatrix} 2 & 1 & 3 & 4 & 2 \\ 0 & 11 & 3 & 10 & 18 \\ 0 & 0 & 19 & 56 & 4 \\ 0 & 0 & 0 & 0 & 0 \end{bmatrix}.$$

The rank is three, since the first three columns are clearly independent and every four by four determinant is zero. To find α_4 in terms of α_1, α_2, α_3 we would have to find constants a, b, c such that $\alpha_4 = a\alpha_1 + b\alpha_2 + c\alpha_3$, that is,

$$(8) \qquad \begin{cases} 2a + b + 3c = 4 \\ -a + 5b = 3 \\ 4a + b + 4c = 2 \\ 9a - 2b + 10c = 7. \end{cases}$$

Each elementary row transformation on matrix (6) can be considered as an operation on the set of equations (8). These operations — interchanging two equations, multiplying one equation by a nonzero constant, adding the left sides and right sides of two equations — can only change the system (8) into an **equivalent system**; that is, one yielding the same solution for a, b, c. It follows that an equivalent system can be read from matrix (7), using the first four columns, as

$$\begin{cases} 2a + b + 3c = 4 \\ 11b + 3c = 10 \\ 19c = 56. \end{cases}$$

From this, solving successively for c, b, a, one finds

$$c = \tfrac{56}{19}, \quad b = \tfrac{2}{19}, \quad a = -\tfrac{47}{19},$$

$$\alpha_4 = -\tfrac{47}{19}\alpha_1 + \tfrac{2}{19}\alpha_2 + \tfrac{56}{19}\alpha_3.$$

Similarly one can find α_5 in terms of α_1, α_2, α_3 by use of columns 1, 2, 3, and 5 of matrix (7).

Exercise 2.4

1. Find the characteristic function of

$$\begin{bmatrix} 1 & 2 & 3 \\ 3 & 0 & 2 \\ 1 & 1 & -1 \end{bmatrix}.$$

Then use equation (2) of the text to find the inverse.

2. Calculate the inverse of the matrix of Exercise 1 by use of elementary row transformations.

3. For the following matrices find the rank r. Find the first r linearly independent columns and write the others as linear combinations of the first r independent ones.

(a) $$\begin{bmatrix} 2 & 0 & 1 & -3 & 3 \\ -1 & 2 & 3 & 2 & 1 \\ 3 & 2 & 1 & 6 & 0 \\ 1 & 2 & 3 & -2 & 4 \end{bmatrix}$$
(b) $$\begin{bmatrix} 1 & 2 & 3 & 2 \\ 3 & 4 & 1 & 2 \end{bmatrix}$$

(c) $$\begin{bmatrix} 3 & 1 \\ 6 & 2 \\ 2 & 4 \\ 1 & 1 \end{bmatrix}$$
(d) $$\begin{bmatrix} 1 & -2 & 0 & -1 \\ 3 & -6 & 1 & -2 \\ -1 & 2 & 2 & 3 \\ 2 & -4 & 4 & 2 \end{bmatrix}$$

4. (a) Verify that elementary matrices are nonsingular.
(b) Show that the inverse of an elementary matrix is also an elementary matrix.

5. Without interpreting an elementary row transformation as premultiplication by a matrix, show that elementary row transformations cannot change the rank of a matrix $[A]$ by considering the submatrices of the resulting matrix.

6. Prove that a necessary and sufficient condition that for a given $n \times n$ matrix $[A]$ there exist an $n \times n$ matrix $[B]$ not identically zero such that $[A][B] = [0]$ is that $[A]$ be singular.

7. The rank of the product of two matrices cannot exceed the rank of either of the matrices.

8. If a matrix of rank r is multiplied by a nonsingular matrix, the rank of the product is r.

9. (a) Show that by use of both elementary row transformations and elementary column transformations any $n \times n$ matrix $[A]$ of rank r can be reduced to

$$[B] = \begin{bmatrix} 1 & 0 & \ldots\ldots & 0 \\ 0 & 1 & & \\ \cdot & & & \\ \cdot & & 1 & \\ \cdot & & & 0 \\ 0 & \ldots\ldots & & 0 \end{bmatrix},$$

a matrix with r 1's along the diagonal, and the rest of the elements zero.

(b) Show that $[B] = [C][A][D]$ where $[C]$, $[D]$ are nonsingular.

(c) The matrix $[B]$ can be written as a sum of r matrices of rank 1. Hence show that any $n \times n$ matrix of rank r can be written as the sum of r matrices of rank 1.

10. Find the values of c such that the matrix

$$\begin{bmatrix} 2 & 1 & 3 & 2 \\ 1 & 3 & 2 & 4 \\ c & 2 & 1 & 1 \\ 1 & c & 2 & 3 \end{bmatrix}$$

is of rank three.

11. (a) Suppose the $n \times n$ matrices $[A]$ and $[B]$ are singular. Is $[A] + [B]$ singular?

(b) Suppose $[A]$ and $[B]$ are nonsingular. Is $[A] + [B]$ nonsingular?

12. Find $\int t^2 \sin t \, dt$ by matrix inversion. *Hint:* Consider the basis $t^2 \sin t$, $t^2 \cos t$, $t \sin t$, $t \cos t$, $\sin t$, $\cos t$.

13. Find $\int t^3 e^t \, dt$ by matrix inversion.

14. Let T be a linear transformation on a vector space $\mathscr{V}$ to $\mathscr{V}$ with domain $\mathscr{V}$. Let $\sigma_1, \ldots, \sigma_n$ be a basis for $\mathscr{V}$ and $T \overset{\sigma}{\leftrightarrow} [T]$. Show that the rank of $[T]$ is equal to the dimension of the range of T. *Hint:* $[T][x_i]$ is a linear combination of the columns of $[T]$.

15. Find the inverse of each of the following.

(a) $\begin{bmatrix} 1 & 2 & 3 \\ 2 & 3 & 1 \\ 3 & 1 & 2 \end{bmatrix}$
(b) $\begin{bmatrix} 1 & 2 & 3 & 4 \\ 2 & 3 & 4 & 1 \\ 3 & 4 & 1 & 2 \\ 4 & 1 & 2 & 3 \end{bmatrix}$
(c) $\begin{bmatrix} 1 & 2i & 1 \\ -2i & 3 & 1+i \\ 1 & 1-i & 2 \end{bmatrix}$

16. (a) Show that the characteristic function of the $n \times n$ matrix

$$\begin{bmatrix} 0 & 1 & 0 \ldots 0 \\ 0 & 0 & 1 \ldots 0 \\ \cdots\cdots\cdots\cdots \\ 0 & 0 & 1 \\ \dfrac{-a_n}{a_0} & \dfrac{-a_{n-1}}{a_0} & \cdots & \dfrac{-a_1}{a_0} \end{bmatrix} = [a_{ij}]$$

whose only nonzero elements are $a_{i,i+1} = 1$ for $i = 1, 2, \ldots, n-1$ and $a_{ni} = -\dfrac{a_{n-i+1}}{a_0}$, $i = 1, 2, \ldots, n$, is

$$a_0 x^n + a_1 x^{n-1} + a_2 x^{n-2} + \ldots + a_n.$$

(b) Hence prove that every polynomial equation $\sum\limits_{i=0}^{n} d_i [B]^i = [0]$, where $[B]$ is an $n \times n$ matrix, has a solution.

2.5

LINEAR EQUATIONS

Determinants were originally studied in connection with the problem of finding solutions for a system of linear equations. The basic theorems relating to such systems will now be derived.

Suppose first that $[a_{ij}]_{n,n}$ and $[y_i]_n$ are given and that there exists a vector $[x_i]_n$ such that

(1) $$[a_{ij}][x_i] = [y_i].$$

The relation (1) may be written

(2) $$\begin{cases} a_{11} x_1 + \cdots + a_{1n} x_n = y_1 \\ \quad \vdots \\ a_{n1} x_1 + \cdots + a_{nn} x_n = y_n \end{cases}$$

or

(3) $$\sum_{j=1}^{n} a_{ij} x_j = y_i, \qquad i = 1, \ldots, n.$$

We may write

$$x_k \begin{vmatrix} a_{11}, & \ldots, & a_{1n} \\ & \cdot & \\ & \cdot & \\ & \cdot & \\ a_{n1}, & \ldots, & a_{nn} \end{vmatrix} = \begin{vmatrix} a_{11}, & \ldots, & x_k\, a_{1k}, & \ldots & a_{1n} \\ & & \cdot & \\ & & \cdot & \\ & & \cdot & \\ a_{n1}, & \ldots, & x_k\, a_{nk}, & \ldots & a_{nn} \end{vmatrix}.$$

If we add x_i times the ith column, for each $i \neq k$, to the kth column, we obtain

$$x_k \det [a_{ij}] = \begin{vmatrix} a_{11}, & \ldots, & \sum_{j=1}^{n} a_{ij}\, x_j, & \ldots, & a_{1n} \\ & & \cdot & \\ & & \cdot & \\ & & \cdot & \\ a_{n1}, & \ldots, & \sum_{j=1}^{n} a_{nj}\, x_j, & \ldots, & a_{nn} \end{vmatrix} = \begin{vmatrix} a_{11}, & \ldots, & y_1, & \ldots, & a_{1n} \\ & & \cdot & \\ & & \cdot & \\ & & \cdot & \\ a_{n1}, & \ldots, & y_n, & \ldots, & a_{nn} \end{vmatrix},$$

where the determinant on the right side is obtained from $\det [a_{ij}]$ by replacing the kth column by the vector $[y_i]$. Thus if $\det [a_{ij}] \neq 0$,

(4)
$$x_k = (\det [a_{ij}])^{-1} \begin{vmatrix} a_{11}, & \ldots, & y_1, & \ldots, & a_{1n} \\ & & \cdot & \\ & & \cdot & \\ & & \cdot & \\ a_{n1}, & \ldots, & y_n, & \ldots, & a_{nn} \end{vmatrix}$$

where $[y_i]$ occurs in the kth column. This result is known as **Cramer's rule.**

A more sophisticated argument using co-factors is instructive. Multiply the ith equation of (2) by A_{ki}, the co-factor of a_{ik}, and sum with respect to i, to obtain

$$\sum_{i=1}^{n} A_{ki}\, y_i = \sum_{j=1}^{n} \sum_{i=1}^{n} A_{ki}\, a_{ij}\, x_j = \sum_{j=1}^{n} \det [a_{ij}] \delta_{kj}\, x_j$$

$$= \det [a_{ij}] \cdot x_k.$$

Hence

$$x_k = \left\{ \sum_{i=1}^{n} A_{ki} y_i \right\} \Big/ \det [a_{ij}],$$

where the numerator is readily seen to be determinant on the right side of (4).

We have shown, in the case where det $[a_{ij}] \neq 0$, that if a solution $[x_i]$ of (1) exists, it is unique and may be obtained by Cramer's rule. Conversely, it is apparent that $[x_i] = [a_{ij}]^{-1}[y_i]$ is a solution of (1). Thus the solution of a system of type (2), with a nonsingular "matrix of coefficients" $[a_{ij}]$, may be obtained by the calculation of an inverse. The same inverse may be used independent of the vector $[y_i]$.

A summary of the results obtained is given as

THEOREM 2.5A   If the matrix $[a_{ij}]$ formed by the coefficients in a system of n linear equations in n unknowns $x_1, \ldots, x_n$, given by equations (2), is nonsingular, then there is a unique solution, the vector $[x_i]$ being given by

$$[x_i] = [a_{ij}]^{-1}[y_i].$$

The unknown x_k may also be obtained as the quotient of two determinants, $\dfrac{\det [b_{ij}]}{\det [a_{ij}]}$, where $[b_{ij}]$ is obtained from $[a_{ij}]$ by replacing the kth column by the vector $[y_i]$.

When dealing with m equations in n unknowns, given by

$$(5) \qquad \sum_{j=1}^{n} a_{ij}x_j = y_i, \qquad i = 1, \ldots, m,$$

it is useful to define the **augmented matrix** $[a_{ij}; y_i]$ as the $m \times (n + 1)$ matrix obtained by adding $[y_i]$ as a final column to the matrix $[a_{ij}]$.

THEOREM 2.5B   A solution for the system (5) exists if and only if the rank r of $[a_{ij}]$ is equal to the rank of the augmented matrix $[a_{ij}; y_i]$. When the ranks are equal, it is possible to assign arbitrary values to certain $n - r$ of the unknowns x_i and there will be a unique determination of the remaining r making $[x_i]$ a solution.

Proof   The rank of the augmented matrix is equal to the rank r of $[a_{ij}]$ if and only if $[y_i]$ is a linear combination of the columns of $[a_{ij}]$, that is, if and only if there exist scalars $x_1, \ldots, x_n$ satisfying (5).

For notational convenience we may assume the $r \times r$ matrix formed by deleting from $[a_{ij}]$ all rows and columns except the first r is nonsingular. Considering $x_{r+1}, \ldots, x_n$ as parameters and using Theorem 2.5A we may solve uniquely for $x_1, \ldots, x_r$ in terms of $x_{r+1}, \ldots, x_n$ by using only the first

r equations of (5). When the rank of the augmented matrix is r, the sth row, $s = r + 1, \ldots, m$ is a linear combination of the first r.

$$a_{sj} = \sum_{i=1}^{r} c_{si} a_{ij}, \quad j = 1, \ldots, n,$$

$$y_s = \sum_{i=1}^{r} c_{si} y_i.$$

From these we deduce

$$\sum_{j=1}^{n} a_{sj} x_j - y_s = \sum_{i=1}^{r} c_{si} \left\{ \sum_{j=1}^{n} a_{ij} x_j - y_i \right\}.$$

This shows that if the first r equations are satisfied by $x_1, \ldots, x_n$, the remaining $m - r$ equations will also be satisfied.   ★

Corollary 1

The system

(6) $$\sum_{j=1}^{n} a_{ij} x_j = 0, \quad i = 1, \ldots, m,$$

always has a solution. If $m = n$, a nonzero solution $[x_i]$ exists if and only if $\det [a_{ij}] = 0$.

The system (6), obtained from (5) by setting all $y_i = 0$, is called a **homogeneous system.** From the form of the solution obtained in Theorem 2.5B where $x_1, \ldots, x_r$ is obtained in terms of $x_{r+1}, \ldots, x_n$, one can deduce that (6) has exactly $n - r$ linearly independent vector solutions. We obtain this result in a different fashion in

THEOREM 2.5C   If r is the rank of $[a_{ij}]$, the system (6) has exactly $n - r$ linearly independent solutions.

Proof $[x_i]$ is a solution of (6) if and only if it lies in the null space of the linear transformation $[a_{ij}]$ on $\mathscr{E}_n^*$ to $\mathscr{E}_m^*$. The range of this transformation is the set of all vectors of the form $[a_{ij}][z_i]$, for $[z_i]$ in $\mathscr{E}_n^*$, each of which is seen to be a linear combination of the columns of $[a_{ij}]$. Thus the range is spanned by the columns of $[a_{ij}]$ and the dimension of the range is r. It follows that the dimension of the null space is $n - r$, in view of Theorem 1.4A.   ★

EXAMPLE 1 The system

$$\begin{cases} 2x_1 + 3x_2 = 0 \\ x_1 + 3x_2 = 0 \\ x_1 - x_2 = 0 \end{cases}$$

has

$$[a_{ij}] = \begin{bmatrix} 2 & 3 \\ 1 & 3 \\ 1 & -1 \end{bmatrix}$$

with rank 2, so there are $n - r = 2 - 2 = 0$ linearly independent solutions. The only solution is

$$\begin{bmatrix} x_1 \\ x_2 \end{bmatrix} = \begin{bmatrix} 0 \\ 0 \end{bmatrix}.$$

EXAMPLE 2 The augmented matrix of the system

$$\begin{cases} x + y + 3z - u + 4v = 3 \\ 2x + y + 4z - u + 6v = 5 \\ 3x + 2y + 7z - 2u + 10v = 8 \\ - 2x + y - u - 2v = -3 \end{cases}$$

is

$$\begin{bmatrix} 1 & 1 & 3 & -1 & 4 & 3 \\ 2 & 1 & 4 & -1 & 6 & 5 \\ 3 & 2 & 7 & -2 & 10 & 8 \\ -2 & 1 & 0 & -1 & -2 & -3 \end{bmatrix}.$$

By elementary row transformations (subtract twice the first row from the second, three times the first row from the third, add twice the first row to the fourth; then add the second row to the first, subtract the second row from the third, and add three times the second to the fourth) the matrix is changed into

$$\begin{bmatrix} 1 & 0 & 1 & 0 & 2 & 2 \\ 0 & -1 & -2 & 1 & -2 & -1 \\ 0 & 0 & 0 & 0 & 0 & 0 \\ 0 & 0 & 0 & 0 & 0 & 0 \end{bmatrix}.$$

From this we see that the ranks of the matrix of coefficients and the augmented matrix are both 2. Moreover, since elementary row transformations change

the original system of equations into an equivalent system, we can read from
the last matrix

$$\begin{cases} x = 2 - z - 2v \\ y = 1 - 2z + u - 2v. \end{cases}$$

Restricting our attention again to the case when the number of equations
is equal to the number of unknowns we derive a result relating the homogeneous and nonhomogeneous systems. Let $[a_{ij}]$ be an $n \times n$ matrix, whose
conjugate transpose is denoted by $[a_{ij}]^*$. The following four systems will be
considered:

(7) $[a_{ij}] [x_i] = [y_i]$,

(8) $[a_{ij}] [x_i] = [0]$,

(9) $[a_{ij}]^* [x_i] = [y_i]$,

(10) $[a_{ij}]^* [x_i] = [0]$.

THEOREM 2.5D The following alternative holds: Either, I. There
is a unique solution $[x_i]$ in $\mathscr{E}_n^*$ of (7) for each vector $[y_i]$, in particular system
(8) has only the zero solution. Moreover in this case (9) also has a unique
solution for each vector $[y_i]$; or, II. The system (8) has a finite number $m > 0$
orthonormal solutions $[z_{i1}], \ldots, [z_{im}]$. In this case system (10) has m orthonormal solutions $[v_{i1}], \ldots, [v_{im}]$. A solution for (7) exists if and only if
$[y_i]$ is orthogonal to each vector $[v_{ij}], j = 1, \ldots, m$. The solution of (7) is
not unique, but any two solutions of (7) differ by a linear combination of
$[z_{ij}], \quad j = 1, \ldots, m$.

Proof The system (7) has a unique solution for every vector $[y_i]$ if
$\det [a_{ij}] \neq 0$. In this case the system (8) has no nonzero solution and
$\det [a_{ij}]^* \neq 0$ so that system (9) also has a unique solution for each $[y_i]$. On
the other hand, if $\det [a_{ij}] = 0$, the system (8) has at least one nonzero
solution, by the corollary to Theorem 2.5B. This implies system (7) cannot
have a unique solution. Indeed if $[x_i]$ is a solution of (7) and $[u_i]$ is a nonzero
solution of (8) then $[x_i] + [u_i]$ is a solution of (7) different from $[x_i]$.

We have proved that one and only one of Case I and Case II can hold.
It remains to investigate Case II. The rank of $[a_{ij}]^*$ is equal to the rank of
$[a_{ij}]$, and Theorem 2.5C implies that the number of linearly independent
solutions $[v_{ij}]$ of system (10) is equal to the number of linearly independent
solutions $[z_{ij}], j = 1, \ldots, m$ of system (8). A linear combination of solutions

of (8) is also a solution of (8) so we may assume $[z_{ij}]$ orthonormal, and $[v_{ij}]$ also. We must show

$$(11) \qquad \sum_{j=1}^{n} a_{ij} x_j = y_i, \qquad i = 1, \ldots, n,$$

has a solution $[x_i]$ if and only if

$$(12) \qquad \sum_{i=1}^{n} y_i \bar{v}_i = 0$$

whenever

$$(13) \qquad \sum_{j=1}^{n} \overline{a_{ji}} v_j = 0, \qquad i = 1, \ldots, n.$$

The identity

$$\sum_{i=1}^{n} \sum_{j=1}^{n} a_{ij} x_j \bar{v}_i = \overline{\sum_{i=1}^{n} \sum_{j=1}^{n} \overline{a_{ji}} v_j \bar{x}_i}$$

indicates that if (11) has a solution then (12) is valid whenever (13) is. Conversely, if (12) and (13) are true then the vector $[y_i]$ is orthogonal to all vectors which are orthogonal to the rows of the transpose of $[a_{ij}]$, that is, $[y_i]$ is orthogonal to all vectors orthogonal to the columns of $[a_{ij}]$, and thus $[y_i]$ is a linear combination of the columns of $[a_{ij}]$. It follows that the rank of the augmented matrix $[a_{ij}; y_i]$ is equal to that of $[a_{ij}]$ and (11) has a solution.

The difference of any two solutions of (7) is a solution of (8) and hence is a linear combination of the linearly independent solutions $[z_{ij}]$ of (8). ★

Exercise 2.5

1. If

$$[A] = \begin{bmatrix} 1 & 1 & 1 \\ 0 & 1 & 0 \\ 2 & 0 & 1 \end{bmatrix}, \text{ calculate } [A]^{-1}.$$

Hence solve the system

$$\begin{cases} x + y + z = 1 \\ \quad\ y \quad\ = 3 \\ 2x \quad\ + z = 5. \end{cases}$$

2. Discuss the system

$$\begin{cases} 5x + 3y - 3z + 2w = 0 \\ x + y - z + 4w = 0 \\ 3x + 4y - 2z + 3w = 0. \end{cases}$$

3. Discuss the system

$$\begin{cases} 2x + y + z = 12 \\ x - y + 3z = 13 \\ 3x + 2y - 5z = -1 \\ 4x + y + z = 18. \end{cases}$$

4. A linear equation in three unknowns may be considered as a plane in 3-space. By investigating the rank of the matrix of coefficients of x, y, z and the augmented matrix determine whether the following systems of planes (1) meet in a point, (2) meet in a line, (3) are parallel, (4) have two of the planes intersecting in a line parallel to the third, (5) are coincident. Are there any other possibilities?

(a) $\begin{cases} x + y + z = 3 \\ 2x + y + z = 4 \\ x - y - z = -1 \end{cases}$ (b) $\begin{cases} x + y + z = 1 \\ x + y + z = 2 \\ x + y + z = 3 \end{cases}$

(c) $\begin{cases} 2x + 2y = 1 \\ 3x + 3y - z = 1 \\ x + y - z = 0 \end{cases}$ (d) $\begin{cases} -x + y + z = 0 \\ 2y + 2z = 1 \\ x + y + z = 0 \end{cases}$

5. The vectors $\alpha_1, \ldots, \alpha_n$ lie in a Euclidean vector space. Show that a necessary and sufficient condition that the vectors are linearly independent is that the **Gramian**, $\det [(\alpha_i, \alpha_j)]$, be different from zero. *Hint:* If α_i are dependent, there exist scalar a_i, not all zero, such that $\sum\limits_{i=1}^{n} a_i \alpha_i = \theta$. Hence $(\sum\limits_{i=1}^{n} a_i \alpha_i, \alpha_j) = 0$ for each j. This yields a system of equations in a_i to which one may apply the corollary to Theorem 2.5B. Prove the converse.

6. Discuss the system

$$\begin{cases} -7x + 3y - z + w = 4 \\ 2x + y + 2z - w = 1 \\ -x + 2y - 3z + 4w = 3 \\ -3x + 3y - z + 2w = 4. \end{cases}$$

7. The diagram illustrates a steady current electrical network composed of resistances given in multiples of the unit R and electromotive forces, abbreviated E.M.F., given in multiples of the unit E.

It is desired to find the currents in the wires using Kirchoff's laws which state:

1. Assume a direction for the current in each wire so that at each junction of wires the sum of the currents approaching is equal to the sum of the currents leaving. (If the algebraic sign of the current is negative, the true direction is opposite the assumed direction.)

2. In passing around a closed circuit the total change in potential is zero. That is, the sum of the potential drops is equal to the sum of the potential rises obtained from the E.M.F.'s. In passing from P_1 to P_2 through a resistance R in which a current I flows, the potential drop is IR if the direction from P_1 to P_2 is the direction assumed for the current and $-IR$ otherwise.

In passing through an E.M.F. the potential rise is equal to the value of the E.M.F. if the circuit direction is from −terminal to +terminal, and otherwise is the negative of the value of the E.M.F.

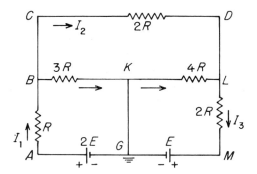

For example, if the current from A to B in the diagram is I_1 and the current from B to C is I_2 then the current from B to K is $I_1 - I_2$. Passing clockwise around $ABKG$, $KLMG$, $CDLB$ in turn we obtain

$$I_1R + 3(I_1 - I_2)R = 2E$$

$$4(I_3 - I_2)R + 2I_3R = -E$$

$$2I_2R - 4(I_3 - I_2)R - 3(I_1 - I_2)R = 0.$$

Solve for I_1, I_2, I_3 in terms of E/R.

8. Let $[A]$ have order n. Show that the rank of adj $[A]$ is n, 1, or 0 according as the rank of $[A]$ is n, $n - 1$ or less than $n - 1$ respectively. *Hint:* When the rank of $[A]$ is $n - 1$, use Theorem 2.3G and Theorem 2.5C.

9. Show that the system

$$\begin{cases} x_1 + x_2 + x_3 + \ldots + x_n = 1 \\ x_1 + 2x_2 + 2x_3 + \ldots + 2x_n = 2 \\ x_1 + 2x_2 + 3x_3 + \ldots + 3x_n = 3 \\ \quad . \\ \quad . \\ \quad . \\ x_1 + 2x_2 + 3x_3 + \ldots + nx_n = n \end{cases}$$

has a unique solution.

10. Solve

$$\begin{vmatrix} 1 & 1 & 1 & \ldots & 1 \\ 1 & 1-x & 1 & \ldots & 1 \\ 1 & 1 & 2-x & \ldots & 1 \\ & & & & \\ 1 & 1 & 1 & \ldots & n-x \end{vmatrix} = 0.$$

11. Show that a necessary and sufficient condition that the system (6) have a nonzero solution is that the rank of $[a_{ij}]$ be less than the number of unknowns.

12. In considering the system (5), let $A = [a_{ij}]$, $\sigma = [x_i]$, $\beta = [y_i]$, and suppose that the rank of A is r. Then (5) can be written as $A\sigma = \beta$. Let α_i, $i = 1, \ldots,$ $n - r$ be linearly independent solutions of $A\sigma = \theta$.

   (a) If σ is a particular solution of $A\sigma = \beta$, show that every solution is of the form $\sigma + \sum\limits_{i=1}^{n-r} c_i \alpha_i$, where c_i are constants.

   (b) Assume $\beta \neq \theta$. Show that $A\sigma = \beta$ has $n - r + 1$ linearly independent solutions, if it has one solution σ. *Hint:* Try σ and $\sigma + \alpha_i$.

   (c) Show that there are at most $n - r + 1$ linearly independent solutions of $A\sigma = \beta$. *Hint:* If $\sigma_1, \ldots, \sigma_k$ are linearly independent solutions, then $\sigma_1 - \sigma_j$, $j = 2, \ldots k$ are linearly independent solutions of $A\sigma = \theta$.

   (d) Use (c) to show that every solution σ of $A\sigma = \beta$, $\beta \neq \theta$, is a linear combination of any $n - r + 1$ linearly independent solutions σ_i, $i = 1,$ $\ldots, n - r + 1$. Moreover if $\sigma = \sum\limits_{i=1}^{n-r+1} c_i \sigma_i$, then $\sum\limits_{i=1}^{n-r+1} c_i = 1$.

2.6

DIAGONALIZATION

Let $\mathscr{V}$ be an n dimensional vector space and T a linear transformation on $\mathscr{V}$ to $\mathscr{V}$ with domain $\mathscr{V}$. A vector α in $\mathscr{V}$ is said to be an **eigenvector** of T if $\alpha \neq \theta$ and, for some scalar r, the relation $T\alpha = r\alpha$ is satisfied. The scalar r is called an **eigenvalue**. For each eigenvalue r there may be many eigenvectors. The set of all eigenvectors of T with eigenvalue r together with the zero vector is a linear manifold since $T\alpha = r\alpha$, $T\beta = r\beta$ imply $T(a\alpha + b\beta) = aT\alpha + bT\beta = r(a\alpha + b\beta)$. We refer to this set as the **eigenvector manifold associated with** r.

THEOREM 2.6A   Let $T \overset{\sigma}{\leftrightarrow} [t_{ij}]$. Each eigenvalue of T is a root of the characteristic equation $\det [x\delta_{ij} - t_{ij}] = 0$. If $\mathscr{W}$ is the eigenvector manifold associated with eigenvalue r, then

$$\dim \mathscr{W} = n - \operatorname{rank} [r\delta_{ij} - t_{ij}].$$

Proof To say $\alpha \overset{\sigma}{\leftrightarrow} [x_i]$ is a nonzero solution of $(rI - T)\alpha = \theta$ is to say $[x_i]$ is a nonzero solution of $[r\delta_{ij} - t_{ij}][x_i] = [0]$, a condition which holds if and only if $\det [r\delta_{ij} - t_{ij}] = 0$. The dimension of $\mathscr{W}$ is the number of linearly independent solutions $[x_i]$ which, by Theorem 2.5C, is $n - \operatorname{rank} [r\delta_{ij} - t_{ij}]$. ★

Theorem 2.6A does not state that the roots of the characteristic equation of $[t_{ij}]$ are also eigenvalues. This would be true if $\mathscr{V}$ were a complex vector space, but is not necessarily true if $\mathscr{V}$ is a real vector space since the roots of the characteristic equation need not be real. From the theorem it is clear that the number of distinct eigenvalues cannot exceed n, the degree of the characteristic equation. Moreover the number of linearly independent eigenvectors cannot exceed n, the dimension of $\mathscr{V}$.

From the definition one sees that the eigenvalues are independent of the basis in which T is represented. The next theorem shows that the characteristic function is also an invariant. We may therefore speak of the characteristic function of T and write it as det $[xI - T]$.

THEOREM 2.6B Let

$$T \overset{\sigma}{\leftrightarrow} [t_{ij}], \quad T \overset{\sigma'}{\leftrightarrow} [t'_{ij}].$$

Then

$$\det [x\delta_{ij} - t_{ij}] = \det [x\delta_{ij} - t'_{ij}].$$

Proof We have, for some nonsingular P,

$$[t'_{ij}] = [P]^{-1}[t_{ij}][P]$$

so that

$$[x\delta_{ij} - t'_{ij}] = [P]^{-1}[x\delta_{ij} - t_{ij}][P]$$

and

$$\det [x\delta_{ij} - t'_{ij}] = \det [P]^{-1} \det [x\delta_{ij} - t_{ij}] \det [P]$$
$$= \det [x\delta_{ij} - t_{ij}]$$

in view of Exercise 2.3–6. ★

With $x = 0$, we obtain

Corollary 1
The determinant of the matrix representing a linear transformation is independent of the basis.

THEOREM 2.6C Let $r_1, \ldots, r_m$ be distinct eigenvalues of T and let α_i be an eigenvector associated with r_i. Then the vectors $\alpha_1, \ldots, \alpha_m$ are linearly independent.

Proof Being eigenvectors, none of the α_i is zero. By reordering, if necessary, we may assume $\alpha_1, \alpha_2, \ldots, \alpha_j$ are linearly independent and form a basis for the linear manifold spanned by α_i, $i = 1, 2, \ldots, m$. If $j \neq m$, there exist constants c_i such that

(1) $$\alpha_{j+1} = c_1 \alpha_1 + \ldots + c_j \alpha_j.$$

Operating on both sides of (1) with T, we obtain

(2) $$r_{j+1} \alpha_{j+1} = c_1 r_1 \alpha_1 + \ldots + c_j r_j \alpha_j.$$

Multiplying (1) by r_{j+1} and subtracting the result from (2) yields

$$\theta = c_1\{r_1 - r_{j+1}\} \alpha_1 + \ldots + c_j \{r_j - r_{j+1}\} \alpha_j.$$

By hypothesis r_{j+1} is different from $r_1, \ldots, r_j$. The linear independence of $\alpha_1, \ldots, \alpha_j$ implies $c_i = 0$ for $i = 1, \ldots, j$ contradicting, by equation (1), the fact that $\alpha_{j+1} \neq \theta$. This proves $j = m$.   ★

Corollary 1

Let $r_1, \ldots, r_m$ be the distinct eigenvalues of T and $\mathcal{W}_1, \ldots, \mathcal{W}_m$ the associated eigenvector manifolds. For each i, $i = 1, \ldots, m$, let α_{ij} with $j = 1, \ldots, \dim \mathcal{W}_i$, be a basis for $\mathcal{W}_i$. Then all the vectors α_{ij}, $i = 1, \ldots, m$, $j = 1, \ldots, \dim \mathcal{W}_i$, are linearly independent.

Indeed, if $\sum_i \sum_j c_{ij} \alpha_{ij} = \theta$, the theorem implies that $\sum_j c_{ij} \alpha_{ij} = \theta$ for each i. The linear independence of α_{ij} in $\mathcal{W}_i$ then yields $c_{ij} = 0$ for each j and each i.

Since there cannot be more than n linearly independent vectors in $\mathcal{V}$, we obtain

Corollary 2

$$\dim \mathcal{W}_1 + \ldots + \dim \mathcal{W}_m \leq n.$$

A very important case arises when $\dim \mathcal{W}_1 + \ldots + \dim \mathcal{W}_m = n$.

THEOREM 2.6D   Let $r_1, \ldots, r_m$ be the distinct eigenvalues with associated eigenvector manifolds $\mathcal{W}_1, \ldots, \mathcal{W}_m$ of the linear transformation T on the n dimensional vector space $\mathcal{V}$ to $\mathcal{V}$ with domain $\mathcal{V}$. Then the following statements are equivalent:

(a)   Every α in $\mathcal{V}$ has a unique representation $\alpha = \mu_1 + \ldots + \mu_m$ with μ_i in $\mathcal{W}_i$.

(b) $\sum_{i=1}^{m} \dim \mathcal{W}_i = n$.

(c)   There is a basis $\alpha_1, \ldots, \alpha_n$ such that $T\alpha_i = s_i \alpha_i$ for constants s_i, $i = 1, \ldots, n$.

(d) There is a basis $\alpha_1, \ldots, \alpha_n$ in which T has the representation

$$T \overset{\alpha}{\leftrightarrow} \begin{bmatrix} s_1 & 0 \ldots 0 \\ 0 & s_2. \ldots 0 \\ 0 & 0 \ldots 0 \\ \cdot & \cdot \quad \cdot \\ \cdot & \cdot \quad \cdot \\ \cdot & \cdot \quad \cdot \\ 0 & 0 \ldots s_n \end{bmatrix}$$

where each element in the ith row and j^{th} column is zero if $i \neq j$.

Proof Suppose that (a) is true. Then $n = \dim \mathscr{V} \leq \sum_{i-1}^{m} \dim \mathscr{W}_i \leq n$ and (b) is true. For each i, choose $\dim \mathscr{W}_i$ linearly independent vectors from $\mathscr{W}_i$. By Corollary 1 of Theorem 2.6C, these are $\sum_{i=1}^{m} \dim \mathscr{W}_i$ linearly independent eigenvectors. If (b) holds, we have found n linearly independent eigenvectors $\alpha_1, \ldots, \alpha_n$ satisfying $T\alpha_i = s_i \alpha_i$. Thus (c) is true. The scalars s_i need not be distinct since different α_i may be associated with the same eigenvalue. That (c) implies (d) follows from Section 2.1. Finally, we must show that (d) implies (a). From (d) it follows that α_i are eigenvectors with eigenvalues s_i so that each s_i is contained in the set $r_1, \ldots, r_m$ and each α_i lies in one of the manifolds $\mathscr{W}_j$. Writing $\alpha = d_1 \alpha_1 + \ldots + d_n \alpha_n$ and adding vectors which lie in the same $\mathscr{W}_j$, we obtain (a). The representation is unique in virtue of Theorem 2.6C. ★

A square matrix $[a_{ij}]$ with $a_{ij} = 0$ for $i \neq j$ is called a **diagonal matrix**. The linear transformation T is said to be **diagonalizable** if there is a basis in which T has a representation as a diagonal matrix. Theorem 2.6D states that T is diagonalizable if and only if T has n linearly independent eigenvectors. It also states that the diagonal representation will be achieved in that basis whose elements are eigenvectors. Thus if $\sigma_1, \ldots, \sigma_n$ is a basis in which T has the representation $[t_{ij}]$ and T has n linearly independent eigenvectors $\alpha_i = \sum_{i=1}^{n} p_{ji} \sigma_j$, the discussion in Section 2.2 indicates that the diagonal representation will be

(3) $[p_{ij}]^{-1} [t_{ij}] [p_{ij}].$

The matrix $[p_{ij}]$ is the matrix whose k^{th} column is the representation of the kth eigenvector in the σ basis.

In view of Theorem 2.6C, an example of a diagonalizable operator is one which has n distinct eigenvalues.

The diagonal matrix represented in Theorem 2.6D can be written more compactly as $\operatorname{diag} [s_1, \ldots, s_n]$. This notation will be frequently employed.

THEOREM 2.6E If T has distinct eigenvalues $r_1, \ldots, r_m$ with associated eigenvector manifolds $\mathscr{W}_1, \ldots, \mathscr{W}_m$ respectively and if T can be diagonalized, then the roots of the characteristic equation are r_i with multiplicity dim $\mathscr{W}_i$.

Proof The characteristic equation of T computed with respect to the basis $\alpha_1, \ldots, \alpha_n$ for which $T\alpha_i = s_i \alpha_i$ is

$$
\det \begin{bmatrix}
x - s_1 & 0 & \ldots 0 \\
0 & x - s_2 & \ldots 0 \\
\vdots & \vdots & \vdots \\
0 & 0 & x - s_n
\end{bmatrix} = 0.
$$

The desired result is now evident.   ★

The terminology used above is applicable to matrices. For a given basis, each matrix $[a_{ij}]$ defines a linear transformation whose eigenvalues will be calculated as numbers r satisfying, for $[x_i] \neq [0]$, $[r\delta_{ij} - a_{ij}][x_i] = [0]$. For a real vector space we of course admit only real solutions. For different bases, the same matrix will define different linear transformations all having the same eigenvalues and eigenvectors with the same representations. We therefore speak of the eigenvalues and eigenvectors of the matrix. If, for some matrix $[p_{ij}]$, the product given by equation (3) is a diagonal matrix, we say $[t_{ij}]$ is diagonalized by a similarity transformation.

EXAMPLE 1 Consider the transformation T whose representation in a given basis is

$$
[t_{ij}] = \begin{bmatrix}
8 & -12 & 5 \\
15 & -25 & 11 \\
24 & -42 & 19
\end{bmatrix}.
$$

The characteristic equation is

$$(x - 1)(x + 1)(x - 2) = 0.$$

The eigenvector associated with the eigenvalue 1 is obtained by solving $T\alpha = 1\alpha$ or

$$
\begin{bmatrix}
7 & -12 & 5 \\
15 & -26 & 11 \\
24 & -42 & 18
\end{bmatrix}
\begin{bmatrix}
x_1 \\
x_2 \\
x_3
\end{bmatrix} =
\begin{bmatrix}
0 \\
0 \\
0
\end{bmatrix}.
$$

We obtain $x_1 = x_2 = x_3$ and choose

$$\alpha_1 \leftrightarrow \begin{bmatrix} 1 \\ 1 \\ 1 \end{bmatrix}$$

as an eigenvector with eigenvalue 1.

The eigenvectors associated with eigenvalues -1 and 2 are obtained by solving $T\alpha = -\alpha$ and $T\alpha = 2\alpha$ respectively and a similar calculation shows we may choose

$$\alpha_2 \leftrightarrow \begin{bmatrix} 1 \\ 2 \\ 3 \end{bmatrix}, \quad \alpha_3 \leftrightarrow \begin{bmatrix} 1 \\ 3 \\ 6 \end{bmatrix}.$$

Taking

$$[p_{ij}] = \begin{bmatrix} 1 & 1 & 1 \\ 1 & 2 & 3 \\ 1 & 3 & 6 \end{bmatrix}$$

we find

$$[p_{ij}]^{-1}\,[t_{ij}]\,[p_{ij}] = \begin{bmatrix} 1 & 0 & 0 \\ 0 & -1 & 0 \\ 0 & 0 & 2 \end{bmatrix}.$$

EXAMPLE 2 Let $T^2 = I$. Show that T is diagonalizable and that the eigenvalues are of the form ± 1.

If every α in $\mathscr{V}$ satisfies $T\alpha = \alpha$ or $T\alpha = -\alpha$ then any n linearly independent vectors will be eigenvectors with eigenvalues ± 1 and there can be no other eigenvalues in view of Theorem 2.6C. Moreover T is diagonalizable having n linearly independent eigenvectors.

If, however, $T\alpha + \alpha \neq \theta$, $T\alpha - \alpha \neq \theta$ for some α, then

$$T(T\alpha + \alpha) = T^2\alpha + T\alpha = \alpha + T\alpha = T\alpha + \alpha,$$

$$T(T\alpha - \alpha) = T^2\alpha - T\alpha = \alpha - T\alpha = -(T\alpha - \alpha),$$

showing that $T\alpha + \alpha$ and $T\alpha - \alpha$ are linearly independent eigenvectors corresponding to eigenvalues 1 and -1 respectively. The relation $\alpha = \frac{1}{2}\{(T\alpha + \alpha) - (T\alpha - \alpha)\}$ proves that every vector is a linear combination of eigenvectors from which we conclude that the eigenvector manifolds corresponding to 1 and -1 together contain n linearly independent eigenvectors. Thus T is diagonalizable and the only eigenvalues are ± 1.

EXAMPLE 3   Show that TR and RT have the same eigenvalues.
Let α be an eigenvector of TR so that

(4) $$TR\alpha = r\alpha.$$

This implies $RT(R\alpha) = rR\alpha$ showing that r is an eigenvalue of RT if $R\alpha \neq \theta$. If, however, $R\alpha = \theta$ then (4) implies $r = 0$. Thus all nonzero eigenvalues of TR are eigenvalues of RT. Suppose now $r = 0$. As above, if $R\alpha \neq \theta$, then 0 is an eigenvalue of RT. If however $R\alpha = \theta$, $\alpha \neq \theta$, then we apply Theorem 1.4A two times to show that the dimension of the range of R and hence the range of RT is less than n and the dimension of the null space of RT is greater than zero. Consequently there exists a vector $\mu \neq \theta$ such that $RT\mu = \theta = 0\mu$; that is, 0 is an eigenvalue of RT.

We can obtain a better result. We shall show that the characteristic function of TR is that of RT. Let $[T]$, $[R]$ be matrix representations of T and R in some basis. If $[R]$ is nonsingular, let $[P] = [R]^{-1}$ and write $[P]^{-1}[T][R][P] = [R][T]$. This shows that $[T][R]$ and $[R][T]$ are similar and, by Theorem 2.6B,

(5) $$\det [xI - RT] = \det [xI - TR].$$

Equation (5) is a statement of equality between two polynomials in x, valid whenever $\det [R] \neq 0$. From this we can deduce that (5) is valid even when $[R]$ is singular. We leave the deduction as problem 2.6–17.

A diagonalizable transformation T has been characterized in Theorem 2.6D in terms of eigenvectors. It may also be characterized by its structure. Let $r_1, \ldots, r_m$ be the distinct eigenvalues with eigenvector manifolds $\mathscr{W}_1, \ldots, \mathscr{W}_m$. For some basis $\sigma_1, \ldots, \sigma_n$, T has the diagonal representation

$$[T] = \text{diag} [r_1, \ldots, r_1, r_2, \ldots, r_2, \ldots, r_m, \ldots, r_m],$$

where r_i is repeated along the diagonal dim $\mathscr{W}_i$ times. Let $[E_i]$ be the diagonal matrix obtained from $[T]$ by replacing r_i by 1 and r_j, $j \neq i$, by 0. Then it is clear that

(6) $$[T] = r_1 [E_1] + \cdots + r_m [E_m].$$

(7) $$[I] = [E_1] + \cdots + [E_m].$$

(8) $$[E_i][E_j] = [0], \quad i \neq j, \quad [E_i][E_i] = [E_i] \neq [0].$$

If E_i is the linear transformation whose representation is $[E_i]$ in the σ basis, it follows from Theorem 2.1B that

(9) $$T = r_1 E_1 + \cdots + r_m E_m, \quad r_i \text{ distinct}.$$

(10) $$I = E_1 + \cdots + E_m.$$

(11) $$E_i E_j = 0, \qquad i \neq j, \qquad E_i^2 = E_i \neq 0.$$

Moreover if $\sigma_1', \ldots, \sigma_n'$ is any other basis and $T \overset{\sigma'}{\leftrightarrow} [T']$, $E_i \overset{\sigma'}{\leftrightarrow} [E_i']$ then Theorem 2.1B indicates that (6), (7), (8) are valid with $[T]$ and $[E_i]$ replaced by $[T']$ and $[E_i']$ respectively.

It seems natural to try to characterize the property of being diagonalizable by a condition regarding the structure of T and this is done in

THEOREM 2.6F If T is diagonalizable then there exist linear transformations $E_1, \ldots, E_m$ satisfying (9), (10), (11). Conversely if (9), (10), (11) are valid then T is diagonalizable and $r_1, \ldots, r_m$ are the only eigenvalues of T.

Proof The first part of the theorem has already been proved. Suppose that (9), (10), (11) hold. For fixed i, the set of all vectors of the form $E_i \alpha$ (the range $\mathscr{R}(E_i)$ of E_i) is a linear manifold whose dimension we may denote by d_i. By (9) and (11),

$$T(E_i \alpha) = \sum_{j=1}^{m} r_j E_j (E_i \alpha) = r_i E_i \alpha,$$

indicating that every nonzero element in $\mathscr{R}(E_i)$ is an eigenvector of T corresponding to r_i. By the corollary to Theorem 2.6C, T has at least $\sum_{i=1}^{m} d_i$ linearly independent eigenvectors. If α is in $\mathscr{V}$, (10) implies

$$\alpha = I\alpha = E_1 \alpha + \ldots + E_m \alpha$$

so that there must be n linearly independent vectors in the sets $\mathscr{R}(E_i)$ taken together. It follows that $\sum_{i=1}^{m} d_i = n$, T has n linearly independent eigenvectors, and T can be diagonalized. There can be no other eigenvalues in view of Theorem 2.6C. ★

Corollary 1
The transformations E_i in (9), (10), (11) are uniquely determined.
In fact, if we had also

$$T = r_1 F_1 + \ldots r_m F_m,$$

$$I = F_1 + \ldots + F_m,$$

$$F_i F_j = 0, \qquad i \neq j, \qquad F_i^2 = F_i \neq 0,$$

then the following relations would be valid when $i \neq j$;

$$E_i(TF_j) = E_i\Big(\sum_k r_k F_k F_j\Big) = E_i r_j F_j = r_j E_i F_j,$$

$$E_i T = E_i\Big(\sum_k r_k E_k\Big) = r_i E_i,$$

$$E_i(TF_j) = (E_i T)F_j = r_i E_i F_j,$$

yielding

$$\{r_i - r_j\} E_i F_j = 0,$$

$$E_i F_j = 0.$$

As a result, we obtain

$$E_i = E_i I = E_i\sum_{j=1}^m F_j = E_i F_i = \Big(\sum_{j=1}^m E_j\Big)F_i = IF_i = F_i.$$

Corollary 2

The range of E_i is the eigenvector manifold $\mathscr{W}_i$ corresponding to r_i.

Since $r_1, \ldots, r_m$ are distinct, the proof of the theorem indicates there are exactly d_i linearly independent eigenvectors with eigenvalue r_i.

The decomposition given by (9), (10), (11) is called a **spectral decomposition** of T. This terminology is also used for matrices. To find the spectral decomposition of a matrix $[T]$ is to find the decomposition given by (6), (7), (8).

The spectral decomposition is useful in studying functions of the diagonalizable transformation T. For example,

$$T^2 = \Big(\sum_{i=1}^m r_i E_i\Big)^2 = \sum_{i=1}^m r_i^2 E_i$$

and in general

$$T^j = \sum_{i=1}^m r_i^j E_i.$$

If $p(y) = \sum_{j=0}^q c_j y^j$ is any polynomial in y, it follows that

$$p(T) = \sum_{j=0}^q c_j T^j = \sum_{j=0}^q c_j \sum_i r_i^j E_i = \sum_{i=1}^m \sum_{j=0}^q c_j r_i^j E_i,$$

$$p(T) = p(r_1) E_1 + \ldots + p(r_m) E_m.$$

This proves that $p(T)$ has eigenvalues $p(r_i)$. If $\mathscr{S}_i$ is the set of indices k such that $p(r_k) = p(r_i)$, then the multiplicity of $p(r_i)$ as a root of the characteristic equation of $p(T)$ is $\sum\limits_{k \text{ in } \mathscr{S}_i} \dim \mathscr{W}_k$, $\mathscr{W}_k$ being the eigenvector manifold of r_k as an eigenvalue of T.

That $p(T)$ has eigenvalues $p(r_i)$ can also be inferred from the diagonal representation.

EXAMPLE 4   Let $[T] = \begin{bmatrix} 1 & 0 \\ 1 & 3 \end{bmatrix}$. The eigenvalues of $[T]$ are found to be 3 and 1 with corresponding eigenvectors $\begin{bmatrix} 0 \\ 1 \end{bmatrix}$ and $\begin{bmatrix} -2 \\ 1 \end{bmatrix}$. When $[P] = \begin{bmatrix} 0 & -2 \\ 1 & 1 \end{bmatrix}$, then

$$[P]^{-1}[T][P] = \begin{bmatrix} \frac{1}{2} & 1 \\ -\frac{1}{2} & 0 \end{bmatrix} \begin{bmatrix} 1 & 0 \\ 1 & 3 \end{bmatrix} \begin{bmatrix} 0 & -2 \\ 1 & 1 \end{bmatrix} = \begin{bmatrix} 3 & 0 \\ 0 & 1 \end{bmatrix}.$$

The spectral decomposition of $[T]$ is obtained as follows:

$$\begin{bmatrix} 1 & 0 \\ 1 & 3 \end{bmatrix} = \begin{bmatrix} 0 & -2 \\ 1 & 1 \end{bmatrix} \left\{ 3 \begin{bmatrix} 1 & 0 \\ 0 & 0 \end{bmatrix} + \begin{bmatrix} 0 & 0 \\ 0 & 1 \end{bmatrix} \right\} \begin{bmatrix} \frac{1}{2} & 1 \\ -\frac{1}{2} & 0 \end{bmatrix}$$

$$= 3 \begin{bmatrix} 0 & 0 \\ \frac{1}{2} & 1 \end{bmatrix} + \begin{bmatrix} 1 & 0 \\ -\frac{1}{2} & 0 \end{bmatrix} = 3\,[E_1] + [E_2].$$

The range of $[E_1]$ is the set of vectors

$$\begin{bmatrix} 0 & 0 \\ \frac{1}{2} & 1 \end{bmatrix} \begin{bmatrix} x_1 \\ x_2 \end{bmatrix} = \{\tfrac{1}{2}x_1 + x_2\} \begin{bmatrix} 0 \\ 1 \end{bmatrix}.$$

The range of $[E_2]$ is the set of vectors

$$\begin{bmatrix} 1 & 0 \\ -\frac{1}{2} & 0 \end{bmatrix} \begin{bmatrix} x_1 \\ x_2 \end{bmatrix} = -\tfrac{1}{2}x_1 \begin{bmatrix} -2 \\ 1 \end{bmatrix}.$$

The matrix $[T]^2 - 4[T] = \begin{bmatrix} -3 & 0 \\ 0 & -3 \end{bmatrix}$ has eigenvalue -3 repeated twice, as would be expected from the fact that $p(1) = -3$ and $p(3) = -3$ for the polynomial $p(y) = y^2 - 4y$.

Exercise 2.6

1. Let

$$[A] = \begin{bmatrix} 0 & 2 \\ 0 & 0 \end{bmatrix}, \ [B] = \begin{bmatrix} 0 & 1 \\ 1 & 0 \end{bmatrix}, \ [C] = \begin{bmatrix} 0 & 1 \\ -1 & 0 \end{bmatrix}.$$

   (a) Find the eigenvalues and eigenvectors when these matrices are considered as transformations on $\mathscr{E}_2$.
   (b) Find the eigenvalues and eigenvectors of A, B, C, A^2, B^2, C^2 considered as transformations on $\mathscr{E}_2^*$.

2. Let the representation of a linear transformation T with respect to an ortho-normal basis in $\mathscr{E}_3$ be given by

$$\begin{bmatrix} -2 & 2 & -5 \\ -3 & 7 & -1 \\ -3 & 1 & 5 \end{bmatrix}.$$

   Are the eigenvectors orthogonal to each other?

3. Let L be a linear transformation on $\mathscr{V}$ to $\mathscr{V}$, where $\mathscr{V}$ is any vector space.

   (a) Show L has an inverse if and only if zero is not an eigenvalue.
   (b) If L^{-1} exists, show the eigenvalues of L^{-1} are reciprocals of the eigenvalues of L.

4. Let

$$[T] = \begin{bmatrix} 3 & -3 & 1 \\ 4 & -4 & 1 \\ 4 & -6 & 3 \end{bmatrix}.$$

   Find a matrix $[P]$ such that $[P]^{-1}[T][P]$ is a diagonal matrix.

5. (a) The Pauli matrices $[P_1] = \begin{bmatrix} 0 & 1 \\ 1 & 0 \end{bmatrix}$, $[P_2] = \begin{bmatrix} 0 & -i \\ i & 0 \end{bmatrix}$, $[P_3] = \begin{bmatrix} 1 & 0 \\ 0 & -1 \end{bmatrix}$

   occur in the quantum mechanical theory of electron spin. In $[P_2]$, $i^2 = -1$. Show that

   $$[P_1]^2 = [P_2]^2 = [P_3]^2 = [I],$$
   $$[P_k][P_j] = -[P_j][P_k] \quad \text{for } k \neq j,$$
   $$[P_m][P_j] = i[P_k] \quad \text{if } (m, j, k) \text{ is } (1, 2, 3), (2, 3, 1) \text{ or } (3, 1, 2).$$

   Verify that the eigenvalues are all ± 1.

   (b) The spin operators are defined by $[S_j] = (\hbar/2)[P_j]$ where $\hbar$ is a constant. Show that their eigenvalues are $\pm \hbar/2$. Show that $[S_j]$ satisfy $[S_m][S_j] - [S_j][S_m] = i\hbar[S_k]$ whenever (m, j, k) is $(1, 2, 3), (2, 3, 1),$ or $(3, 1, 2)$.

6. Consider the matrices

$$[E_1] = \begin{bmatrix} 0 & 1 & 0 & 0 \\ 1 & 0 & 0 & 0 \\ 0 & 0 & 0 & 1 \\ 0 & 0 & 1 & 0 \end{bmatrix}, \quad [E_2] = \begin{bmatrix} 0 & -i & 0 & 0 \\ i & 0 & 0 & 0 \\ 0 & 0 & 0 & -i \\ 0 & 0 & i & 0 \end{bmatrix}, \quad [E_3] = \begin{bmatrix} 1 & 0 & 0 & 0 \\ 0 & -1 & 0 & 0 \\ 0 & 0 & 1 & 0 \\ 0 & 0 & 0 & -1 \end{bmatrix},$$

$$[D_1] = \begin{bmatrix} 0 & 0 & 1 & 0 \\ 0 & 0 & 0 & 1 \\ 1 & 0 & 0 & 0 \\ 0 & 1 & 0 & 0 \end{bmatrix}, \quad [D_2] = \begin{bmatrix} 1 & 0 & 0 & 0 \\ 0 & 1 & 0 & 0 \\ 0 & 0 & -1 & 0 \\ 0 & 0 & 0 & -1 \end{bmatrix}.$$

These are the Dirac matrices used in the solution of the quantum mechanical relativistic wave equation. Show that

$$[E_j]^2 = [D_j]^2 = ([E_m][D_j])^2 = [I], \quad [E_m][D_j] = [D_j][E_m],$$

and, if $m \neq j$,

$$[E_m][E_j] = -[E_j][E_m], \quad [D_m][D_j] = -[D_j][D_m],$$
$$([E_m][E_j])^2 = ([D_m][D_j])^2 = -[I].$$

What are the eigenvalues of $[E_m]$, $[D_m]$, and $[E_m][D_m]$?

What are the eigenvalues of $[D_m][D_j]$ and $[E_m][E_j]$ when $m \neq j$?

7. T is a linear transformation on an n dimensional complex vector space and $T^2 = -I$. Show that the eigenvalues of T are of the form $\pm i$.

8. (a) If α is an eigenvector of T corresponding to the eigenvalue r, then it is also an eigenvector of T^k corresponding to the eigenvalue r^k, k being a positive integer.

(b) If T is diagonalizable, so is T^k.

9. Find the spectral decomposition of

$$\begin{bmatrix} -4 & 5 & 2 \\ 5 & -4 & 2 \\ 2 & 2 & 8 \end{bmatrix}.$$

10. Show that the dimension of the eigenvector manifold corresponding to the eigenvalue r_i of the diagonalizable transformation T given by (9), (10), (11) when $r_1, \ldots, r_m$ are distinct is equal to the rank of any matrix representing E_i.

11. Prove that the determinant of a matrix diagonalizable by a similarity transformation is the product of the eigenvalues.

12. Show that the characteristic function of a square matrix is the characteristic function of the transposed matrix.

13. Show that the eigenvalues of $[T]$ are the conjugates of the eigenvalues of $[T]^*$.

14. Show that if the $n \times n$ matrices $[A]$ and $[B]$ are diagonalizable and have the same characteristic function, they must be similar.

15. Show that the matrices

$$\begin{bmatrix} 1 & 1 \\ 0 & 1 \end{bmatrix} \quad \text{and} \quad \begin{bmatrix} 1 & 0 \\ 0 & 1 \end{bmatrix}$$

have the same eigenvalues but are not similar.

16. (a) Let $p(x)$ be a polynomial in x of degree n. If p vanishes at $n + 1$ distinct points, show that p must be identically zero.

(b) Let $p(x, y)$ be a polynomial in x and y of degree n in x and of degree m in y. Show that if p vanishes at $(n + 1)(m + 1)$ distinct points (x_i, y_j), $i = 1, \ldots, n + 1, j = 1, \ldots, m + 1$, then p must be identically zero. *Hint:* Write $p = c_1(x)y^m + c_2(x)y^{m-1} + \ldots + c_{m+1}(x)$.

(c) State the generalization of part (b) to polynomials in n variables.

(d) Prove that a necessary and sufficient condition that two polynomials in the variables $x_1, \ldots, x_n$ be identically equal is that they be equal for all points $x_1, \ldots, x_n$ satisfying $\{x_1 - a_1\}^2 + \ldots + \{x_n - a_n\}^2 \leq r^2$, where $(a_1, \ldots, a_n)$ is any given point and $r > 0$, that is, for all points in an n dimensional sphere about $(a_1, \ldots, a_n)$ of radius r.

17. Show that if equation (5) of the text holds for values of r_{ij} such that det $[r_{ij}] \neq 0$, then it also holds when det $[r_{ij}] = 0$. *Hint:* Let r_{ij} be a given set with det $[r_{ij}] \neq 0$. Then for fixed x, (5) is valid. Consider both sides of (5) as polynomials in parameters y_{ij} replacing r_{ij}. For values of y_{ij} near r_{ij} we have det $[y_{ij}] \neq 0$ by continuity. Hence (5) is valid for such values of y_{ij} and thus for all values by problem **16(d)**.

18. Use the method of problem **17** to prove
$$\text{adj} \{[A][B]\} = \text{adj} [B] \, \text{adj} [A] \text{ for } n \times n \text{ matrices } [A] \text{ and } [B].$$

19. Consider vectors in the plane emanating from the origin and the operation which reflects every vector with respect to the line $y = x$. What are the eigenvalues?

20. Let T be a linear transformation on an n dimensional vector space. If $\mathscr{W}$ is the eigenvector manifold corresponding to eigenvalue r and m is the multiplicity of r as a root of the characteristic equation, show that dim $\mathscr{W} \leq m$. *Hint:* Let $\alpha_j, j = 1, \ldots, d$, where $d = \dim \mathscr{W}$, be independent eigenvectors of T with eigenvalue r. Choose $\alpha_j, j = d + 1, \ldots, n$, so as to obtain a basis $\alpha_1, \ldots, \alpha_n$. Show that the representation of T in the basis $\alpha_1, \ldots, \alpha_n$ is of the form $\begin{bmatrix} r[I] & [A] \\ [0] & [B] \end{bmatrix}$ where $[I]$ is the $d \times d$ identity matrix, and hence $(x - r)^d$ is a factor of the characteristic function. Compare with Theorem 2.6E.

21. (a) Show that a necessary and sufficient condition that T in problem **20** be diagonalizable is that for each eigenvalue r with multiplicity m and eigenvector manifold $\mathscr{W}$, we have dim $\mathscr{W} = m$. Here $\mathscr{V}$ is complex.

(b) Use this fact and Theorem 2.6A to decide whether the following matrices can be diagonalized by a similarity transformation.

$$\begin{bmatrix} 1 & 0 & 0 \\ -6 & 4 & -6 \\ 4 & 2 & -3 \end{bmatrix}, \quad \begin{bmatrix} 2 & -1 & 1 \\ 2 & 2 & -1 \\ 1 & 2 & -1 \end{bmatrix}.$$

22. If T has a spectral decomposition given by (9), (10), (11) and T^{-1} exists, then

$$T^{-1} = r_1^{-1}E_1 + \ldots + r_m^{-1}E_m.$$

23. When the $n \times n$ matrix $[P]$ is nonsingular, its columns are linearly independent. If $[P]^{-1}[A][P] = [D]$ where $[D]$ is a diagonal matrix, equate the columns of $[A][P] = [P][D]$ and thus show in a different fashion that $[A]$ is diagonalizable by a similarity transformation if and only if $[A]$ has n linearly independent eigenvectors.

24. (a) Obtain the results of Example 3 by taking determinants in the identity

$$\begin{bmatrix} [xI - TR] & [T] \\ [0] & [xI] \end{bmatrix} \begin{bmatrix} [I] & [0] \\ [R] & [I] \end{bmatrix} = \begin{bmatrix} [I] & [0] \\ [R] & [I] \end{bmatrix} \begin{bmatrix} [xI] & [T] \\ [0] & [xI - RT] \end{bmatrix}.$$

(b) If $[T]$ is $m \times n$ and $[R]$ is $n \times m$, prove that

$$x^n \det [xI_m - TR] = x^m \det [xI_n - RT].$$

Here $[I_m]$ refers to the $m \times m$ identity matrix.

2.7

SYMMETRIC OPERATORS

Let $\mathscr{E}$ be an n dimension *real* Euclidean vector space. We shall discuss a type of linear transformation on $\mathscr{E}$ to $\mathscr{E}$ with domain $\mathscr{E}$ which has only real eigenvalues and is diagonalizable.

The linear transformation T is called **symmetric** if $(T\alpha, \beta) = (\alpha, T\beta)$ for every α and β in $\mathscr{E}$.

THEOREM 2.7A Let $\sigma_1, \ldots, \sigma_n$ be an orthonormal basis for $\mathscr{E}$ and let $T \overset{\sigma}{\leftrightarrow} [t_{ij}]$. Then T is symmetric if and only if $t_{ij} = t_{ji}$, $i, j = 1, 2, \ldots, n$.

Proof $[t_{ij}]$ is the representation for T when $T\sigma_i = \sum_{j=1}^{n} t_{ji}\sigma_j$. Form the scalar product of $T\sigma_i$ with σ_k to get

$$(T\sigma_i, \sigma_k) = t_{ki}.$$

Thus if T is symmetric,

$$t_{ki} = (T\sigma_i, \sigma_k) = (\sigma_i, T\sigma_k) = (T\sigma_k, \sigma_i) = t_{ik}.$$

Conversely, if $t_{ij} = t_{ji}$ for all i and j, and if

$$\alpha = \sum_{i=1}^{n} x_i \sigma_i, \qquad \beta = \sum_{k=1}^{n} y_k \sigma_k$$

then

$$(T\alpha, \beta) = \left(\sum_i x_i \sum_k t_{ki} \sigma_k, \sum_j y_j \sigma_j \right) = \sum_k \sum_i x_i \, t_{ki} \, y_k$$

and

$$(\alpha, T\beta) = \left(\sum_i x_i \sigma_i, \sum_{k=1}^{n} y_k \sum_j t_{jk} \sigma_j \right) = \sum_k \sum_i x_i \, t_{ik} \, y_k$$

are equal.   ★

A matrix $[t_{ij}]$ with $t_{ij} = t_{ji}$ is called a **symmetric matrix.** $[t_{ij}]$ is symmetric if and only if it is equal to its transpose.

THEOREM 2.7B   Every symmetric transformation T has at least one eigenvalue.

Proof   Let $\sigma_1, \ldots, \sigma_n$ be an orthonormal basis for $\mathscr{E}$, and $T \overset{\sigma}{\leftrightarrow} [t_{ij}]$. If r is a root of the characteristic equation, there exists a nonzero solution $[z_i]$ of

$$\sum_{j=1}^{n} \left\{ r\delta_{ij} - t_{ij} \right\} z_j = 0, \qquad i = 1, \ldots, n,$$

by corollary 1 of Theorem 2.5B. Multiply by $\bar{z}_i$ and sum to obtain

$$\sum_{i,j=1}^{n} t_{ij} z_j \bar{z}_i = \sum_{i,j=1}^{n} r\delta_{ij} z_j \bar{z}_i = r \sum_{i=1}^{n} |z_i|^2.$$

The coefficient of r is real and not zero. The left side of the equation is also real, since $t_{ij} = t_{ji}$ implies

$$\overline{\sum_{i,j=1}^{n} t_{ij} z_j \bar{z}_i} = \sum_{i,j=1}^{n} t_{ij} \bar{z}_j z_i = \sum_{i,j=1}^{n} t_{ji} \bar{z}_j z_i = \sum_{i,j=1}^{n} t_{ij} \bar{z}_i z_j.$$

Hence r is real.   ★

Corollary 1
All the roots of the characteristic equation of a symmetric transformation are real.

It has already been proved that eigenvectors corresponding to distinct eigenvalues are linearly independent. When the transformation is symmetric, a better result is obtained.

THEOREM 2.7C Eigenvectors of a symmetric transformation T corresponding to distinct eigenvalues are orthogonal.

Proof If $T\alpha = r\alpha$, $T\beta = s\beta$, $r \neq s$, then

$$r(\alpha, \beta) = (T\alpha, \beta) = (\alpha, T\beta) = s(\alpha, \beta)$$

and thus $(r - s)(\alpha, \beta) = 0$, $(\alpha, \beta) = 0$. ★

The next theorem shows that a symmetric transformation is diagonalizable.

THEOREM 2.7D If T is symmetric, there is an orthonormal basis $\alpha_1, \ldots, \alpha_n$ of $\mathscr{E}$ such that $T\alpha_i = s_i \alpha_i$, $i - 1, \ldots, n$.

Proof We proceed by induction on the dimension of $\mathscr{E}$. The statement to be proved is true if the dimension of $\mathscr{E}$ is 1. Suppose the theorem true for Euclidean vector spaces of dimension $n - 1$. We will then show it is true for Euclidean vector spaces of dimension n. By theorem 2.7B, there is a vector α_n, $\|\alpha_n\| = 1$, and a real number s_n such that $T\alpha_n = s_n \alpha_n$. Let $\mathscr{W}$ be the set of vectors in $\mathscr{E}$ orthogonal to α_n. $\mathscr{W}$ is a linear manifold of dimension $n - 1$. In fact, if α_n is the first element of an orthonormal basis of $\mathscr{E}$, then $\mathscr{W}$ is the manifold spanned by the last $n - 1$ elements of that basis.

When α is in $\mathscr{W}$,

$$(T\alpha, \alpha_n) = (\alpha, T\alpha_n) = s_n (\alpha, \alpha_n) = 0$$

so that $T\alpha$ is in $\mathscr{W}$. Thus T is a symmetric transformation on $\mathscr{W}$ to $\mathscr{W}$. By the induction assumption, there is an orthonormal basis $\alpha_1, \ldots, \alpha_{n-1}$ for $\mathscr{W}$ such that

$$T\alpha_i = s_i \alpha_i, \qquad i = 1, \ldots, n - 1.$$

The vectors $\alpha_1, \ldots, \alpha_n$ now have the desired properties. ★

Corollary 1

If $[t_{ij}]$ is a symmetric matrix then there exists an orthogonal matrix $[p_{ij}]$ so that $[p_{ij}]^T [t_{ij}][p_{ij}]$ is a diagonal matrix

$$\text{diag } [s_1, \ldots, s_n]$$

where $s_1, \ldots, s_n$ are the roots of $\det [x\delta_{ij} - t_{ij}] = 0$.

As indicated in Section 2.6 the matrix $[p_{ij}]$ has for its columns the representations of the orthonormal eigenvectors of the matrix.

EXAMPLE 1

$$\text{Let } [t_{ij}] = \begin{bmatrix} 13 & -4 & 2 \\ -4 & 13 & -2 \\ 2 & -2 & 10 \end{bmatrix}.$$

The characteristic equation is $x^3 - 36x^2 + 405x - 1458 = 0$ whose roots are 9, 9, 18.

An eigenvector for eigenvalue 9 is obtained by solving

$$\begin{bmatrix} -4 & 4 & -2 \\ 4 & -4 & 2 \\ -2 & 2 & -1 \end{bmatrix} \begin{bmatrix} x_1 \\ x_2 \\ x_3 \end{bmatrix} = \begin{bmatrix} 0 \\ 0 \\ 0 \end{bmatrix}.$$

This implies $2x_1 - 2x_2 + x_3 = 0$. Choosing $x_1 = 1$, $x_2 = 2$, we obtain $x_3 = 2$. A first eigenvector, normalized, is then

$$\frac{1}{3} \begin{bmatrix} 1 \\ 2 \\ 2 \end{bmatrix}.$$

The second eigenvector for eigenvalue 9 can be chosen orthogonal to the first. Denoting it by $\begin{bmatrix} x_1 \\ x_2 \\ x_3 \end{bmatrix}$, we must solve

$$2x_1 - 2x_2 + x_3 = 0$$
$$x_1 + 2x_2 + 2x_3 = 0,$$

whence $x_1 = -x_3 = 2x_2$. Choosing $x_2 = 1$ we have $x_1 = 2$, $x_3 = -2$, and a second normalized eigenvector is

$$\frac{1}{3} \begin{bmatrix} 2 \\ 1 \\ -2 \end{bmatrix}.$$

The eigenvector corresponding to eigenvalue 18 is obtained by solving

$$\begin{bmatrix} 5 & 4 & -2 \\ 4 & 5 & 2 \\ -2 & 2 & 8 \end{bmatrix} \begin{bmatrix} x_1 \\ x_2 \\ x_3 \end{bmatrix} = \begin{bmatrix} 0 \\ 0 \\ 0 \end{bmatrix},$$

one normalized solution being

$$\frac{1}{3}\begin{bmatrix} 2 \\ -2 \\ 1 \end{bmatrix}.$$

The orthogonal matrix $[p_{ij}]$ is then

$$\frac{1}{3}\begin{bmatrix} 1 & 2 & 2 \\ 2 & 1 & -2 \\ 2 & -2 & 1 \end{bmatrix}.$$

We shall give an application of the theory to geometry. In plane analytic geometry one studies the conic sections

$$ax^2 + bxy + cy^2 + dx + ey + f = 0$$

and draws the locus by finding a new coordinate system with respect to which the equation of the locus is in a simple form. The theory developed above permits us to obtain similar results in higher dimensional space.

An expression of the form

$$A(x) = \sum_{i,j=1}^{n} a_{ij} x_i x_j$$

is called a **quadratic form** in the n variables $x_1, \ldots, x_n$. There is no loss of generality in assuming $a_{ij} = a_{ji}$, for we may always define

$$b_{ij} = \frac{a_{ij} + a_{ji}}{2}$$

and note that $b_{ij} = b_{ji}$, and $\sum_{i,j=1}^{n} a_{ij} x_i x_j = \sum_{i,j=1}^{n} b_{ij} x_i x_j$. We shall therefore assume a_{ij} are real numbers with $a_{ij} = a_{ji}$. Then there is a one-to-one correspondence between quadratic forms and symmetric matrices

$$A(x) \leftrightarrow \begin{bmatrix} a_{11} \cdots\cdots a_{1n} \\ \cdot \\ \cdot \\ \cdot \\ a_{n1} \cdots\cdots a_{nn} \end{bmatrix}$$

and $A(x)$ is related to $[a_{ij}]$ by

(1) $$A(x) = [x_i]^T [a_{ij}][x_i].$$

A change of variable

$$x_i = \sum_{j=1}^{n} p_{ij} y_j$$

will change $A(x)$ into a new quadratic form $A'(y)$. Rewrite this as

$$[x_i] = [p_{ij}] [y_i]$$

and insert in (1) to obtain

$$A'(y) = [y_i]^T [p_{ij}]^T [a_{ij}] [p_{ij}] [y_i].$$

The symmetric matrix corresponding to $A'(y)$ is therefore

$$[p_{ij}]^T [a_{ij}] [p_{ij}].$$

Now apply the corollary to theorem 2.7D to get

THEOREM 2.7E   If $A(x) \leftrightarrow [a_{ij}]$ is a quadratic form in $x_1, \ldots, x_n$, there is an orthogonal matrix $[p_{ij}]$ such that if

$$x_i = \sum_{j=1}^{n} p_{ij} y_j, \qquad i = 1, \ldots n,$$

then $A(x)$, expressed in terms of $y_1, \ldots, y_n$, is

$$A'(y) = s_1 |y_1|^2 + \ldots + s_n |y_n|^2$$

where $s_1, \ldots, s_n$ are the eigenvalues of $[a_{ij}]$.

EXAMPLE 2   Identify the quadric surface

$$A(x) = 13x^2 + 13y^2 + 10z^2 - 8xy + 4xz - 4yz = 12$$

and find the equations of the transformation needed to eliminate the cross product terms.

The matrix of the quadratic form $A(x)$ is

$$[A] = \begin{bmatrix} 13 & -4 & 2 \\ -4 & 13 & -2 \\ 2 & -2 & 10 \end{bmatrix}.$$

This is the matrix studied in Example 1. Its eigenvalues are 9, 9, 18, and we can find an orthogonal transformation reducing $A(x)$ to

$$9\{(x')^2 + (y')^2 + 2(z')^2\} = 12.$$

The surface is an ellipsoid. The equations of transformation are given by

$$\begin{bmatrix} x \\ y \\ z \end{bmatrix} = \frac{1}{3} \begin{bmatrix} 1 & 2 & 2 \\ 2 & 1 & -2 \\ 2 & -2 & 1 \end{bmatrix} \begin{bmatrix} x' \\ y' \\ z' \end{bmatrix},$$

using the matrix $[p_{ij}]$ found in Example 1.

It is to be noted that the determinant of $[p_{ij}]$ is equal to -1. By Exercise 2.3–3, the determinant of a real orthogonal matrix is 1 or -1. If the determinant is $+1$, the linear transformation determined in Theorem 2.7E is called a **rotation**. If we desire that det $[p_{ij}] = 1$ instead of -1, we need merely replace one of the eigenvectors by its negative.

Of course, the cross product terms of a quadratic form may be eliminated by applying a change of variable which does not correspond to an orthogonal transformation. Suppose that the quadratic form $A(x)$ is carried into $A'(y)$ by an orthogonal transformation $[x_i] = [p_{ij}][y_i]$ in such a manner that the diagonal matrix corresponding to $A'(y)$ is

$$[A'] = [P]^T [A] [P] = \text{diag} [q_1, \ldots, q_r, 0, \ldots, 0]$$

where $q_1, \ldots, q_r$ are the nonzero eigenvalues of $[A]$ and the first s eigenvalues $q_1, \ldots, q_s$ are positive. This is accomplished by placing the eigenvector corresponding to q_1 in the first column of $[P]$, etc. Then there exist real numbers $v_1, \ldots, v_r$ such that $v_i^2 = q_i^{-1}$, $i = 1, \ldots s$, and $-v_i^2 = q_i^{-1}$, $i = s + 1, \ldots, r$. If the $n \times n$ matrix $[V]$ is defined by $[V] = \text{diag} [v_1, \ldots, v_r, 1, \ldots 1]$, it is clear that $[V]^T [A'] [V] = ([P][V])^T [A] [P][V]$ is a diagonal matrix with 1 and -1 appearing along the diagonal s and $r - s$ times respectively. It follows that the nonsingular transformation $[x_i] = [P] [V] [z_i]$ transforms $A(x)$ into the quadratic form

$$A''(z) = z_1^2 + \ldots + z_s^2 - z_{s+1}^2 - \ldots - z_r^2.$$

It is interesting to note that whenever $A(x)$ is carried into $A'(y)$ with no cross product terms by the transformation $[x_i] = [R][y_i]$, with $[R]$ nonsingular, the number of positive elements of the diagonal matrix $[R]^T [A] [R]$ corresponding to $A'(y)$ (**index**) and the number of nonzero elements (**rank**) is independent of $[R]$. Clearly the rank is independent of $[R]$ since the rank of $[R]^T [A] [R]$ is that of $[A]$ by Exercise 2.4–8. To prove the invariance of index, let $[x_i] = [P] [y_i]$ and $[x_i] = [Q] [z_i]$, with $[P]$ and $[Q]$ nonsingular, carry $A(x)$ into $A'(y)$ and $A''(z)$ respectively with no cross product terms. In view of the discussion above, we may suppose that

$$A'(y) = y_1^2 + \ldots + y_s^2 - y_{s+1}^2 - \ldots - y_r^2,$$
$$A''(z) = z_1^2 + \ldots + z_t^2 - z_{t+1}^2 - \ldots - z_r^2.$$

When $[y_i]$ and $[z_i]$ are related by

(2) $[y_i] = [P]^{-1} [Q] [z_i] = [d_{ij}] [z_i]$

we must have $A'(y) = A''(z)$. If $s < t$, we may, in view of Theorem 2.5C, choose $z_1, \ldots, z_n$ not all zero such that

$$y_1 = d_{11} z_1 + \cdots + d_{1n} z_n = 0,$$
$$\cdots\cdots\cdots\cdots\cdots\cdots$$
$$y_s = d_{s1} z_1 + \cdots + d_{sn} z_n = 0,$$
$$z_{t+1} = z_{t+2} = \cdots = z_n = 0.$$

With $y_{s+1}, \ldots, y_n$ now determined by (2), we see that $A'(y) \leq 0$ while $A''(z) > 0$, since $z_1, \ldots, z_t$ cannot all be zero. This contradiction shows that $s \geq t$. Similarly $t \geq s$ and hence $t = s$.

When can two symmetric transformations L and M be simultaneously diagonalized in an orthonormal basis? Since the basis consists of eigenvectors, the question may be rephrased: When will there exist an orthonormal basis whose elements are eigenvectors of L and M? If $L \overset{\sigma}{\leftrightarrow} [l_{ij}]$, $M \overset{\sigma}{\leftrightarrow} [m_{ij}]$, we seek an orthogonal matrix $[p_{ij}]$ such that $[p_{ij}]^T[l_{ij}] [p_{ij}]$ and $[p_{ij}]^T [m_{ij}] [p_{ij}]$ are both diagonal matrices.

THEOREM 2.7F   If L and M are symmetric, there exists an orthonormal basis of eigenvectors for both L and M if and only if $LM = ML$.

Proof   Let $\alpha_1, \ldots, \alpha_n$ be a basis and

$$L\alpha_i = r_i \alpha_i, \qquad M\alpha_i = s_i \alpha_i, \qquad i = 1, \ldots n.$$

Then

$$LM\alpha_i = L s_i \alpha_i = s_i L\alpha_i = s_i r_i \alpha_i,$$
$$ML\alpha_i = M r_i \alpha_i = r_i M\alpha_i = r_i s_i \alpha_i.$$

If $\alpha = \sum_{i=1}^{n} x_i \alpha_i$ is any vector in $\mathscr{E}$,

$$LM\alpha = \sum_{i=1}^{n} x_i LM\alpha_i = \sum_{i=1}^{n} x_i ML\alpha_i = ML\alpha.$$

Thus $LM = ML$.

Conversely, suppose $LM = ML$. Let $r_1, \ldots, r_m$ be the distinct eigenvalues of L and let $\mathscr{W}_1, \ldots, \mathscr{W}_m$ be the corresponding eigenvector manifolds.

If α is in $\mathscr{W}_i$, the equation

$$LM\alpha = ML\alpha = Mr_i\alpha = r_i M\alpha$$

shows that either $M\alpha = 0$ or $M\alpha$ is an eigenvector of L with eigenvalue r_i. In either case $M\alpha$ lies in the eigenvector manifold $\mathscr{W}_i$. This means that the transformation M', defined as the transformation M with domain restricted to $\mathscr{W}_i$, has its range in $\mathscr{W}_i$. M' is also symmetric and there must exist $d_i = \dim \mathscr{W}_i$ orthonormal vectors $\beta_1, \ldots, \beta_{d_i}$ in $\mathscr{W}_i$ such that $M\beta_j = M'\beta_j = t_j \beta_j$. These β_j, belonging to $\mathscr{W}_i$, are also eigenvectors of L. In this way, we obtain $\sum_{i=1}^{m} \dim \mathscr{W}_i = n$ eigenvectors of both L and M. By Theorem 2.7C, the eigenvectors are orthonormal. $\star$

The above theorem does not state that L and M have the same eigenvectors. Consider the transformations I and M which commute. Every vector in $\mathscr{E}$ is an eigenvalue of I (corresponding to eigenvalue 1), but this need not be true for M. Note also that I commutes with any two symmetric transformations R and S but R need not commute with S. In this case I and R or I and S can be simultaneously diagonalized while R and S cannot be simultaneously diagonalized. If, however, $L_1, \ldots, L_p$ are symmetric transformations which commute with each other, a slight extension of the proof shows that all L_i can be simultaneously diagonalized in an orthonormal basis. The details are left to the reader as Exercise 2.7–13.

The remainder of this section is devoted to a discussion of an analogous operator in an n dimensional *complex* Euclidean vector space $\mathscr{E}$. Let the domain of T be $\mathscr{E}$. We again define T to be symmetric if $(T\alpha, \beta) = (\alpha, T\beta)$ for every α and β in $\mathscr{E}$. By a proof similar to that of Theorem 2.7A, we get

THEOREM 2.7G   Let $\sigma_1, \ldots, \sigma_n$ be an orthonormal basis for $\mathscr{E}$ and let $T \overset{\sigma}{\leftrightarrow} [t_{ij}]$. Then T is symmetric if and only if $t_{ij} = \overline{t_{ji}}$, $i, j = 1, \ldots n$.

A matrix $[t_{ij}]$ with $t_{ij} = \overline{t_{ji}}$ is called **Hermitian.** Thus $[T]$ is Hermitian when it is equal to its adjoint (conjugate transpose). Theorem 2.7B is immediate since there is always a nonzero solution α of $T\alpha = r\alpha$ whenever r is a root of the characteristic equation. But the proof of the theorem is still valid, so that all eigenvalues of T are real when T is symmetric. Theorems 2.7C, 2.7D, 2.7F remain valid for the complex case.

An expression of the form $\sum_{i,j=1}^{n} a_{ij} x_j \overline{x_i}$ with $a_{ij} = \overline{a_{ji}}$ is called an **Hermitian form.** Theorem 2.7E and the corollary to theorem 2.7D are valid when the words symmetric, quadratic form, orthogonal and $[p_{ij}]^T$ are replaced respectively by Hermitian, Hermitian form, unitary and $[p_{ij}]^*$. Only slight changes are needed in the proofs.

When $[t_{ij}]$ is the representation of a linear transformation T in an ortho-normal basis $\sigma_1, \ldots, \sigma_n$ of $\mathscr{E}$, it is often useful to consider that transformation whose representation in the σ basis is $[t_{ij}]^*$. We denote this transformation by T^* and call it the **adjoint transformation.** We shall show that for every α and β in $\mathscr{E}$,

(3) $(T\alpha, \beta) = (\alpha, T^*\beta).$

In fact, if

$$\alpha \overset{\sigma}{\longleftrightarrow} \begin{bmatrix} x_1 \\ \cdot \\ \cdot \\ \cdot \\ x_n \end{bmatrix}, \qquad \beta \overset{\sigma}{\longleftrightarrow} \begin{bmatrix} y_1 \\ \cdot \\ \cdot \\ \cdot \\ y_n \end{bmatrix},$$

then

$$(T\alpha, \beta) = \sum_{i=1}^{n} \sum_{j=1}^{n} t_{ij}\, x_j\, \overline{y_i},$$

$$(\alpha, T^*\beta) = \sum_{i=1}^{n} \sum_{j=1}^{n} x_i\, t_{ji}\, \overline{y_j} = (T\alpha, \beta).$$

Equation (3) is the determining equation for T^*. In other words, for each T, there is only one linear transformation T^* satisfying (3) for every α, β in $\mathscr{E}$ and its representation in any orthonormal basis is the conjugate transpose of the representation of T in that basis. To see this, suppose

(4) $(T\alpha, \beta) = (\alpha, M\beta)$ for α and β in $\mathscr{E}$

and T^* is the transformation whose representation in a given orthonormal basis $\sigma_1, \ldots, \sigma_n$ is $[t_{ij}]^*$ where $[t_{ij}]$ is the representation of T in that basis. By the above proof, (3) is valid and yields, together with (4), the relation

(5) $(\alpha, (T^* - M)\beta) = 0$

for every α and β. Choosing $\alpha = (T^* - M)\beta$ we have $(T^* - M)\beta = \theta$ for every β. This proves $M = T^*$.

In a similar fashion, when dealing with a real Euclidean vector space, one might have considered the transformation whose representation was the transpose of $[T]$ in an orthonormal basis and called it the transpose transformation T^T. However, it is customary, even in the real case, to call it the adjoint transformation and denote it by T^*. Equation (3) is the defining equation for T^* in the real or complex case.

When $T = T^*$, the transformation T is called **self-adjoint.** In view of (3), T is self-adjoint if and only if it is symmetric. For real Euclidean vector spaces, the matrix representation in an orthonormal basis will be symmetric, while for complex vector spaces, the matrix will be Hermitian.

Exercise 2.7

1. What is the quadric surface represented by

$$5x^2 + 4xy + 4xz + 2y^2 + 2yz + 2z^2 = 9?$$

   Obtain a rotation matrix transforming this equation into an equation with no cross product terms.

2. Find the conic represented by

$$x^2 + y^2 - 4xy + 6x - 2 = 0.$$

   Rotate the axis so that no cross product terms are present. Sketch the conic with respect to the original axes.

3. (a) Identify the quadric surface

$$-x^2 - y^2 - 7z^2 + 16xy + 8xz + 8yz = 3.$$

   (b) Replace the right side of the equation in (a) by $3 - 2x + y$ instead of 3. What is the relation between the new quadric surface and that given in (a)?

4. If T is symmetric, then
   (a) T^{-1} is symmetric, when it exists.
   (b) $B^* TB$ is symmetric for every transformation B.
   (c) T^n is symmetric for every positive integer n.

5. If T and R are symmetric, then
   (a) $T + R$ is symmetric.
   (b) TR is symmetric if and only if T and R commute.

6. (a) $[A][A]^T$ is symmetric for every matrix $[A]$.
   (b) $[A][A]^*$ is Hermitian for every matrix $[A]$.

7. Let T be a linear transformation on an n dimensional complex Euclidean vector space $\mathscr{E}$. Show that $(T\alpha, \alpha)$ is real for every α in $\mathscr{E}$, if and only if T is symmetric. *Hint:* Consider $(T(\alpha + r\beta), \alpha + r\beta)$.

8. Show that the eigenvalues of a unitary transformation (see Exercise 2.2–10) have absolute value equal to 1.

9. Let U be a unitary transformation on an n dimensional complex Euclidean vector space $\mathscr{E}$.
   (a) If β is an eigenvector of U with eigenvalue r (different from zero according to Exercise 8) and α is orthogonal to β, then $U\alpha$ is orthogonal to β.
   (b) Using the result of (a) and the method of proof outlined in Theorem 2.7D, prove that there is an orthonormal basis $\alpha_1, \ldots, \alpha_n$ such that $U\alpha_i = s_i\alpha_i, i = 1, \ldots, n$.
   (c) Show that eigenvectors corresponding to distinct eigenvalues are orthogonal.

10. Show that if T is a linear transformation over a real Euclidean n dimensional vector space and can be diagonalized in an orthonormal basis then T must be symmetric.

Note. The property expressed by Exercise 10 does not carry over to complex vector spaces. Consider the transformation T on $\mathscr{E}$ whose matrix in an orthonormal basis is

$$[T] = \begin{bmatrix} 0 & 1 \\ -1 & 0 \end{bmatrix}.$$

T is not Hermitian but since $[T]$ is unitary, there is a unitary matrix $[P]$ such that $[P]^*[T][P]$ is diagonal (Exercise 9).

As another indication of the difference between real and complex spaces, note that although Exercise 9 indicates that a unitary matrix with real elements may be diagonalized when considered as a matrix over $\mathscr{E}_n^*$, it may not be diagonalizable when considered as a matrix over $\mathscr{E}_n$.

11. Prove that if $[A]$, $[B]$, $[C]$, $[D]$ are square matrices such that $[A][A]^* + [B][B]^* + [C][C]^* + [D][D]^* = [0]$ then $[A]$, $[B]$, $[C]$, $[D]$ are all zero. Hence if $[A]$, $[B]$, $[C]$, $[D]$ are Hermitian and $[A]^2 + [B]^2 + [C]^2 + [D]^2 = [0]$, we have $[A]$, $[B]$, $[C]$, $[D]$ all zero. This example indicates that Hermitian matrices act, in some respects, like real numbers.

12. Let $T_1, \ldots, T_p$ be linear transformations on an n dimensional vector space $\mathscr{V}$ to $\mathscr{V}$ and suppose they can be simultaneously diagonalized. The basis need not be orthonormal. Show $T_iT_j = T_jT_i$, $i, j = 1, \ldots, p$.

13. Let $T_1, \ldots, T_p$ be symmetric transformations on a finite dimensional Euclidean vector space with $T_iT_j = T_jT_i$, $i, j = 1, \ldots, p$. Use the proof of theorem 2.7F together with induction on p to show there exists an orthonormal basis in which T_i can be simultaneously diagonalized.

14. Let L and M be diagonalizable linear transformations on the n dimensional vector space $\mathscr{V}$ to $\mathscr{V}$, and suppose L and M commute. Let r_i, $i = 1, \ldots, m$ be the distinct eigenvalues of L with corresponding eigenvector manifolds $\mathscr{W}_i$ having dimension d_i. Show that M has d_i linearly independent eigenvectors in $\mathscr{W}_i$.

    Hint: Let $M\beta_j = s_j\beta_j$ for linearly independent β_j, $j = 1, \ldots, n$. Each β_j has a unique representation $\beta_j = \sum\limits_{i=1}^{m} \alpha_{ij}$ with α_{ij} in $\mathscr{W}_i$. Thus $\sum\limits_{i=1}^{m} s_j\alpha_{ij} = s_j\beta_j = M\beta_j = \sum\limits_{i=1}^{m} M\alpha_{ij}$. Show that $M\alpha_{ij}$ is in $\mathscr{W}_i$ and deduce $M\alpha_{ij} = s_j\alpha_{ij}$. It remains to show that for fixed i there are at least (and hence exactly) d_i linearly independent vectors α_{ij}. Each of d_i linearly independent eigenvectors $\mu_k = \mu_{ki}$ of L in $\mathscr{W}_i$ has the representation

$$\mu_k = \sum_{j=1}^{n} c_{jk}\beta_j = \sum_{t=1}^{m} \sum_{j=1}^{n} c_{jk}\alpha_{tj}.$$

Deduce $\mu_k = \sum\limits_{j=1}^{n} c_{jk}\alpha_{ij}$ and from this the desired result.

15. (a) Using the notation and result of Exercise 14, show that if L and M are diagonalizable and commute, there is a basis in which L and M may be simultaneously diagonalized.

    (b) Let $T_1, \ldots, T_p$ be diagonalizable linear transformations on the n dimensional vector space $\mathscr{V}$ to $\mathscr{V}$ and suppose $T_iT_j = T_jT_i$, $i, j = 1, \ldots, p$. Show that T_i can be simultaneously diagonalized. Use the method of Exercise 13.

16. (a) Let L and M be unitary transformations on an n dimensional complex Euclidean vector space $\mathscr{E}$ with $LM = ML$. Using the proof of Theorem 2.7F, show that there is an orthonormal basis $\alpha_1, \ldots, \alpha_n$ of $\mathscr{E}$ such that α_i are eigenvectors of both L and M. Use the results of Exercise 9.

(b) Let $T_1, \ldots, T_p$ be unitary transformations on $\mathscr{E}$ with $T_i T_j = T_j T_i$, $i, j = 1, \ldots, p$. Show there is an orthonormal basis in which T_i can be simultaneously diagonalized. See Exercise 13.

17. Let

$$[A] = \begin{bmatrix} 1 & 0 \\ 0 & 1 \end{bmatrix}, \qquad [B] = \begin{bmatrix} 0 & -1 \\ 2 & 3 \end{bmatrix}.$$

Show that $[A]$ and $[B]$ commute but that there does not exist any orthogonal matrix $[U]$ such that $[U]^T[A][U]$ and $[U]^T[B][U]$ are diagonal.

18. Find the normalized eigenvectors of the following matrices (the matrix in part (c) is unitary so that the results in Exercise 9 are applicable).

(a) $\begin{bmatrix} 1 & 0 & 2 \\ 0 & c & 0 \\ 2 & 0 & 4 \end{bmatrix}$ (b) $\begin{bmatrix} -1 & 0 & 0 & 0 \\ 0 & -1 & 0 & 0 \\ 0 & 0 & 2 & 1 \\ 0 & 0 & 1 & 2 \end{bmatrix}$ (c) $\begin{bmatrix} \dfrac{1}{3} & \dfrac{-3+i}{\sqrt{18}} & \dfrac{-1-i}{\sqrt{6}} \\[2mm] \dfrac{3-i}{\sqrt{18}} & \dfrac{1-3i}{6} & \dfrac{-1+i}{\sqrt{12}} \\[2mm] \dfrac{1+i}{\sqrt{6}} & \dfrac{-1+i}{\sqrt{12}} & \dfrac{1+i}{2} \end{bmatrix}$

19. Let T be a linear transformation on $\mathscr{V}$ to $\mathscr{V}$ with domain $\mathscr{V}$. Let $\sigma_1, \ldots, \sigma_n$ be a basis for $\mathscr{V}$ and $T \overset{\sigma}{\leftrightarrow} [T]$. Show that the rank of $[T]^*[T]$ is equal to the rank of $[T]$. *Hint:* By Exercise 2.4–14 we need only show that the dimension of the range of T^*T is equal to the dimension of the range of T. The equation $(T\alpha, \beta) = (\alpha, T^*\beta)$ indicates that β is in the null space of T^* if and only if it is orthogonal to the range of T. Use this fact to prove that $T^*T\alpha_1, \ldots, T^*T\alpha_r$ are linearly independent whenever $T\alpha_1, \ldots, T\alpha_r$ span the range of T, and hence dimension of the range of $T^*T \geq$ dimension of the range of T.

2.8

EXTREMAL PROPERTIES

OF EIGENVALUES

It was shown in Example 2 of the previous section that the family of ellipsoids

$$13x^2 + 13y^2 + 10z^2 - 8xy + 4xz - 4yz = c \qquad (c > 0)$$

can be represented in another rectangular coordinate system by

$$9(x')^2 + 9(y')^2 + 18(z')^2 = c$$

where the coefficients 9, 9, 18 are the eigenvalues of the matrix associated with the quadratic form. It is evident from the latter representation that the values 9, 9, 18 are the values of c when (x', y', z') are $(1, 0, 0)$, $(0, 1, 0)$, $(0, 0, 1)$ respectively. In other words, 9, 9, 18 are the values of the quadratic form for those points on the unit sphere pierced by the common axes of the family. The adjoining diagram shows that these points are located where the quadratic form has its largest value ($c = 18$) and its smallest value ($c = 9$) for points on the unit sphere. Such geometrical considerations lead us to investigate the possibility of obtaining the eigenvalues as extremal values of the quadratic form for points of the unit sphere.

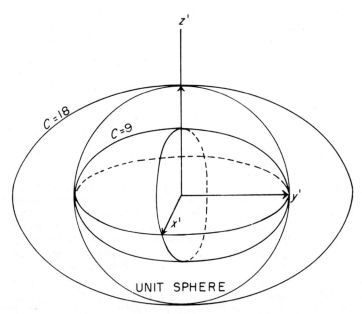

A set $\mathcal{R}$ of real numbers is said to be **bounded above** if there is a real number M greater than or equal to all the members of $\mathcal{R}$. Any such number M is called an **upper bound** for the set $\mathcal{R}$. The number M is called the **least upper bound** for $\mathcal{R}$ (abbreviated l.u.b.) if M is an upper bound and if for every positive number p there is a member of $\mathcal{R}$ greater than $M - p$. We then write l.u.b. $\mathcal{R} = M$. A property of the real number system states that every set bounded above has a least upper bound. If $\mathcal{R}$ is not bounded above, it is common to write l.u.b. $\mathcal{R} = \infty$. In case the set $\mathcal{R}$ has a **maximum**, that is, a member of $\mathcal{R}$ greater than or equal to every member of $\mathcal{R}$, then it is evident that the maximum is the least upper bound. We leave to the reader the corresponding definition of the terms **bounded below, lower bound, greatest lower bound** (abbreviated g.l.b.) and **minimum**.

A set $\mathcal{R}$ of real numbers may be defined by a property which specifies uniquely the members of $\mathcal{R}$. Thus the set of roots of the equation $x^3 - 6x^2 + 11x - 6 = 0$ may be written as

$$\mathcal{R} = \{x \mid x^3 - 6x^2 + 11x - 6 = 0\}$$

indicating that $\mathcal{R}$ is the set of values x which satisfy the condition listed at the right of the vertical bar.

In this section $\mathcal{E}$ will denote either a real or complex n dimensional Euclidean vector space, the theorems and proofs being valid in either case. T will be a symmetric operator and $\alpha_1, \ldots, \alpha_n$ an orthonormal basis such that $T\alpha_i = s_i \alpha_i$, $i = 1, \ldots, n$. Thus s_i are the eigenvalues of T. If $\sigma_1, \ldots, \sigma_n$ is any orthonormal basis and $\alpha \overset{\sigma}{\leftrightarrow} [x_i]$, $T \overset{\sigma}{\leftrightarrow} [t_{ij}]$, then $(T\alpha, \alpha) = \sum\limits_{i,j=1}^{n} t_{ij} x_j \overline{x_i}$ is an Hermitian form in the variables $x_1, \ldots, x_n$. It assumes only real values. The next theorem yields the relationship between eigenvalues and extremal values suggested above.

THEOREM 2.8A If $s_1 \geq s_2 \ldots \geq s_n$ then, for $i = 1, \ldots, n$,

$$s_i = \text{l.u.b.} \{(T\alpha, \alpha) \mid \|\alpha\| = 1, \alpha \perp \alpha_j, j = 1, \ldots, i-1\}.$$

Proof Any vector $\alpha \perp \alpha_j, j = 1, \ldots, i-1$ is of the form

$$\alpha = x_i \alpha_i + x_{i+1} \alpha_{i+1} + \ldots + x_n \alpha_n$$

while $\|\alpha\| = 1$ implies

$$|x_i|^2 + \cdots + |x_n|^2 = 1.$$

By direct computation,

$$(T\alpha, \alpha) = s_i |x_i|^2 + \ldots + s_n |x_n|^2 \leq s_i \{|x_i|^2 + \ldots + x_n|^2\} = s_i.$$

Thus

$$\text{l.u.b.} \{(T\alpha, \alpha) \mid \|\alpha\| = 1, \alpha \perp \alpha_j, j = 1, \ldots, i-1\} \leq s_i.$$

Now choose $\alpha = \alpha_i$. Then $\alpha \perp \alpha_j, j = 1, \ldots, i-1$, $\|\alpha\| = 1$, and $(T\alpha, \alpha) = s_i (\alpha_i, \alpha_i) = s_i$ so that

$$\text{l.u.b.} \{(T\alpha, \alpha) \mid \|\alpha\| = 1, \alpha \perp \alpha_j, j = 1, \ldots, i-1\} \geq s_i.$$

The two inequalities derived yield the desired result. $\star$

For the calculation of eigenvalues by Theorem 2.8A it is necessary to know the eigenvectors $\alpha_1, \ldots, \alpha_n$. This requirement is dropped in the following

THEOREM 2.8 B   If $s_1 \geq s_2 \ldots \geq s_n$, then

$$s_i = \underset{\beta}{\text{g.l.b.}} \left[\underset{\alpha}{\text{l.u.b.}} \left\{ (T\alpha, \alpha) \mid \alpha \perp \beta_j, j = 1, \ldots, i - 1, \|\alpha\| = 1 \right\} \right]$$

Proof   The theorem states that if for fixed $\beta_1, \ldots, \beta_{i-1}$ we set

$$f(\beta_1, \ldots, \beta_{i-1}) = \text{l.u.b.} \{ (T\alpha, \alpha) \mid \alpha \perp \beta_j, j = 1, \ldots, i - 1, \|\alpha\| = 1 \}$$

then

$$s_i = \text{g.l.b.} f(\beta_1, \ldots, \beta_{i-1})$$

the greatest lower bound being taken over every set $\beta_1, \ldots, \beta_{i-1}$ of $i - 1$ vectors of $\mathscr{E}$.

To prove the theorem, let $\beta_1, \ldots, \beta_{i-1}$ be fixed and let α be a vector of the form

$$\alpha = x_1 \alpha_1 + \ldots + x_i \alpha_i.$$

By suitably choosing $x_1, \ldots, x_i$ we can be sure that

$$\|\alpha\| = 1 \text{ and } \alpha \perp \beta_j, \qquad j = 1, \ldots, i - 1.$$

In fact, the condition $\alpha \perp \beta_j, j = 1, \ldots, i - 1$ yields a set of $i - 1$ equations in i unknowns $x_1, \ldots, x_i$ for which there is a nonzero solution which can always be normalized.

Then

$$(T\alpha, \alpha) = s_1 |x_1|^2 + \ldots + s_i |x_i|^2$$
$$\geq s_i \{ |x_1|^2 + \ldots + |x_i|^2 \} = s_i$$

and

$$f(\beta_1, \ldots, \beta_{i-1}) \geq s_i.$$

Since this is true for every set $\beta_1, \ldots, \beta_{i-1}$ we have

$$\text{g.l.b.} f(\beta_1, \ldots, \beta_{i-1}) \geq s_i.$$

In view of Theorem 2.8A

$$f(\alpha_1, \ldots, \alpha_{i-1}) = s_i,$$

hence also

$$\underset{\beta}{\text{g.l.b.}} f(\beta_1, \ldots, \beta_{i-1}) \leq s_i. \quad \star$$

An application of the preceding theorems will now be given. Consider the Hermitian $n \times n$ matrix $[a_{ij}]$ whose eigenvalues are $a_1 \geq a_2 \ldots \geq a_n$. By deleting all but the first m rows and columns we obtain an $m \times m$

Hermitian matrix $[b_{ij}]$, $b_{ij} = a_{ij}$, $i, j = 1, \ldots, m$, whose eigenvalues may be denoted by $b_1 \geq b_2 \ldots \geq b_m$. We shall show that certain bounds on the eigenvalues a_i may be obtained in terms of the eigenvalues b_i. More specifically,

(1) $$a_{n-m+i} \leq b_i \leq a_i, \qquad i = 1, \ldots, m.$$

EXAMPLE 1 The eigenvalues of the matrix

$$\begin{bmatrix} 5 & -1 & 0 & -2 \\ -1 & 5 & 2 & 0 \\ 0 & 2 & 5 & 1 \\ -2 & 0 & 1 & 5 \end{bmatrix}$$

are $\{8, 6, 4, 2\}$ while the eigenvalues of

$$\begin{bmatrix} 5 & -1 & 0 \\ -1 & 5 & 2 \\ 0 & 2 & 5 \end{bmatrix}, \quad \begin{bmatrix} 5 & -1 \\ -1 & 5 \end{bmatrix}, \quad [5]$$

are $\{5 + \sqrt{5}, 5, 5 - \sqrt{5}\}$, $\{6, 4\}$, $\{5\}$ respectively. The following table exhibits the inequalities specified by relation (1).

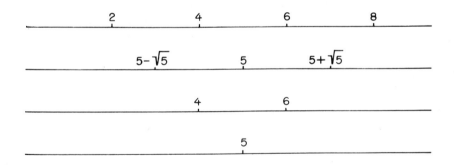

For the proof of relation (1), let σ_k, $k = 1, \ldots, n$, be vectors in $\mathscr{E}_n{}^*$ such that σ_k has its kth coordinate equal to 1 and its other coordinates equal to 0, and let A be the linear transformation on $\mathscr{E}_n{}^*$ to $\mathscr{E}_n{}^*$ with $A \overset{\sigma}{\leftrightarrow} [a_{ij}]$. Also let σ'_k, $k = 1, \ldots, m$, be vectors in $\mathscr{E}_m{}^*$ such that σ'_k has its kth coordinate equal to 1 and its other coordinates equal to 0, and let B be the linear transformation on $\mathscr{E}_m{}^*$ to $\mathscr{E}_m{}^*$ with $B \overset{\sigma'}{\leftrightarrow} [b_{ij}]$ where $b_{ij} = a_{ij}$, $i, j = 1, \ldots, m$.

If $\beta_1, \ldots, \beta_{i-1}$ are any $i-1$ vectors in $\mathscr{E}_n{}^*$, $i-1 < m$, write $\beta_j = \sum\limits_{k=1}^{n} c_{kj}\sigma_k$

and define $\beta_j' = \sum\limits_{k=1}^{m} c_{kj}\sigma_k'$, $j = 1, \ldots, i-1$. For any vector $\alpha' = \sum\limits_{k=1}^{m} d_k\sigma_k'$

with $\|\alpha'\| = 1$ and $\alpha' \perp \beta_j'$, $j = 1, \ldots, i-1$, the vector $\alpha = \sum\limits_{k=1}^{n} d_k\sigma_k$ with

$d_k = 0$ for $k = m+1, \ldots, n$ is a vector in $\mathscr{E}_n{}^*$ with $\|\alpha\| = 1$, $\alpha \perp \beta_j$,
$j = 1, \ldots, i-1$ and

$$(A\alpha, \alpha) = \sum_{k,i=1}^{n} a_{ki}\, d_i\, \overline{d}_k = \sum_{k,i=1}^{m} a_{ki}\, d_i\, \overline{d}_k = (B\alpha', \alpha').$$

Thus

$$\underset{\alpha'}{\text{l.u.b.}}\, \{(B\alpha', \alpha') \mid \|\alpha'\| = 1, \alpha' \perp \beta_j'\} \leq \underset{\mu}{\text{l.u.b.}}\, \{(A\mu, \mu) \mid \|\mu\| = 1, \mu \perp \beta_j\}.$$

Letting $\beta_1, \ldots, \beta_{i-1}$ vary over $\mathscr{E}_n{}^*$, we obtain

$$\underset{\beta}{\text{g.l.b.}}\,[\underset{\alpha'}{\text{l.u.b.}}\{(B\alpha', \alpha') \mid \|\alpha'\| = 1, \alpha' \perp \beta_j', j = 1, \ldots, i-1\}] \leq a_i.$$

Since any set of β_j' can be obtained by varying β_j, we may take the greatest lower bound on the left side of the inequality over all sets $\beta_1', \ldots, \beta_{i-1}'$. In this way we obtain $b_i \leq a_i$.

Moreover, with β_j, β_j', α', α defined as above, we have

$$\underset{\alpha'}{\text{l.u.b.}}\{(B\alpha', \alpha') \mid \|\alpha'\| = 1, \alpha' \perp \beta_j', j = 1, \ldots, i-1\} =$$
$$\underset{\alpha}{\text{l.u.b.}}\{(A\alpha, \alpha) \mid \|\alpha\| = 1, \alpha \perp \beta_j, j = 1, \ldots, i-1,$$
$$\alpha \perp \sigma_j, j = m+1, \ldots n\}.$$

Take the greatest lower bound of both sides as β_j vary. On the left side of the equation, we obtain the same result by varying β_j' over $\mathscr{E}_m{}^*$. It follows that

$$b_i = \underset{\beta}{\text{g.l.b.}}\, [\underset{\alpha}{\text{l.u.b.}}\, \{(A\alpha, \alpha) \mid \|\alpha\| = 1, \alpha \perp \beta_j, j = 1, \ldots, i-1,$$
$$\alpha \perp \sigma_j, j = m+1, \ldots, n\}]$$

$$\geq \underset{\beta}{\text{g.l.b.}}\, [\underset{\alpha}{\text{l.u.b.}}\, \{(A\alpha, \alpha) \mid \|\alpha\| = 1, \alpha \perp \beta_j, j = 1, \ldots, n-m+i-1\}]$$

where the greatest lower bound on the right side of the inequality is taken over all sets $\beta_1, \ldots, \beta_{n-m+i-1}$. By Theorem 2.8B, the right side is exactly a_{n-m+i}.

The next theorem illustrates an important property of linear transformations on finite dimensional spaces.

THEOREM 2.8C If the linear transformation A has a representation $A \overset{\sigma}{\leftrightarrow} [a_{ij}]$ where $\sigma_1, \ldots, \sigma_n$ is an orthonormal basis of $\mathscr{E}$ and if M is the larger of l.u.b. $\{\sum_{j=1}^{n} |a_{ij}| \mid i = 1, \ldots, n\}$ and l.u.b. $\{\sum_{i=1}^{n} |a_{ij}| \mid j = 1, \ldots, n\}$ then

$$(2) \qquad \qquad \|A\alpha\| \le M \|\alpha\|$$

for every vector α in $\mathscr{E}$.

Proof When $\alpha \overset{\sigma}{\leftrightarrow} [x_i]$, then $A\alpha \overset{\sigma}{\leftrightarrow} [a_{ij}][x_i]$ and $\|A\alpha\|^2 = \sum_{i=1}^{n} |\sum_{j=1}^{n} a_{ij} x_j|^2$.

By Schwarz's inequality,

$$\left| \sum_{j=1}^{n} a_{ij} x_j \right|^2 \le \sum_{j=1}^{n} |a_{ij}| |x_j|^2 \sum_{j=1}^{n} |a_{ij}| \le M \sum_{j=1}^{n} |a_{ij}| |x_j|^2.$$

Thus

$$\|A\alpha\|^2 \le M \sum_{i=1}^{n} \sum_{j=1}^{n} |a_{ij}| |x_j|^2 = M \sum_{j=1}^{n} |x_j|^2 \sum_{i=1}^{n} |a_{ij}|$$

$$\le M^2 \sum_{j=1}^{n} |x_j|^2 = M^2 \|\alpha\|^2. \quad \bigstar$$

A linear transformation L on a Euclidean vector space $\mathscr{E}$ to another Euclidean vector space $\mathscr{F}$ satisfying

$$\|L\alpha\| \le M \|\alpha\|$$

for every α in $\mathscr{E}$ and a fixed positive number M is called a **bounded transformation**. The least such number M is called the **norm of the transformation** L and denoted by $\|L\|$. That is,

$$(3) \qquad \|L\| = \text{g.l.b.} \{M \mid \|L\alpha\| \le M \|\alpha\| \text{ for all } \alpha \text{ in } \mathscr{E}\}.$$

Equivalent definitions for the norm of L are given by

$$(4) \qquad \|L\| = \text{l.u.b.} \{\|L\alpha\| \mid \|\alpha\| = 1\},$$

$$(5) \qquad \|L\| = \text{l.u.b.} \{\|L\alpha\| \mid \|\alpha\| \le 1\},$$

$$(6) \qquad \|L\| = \text{l.u.b.} \left\{ \frac{\|L\alpha\|}{\|\alpha\|} \mid \|\alpha\| \ne 0 \right\}.$$

To show the equivalence, denote the right sides of (3), (4), (5), and (6) by a, b, c, d respectively. We shall show $a \leq b \leq c \leq d \leq a$ and thus prove the equality. If $a = \infty$, for every integer n there is a vector α_n such that $\|L\alpha_n\| > n\|\alpha_n\|$. Then $\left\|L \dfrac{\alpha_n}{\|\alpha_n\|}\right\| > n$ and $b = \infty$. If a is finite, for every $p > 0$ we can find a vector $\alpha \neq \theta$ such that $\|L\alpha\| > (a - p)\|\alpha\|$. Then $\left\|L \dfrac{\alpha}{\|\alpha\|}\right\| > a - p$ and $b \geq a - p$. Since p is arbitrary, $b \geq a$. Clearly $b \leq c$. If $\|\alpha\| \leq 1$, $\alpha \neq \theta$, then $\dfrac{\|L\alpha\|}{\|\alpha\|} \geq \|L\alpha\|$ so that $c \leq d$. It remains to prove $d \leq a$. If $\|L\alpha\| \leq M\|\alpha\|$, then $M \geq \dfrac{\|L\alpha\|}{\|\alpha\|}$ for $\alpha \neq \theta$ so that $M \geq d$. From this it follows that $a \geq d$.

Every linear transformation A on an n dimensional vector space $\mathscr{E}$ to $\mathscr{E}$ with domain $\mathscr{E}$ is bounded and an explicit bound is given by Theorem 2.8C. In view of (3), we have, for $p > 0$,

$$\|A\alpha\| \leq (\|A\| + p)\|\alpha\| \text{ for every } \alpha$$

and hence, since p is arbitrary,

$$\|A\alpha\| \leq \|A\|\,\|\alpha\|.$$

If α is an eigenvector of A corresponding to the eigenvalue s, then

$$\|A\|\,\|\alpha\| \geq \|A\alpha\| = \|s\alpha\| = |s|\,\|\alpha\|$$

yielding

(7) $$|s| \leq \|A\|.$$

Thus the largest of the absolute values of the eigenvalues of A is less than or equal to the norm of A.

For symmetric operators we can say more.

THEOREM 2.8D If T is a symmetric operator on the n dimensional Euclidean vector space $\mathscr{E}$ to $\mathscr{E}$, then

(8) $$\|T\| = \text{l.u.b.} \{|s_1|, \ldots, |s_n|\}.$$

where s_i are the eigenvalues of T.

Proof Denote the right side of (8) by z. We shall show that $\|T\| \leq z$. This, combined with (7), will prove the theorem. Take $\alpha_1, \ldots, \alpha_n$ to be an orthonormal basis of $\mathscr{E}$ such that $T\alpha_i = s_i\alpha_i$. If α is in $\mathscr{E}$ and has $\|\alpha\| = 1$, write $\alpha = \sum\limits_{i=1}^{n} x_i\alpha_i$, $T\alpha = \sum\limits_{i=1}^{n} x_i s_i\alpha_i$,

$$(T\alpha, T\alpha) = \sum_{i=1}^{n} |x_i|^2 |s_i|^2 \leq z^2 \sum_{i=1}^{n} |x_i|^2 = z^2.$$

Hence

$$\|T\| = \text{l.u.b.} \{\|T\alpha\| \mid \|\alpha\| = 1\} \leq z. \quad \star$$

EXAMPLE 2 Calculate the norm of the matrix $\begin{bmatrix} 1 & 3 \\ 4 & 2 \end{bmatrix} = M$ defined on $\mathscr{E}_2$.

Let $\alpha = \begin{bmatrix} x_1 \\ x_2 \end{bmatrix}$. Then $M\alpha = \begin{bmatrix} x_1 + 3x_2 \\ 4x_1 + 2x_2 \end{bmatrix}$ and

$$\|M\alpha\|^2 = \{x_1 + 3x_2\}^2 + \{4x_1 + 2x_2\}^2 = 17x_1^2 + 22x_1 x_2 + 13x_2^2 = A(x).$$

The least upper bound of $A(x)$ for $x_1^2 + x_2^2 = 1$ is given by Theorem 2.8A as the largest eigenvalue of the matrix $\begin{bmatrix} 17 & 11 \\ 11 & 13 \end{bmatrix}$, a value calculated to be $15 + 5\sqrt{5}$.

Hence

$$\|M\| = \text{l.u.b.} \{\|M\alpha\| \mid \|\alpha\| = 1\} = \sqrt{15 + 5\sqrt{5}} = 5.12.$$

The eigenvalues of M are 5 and -2 and we see they are less, in absolute value, than $\|M\|$. Another method is suggested in Exercise 2.8–5.

Exercise 2.8

1. Find the l.u.b. and g.l.b. for the following sequences:

(a) $\left\{1 + (-1)^n - \dfrac{1}{n}\right\}$, $\quad n = 1, 2, 3, \ldots$

(b) $\left\{(-1)^n \dfrac{n+1}{2n+1}\right\}$, $\quad n = 1, 2, \ldots$

(c) $\left\{\dfrac{1}{m} + \dfrac{1}{n}\right\}$, $\quad m = 1, 2, \ldots, \quad n = 1, 2, \ldots$

2. Let L be a linear transformation on a Euclidean vector space $\mathscr{E}$ to $\mathscr{E}$, not necessarily finite dimensional. Show that

$$\|L\| = \text{l.u.b.} \{|(L\alpha, \beta)| \mid \|\alpha\| = 1, \|\beta\| = 1\},$$

Hint: Denote the right side by z. Use the Schwarz inequality to show $z \leq \|L\|$. Then show $\|L\| \leq z$.

3. Let $[A] = [a_{ij}]$, $[B] = [b_{ij}]$ be $n \times n$ matrices and $[C] = [c_{ij}] = [a_{ij}][b_{ij}]$.

Define $S[A] = \text{l.u.b.}\left\{ \sum_{j=1}^{n} |a_{ij}| \mid i = 1, \ldots n \right\}$

$S'[A] = \text{l.u.b.}\left\{ \sum_{i=1}^{n} |a_{ij}| \mid j = 1, \ldots n \right\}$

Show that $S[C] \leq S[A] S[B]$, $S'[C] \leq S'[A] S'[B]$. This result yields a bound for the eigenvalues of $[A][B]$ in terms of certain bounds on the eigenvalues of $[A]$ and $[B]$ by use of equations (2) and (7) in the text. A better result can be obtained using the next exercise.

4. Let A and B be bounded linear transformations on $\mathscr{E}$ to $\mathscr{E}$ with domain $\mathscr{E}$. Show that $\|AB\| \leq \|A\| \|B\|$.

5. (a) Use Exercise (2) to show $\|L^*\| = \|L\|$, L being any linear transformation and L^* related to L by equation 2.7(3).
    (b) Write $\|L\|^2 = \text{l.u.b.}\{(L\alpha, L\alpha) \mid \|\alpha\| = 1\}$
        $\leq \text{l.u.b.} \{|(L\alpha, L\beta)| \mid \|\alpha\| = 1, \|\beta\| = 1\}$
        $= \text{l.u.b.} \{|(\alpha, L^*L\beta)| \mid \|\alpha\| = 1, \|\beta\| = 1\}$
        and obtain $\|L\|^2 \leq \|L^*L\|$. Also show $\|L^*L\| \leq \|L\|^2$. Thus prove $\|L\|^2 = \|L^*L\| = \|LL^*\|$.
    (c) Using the notation of Example (2) of the text, show that
        $$[M]^*[M] = \begin{bmatrix} 17 & 11 \\ 11 & 13 \end{bmatrix}.$$
        By Exercise 2.7(6), $[M]^*[M]$ is Hermitian for every matrix $[M]$. Obtain the value $\sqrt{15 + 5\sqrt{5}}$ in Example (2) by use of part b.

6. Calculate the norm of
    $$\begin{bmatrix} 1 & 1 & 1 \\ -1 & 1 & 1 \\ -1 & -1 & 1 \end{bmatrix}.$$

7. Show that the matrix
    $$\begin{bmatrix} 4 & 0 & 1 & 6i \\ 0 & 4 & 0 & 2 \\ 1 & 0 & 4 & 0 \\ -6i & 2 & 0 & 7 \end{bmatrix}$$
    has at least one eigenvalue greater than or equal to 5 and at least three eigenvalues less than or equal to 5.

8. Use Theorem 2.8C to obtain a bound on the absolute value of the eigenvalues of the matrix in Exercise 7.

9. (a) If, for each i, $|a_{ii}| > \sum_{k \neq i} |a_{ik}|$, then show that $\det [a_{ij}] \neq 0$. Hint: if the determinant is zero, there exist constants $x_1, \ldots, x_n$ not all zero, such that $\sum_{j=1}^{n} a_{ij}x_j = 0$, $i = 1, \ldots, n$. Let r be an integer such that
        $$|x_r| = \text{l.u.b.} \{|x_i| \mid i = 1, \ldots, n\}.$$

The rth equation yields

$$|a_{rr}x_r| \leq \sum_{j \neq r} |a_{rj}x_j| \leq |x_r| \sum_{j \neq r} |a_{rj}|.$$

Finish the proof.

(b)   Each eigenvalue s of $[a_{ij}]$ lies, for some i, in a circle in the complex plane about a_{ii} of radius $\sum_{k \neq i} |a_{ik}|$. *Hint:* We have $\det [s\delta_{ij} - a_{ij}] = 0$. Now apply the result of part a.

10. (a)   Prove the following analogue of Theorem 2.8A.
If $s_1 \geq s_2 \ldots \geq s_n$ then for $i = 1, \ldots, n$ we have
$$s_i = \text{g.l.b.} \{(T\alpha, \alpha) \mid \|\alpha\| = 1, \alpha \perp \alpha_j, j = i + 1, \ldots, n\},$$
where T, α_j, s_i are as in Theorem 2.8A.

(b)   Hence, using Theorem 2.8D, show that $\|T\| = \text{l.u.b.} \{|(T\alpha, \alpha)| \mid \|\alpha\| = 1\}$.

11. (a)   Show that if $\|L\| = 0$, then $L = 0$ for any linear transformation L on a Euclidean vector space $\mathscr{E}$.

(b)   If T is a symmetric operator on an n dimensional Euclidean vector space $\mathscr{E}$, and $(T\alpha, \alpha) = 0$ for every α, then $T = 0$. *Hint:* Use Exercise 10.

12. Let $[A]$ be a nonsingular $n \times n$ Hermitian matrix. Change the values of the elements of $[A]$ slightly to form another Hermitian matrix $[B]$. Show that if $p > 0$ is chosen sufficiently small and $\|B - A\| < p$ then $[B]$ has the same number of positive and negative eigenvalues that $[A]$ has. *Hint:* Write $(B\alpha, \alpha) = ((B - A)\alpha, \alpha) + (A\alpha, \alpha)$ and use Theorem 2.8B.

13. Let T be Hermitian, $\|\beta\| = 1$, $a = (T\beta, \beta)$, $b = (\|T\beta\|^2 - a^2)^{1/2}$. Show that there is an eigenvalue of T in the circle $|z - a| \leq b$. *Hint:* Write $\beta = \Sigma b_i \alpha_i$ where $\{\alpha_i\}$ is an orthonormal basis of eigenvectors. Then $b^2 = ((T - aI)\beta, (T - aI)\beta) = \sum_i |s_i - a|^2 |b_i|^2 \geq \min |s_i - a|^2$ where $T\alpha_i = s_i \alpha_i$.

2.9

POSITIVE DEFINITE

OPERATORS

When T is symmetric, it has real eigenvalues and $(T\alpha, \alpha)$ is real. Thus certain properties are characterized by real numbers. A closer connection with real numbers is apparent when the domain is a complex Euclidean vector space. Indeed the relation of symmetric transformations to the class of all linear transformations becomes somewhat analogous to the relation between real and complex numbers. One illustration is afforded by Exercise 2.7–11 which states that a sum of squares of symmetric transformations is zero only when each transformation is zero. This is a property characteristic of real numbers. Again, for any L we may write

$$L = \frac{L + L^*}{2} + i\frac{-iL + iL^*}{2} = A + iB$$

where $A = \dfrac{L + L^*}{2}$ and $B = \dfrac{-iL + iL^*}{2}$ are symmetric since $A^* = A$, $B^* = B$. The decomposition is unique, since $L = A + iB$ implies $L^* = A - iB$ and the two equations may be solved uniquely for A and B to obtain $A = \dfrac{L + L^*}{2}$, $B = \dfrac{-iL + iL^*}{2}$. This result is analogous to the familiar decomposition $z = a + ib$, a and b real, of the complex number z.

Certain symmetric transformations called positive definite transformations have properties related to positive numbers. The symmetric transformation P on the n dimensional real or complex Euclidean vector space $\mathscr{E}$ to $\mathscr{E}$ is said to be **positive definite** if $(P\alpha, \alpha) > 0$, unless $\alpha = \theta$. It is easily seen that P is positive definite if and only if all its eigenvalues are positive. In fact, if P is positive definite and $P\alpha = r\alpha$, $\alpha \neq \theta$, then $0 < (r\alpha, \alpha) = r(\alpha, \alpha)$ so that $r > 0$. Conversely, if $\alpha_1, \ldots, \alpha_n$ is an orthonormal basis of eigenvectors of P corresponding to positive eigenvalues $s_1, \ldots, s_n$ respectively, then every vector α in $\mathscr{E}$ may be written as $\alpha = \sum_{i=1}^{n} x_i \alpha_i$ so that

$$(P\alpha, \alpha) = \left(\sum_{i=1}^{n} x_i s_i \alpha_i, \sum_{i=1}^{n} x_i \alpha_i\right) = \sum_{i=1}^{n} s_i |x_i|^2 > 0$$

unless $\alpha = \theta$.

THEOREM 2.9A   Let $\sigma_1, \ldots, \sigma_n$ be an orthonormal basis of $\mathscr{E}$. The symmetric transformation P with representation $P \overset{\sigma}{\leftrightarrow} [p_{ij}]$ is positive definite if and only if $\det [P_m] > 0$, $m = 1, 2, \ldots, n$, where $[P_m]$ is the matrix of order m obtained from $[p_{ij}]$ by deleting all elements except those in the first m rows and m columns.

Proof   The representation $[x_i]$ of α in $\mathscr{E}$ lies in $\mathscr{E}_n$ or $\mathscr{E}_n^*$ according as $\mathscr{E}$ is a real or complex vector space. The condition that P be positive definite is

(1) $$\sum_{i,j=1}^{n} p_{ij} x_j \bar{x}_i > 0 \text{ whenever } \sum_{i=1}^{n} |x_i|^2 \neq 0.$$

If, in particular, we use in (1) a set of values where $x_j = 0$ for $j = m + 1, \ldots, n$ we obtain

$$\sum_{i,j=1}^{m} p_{ij} \, x_j \, \overline{x_i} > 0 \text{ whenever } \sum_{i=1}^{m} |x_i|^2 \neq 0.$$

This states that the matrix $[P_m]$ defines a positive definite transformation on the linear manifold spanned by $\sigma_1, \ldots, \sigma_m$. The determinants $\det [P_m]$ must then all be positive since the determinant of a symmetric transformation is equal to the product of its eigenvalues.

Conversely, suppose $\det [P_m] > 0$ for $m = 1, \ldots, n$. Since $[P_1] = p_{11} > 0$, equation (1) indicates that $[P_1]$ defines a positive definite transformation. We proceed by induction. Suppose that $[P_m]$ defines a positive definite transformation. The eigenvalues of $[P_m]$ are positive and, when arranged in order of magnitude, are less than or equal to the first m eigenvalues of $[P_{m+1}]$ by virtue of equation 2.8 (1). Thus $[P_{m+1}]$ can have at most one negative or zero eigenvalue. If one were present, then $\det [P_{m+1}]$, being equal to the product of its eigenvalues, could not be positive. It follows that $[P_{m+1}]$ has only positive eigenvalues and defines a positive definite transformation. This completes the induction and shows that P, with representation $[P_n]$, is positive definite.   ★

The representation of a positive definite transformation in an orthonormal basis is called a **positive definite matrix**. Thus a positive definite matrix $[p_{ij}]$ may be defined as a Hermitian matrix satisfying (1) or as a Hermitian matrix with positive eigenvalues or as a Hermitian matrix with minors $[P_m]$ (defined in the theorem) all positive.

We now turn our attention to the equation

$$(2) \qquad\qquad T\alpha = rP\alpha$$

where T is symmetric and P is positive definite.

The transformation P^{-1} exists since P has no zero eigenvalues (Exercise 2.6–3) and equation (2) may be written

$$(3) \qquad\qquad P^{-1}T\alpha = r\alpha,$$

showing that the nonzero solutions of (2) are the eigenvectors of $P^{-1}T$ P and T and hence P^{-1} are symmetric but $P^{-1}T$ need not be. However, we shall see it is still possible to apply the theory obtained for symmetric operators. To do this, we define a second inner product on $\mathscr{E}$. It is readily verified that

$$(4) \qquad\qquad (\alpha, \beta)_P = (P\alpha, \beta)$$

satisfies the axioms required for an inner product. We have

$$(\alpha, \beta)_P = (P\alpha, \beta) = (\alpha, P\beta) = \overline{(P\beta, \alpha)} = \overline{(\beta, \alpha)_P},$$

$$(\alpha + \mu, \beta)_P = (P(\alpha + \mu), \beta) = (P\alpha, \beta) + (P\mu, \beta) = (\alpha, \beta)_P + (\mu, \beta)_P,$$

$$(\alpha, \alpha)_P = (P\alpha, \alpha) > 0 \text{ unless } \alpha = \theta,$$

and we shall call $(\alpha, \beta)_P$ the P **inner product.** All the results proved for an arbitrary inner product are now valid for the P inner product. For example, if we define the P **norm** of α by $\|\alpha\|_P{}^2 = (\alpha, \alpha)_P$, the Schwarz inequality $|(\alpha, \beta)_P| \leq \|\alpha\|_P \|\beta\|_P$ yields

$$|(P\alpha, \beta)| \leq (P\alpha, \alpha)^{1/2}(P\beta, \beta)^{1/2}.$$

Vectors α and β are P **orthogonal** if $(\alpha, \beta)_P = 0$. The vectors $\alpha_1, \ldots, \alpha_n$ are P **orthonormal** if $(\alpha_i, \alpha_j)_P = \delta_{ij}, i, j = 1, \ldots, n$. By Section 1.3, P orthonormal vectors are linearly independent. If $\alpha_1, \ldots, \alpha_n$ is a P orthonormal basis and $\alpha = \sum_{i=1}^{n} x_i \alpha_i, \beta = \sum_{i=1}^{n} y_i \alpha_i$, then $(\alpha, \beta)_P = \sum x_i \overline{y_i}$ and $\|\alpha\|_P{}^2 = \sum_{i=1}^{n} |x_i|^2$.

The connection with symmetric operators becomes clear in virtue of

THEOREM 2.9B   With respect to the P inner product, the transformation $P^{-1}T$ is symmetric.

Proof   We must show that $(P^{-1}T\alpha, \beta)_P = (\alpha, P^{-1}T\beta)_P$ for every α and β in $\mathcal{E}$.

$$(P^{-1}T\alpha, \beta)_P = (T\alpha, \beta) = \overline{(\beta, T\alpha)} = \overline{(T\beta, \alpha)} = \overline{(P^{-1}T\beta, \alpha)_P} = (\alpha, P^{-1}T\beta)_P. \quad \star$$

The nonzero solutions of (2) are the eigenvectors of (3).
Theorem 2.9B implies the following:

Corollary 1
The values of r for which (2) has a nonzero solution are real. They are the roots of $\det [xI - P^{-1}T] = 0$ and hence of

(5) $\det [x\, p_{ij} - t_{ij}] = 0.$

If α_1 and α_2 are nonzero solutions of (2) corresponding to distinct values r_1 and r_2, then α_1 and α_2 are P orthogonal.

Corollary 2

There exists a P orthonormal basis $\alpha_1, \ldots, \alpha_n$ such that $T\alpha_k = s_k P\alpha_k$ for real numbers s_k, $k = 1, \ldots, n$.

From Corollary 2 we derive

$$(T\alpha_k, \alpha_k) = s_k (P\alpha_k, \alpha_k)$$

showing that s_k is positive if T is also positive definite. Conversely, if s_k is positive, $k = 1, 2, \ldots, n$, and $\alpha = \sum_{i=1}^{n} x_i \alpha_i$ is any nonzero vector in $\mathscr{E}$, then

$$T\alpha = \sum_{i=1}^{n} x_i T\alpha_i = \sum_{i=1}^{n} x_i s_i P\alpha_i \text{ and}$$

$$(T\alpha, \alpha) = \sum_{i=1}^{n} \sum_{j=1}^{n} x_i s_i \bar{x}_j (P\alpha_i, \alpha_j) = \sum_{i=1}^{n} |x_i|^2 s_i(P\alpha_i, \alpha_i) > 0$$

since α_i are P orthonormal. We have therefore proved

Corollary 3

A necessary and sufficient condition that the numbers s_i in Corollary 2 be positive is that T also be positive definite.

Let the vectors α_k of Corollary 2 be represented in the original orthonormal system $\sigma_1, \ldots, \sigma_n$ by $\alpha_k \overset{\sigma}{\leftrightarrow} [a_{ik}]$. For fixed k, $k = 1, \ldots, n$, these representations satisfy

(6) $$[t_{ij}][a_{ik}] = s_k [p_{ij}][a_{ik}].$$

Since $\alpha_k = \sum_{i=1}^{n} a_{ik}\sigma_i$ are P orthonormal,

$$\delta_{ke} = (P\alpha_k, \alpha_e) = \sum_{j, i=1}^{n} p_{ij} a_{jk} \bar{a}_{ie};$$

or, in matrix form,

(7) $$[I] = [a_{ij}]^*[p_{ij}][a_{ij}].$$

In view of Corollary 2 and Theorem 2.2B, the representation of $P^{-1}T$ in the basis $\alpha_1, \ldots, \alpha_n$ is

$$[a_{ij}]^{-1}[p_{ij}]^{-1}[t_{ij}][a_{ij}] = \text{diag } [s_1, \ldots, s_n].$$

Using (7), this may be written as

(8) $$[a_{ij}]^*[t_{ij}][a_{ij}] = \text{diag } [s_1, \ldots, s_n].$$

The results obtained may be summarized as

THEOREM 2.9C If $[t_{ij}]$ is Hermitian and $[p_{ij}]$ is positive definite, there is a nonsingular matrix $[a_{ij}]$ such that (7) and (8) hold, that is, upon multiplication on the left by $[a_{ij}]^*$ and on the right by $[a_{ij}]$, the matrices $[t_{ij}]$ and $[p_{ij}]$ are brought into diagonal form, $[p_{ij}]$ being carried into the identity. The matrix $[a_{ij}]$ has as its columns n P-orthonormalized solutions satisfying (6).

The next corollary will be stated for quadratic forms. A corresponding corollary is true for Hermitian forms.

Corollary 1

The change of variables $x_i = \sum\limits_{j=1}^{n} a_{ij} y_j$ reduces the symmetric quadratic

forms $\sum\limits_{i,j=1}^{n} t_{ij} x_i x_j$ and $\sum\limits_{i,j=1}^{n} p_{ij} x_i x_j$, the latter being positive definite, to

$\sum\limits_{i=1}^{n} s_i y_i^2$ and $\sum\limits_{i=1}^{n} y_i^2$ respectively.

This is an immediate consequence of the fact that the transformation

$x_i = \sum\limits_{j=1}^{n} a_{ij} y_j$ carries the symmetric matrix $[q_{ij}]$ of a quadratic form into $[a_{ij}]^T [q_{ij}][a_{ij}]$.

EXAMPLE 1 Determine a change of variables which eliminates the cross product terms in the forms

$$T(x) = 84x_1^2 + 66x_1x_2 + 13x_2^2, \qquad P(x) = 34x_1^2 + 26x_1x_2 + 5x_2^2.$$

The symmetric matrices corresponding to these forms are

$$[t_{ij}] = \begin{bmatrix} 84 & 33 \\ 33 & 13 \end{bmatrix}, \qquad [p_{ij}] = \begin{bmatrix} 34 & 13 \\ 13 & 5 \end{bmatrix},$$

determining symmetric transformations T and P which are also positive definite.

The eigenvalues of $P^{-1}T$ are obtained by solving

$$0 = \det [xp_{ij} - t_{ij}] = \begin{vmatrix} 34x - 84 & 13x - 33 \\ 13x - 33 & 5x - 13 \end{vmatrix} = (x - 3)(x - 1)$$

and hence are 3 and 1.

An eigenvector $\beta = \begin{bmatrix} z_1 \\ z_2 \end{bmatrix}$ associated with eigenvalue 3 satisfies

$$\begin{bmatrix} 18 & 6 \\ 6 & 2 \end{bmatrix} \begin{bmatrix} z_1 \\ z_2 \end{bmatrix} = \begin{bmatrix} 0 \\ 0 \end{bmatrix}.$$

This equation is satisfied if we choose $\beta = \begin{bmatrix} -1 \\ 3 \end{bmatrix}$. A P normalized eigenvector is $\alpha_1 = \beta/\|\beta\|_P = \beta/(P\beta, \beta)^{1/2}$. Since $(P\beta, \beta)$ is calculated to be 1, we have $\alpha_1 = \begin{bmatrix} -1 \\ 3 \end{bmatrix}$.

A P normalized eigenvector associated with eigenvalue 1 is found, in a similar fashion, to be $\alpha_2 = \begin{bmatrix} -2 \\ 5 \end{bmatrix}$. Hence the matrix to be used in Corollary 1 is

$$[a_{ij}] = \begin{bmatrix} -1 & -2 \\ 3 & 5 \end{bmatrix}$$

and the desired change of variables is $\begin{cases} x_1 = -y_1 - 2y_2, \\ x_2 = 3y_1 + 5y_2. \end{cases}$

EXAMPLE 2 It is of interest to note that physical problems motivated many of the theoretical developments in this chapter. Let us consider an application to the theory of small vibrations. It is assumed that the motion of a system is described in terms of parameters q_i, $i = 1, 2, \ldots, n$ where q_i are all zero at a fixed position of equilibrium, that is, a point where the forces are zero. The analysis deals with motion near this equilibrium position and it is assumed that the potential energy, when expanded as an infinite series in q_i about the equilibrium position, may have its terms of third or higher order neglected. In this case the potential energy $V(q) = V(q_1, \ldots, q_n)$ may be written

$$V(q) = \sum_{i,j=1}^{n} t_{ij} q_i q_j,$$

for constants $t_{ij} = t_{ji}$. When $V(q) > 0$ unless $q_i = 0$ for all i, the position $(q_1, \ldots, q_n) = (0, \ldots, 0)$ is said to be a position of **stable equilibrium.** The kinetic energy near the equilibrium position is approximately

$$T(q) = \sum_{i,j=1}^{n} p_{ij} q_i' q_j'$$

for constants $p_{ij} = p_{ji}$, where the prime denotes differentiation with respect to time. The system is said to have n **degrees of freedom** if n is the minimum number of variables needed to characterize the motion. In this case it may be shown that $[p_{ij}]$ is positive definite. If the expressions for $T(q)$ and $V(q)$ are substituted into the Lagrangian equations of motion,

$$\frac{d}{dt}\frac{\partial(T-V)}{\partial q_i'} - \frac{\partial(T-V)}{\partial q_i} = 0, \qquad i = 1, 2, \ldots, n,$$

one obtains a system of differential equations

$$\sum_{j=1}^{n} p_{ij} q_j'' + t_{ij} q_j = 0, \qquad i = 1, 2, \ldots, n,$$

which may be difficult to solve. If, however, one makes the substitution

$$q_i = \sum_{j=1}^{n} a_{ij} y_j$$

where a_{ij} is obtained as in Theorem 2.9C, T and V are respectively carried into

$$T = \sum_{i=1}^{n} (y_i')^2, \qquad V = \sum_{i=1}^{n} s_i y_i^2.$$

Now application of the Lagrangian equations taken with respect to the variables y_i yields

$$y_i'' + s_i y_i = 0, \qquad i = 1, 2, \ldots, n, \qquad s_i > 0,$$

with solutions

$$y_i = b_i \sin \sqrt{s_i}\, t + c_i \cos \sqrt{s_i}\, t.$$

The solution for the original system is given by

$$[q_i] = [a_{ij}]\, [b_i \sin \sqrt{s_i}\, t + c_i \cos \sqrt{s_i}\, t].$$

The variables y_i are called the **normal coordinates** of the problem. Each of these variables has a purely sinusoidal variation. The numbers $\sqrt{s_i}$ are called the **angular frequencies** of the normal coordinates.

As a further indication of the analogy between positive definite matrices and positive numbers, we shall show that every nonsingular transformation L on an n dimensional complex vector space can be uniquely written as $L = TU$ where T is positive definite and U is unitary. When $n = 1$, this becomes the polar form $z = re^{i\phi}$, $r > 0$, $|e^{i\phi}| = 1$, of complex numbers. We have $(LL^*\alpha, \alpha) = (L^*\alpha, L^*\alpha) > 0$ unless $L^*\alpha = \theta$ in which case multiplication by $(L^*)^{-1}$ shows $\alpha = \theta$. Thus the symmetric transformation LL^* is positive definite and has a diagonal representation with all elements on the diagonal positive. This matrix may be written as the product $[T][T]$ where $[T]$ is a diagonal matrix whose entries are the square roots of the diagonal elements of $[LL^*]$. Hence there is a positive definite transformation $T = T^*$ such that $T^2 = LL^*$. Let $U = T(L^*)^{-1}$. Then $U^*U = L^{-1}T^*T(L^*)^{-1} = L^{-1}LL^*(L^*)^{-1} = I$ proving that U is unitary. The equation $L = TT(L^*)^{-1} = TU$ now gives the desired representation. It remains to prove the uniqueness. If $T_1U_1 = T_2U_2$ where T_1 and T_2 are positive definite while U_1 and U_2 are unitary, then $T_2^{-1}T_1 = U_2U_1^{-1}$ is unitary and has eigenvalues equal to 1 in absolute value by Exercises 2.2–7 and 2.7–8. However $T_2^{-1}T_1$ has positive eigenvalues in view of Corollary 3 of Theorem 2.9B. It follows that all the eigenvalues of $T_2^{-1}T_1$ are 1. By Corollary 2 of Theorem 2.9B we can find a basis $\alpha_1, \ldots, \alpha_n$ for which $T_1\alpha_i = T_2\alpha_i$, $i = 1, \ldots, n$. From this one obtains $T_1\alpha = T_2\alpha$ for every α. Thus $T_1 = T_2$, $U_1 = U_2$.

Exercise 2.9

1. Let the domain of the transformation L be an n dimensional complex Euclidean vector space. L is called *normal* if it commutes with its adjoint, that is, if $LL^* = L^*L$.

   (a) Show that symmetric and unitary transformations are normal.

   (b) Show that if $L = A + iB$ with A and B symmetric and if A and B commute, then L is normal.

   (c) Conversely, show that if L is normal, then $L = A + iB$ where $A = \dfrac{L + L^*}{2}$ and $B = \dfrac{-iL + iL^*}{2}$ are symmetric and commute.

   (d) Let $[L]$ be the representation of L in an orthonormal basis. Prove that a necessary and sufficient condition that there exists a unitary matrix $[U]$ such that $[U]^* [L][U]$ is diagonal is that L be normal. Use the results on commutivity in Section 2.7.

2. (a) Determine a change of variables which reduces the quadratic forms $5x^2 + 4xy + 3y^2$ and $x^2 + 2y^2$ to forms having no cross product terms.

   (b) Do the same for the quadratic forms
   $2x^2 + 12y^2 + 5z^2 + 2xz - 4yz$ and $2x^2 + 4y^2 + 8xz + 24yz + 24xy$.

3. Find an orthogonal matrix $[R]$ such that $[R]^T[A][R]$ and $[R]^T[B][R]$ are diagonal when

$$[A] = \begin{bmatrix} 6 & -2 & 4 \\ -2 & 2 & 0 \\ 4 & 0 & 3 \end{bmatrix}, \quad [B] = \begin{bmatrix} 5 & -1 & 4 \\ -1 & 1 & 0 \\ 4 & 0 & 5 \end{bmatrix}.$$

4. In applications, the matrices of a system of equations may not be symmetric. However an equivalent system may often be derived to bring the problem within the scope of our theory. In the diagram, $L > 0$ is the inductance of the coil, $c > 0$ is the capacitance of the condenser, I is the current. If Q is the charge on the condenser, the current "through" it is $\dfrac{dQ}{dt}$. Kirchoff's law states that the total change in potential around a closed circuit is zero. The potential is decreased $L\dfrac{dI}{dt}$ in passing through a coil in the direction of the current and decreased Q/c in passing through a condenser in the direction of the current. See Exercise 2.5–7. Closing the circuit we obtain

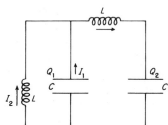

$$\begin{cases} L\dfrac{dI_2}{dt} - \dfrac{Q_1}{c} = 0 \\[2mm] L\dfrac{d(I_1 + I_2)}{dt} + \dfrac{Q_2}{c} + \dfrac{Q_1}{c} = 0 \end{cases}$$

where Q_1, Q_2 are the charges on the condensers at time t.

Show that if the currents at resonance are

$$I_1 = A_1 \sin(wt + \phi)$$
$$I_2 = A_2 \sin(wt + \phi)$$

then the eigenvalue problem for determining the frequencies w can be put in the form

$$2A_1 + A_2 = r(A_1 + A_2)$$
$$A_1 + A_2 = r(A_1 + 2A_2)$$

where $r = w^2 LC$. Then find w in terms of LC.

5. (a) If P is positive definite, show that P^n is positive definite for integral n.

  (b) If P is positive definite, show that P^{-1} is positive definite.

6. (a) Show that a necessary and sufficient condition that P be positive definite is that there exist a transformation B with nonsingular determinant such that $P = B^*B$.

  (b) Show that the equation $X^n = P$, where P is positive definite, has a positive definite solution X for every positive integer n.

7. With $[t_{ij}]$, $[p_{ij}]$, s_i defined as in the corollaries to Theorem 2.9B, show that

$$\det[xp_{ij} - t_{ij}] = \det\begin{bmatrix} x - s_1 & \cdot & \cdot & 0 \\ \cdot & & & \\ \cdot & & & \\ 0 & & & x - s_n \end{bmatrix} \cdot \det[p_{ij}].$$

8. (a) Let the numbers s_i in Corollary 2 of Theorem 2.9B be arranged so that $s_1 \geq s_2 \ldots \geq s_n$. Show that

$$s_i = \text{l.u.b.}\{(T\alpha, \alpha) \mid \|\alpha\|_p = 1, \alpha \, P \text{ orthogonal to } \alpha_j, j = 1, 2, \ldots, i - 1\}.$$

$$= \text{l.u.b.} \left\{ \frac{(T\alpha, \alpha)}{(P\alpha, \alpha)} \, \middle| \, \alpha \, P \text{ orthogonal to } \alpha_j, j = 1, \ldots, i - 1 \right\}.$$

(b) Show that
$$s_i = \text{g.l.b.} \{(T\alpha, \alpha) \mid \|\alpha\|_p = 1, \alpha \, P \text{ orthogonal to } \alpha_j, j = i + 1, \ldots, n\}.$$

9. (a) Find the maximum and minimum values of $T(x) = 17x^2 - 30xy + 17y^2$ subject to the condition $5x^2 - 6xy + 5y^2 = 1$. *Hint:* By problem 8, the maximum and minimum values are the largest and smallest eigenvalues respectively for a problem of the form $T\alpha = rP\alpha$.

(b) Find the maximum and minimum values of $T(x)$ subject to $5x^2 - 6xy + 5y^2 = 9$.

10. Prove Theorem 2.9C as follows: Carry $[p_{ij}]$ into a diagonal matrix (using the counterpart of Corollary 1 of Theorem 2.7D for Hermitian matrices) and then determine another transformation carrying this diagonal matrix into the identity matrix. Under these transformations $[t_{ij}]$ will be carried into a Hermitian matrix $[v_{ij}]$. Finally a third transformation will carry $[v_{ij}]$ into a diagonal matrix. Show that the product of the three transformations yields the desired result.

11. The **principal minors** of an $n \times n$ matrix are those obtained by deleting certain rows and the same numbered columns. Show, by reordering the terms in equation (1), that if $[p_{ij}]$ is positive definite, all the principal minors are positive.

12. (a) Let $[t_{ij}]$ be Hermitian with eigenvalues $s_1, \ldots, s_n$. Write
$$\det [x\delta_{ij} - t_{ij}] = x^n - t_1 x^{n-1} + t_2 x^{n-2} - \ldots + (-1)^n t_n.$$
Show that $t_1 = s_1 + \ldots + s_n$.

$$\vdots$$

$$t_k = \Sigma \, s_{i_1} s_{i_2} \ldots s_{i_k} \text{ where } i_1, i_2, \ldots, i_k \text{ are distinct and vary}$$
over the set $1, 2, \ldots, n$.

$$\vdots$$

$$t_n = \prod_{i=1}^{n} s_i = \det [t_{ij}].$$

(b) Show that $[t_{ij}]$ is positive definite if and only if all the t_i are positive. *Hint:* Use Descartes' rule of signs.

13. Using an equation in the text, show that if $a, b, c, x_1, x_2, y_1, y_2$ are real numbers with $a > 0$, $ab > c^2$ then

$$|ax_1 y_1 + cx_1 y_2 + cx_2 y_1 + bx_2 y_2| \leq$$
$$\{ax_1^2 + 2c \, x_1 x_2 + bx_2^2\}^{1/2}\{ay_1^2 + 2c \, y_1 y_2 + by_2^2\}^{1/2}.$$

14. Give an example of a 2×2 matrix, not the identity matrix, both of whose eigenvalues are equal to 1. Can such a matrix be diagonalized by a similarity transformation?

15. Consider the vibrating system given in the diagram where x_1, x_2, x_3 measure the displacements of the three masses from the unstrained configuration. The points A, B, C indicate the positions of the masses before the configuration was strained.

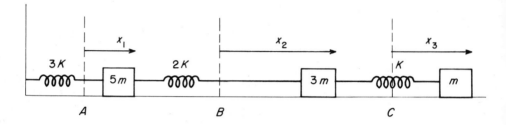

The spring constant, that is, the force needed for unit stretch of the spring, is given as a multiple of a constant K. Newton's laws, applied to the $5m$, $3m$, and m masses in turn, yield

$$5m\frac{d^2x_1}{dt^2} = -3Kx_1 + 2K(x_2 - x_1),$$

$$3m\frac{d^2x_2}{dt^2} = -2K(x_2 - x_1) + K(x_3 - x_2),$$

$$m\frac{d^2x_3}{dt^2} = -K(x_3 - x_2).$$

This may be written in the form

$$[P_{ij}][x''] + \frac{K}{m}[t_{ij}][x_i] = [0].$$

Perform a change of variables $x_i = \sum_{j=1}^{n} a_{ij}y_j$ to apply Theorem 2.9C and obtain

$$y_1'' + \frac{K}{m}\left(1 + \frac{\sqrt{15}}{5}\right)y_1 = 0,$$

$$y_2'' + \frac{K}{m}y_2 = 0,$$

$$y_3'' + \frac{K}{m}\left(1 - \frac{\sqrt{15}}{5}\right)y_3 = 0.$$

Solve this system and thus obtain $x_i(t)$.

2.10

THE GENERAL
LINEAR TRANSFORMATION

The diagonal representation of a diagonalizable linear transformation permits one to see immediately its important properties. If the transformation is not necessarily diagonalizable, it is of interest to seek a coordinate system in which the representation has some simple form. We restrict our attention to linear transformations whose domain is a finite dimensional *complex* Euclidean vector space $\mathscr{E}$ and whose range is in $\mathscr{E}$. This assures us that the transformation has at least one eigenvalue. The results to be obtained are, in general, not valid for a real Euclidean vector space.

The $n \times n$ matrix $[a_{ij}]$ is said to be in **superdiagonal form** if $a_{ij} = 0$ for $i > j$, that is, if all elements below the diagonal crossing from upper left to lower right of the matrix (the **principal diagonal**) are equal to zero. The next theorem states that for every square matrix $[A]$ there is a unitary matrix $[U]$ such that $[U]^{-1}[A][U]$ is superdiagonal.

THEOREM 2.10A   For each T, there exists an orthonormal basis of $\mathscr{E}$ in which the representation of T is superdiagonal. The elements on the principal diagonal are the eigenvalues of T, each appearing a number of times equal to its multiplicity as a root of the characteristic equation.

Proof   It is clear that if $\mathscr{E}$ has dimension 1 then every linear transformation T has a superdiagonal form. In fact, the matrix representation of T in any basis has just one element. We now proceed by induction on the dimension of $\mathscr{E}$. Assume that for every linear transformation whose domain $\mathscr{D}$ is a complex Euclidean vector space of dimension $n - 1$ and whose range is in $\mathscr{D}$ there is an orthonormal basis where the representation is super-diagonal. Let $\mathscr{E}$ have dimension n and T be a linear transformation on $\mathscr{E}$. Choose α_n to satisfy $\|\alpha_n\| = 1$ and $T^*\alpha_n = r\alpha_n$ and choose $\beta_1, \ldots, \beta_{n-1}, \alpha_n$ to be an orthonormal basis for $\mathscr{E}$. If $\mu = \sum_{i=1}^{n-1} c_i \beta_i$ is in the linear manifold $\mathscr{V}$ spanned by $\beta_1, \ldots, \beta_{n-1}$, we have

$$(T\mu, \alpha_n) = (\mu, T^* \alpha_n) = \left(\sum_{i=1}^{n-1} c_i \beta_i, r\alpha_n \right) = 0$$

so that $T\mu$ is also in $\mathscr{V}$. By our induction assumption there exists an orthonormal basis $\alpha_1, \ldots, \alpha_{n-1}$ of $\mathscr{V}$ for which

$$T\alpha_1 = t_{11}\,\alpha_1,$$
$$T\alpha_2 = t_{12}\,\alpha_1 + t_{22}\,\alpha_2,$$
$$\cdot$$
$$\cdot$$
$$\cdot$$
$$T\alpha_{n-1} = t_{1,n-1}\,\alpha_1 + \ldots + t_{n-1,n-1}\,\alpha_{n-1}.$$

The set $\alpha_1, \ldots, \alpha_n$ forms an orthonormal basis for $\mathscr{E}$. Adjoin to the above
set of equations, the equation

$$T\alpha_n = t_{1n}\,\alpha_1 + \ldots + t_{nn}\,\alpha_n$$

and observe that in the α basis T has a superdiagonal representation. This
completes the induction. The last part of the theorem is a consequence of the
first part. In fact, the characteristic equation of T is given by

$$0 = \det \begin{bmatrix} x - t_{11} & -t_{12} & \cdot & \cdot & -t_{1n} \\ 0 & x - t_{22} & \cdot & \cdot & \cdot \\ \cdot & \cdot & \cdot & \cdot & \cdot \\ \cdot & \cdot & \cdot & \cdot & \cdot \\ 0 & 0 & 0 & 0 & x - t_{nn} \end{bmatrix} = \prod_{i=1}^{n} \{x - t_{ii}\}. \quad \bigstar$$

Corollary 1

If $p(x) = \sum_{i=0}^{q} a_i x^i$ and the eigenvalues of T are $s_1, \ldots, s_n$, then the eigenvalues of $p(T)$ are $\sum_{i=1}^{q} a_i s_j{}^i$, $\quad j = 1, \ldots, n$.

It is only necessary to note that the product (or sum) of two superdiagonal
matrices $[A]$ and $[B]$ is also superdiagonal and the diagonal elements of the
resultant matrix are the products (or sums) of the corresponding diagonal
elements of $[A]$ and $[B]$. Therefore, using the basis where the representation
of T is superdiagonal, we find that $[p(T)]$ is superdiagonal with diagonal
elements $\sum_{i=1}^{q} a_i s_j{}^i$, $\quad j = 1, \ldots, n$.

An important representation for T is obtained by reducing the consideration of T with n dimensional domain to the consideration of transformations
with domains of smaller dimension. To discuss these ideas we need an appro-
priate terminology. If T transforms a linear manifold $\mathscr{V}$ of $\mathscr{E}$ into $\mathscr{V}$, then $\mathscr{V}$
is said to **reduce** T or to be **invariant** under T. Let $\alpha_1, \ldots, \alpha_r$ be a basis for $\mathscr{V}$

and $\alpha_1, \ldots, \alpha_n$ be a basis for $\mathscr{E}$. Then the representation of T in the α basis is

(1)
$$T \overset{\alpha}{\longleftrightarrow} \begin{bmatrix} [A] & [B] \\ [0] & [C] \end{bmatrix}$$

where $[A]$ is an $r \times r$ matrix. If also T is reduced by the linear manifold $\mathscr{W}$ spanned by $\alpha_{r+1}, \ldots, \alpha_n$, then $[B] = [0]$ and

$$T \overset{\alpha}{\longleftrightarrow} \begin{bmatrix} [A] & [0] \\ [0] & [C] \end{bmatrix}.$$

Note that every vector α in $\mathscr{E}$ can be written

$$\alpha = \beta_1 + \beta_2$$

where β_1 is in $\mathscr{V}$ and β_2 is in $\mathscr{W}$, and that

$$\mu_1 + \mu_2 = \theta, \qquad \mu_1 \text{ in } \mathscr{V}, \mu_2 \text{ in } \mathscr{W},$$

implies $\mu_1 = \mu_2 = \theta$.

The vector space $\mathscr{E}$ is called the **direct sum** of the linear manifolds $\mathscr{V}_1, \ldots, \mathscr{V}_m$ if every vector in $\mathscr{E}$ can be written as a sum

(3)
$$\alpha = \beta_1 + \ldots + \beta_m, \qquad \beta_i \text{ in } \mathscr{V}_i,$$

and the equation

(4)
$$\mu_1 + \ldots + \mu_m = \theta, \qquad \mu_i \text{ in } \mathscr{V}_i,$$

implies $\mu_i = \theta$, $i = 1, \ldots, m$. The condition (4) assures that the decomposition (3) of α is unique. It is not difficult to verify that the dimension of $\mathscr{E}$ is the sum of the dimensions of the $\mathscr{V}_i$.

Now suppose that $\mathscr{E}$ is the direct sum of $\mathscr{V}_1, \ldots, \mathscr{V}_m$ and each $\mathscr{V}_i$ reduces T. Choose $d_i = \dim \mathscr{V}_i$ linearly independent vectors from $\mathscr{V}_i$ and order them

$$\alpha_1, \ldots, \alpha_{d_1}; \alpha_{d_1+1}, \ldots, \alpha_{d_1+d_2}; \ldots, \alpha_{d_1 + \cdots + d_n}.$$

Since T transforms vectors in $\mathscr{V}_i$ into $\mathscr{V}_i$, the representation of T in the α basis must be

(5)
$$T \overset{\alpha}{\longleftrightarrow} \begin{bmatrix} [A_1] & [0] & \cdots & [0] \\ [0] & [A_2] & & \\ & & \cdot & \\ & & \cdot & \\ & & \cdot & \\ [0] & & & [A_m] \end{bmatrix}$$

where $[A_i]$ is a $d_i \times d_i$ matrix.

The transformation T is said to be **completely reduced** by $\mathscr{V}_1, \ldots, \mathscr{V}_m$ when each $\mathscr{V}_i$ reduces T and $\mathscr{E}$ is the direct sum of $\mathscr{V}_1, \ldots, \mathscr{V}_m$. If we define T_i to be the restriction of T to domain $\mathscr{V}_i$ and decompose α in $\mathscr{E}$ as in (3), then

$$T\alpha = T\beta_1 + \ldots + T\beta_m = T_1\,\beta_1 + \ldots + T_m\,\beta_m..$$

Thus $T\alpha$ may be determined by $T_i\,\beta_i$. Moreover, the matrix $[A_i]$ in (5) is the representation of T_i in the basis $\alpha_{d_1+\cdots+d_{i-1}+1}, \ldots, \alpha_{d_1+\cdots+d_i}$. This is true because the corresponding columns of $[T]$ are the representations of $T\alpha_{d_1+\cdots+d_{i-1}+1}, \ldots, T\alpha_{d_1+\cdots+d_i}$ in terms of the α basis and hence, since $\mathscr{V}_i$ reduces T and $T\sigma = T_i\sigma$ for σ in $\mathscr{V}_i$, the columns of $[A_i]$ are the representations of $T_i\,\alpha_{d_1+\cdots+d_{i-1}+1}, \ldots, T_i\,\alpha_{d_1+\cdots+d_i}$ in terms of $\alpha_{d_1+\cdots+d_{i-1}+1}, \ldots,$ $\alpha_{d_1+\cdots+d_i}$. In this way we can reduce the study of T to the study of transformations with smaller domains.

A diagonalizable transformation can be completely reduced by one dimensional linear manifolds. This means that the eigenvectors span the space. If T is not diagonalizable and does have a representation of the form (5), not all of the basis vectors can satisfy $(T - r_iI)\,\alpha_i = \theta$ for constants r_i. Next in simplicity we might try to obtain basis vectors of the type which satisfy $(T - rI)^k\,\alpha = \theta$ for some k. This motivates the study of transformations N which have the property $N^k = 0$ while $N^{k-1} \neq 0$. Such a transformation is called **nilpotent of index** k. The following theorem is stated without proof.

THEOREM 2.10 B Let $r_1, \ldots, r_m$ be the distinct eigenvalues of T. Let d_i be the multiplicity of r_i as a root of the characteristic equation. Then $\mathscr{E}$ is completely reduced by m linear manifolds $\mathscr{V}_1, \ldots, \mathscr{V}_m$ of dimension $d_1, \ldots, d_m$ respectively. Moreover, if T_i is the restriction of T to domain $\mathscr{V}_i$, then there is a nilpotent transformation N_i on $\mathscr{V}_i$ to $\mathscr{V}_i$ such that

(6) $$T_i = N_i + r_i I.$$

From the first part of the theorem it follows that T has a representation given by (5). The structure of the matrix $[A_i]$ in (5) is determined by the representation of N_i. It can be shown that if N is nilpotent there is a basis for which the only nonzero elements of the representation $[n_{ij}]$ of N lie just below the principal diagonal, that is, $n_{ij} = 0$ unless $i = j + 1$. Moreover, the elements below the principal diagonal are groups of one's followed by a single zero. A typical example of such a representation would be

(7) $$[n_{ij}] = \begin{bmatrix} \begin{array}{ccc|cc|c} 0 & 0 & 0 & 0 & 0 & 0 \\ 1 & 0 & 0 & 0 & 0 & 0 \\ 0 & 1 & 0 & 0 & 0 & 0 \\ \hline 0 & 0 & 0 & 0 & 0 & 0 \\ 0 & 0 & 0 & 1 & 0 & 0 \\ 0 & 0 & 0 & 0 & 0 & 0 \end{array} \end{bmatrix}.$$

Equation (6) then implies that $[A_i]$ may be obtained by placing r_i in each principal diagonal element of the representation of N_i. As indicated in (7), the representation of N_i and hence of T_i is also of the form (5) where each bracketed submatrix has all elements below the principal diagonal equal to 1. These considerations show that T has a representation

$$
(8) \quad [T] =
\begin{bmatrix}
[B_1] & [0] & & & [0] \\
[0] & [B_2] & & & \\
& & \cdot & & \\
& & \cdot & & \\
& & & \cdot & \\
[0] & & & & [B_k]
\end{bmatrix},
\qquad
[B_i] =
\begin{bmatrix}
s_i & 0 & & & & 0 \\
1 & s_i & & & & \\
0 & 1 & \cdot & & & \\
& & \cdot & \cdot & & \\
& & & \cdot & \cdot & \\
0 & & & & 1 & s_i
\end{bmatrix},
$$

where s_i are eigenvalues of T, not necessarily distinct, and $[B_i]$ has s_i along the principal diagonal, every element below the principal diagonal equal to 1 and all other elements equal to zero. Each s_i appears in T a number of times equal to its multiplicity as a root of the characteristic equation. The representation given in (8) is called the **Jordan canonical form** of T.

A set of $n \times n$ matrices is said to be a **canonical set under similarity** if no two matrices in the set are similar but every $n \times n$ matrix is similar to some member of the set. The set of all $n \times n$ matrices of the form (8), where we do not distinguish between matrices which have the same submatrices $[B_i]$ although placed in a different order along the diagonal, forms a canonical set. That is, each matrix is similar to a matrix in Jordan canonical form and two matrices are similar if and only if they have the same Jordan canonical form except perhaps for the order of the $[B_i]$. Proofs of these results are to be found in the references given in the bibliography.

What is the significance of the statement that two transformations T and U have the same canonical form? Then there exist bases such that the representation of T in one basis is similar to the representation of U in the other basis. It follows that T and U have similar representations in any basis. If $[T]$ and $[U]$ are the representations in a fixed σ basis, there is a nonsingular matrix $[P]$ such that $[T] = [P]^{-1}[U][P]$ and therefore, by Theorem 2.1B, $T = P^{-1} UP$, where $P \overset{\sigma}{\leftrightarrow} [P]$. The relation $PT = UP$ shows that if T transforms α into $T\alpha$ then U transforms $P\alpha$ into $P(T\alpha)$. Thus the action of T on the space $\mathscr{E}$ is duplicated by the action of U on the vectors obtained by applying P to $\mathscr{E}$. In this sense, U is geometrically similar to T. For example, if P is the operation of a counterclockwise rotation of $\pi/4$ radians on plane geometrical vectors and T is the operation of doubling the length, then $U = PTP^{-1}$ is also the operation of doubling the length, while if T is the operation of projection on a line d then U is the operation of projection on a line obtained by rotating d $\pi/4$ radians counterclockwise.

Exercise 2.10

1. (a) The $n \times n$ matrix $[a_{ij}]$ is said to be in **subdiagonal form** if $a_{ij} = 0$ for $i < j$. By a renumbering of the elements of the basis, show Theorem 2.10A may be modified by replacing the word "superdiagonal" by "subdiagonal".

   (b) Let $[T]$ be the superdiagonal form of T in Theorem 2.10A. Show that the subdiagonal form obtained by the renumbering suggested in part (a) is $[Q]^{-1}[T][Q]$ where $[Q] = [Q]^{-1} = [q_{ij}]$ is a unitary matrix with $q_{ij} = \delta_{i,n-j+1}$ i.e., $[Q]$ is the matrix with ones along the diagonal crossing from lower left to upper right (**secondary diagonal**) and zeros elsewhere.

2. In an orthonormal basis where $[T]$ is superdiagonal, $[T]^*$ must be subdiagonal. Show that if T commutes with T^* then the superdiagonal representation of T is actually diagonal. (Compare with the result of Exercise 2.9-1.) Note that this result implies much of our previous work on symmetric transformations over complex vector spaces.

3. (a) Show that a transformation is nilpotent if and only if all the eigenvalues are zero. *Hint:* Use the superdiagonal representation and successive multiplication.

   (b) Show that a nonzero nilpotent transformation is not diagonalizable.

4. Consider the transformation with domain $\mathscr{E}_3$ whose matrix in an orthonormal basis σ_1, σ_2, σ_3 is given by

$$T \overset{\sigma}{\leftrightarrow} \begin{bmatrix} -2 & 4 & 1 \\ 2 & 0 & 1 \\ 0 & -2 & -1 \end{bmatrix}. \quad \text{If } \alpha \overset{\sigma}{\leftrightarrow} \begin{bmatrix} x_1 \\ x_2 \\ x_3 \end{bmatrix}, \quad \text{show that}$$

the linear manifold $\mathscr{V}$ defined by $x_1 + x_2 + 2x_3 = 0$ reduces T. Show that

$$\begin{bmatrix} 1 \\ -1 \\ 0 \end{bmatrix}, \quad \begin{bmatrix} 0 \\ 2 \\ -1 \end{bmatrix}$$

are in $\mathscr{V}$. Use the Gram–Schmidt process to obtain an orthonormal basis α_1, α_2 of $\mathscr{V}$ and extend this basis to obtain an orthonormal basis α_1, α_2, α_3 of $\mathscr{E}$. Find the representation of T in this basis.

Limit Processes

3.1

POINT SETS

AND SEQUENCES

Our study of finite dimensional spaces has been essentially **algebraic** in character in the sense that we manipulated at each step with only a finite number of vectors. When dealing with infinite dimensional spaces it will be necessary to use operations involving an infinity of vectors. Such operations are called **limit processes** and are characteristic of the field of **analysis.**

In this section we consider some fundamental concepts which, although previously learned in a more restricted setting, are already familiar to the reader. Here we encounter analytic techniques useful in the sequel.

We shall be considering sets of vectors in a Euclidean vector space $\mathscr{E}$. In order to retain the geometrical model which gave rise to many of the concepts, it will be useful to refer to these vectors as **points.** When α and β are in $\mathscr{E}$, the norm of $\alpha - \beta$, $\|\alpha - \beta\|$, is called the **distance** between the points α and β. In this way we associate with every pair of points α and β a real number $d(\alpha, \beta) = \|\alpha - \beta\|$ satisfying

a. $d(\alpha, \beta) = d(\beta, \alpha)$.

b. $d(\alpha, \beta) > 0$ unless $\alpha = \beta$, $d(\alpha, \alpha) = 0$.

c. $d(\alpha, \beta) + d(\beta, \gamma) \geq d(\alpha, \gamma)$.

The validity of these properties is an immediate consequence of Theorem 1.1B. The function $d(\alpha, \beta)$ is called a **distance function,** and all the concepts to be introduced in this section can be generalized to spaces (**metric spaces**) for which a distance function can be defined.

A set of objects is called **countable** if it can be put into one-to-one correspondence either with the set $1, 2, \ldots, n$ for some n, or with the set of all positive integers. This means that we must be able to arrange the objects in a sequence such that every object occupies a definite place in the sequence.

Let us show that the set of all rational numbers on the interval $0 \leq x \leq 1$ is a countable set. We may order them

$$0, 1, 1/2, 1/3, 2/3, 1/4, 3/4, 1/5, 2/5, 3/5, 4/5, 1/6, \ldots$$

where, after 0 and 1, we select for each integer n, all fractions m/n, $m < n$, which have not been previously chosen.

An example of a noncountable set is the set of real numbers on the interval $0 \le x \le 1$. If this set were countable, we could order their decimal expansions

$$. a_{11}\, a_{12}\, a_{13}\, a_{14} \cdots$$
$$. a_{21}\, a_{22}\, a_{23}\, a_{24} \cdots$$
$$. a_{31}\, a_{32}\, a_{33}\, a_{34} \cdots$$
$$. \quad . \quad . \quad . \quad . \, . \, . \quad .$$

Now form the decimal

$$. b_1\, b_2\, b_3 \ldots ,$$

where $b_i = 3$ if a_{ii} is 5, 6, 7, 8, or 9 and $b_i = 7$ if $a_{ii} = 0, 1, 2, 3,$ or 4. Then the decimal so formed cannot be any of the decimals in the array. This contradicts the assumption that the array contains all numbers x, $0 \le x \le 1$.

Let $\mathscr{B}$ be a collection of point sets $\mathscr{S}$. The collection $\mathscr{B}$ need not be countable. By the **union** or **sum** $\cup \mathscr{S}$ of all sets $\mathscr{S}$ in $\mathscr{B}$ we mean the point set consisting of all points found in any of the sets $\mathscr{S}$. Thus

$$\underset{\mathscr{S} \text{ in } \mathscr{B}}{\cup \mathscr{S}} = \{\alpha \mid \text{For some } \mathscr{S} \text{ in } \mathscr{B}, \alpha \text{ is in } \mathscr{S}\}.$$

When there is no question as to the collection $\mathscr{B}$ under consideration, the sum will be written $\cup \mathscr{S}$. For n sets we write $\mathscr{S}_1 \cup \mathscr{S}_2 \cup \ldots \cup \mathscr{S}_n$.

By the **intersection** or **product** $\cap \mathscr{S}$, we mean the set containing those points found in every set $\mathscr{S}$ in $\mathscr{B}$,

$$\underset{\mathscr{S} \text{ in } \mathscr{B}}{\cap \mathscr{S}} = \{\alpha \mid \alpha \text{ is in } \mathscr{S} \text{ whenever } \mathscr{S} \text{ is in } \mathscr{B}\}.$$

Usually we write just $\cap \mathscr{S}$. For n sets we write $\mathscr{S}_1 \cap \mathscr{S}_2 \cap \ldots \cap \mathscr{S}_n$.

The set of all points β in $\mathscr{E}$ which satisfy the relation $\|\beta - \alpha\| < r$, for a positive real number r, is called the **sphere of radius r with center** α. When $\alpha = (x_1, \ldots, x_n)$ and $\beta = (y_1, \ldots, y_n)$ are in $\mathscr{E}_n$, then

$$\|\beta - \alpha\| = \left(\sum_{i=1}^{n} |y_i - x_i|^2 \right)^{1/2}.$$

Thus in $\mathscr{E}_n$, the sphere of radius r about $\alpha = (x_1, \ldots, x_n)$ is the set of vectors $(y_1, \ldots, y_n)$ satisfying

$$\sum_{i=1}^{n} |y_i - x_i|^2 < r^2.$$

A set $\mathcal{S}$ in $\mathcal{E}$ is called **bounded** if there is a real number b such that $\|\alpha\| < b$ for every α in $\mathcal{S}$. In other words, the set $\mathcal{S}$ is bounded if it is contained in some sphere about the **origin** θ.

A point α in $\mathcal{S}$ is said to be an **interior** point of $\mathcal{S}$ if it is the center of some sphere all of whose points are members of $\mathcal{S}$. A point set $\mathcal{S}$ is called **open** if every point of $\mathcal{S}$ is an interior point. We leave for Exercise 3.1–1 the proof of the fact that every sphere is open.

It is useful to define the **empty set** as the set containing no points. One can verify that the following statements are true:

1. *The empty set and the entire space are open sets.*

2. *Any sum of open sets is open.*

3. *The product of a finite number of open sets is open.*

To prove **1**, note that every point in the empty set or in $\mathcal{E}$ is an interior point. If $\mathcal{B}$ is a collection of open sets $\mathcal{S}$, and α is in $\cup\mathcal{S}$, then α is in some set $\mathcal{S}_1$ in $\mathcal{B}$ and there is a sphere about α containing only points in $\mathcal{S}_1$. This sphere then lies in $\cup\mathcal{S}$ so that α is an interior point of $\cup\mathcal{S}$ and $\cup\mathcal{S}$ is open. Finally, if α is in $\cap\mathcal{S}_i$, $i = 1, \ldots, n$, $\mathcal{S}_i$ open, then α is in each $\mathcal{S}_i$ and there exist numbers $r_i > 0$ so that the sphere of radius r_i about α lies entirely in $\mathcal{S}_i$. With r chosen to be the smallest of the numbers r_i, the sphere of radius r about α lies in each $\mathcal{S}_i$ and hence in $\cap\mathcal{S}_i$. This proves α is an interior point of $\cap\mathcal{S}_i$.

If $\mathcal{S}$ is any set in $\mathcal{E}$, the **complement** of $\mathcal{S}$, written $C(\mathcal{S})$, is the set of points of $\mathcal{E}$ which do not lie in $\mathcal{S}$. The complement of $C(\mathcal{S})$ is the set $\mathcal{S}$ itself. Let $\mathcal{B}$ be a collection of sets $\mathcal{S}$. The next two relations are called **rules of complementation.**

4. $C(\cup\mathcal{S}) = \cap C(\mathcal{S}).$
5. $C(\cap\mathcal{S}) = \cup C(\mathcal{S}).$

To prove **4**, note that α is in $C(\cup\mathcal{S})$ if and only if it is in no one of the sets $\mathcal{S}$, that is, if and only if it is in every set $C(\mathcal{S})$, and hence if and only if it is in $\cap C(\mathcal{S})$. Relation **5** can be derived in a similar manner.

A set $\mathcal{S}$ is called **closed** if its complement is open. Since $C(C(\mathcal{S})) = \mathcal{S}$, a set is open if and only if its complement is closed. Using the fact that the empty set is the complement of the whole space, and relations **1 – 5**, we obtain

6. *The empty set and the entire space are closed sets.*

7. *Any product of closed sets is closed.*

8. *The sum of a finite number of closed sets is closed.*

For example, if $\mathscr{S}$ is closed, then $C(\mathscr{S})$ is open, $\cup C(\mathscr{S}) = C(\cap \mathscr{S})$ is open by **2** and **5**, and hence $\cap \mathscr{S}$ is closed. This proves **7**. **8** may be obtained in a similar fashion.

A point α in $\mathscr{E}$ is called an **accumulation point** of a set $\mathscr{S}$ if each sphere with center α contains at least one point β of $\mathscr{S}$ distinct from α. The point α need not belong to $\mathscr{S}$.

A criterion that a set be closed may be given in terms of the notion of accumulation point. This criterion is the following:

9. $\mathscr{S}$ *is closed if and only if it contains its accumulation points.*

Indeed, if $\mathscr{S}$ is closed and α is not in $\mathscr{S}$, then α is in the open set $C(\mathscr{S})$ and there exists a sphere with α as center containing only points of $C(\mathscr{S})$. Thus α is not an accumulation point of $\mathscr{S}$. It follows that a closed set contains its accumulation points. Conversely, if $\mathscr{S}$ contains its accumulation points, no point α in $C(\mathscr{S})$ is an accumulation point of $\mathscr{S}$ and therefore α must be the center of some sphere containing no points of $\mathscr{S}$. This implies that α is an interior point of $C(\mathscr{S})$, $C(\mathscr{S})$ is open and $\mathscr{S}$ is closed.

The set consisting of $\mathscr{S}$ together with its accumulation points is called the **closure** $\bar{\mathscr{S}}$ of $\mathscr{S}$. A point α is in $\bar{\mathscr{S}}$ if and only if α is in $\mathscr{S}$ or is an accumulation point of $\mathscr{S}$. Hence we have

10. α *is in* $\bar{\mathscr{S}}$ *if and only if every sphere about* α *contains a point of* $\mathscr{S}$.

Two useful relations are given by

11.   If $\mathscr{S}$ is in $\mathscr{T}$, then $\bar{\mathscr{S}}$ is in $\bar{\mathscr{T}}$.
12. $\bar{\bar{\mathscr{S}}} = \bar{\mathscr{S}}$.

Indeed, if $\mathscr{S}$ is in $\mathscr{T}$ and α is in $\bar{\mathscr{S}}$, then every sphere about α contains a point of $\mathscr{S}$ and hence of $\mathscr{T}$ so that α is in $\bar{\mathscr{T}}$. The relation **12** is equivalent to the statement that $\bar{\mathscr{S}}$ contains its accumulation points, that is, $\bar{\mathscr{S}}$ is a closed set. To prove $\bar{\mathscr{S}}$ is closed, let α be an accumulation point of $\bar{\mathscr{S}}$. We must show α is in $\bar{\mathscr{S}}$. Any sphere of radius r about α contains a point β of $\bar{\mathscr{S}}$. By **10** every sphere about β lying entirely in the first sphere contains a point σ in $\mathscr{S}$. But then, using **10** again, α is in $\bar{\mathscr{S}}$.

EXAMPLE 1   The set $\mathscr{S}$ of points (x, y) in $\mathscr{E}_2$ satisfying $a \le x \le b$, $c \le y \le d$ is a closed set.

Suppose $\alpha = (t, u)$ is not in $\mathscr{S}$. Then either $t < a$, or $t > b$, or $u < c$, or $u > d$. To be specific suppose $t < a$. Then the sphere of center α and radius $r = \dfrac{a - t}{2}$ contains no points of $\mathscr{S}$. Indeed if $\beta = (x, y)$ is in the sphere, then

$$|x - t| \le ((x - t)^2 + (y - u)^2)^{1/2} = \|\beta - \alpha\| < r$$

so that

$$x < t + r = t + \frac{a - t}{2} = \frac{t}{2} + \frac{a}{2} < \frac{a}{2} + \frac{a}{2} = a.$$

This shows that (x, y) cannot be a member of $\mathscr{S}$. Hence $C(\mathscr{S})$ is open, and $\mathscr{S}$ is closed.

EXAMPLE 2 Show that $\overline{\mathscr{S} \cap \mathscr{T}}$ is contained in $\overline{\mathscr{S}} \cap \overline{\mathscr{T}}$ but that the converse need not be true.

We have $\mathscr{S} \cap \mathscr{T}$ contained in $\mathscr{S}$ and hence in $\overline{\mathscr{S}}$. Similarly $\mathscr{S} \cap \mathscr{T}$ is contained in $\overline{\mathscr{T}}$. Therefore $\mathscr{S} \cap \mathscr{T}$ is contained in $\overline{\mathscr{S}} \cap \overline{\mathscr{T}}$. The latter is a closed set since $\overline{\mathscr{S}}$ and $\overline{\mathscr{T}}$ are. Using relation **11**, we obtain $\overline{\mathscr{S} \cap \mathscr{T}}$ contained in $\overline{\overline{\mathscr{S}} \cap \overline{\mathscr{T}}} = \overline{\mathscr{S}} \cap \overline{\mathscr{T}}$.

To show that the converse need not be true, let

$$\mathscr{S} = \{(x, y) \mid x > 0, y = 0\}, \quad \mathscr{T} = \{(x, y) \mid x = 0, y > 0\}.$$

Then $\overline{\mathscr{S} \cap \mathscr{T}}$ is the empty set, while $\overline{\mathscr{S}} \cap \overline{\mathscr{T}}$ is the point $(0, 0)$.

The concept of an infinite sequence of vectors, $\{\alpha_i\}$, $i = 1, 2, \ldots$, is already familiar. The vectors α_i need not be distinct. A sequence differs from a point set in that the sequence implies an ordering, while a point set does not. If all the vectors of a sequence are equal, we still have an infinite sequence but a finite point set.

We say α is the **limit** of the sequence $\{\alpha_i\}$ as i approaches infinity, or $\{\alpha_i\}$ **converges** to α, and write

$$\lim_{i \to \infty} \alpha_i = \alpha, \quad \text{if} \quad \lim_{i \to \infty} \|\alpha_i - \alpha\| = 0.$$

Thus $\lim_{i \to \infty} \alpha_i = \alpha$ means that for every positive number ϵ, there is an integer $N = N(\epsilon)$ such that

$$\|\alpha_i - \alpha\| < \epsilon \quad \text{if} \quad i > N.$$

In conformity with common usage, the Greek letters ϵ and δ will be used to represent real numbers and not vectors in $\mathscr{E}$.

It is easy to see that a sequence can have at most one limit. For if $\lim_{i \to \infty} \alpha_i = \alpha$, $\lim_{i \to \infty} \alpha_i = \beta$, then for given ϵ, we may choose i sufficiently large so that

$$\|\alpha - \beta\| \leq \|\alpha - \alpha_i\| + \|\alpha_i - \beta\| < \epsilon + \epsilon.$$

Since ϵ is arbitrary, we have $\|\alpha - \beta\| = 0$. This proof illustrates a fundamental procedure. To prove $\alpha = \beta$, we resort to proving $\|\alpha - \beta\| < \epsilon$ for arbitrary ϵ.

Let $i_1, i_2, i_3, \ldots$ be an increasing sequence of positive integers. Then the sequence $\{\alpha_{i_j}\}$, $j = 1, 2, \ldots$ is called a **subsequence** of the sequence $\{\alpha_i\}$. If the sequence $\{\alpha_i\}$ converges to α, then every subsequence must also converge to α.

If $\alpha_i = \alpha$ for every i, then $\lim\limits_{i = \infty} \alpha_i = \alpha$. However the set of points composed of all α_i has no accumulation point. The relation between limit points and accumulation points is given by

13. α *is an accumulation point of* $\mathscr{S}$ *if and only if* $\lim\limits_{i \to \infty} \alpha_i = \alpha$ *for some*

sequence α_i *of distinct points of* $\mathscr{S}$.

For, if α is an accumulation point of $\mathscr{S}$ we can find a point $\alpha_1 \neq \alpha$ in a sphere of radius < 1, and if $\alpha_1, \ldots, \alpha_j$ are already found we can find $\alpha_{j+1} \neq \alpha$ in a sphere of radius $< \dfrac{1}{j + 1}$ about α and not containing $\alpha_1, \ldots, \alpha_j$. In this way we construct a sequence $\{\alpha_i\}$ converging to α. Conversely, if a sequence $\{\alpha_i\}$ of distinct points of $\mathscr{S}$ converges to α, then every sphere about α contains a point of $\mathscr{S}$ distinct from α.

A sequence $\{x_i\}$ of real numbers which has the property $x_i \leq x_{i+1}$ for every i, or else the property $x_i \geq x_{i+1}$ for every i, is called **monotone**. In the former case the sequence is called **monotone increasing** and in the latter **monotone decreasing**. If the equality signs are not permitted, the sequence is called **strictly monotone**. Thus if $x_i < x_{i+1}$ for every i, the sequence is strictly monotone increasing.

We have

14.   *A bounded monotone increasing sequence converges to its least upper bound.*

For, if $b = $ l.u.b. $\{x_i\}$, then for given $\epsilon > 0$ there is an integer j such that $b \geq x_j > b - \epsilon$, and, since the sequence increases,

$$b \geq x_i > b - \epsilon \quad \text{for} \quad i > j.$$

This proves $\lim\limits_{i \to \infty} x_i = b$.

One may prove in a similar fashion that a bounded monotone decreasing sequence converges to its greatest lower bound. The condition of boundedness given in **14** may be removed if we define **convergence to** ∞. We say $\lim\limits_{i \to \infty} x_i = \infty$ if for every positive number M there is an integer N, depending on M, such that

$$x_i > M \text{ when } i > N.$$

With this definition the reader can show that if $\{x_i\}$ is monotone increasing, and l.u.b. $\{x_i\} = \infty$, then $\lim\limits_{i \to \infty} x_i = \infty$.

There are some important theorems which are valid in $\mathscr{E}_n$ but are not valid in infinite dimensional spaces.

THEOREM 3.1A   The sequence $\{\alpha_i\} = \{(x_{1i},\ x_{2i}, \ldots, x_{ni})\}$ in $\mathscr{E}_n$ converges to $\alpha = (a_1, \ldots, a_n)$ if and only if $\lim\limits_{i \to \infty} x_{ki} = a_k$.

Proof   This follows at once from the inequalities

$$|x_{ki} - a_k| \leq \left(\sum_{k=1}^{n} |x_{ki} - a_k|^2 \right)^{1/2} \leq \sqrt{n}\ \max_k |x_{ki} - a_k|. \quad \star$$

THEOREM 3.1B   Every bounded sequence $\{\alpha_i\} = \{(x_{1i}, \ldots, x_{ni})\}$ in $\mathscr{E}_n$ has a convergent subsequence.

Proof   Consider first the case $n = 1$, where we have just a sequence $\{x_i\}$ of real numbers. If an infinite number of the x_i have a common value x, we immediately obtain a subsequence converging to x. Otherwise, the point set $\mathscr{S}$ formed by the numbers x_i is infinite. Let $\mathscr{T}$ be the set of all numbers t in $\mathscr{E}_1$ for which there are an infinite number of members of $\mathscr{S}$ greater than t. $\mathscr{T}$ is not empty since all numbers less than the greatest lower bound of $\mathscr{S}$ belong to $\mathscr{T}$. Then t_0, the least upper bound of the set $\mathscr{T}$, must be an accumulation point of $\mathscr{S}$. For, any interval $t_0 - r < x < t_0 + r$ must contain a point t_1 of $\mathscr{T}$ less than or equal to t_0, with an infinite number of elements of $\mathscr{S}$ greater than t_1, while any point t_2 greater than t_0 can have only a finite number of elements of $\mathscr{S}$ greater than t_2. Hence the interval contains an infinite number of points of $\mathscr{S}$ and t_0 is an accumulation point of $\mathscr{S}$. By **13** there is a sequence of distinct points $\{x_{i_j}\}, j = 1, 2, \ldots$ of $\mathscr{S}$ converging to t_0. This may not be a subsequence of $\{x_i\}$ since $i_1, i_2, \ldots$ may not be an increasing sequence. However, by dropping those x_{i_j} for which i_j are not in natural order we can obtain a convergent subsequence of $\{x_i\}$.

For $n > 1$, the inequality $|x_{ki}| \leq (\sum\limits_{k=1}^{n} |x_{ki}|^2)^{1/2}$ shows that the boundedness of the sequence $\{\alpha_i\}$ implies the boundedness of the sequence of kth coordinates, $k = 1, 2, \ldots, n$. By the proof for $n = 1$, there is a subsequence $\{\alpha_{i_j}\}, j = 1, 2, \ldots$ whose first coordinate converges. This, in turn, has a subsequence $\{\alpha_{i_{j_k}}\}$ where the first and second coordinates converge. After n steps we obtain a subsequence of $\{\alpha_i\}$ such that the sequence of kth coordinates converges for $k = 1, 2, \ldots, n$. By Theorem 3.1A the subsequence itself converges. $\star$

EXAMPLE 3 Neither Theorem 3.1A nor Theorem 3.1B is valid when $\mathscr{E}_n$ is replaced by $\mathscr{E}_\infty$. If we let α_i be the vector in $\mathscr{E}_\infty$ with 1 for the ith coordinate and 0 for every other coordinate, then $\|\alpha_i\| = 1$ so the sequence $\{\alpha_i\}$ is bounded. If a subsequence $\{\alpha_{i_j}\}$ converges to α, then

$$\|\alpha_{i_j} - \alpha_{i_k}\| \leq \|\alpha_{i_j} - \alpha\| + \|\alpha - \alpha_{i_k}\|$$

indicates $\lim\limits_{k,j\to\infty} \|\alpha_{i_j} - \alpha_{i_k}\| = 0$. However we have, for $i \neq j$, $\|\alpha_i - \alpha_j\| = \sqrt{2}$. Theorem 3.1B is therefore not valid for $\mathscr{E}_\infty$. Moreover, for fixed k, the sequence of kth coordinates of $\{\alpha_i\}$ approaches 0, yet the sequence $\{\alpha_i\}$ does not converge. Hence Theorem 3.1A is not valid for $\mathscr{E}_\infty$.

An equivalent formulation of Theorem 3.1B is the statement

15.   *Every bounded infinite set in $\mathscr{E}_n$ has an accumulation point.*

This form of the theorem is called the **Bolzano-Weierstrass Theorem.** However the form given in Theorem 3.1B is better for our purposes.

A criterion that a sequence converge, without making any statement about the limit of the sequence, is given by the next theorem, called the **Cauchy criterion** for convergence.

THEOREM 3.1C   A necessary and sufficient condition that the sequence $\{\alpha_i\}$ in $\mathscr{E}_n$ converge is that $\lim\limits_{i,j\to\infty} \|\alpha_i - \alpha_j\| = 0$.

Proof If $\lim\limits_{i\to\infty} \alpha_i = \alpha$, we can find an integer $N(\epsilon)$ such that $\|\alpha_i - \alpha\| < \epsilon/2$ when $i > N$. Hence, if $i > N$ and $j > N$ we have

$$\|\alpha_i - \alpha_j\| \leq \|\alpha_i - \alpha\| + \|\alpha - \alpha_j\| < \epsilon.$$

This proves $\lim\limits_{i,j\to\infty} \|\alpha_i - \alpha_j\| = 0$. Conversely, if $\lim\limits_{i,j\to\infty} \|\alpha_i - \alpha_j\| = 0$, then for given $\epsilon > 0$ we can find an integer $N(\epsilon)$ such that

$$\|\alpha_i - \alpha_j\| < \epsilon \quad \text{when} \quad i > N, j > N.$$

In particular for $\epsilon = 1$, there is an integer $N(1)$ such that, for $i > N = N(1)$,

$$\|\alpha_i\| \leq \|\alpha_i - \alpha_{N+1}\| + \|\alpha_{N+1}\| < 1 + \|\alpha_{N+1}\|.$$

If b is chosen larger than each of the values $1 + \|\alpha_i\|$, $i = 1, 2, \ldots, N + 1$, then $\|\alpha_i\| < b$ for every i, proving that the sequence $\{\alpha_i\}$ is bounded. By Theorem 3.1B there is a subsequence $\{\alpha_{i_j}\}$ converging to some point β. That is, there is an integer $M(\epsilon)$ such that $\|\alpha_{i_j} - \beta\| < \epsilon$ for $j > M(\epsilon)$. If we choose $M(\epsilon) > N(\epsilon)$, we have

$$\|\alpha_i - \beta\| \leq \|\alpha_i - a_{i_{M+1}}\| + \|\alpha_{i_{M+1}} - \beta\| < 2\epsilon$$

for $i > N(\epsilon)$.   This shows that the sequence $\{\alpha_i\}$ converges to β.   ★

A sequence $\{\alpha_i\}$ with the property that $\lim\limits_{i,j\to\infty} \|\alpha_i - \alpha_j\| = 0$ is called a **Cauchy sequence.** A vector space $\mathcal{E}$ with the property that every Cauchy sequence converges to an element in $\mathcal{E}$ is called **complete.** We have just proved that the space $\mathcal{E}_n$ is complete. Note that in the proof we have also shown

16.   *Every Cauchy sequence is a bounded sequence.*

Although the proof of Theorem 3.1C used Theorem 3.1B, which is not valid for $\mathcal{E}_\infty$, it is still possible to show that $\mathcal{E}_\infty$ is complete.

THEOREM 3.1D   The space $\mathcal{E}_\infty$ is complete.

Proof   Let $\{\alpha_i\} = \{(x_{1i}, x_{2i}, \dots)\}$ be a Cauchy sequence in $\mathcal{E}_\infty$ so that

$$\lim_{i,j\to\infty} \|\alpha_i - \alpha_j\|^2 = \lim_{i,j\to\infty} \sum_{k=1}^{\infty} |x_{ki} - x_{kj}|^2 = 0.$$

For $\epsilon > 0$, there is an integer $N(\epsilon)$ such that, whenever $i > N, j > N$,

$$|x_{ki} - x_{kj}|^2 \leq \sum_{k=1}^{\infty} |x_{ki} - x_{kj}|^2 < \epsilon.$$

For fixed k, Theorem 3.1C now implies that there exists $y_k = \lim\limits_{i\to\infty} x_{ki}$. We shall show that

$$\beta = (y_1, y_2, \dots)$$

is an element of $\mathcal{E}_\infty$. For this, it is necessary to verify that $\sum_{k=1}^{\infty} |y_k|^2 < \infty$. Use the inequality $|a + b|^2 \leq 2|a|^2 + 2|b|^2$ and write

$$\sum_{k=1}^{p} |y_k|^2 \leq 2 \sum_{k=1}^{p} |y_k - x_{kj}|^2 + 2 \sum_{k=1}^{p} |x_{kj}|^2.$$

For each p, there is a number j such that $|y_k - x_{kj}|^2 \leq 1/2p$, $k = 1, 2, \dots, p$. Also there is a constant M such that $\sum_{k=1}^{p} |x_{kj}|^2 \leq \sum_{k=1}^{\infty} |x_{kj}|^2 = \|\alpha_j\|^2 < M$ independent of j in view of **16.** It follows that $\sum_{k=1}^{p} |y_k|^2 < 1 + 2M$. Thus

$\sum_{k=1}^{\infty} |y_k|^2 < \infty$. Finally we will show that $\lim_{i\to\infty} \alpha_i = \beta$, thus proving $\mathcal{E}_\infty$ is complete. We must show that

$$0 = \lim_{i\to\infty} \|\beta - \alpha_i\| = \lim_{i\to\infty} \sum_{k=1}^{\infty} |y_k - x_{ki}|^2.$$

Given $\epsilon > 0$ and fixed p, there is a $j > N(\epsilon)$ such that $|y_k - x_{kj}|^2 < \epsilon/p$ for $k = 1, 2, \ldots, p$. For $i > N(\epsilon)$, we have

$$\sum_{k=1}^{p} |y_k - x_{ki}|^2 \le 2 \sum_{k=1}^{p} |y_k - x_{kj}|^2 + 2 \sum_{k=1}^{p} |x_{kj} - x_{ki}|^2 \le 2\epsilon + 2\epsilon.$$

Now let $p \to \infty$ and obtain, for $i > N(\epsilon)$,

$$\sum_{k=1}^{\infty} |y_k - x_{ki}|^2 \le 4\epsilon.$$

This concludes the proof.   ★

Not every infinite dimensional space is complete. For an example, see Exercise 3.1–11.

Theorems 3.1A, B, C are valid for $\mathcal{E}_n{}^*$ and Theorem 3.1D is valid for $\mathcal{E}_\infty{}^*$ (see Section 1.1 and Exercise 1.1). The only modifications needed are in the proof of the case $n = 1$ in Theorem 3.1B. Since every complex number $z = x + iy$ can be thought of as the pair (x, y) of real numbers, the case $n = 2$ of Theorem 3.1B for $\mathcal{E}_n$ yields the proof of case $n = 1$ for $\mathcal{E}_n{}^*$.

The concept of completeness will be considered again in a later chapter.

Exercise 3.1

1. Prove that the sphere of radius r and center α is an open set.

2. (a) Show that the sets

$$\mathcal{S}_j = \left\{ x \left| \frac{1}{j} \le x \le 1 - \frac{1}{j} \right. \right\}, \quad j = 1, 2, \ldots$$

    are closed but their sum is open.

    (b) Show that the sets

$$\mathcal{S}_j = \left\{ x \left| -\frac{1}{j} < x < 1 + \frac{1}{j} \right. \right\}, \quad j = 1, 2, \ldots$$

    are open but their product is closed.

3. Show that a finite set of points has no accumulation point and hence is a closed set.

4. Prove that a necessary and sufficient condition that α be an accumulation point of $\mathcal{S}$ is that every sphere with center α contain an infinity of points belonging to $\mathcal{S}$.

5. If $\mathcal{S}$ is any set, then the union of all open subsets of $\mathcal{S}$ is called the **interior** of $\mathcal{S}$. Show that the interior of $\mathcal{S}$ is open. Show that a set is open if and only if it is equal to its interior.

6. Show that the set of points (x, y) in $\mathscr{E}_2$ satisfying $a < x < b$, $c < y < d$ is open. Show also that the set is not closed.

7. Show that the set of accumulation points of $\mathcal{S}$ is a closed set.

8. A point α is said to be a **boundary point** of $\mathcal{S}$ if every sphere about α contains a point of $\mathcal{S}$ and a point of $C(\mathcal{S})$. The set of boundary points is called the **boundary** of $\mathcal{S}$. Show that it is a closed set.

9. Prove relation **5** of the text.

10. (a) Prove that $\overline{\mathcal{S} \cup \mathcal{T}} = \overline{\mathcal{S}} \cup \overline{\mathcal{T}}$.

    (b) Give an example to illustrate $\overline{\cup \mathcal{S}_i}$ need not be equal to $\cup \overline{\mathcal{S}}_i$ for an infinite collection of sets.

11. Let $\mathscr{E}$ be the linear manifold in $\mathscr{E}_\infty$ composed of all vectors which are finite linear combinations of the vectors α_n, $n = 1, 2, \ldots$ where α_n has 1 as its nth coordinate and 0 for all other coordinates. Define $\beta_n = \sum_{j=1}^{n} \alpha_j/j$. Show that $\{\beta_n\}$ is a Cauchy sequence yet there is no vector σ in $\mathscr{E}$ with $\lim_{n \to \infty} \|\beta_n - \sigma\| = 0$. Thus $\mathscr{E}$ is not complete.

12. Let $\mathcal{S}$ be the set of all fractions of the form $\dfrac{p}{2^n}$ where p is a positive odd integer less than 2^n. Find all accumulation points of the set $\mathcal{S}$.

13. If $\mathcal{S}_i$ are closed nonempty sets in $\mathscr{E}_n$ with $\mathcal{S}_{i+1}$ contained in $\mathcal{S}_i$, show that $\cap \mathcal{S}_i$ is not empty.

14. (a) Let $\alpha_i = \{(x_{1i}, x_{2i}, \ldots)\}$ be points in $\mathscr{E}_\infty$ with the property $|x_{ki}| \le \dfrac{1}{k}$, $k = 1, 2, \ldots$ Show that $\lim_{i \to \infty} \alpha_i = \beta = (y_1, y_2, \ldots)$ if and only if $\lim_{i \to \infty} x_{ki} = y_k$.

    Hint: If $\lim_{i \to \infty} x_{ki} = y_k$, then $|y_k| < |x_{ki}| + \dfrac{1}{k}$ for i sufficiently large so $|y_k| < \dfrac{2}{k}$ showing that $\beta = (y_1, y_2, \ldots)$ is in $\mathscr{E}_\infty$. Write $\|\alpha_i - \beta\|^2$
    $$\le \sum_{k=1}^{j} |x_{ki} - y_k|^2 + \sum_{k=j+1}^{\infty} 2|x_{ki}|^2 + \sum_{k=j+1}^{\infty} 2|y_k|^2.$$

    (b) Let $\mathscr{W}$ be the set of all vectors $\alpha = (x_1, \ldots)$ in $\mathscr{E}_\infty$ with the property $|x_k| \le \dfrac{1}{k}$. Show that any sequence from $\mathscr{W}$ has a convergent subsequence.

15. Let $\{x_i\}$ be a sequence of real numbers defined as follows: Select $x_2 > x_1 > 0$. For $n = 2, 3, \ldots$ define $x_{n+1} = \dfrac{1}{2}\left(x_n + x_{n-1}\right)$. Show that
    $$x_1 < x_3 < x_5 < \ldots, \qquad x_2 > x_4 > x_6 > \ldots,$$
    and that $\lim_{i \to \infty} x_i = \dfrac{1}{3}\left(x_1 + 2x_2\right)$.

16. Show that the sum of a countable set of countable sets is countable.

17. Prove the **Heine-Borel Theorem**: If $\mathcal{B}$ is a collection of open sets $\mathcal{S}$ in $\mathcal{E}_n$ and $\mathcal{D}$ is a bounded closed set contained in $\cup \mathcal{S}$, then there is a finite number of sets $\mathcal{S}$ such that their sum contains $\mathcal{D}$. *Hint:* If $\mathcal{I}$ is a "cube", $-a \leq x_i \leq a$, $i = 1, \ldots, n$, containing $\mathcal{D}$, bisect each edge to obtain 2^n cubes of side length a. If the theorem is false, the part of $\mathcal{D}$ in at least one of the 2^n cubes, call it $\mathcal{D}_1$, cannot be covered by a finite number of sets $\mathcal{S}$. Repeat the bisection on $\mathcal{D}_1$. Continue the process to obtain an accumulation point β of $\mathcal{D}$, such that for every $\epsilon > 0$ there is a cube of side length less than ϵ containing β such that the part of $\mathcal{D}$ in the cube cannot be covered by a finite number of sets $\mathcal{S}$. However β itself can be covered by one of the open sets $\mathcal{S}$, and this leads to a contradiction.

3.2

CONTINUOUS

FUNCTIONS

This section is concerned with some simple properties of continuous functions. Our objective is to familiarize the reader with the so-called "ϵ, δ technique" which will be employed in later sections.

A **complex valued function** f with **domain** $\mathcal{D}$ is a correspondence assigning a complex number $f(\alpha)$ to each element α in a point set $\mathcal{D}$. The set of numbers $f(\alpha)$ is the **range** of f. If the range consists of real numbers, f is called a **real valued function**.

If the domain $\mathcal{D}$ is a point set in $\mathcal{E}_n$, f is called a **function of n real variables**, and if $\alpha = (x_1, \ldots, x_n)$ we write $f(\alpha) = f(x_1, \ldots, x_n)$.

The functional values $f(\alpha)$ are said to approach a **limit** b as α approaches an accumulation point β of $\mathcal{D}$ if $\{f(\alpha_i)\}$ converges to b whenever $\{\alpha_i\}$, $\alpha_i \neq \beta$, is a sequence of points in $\mathcal{D}$ converging to β. We then write

$$(1) \qquad\qquad b = \lim_{\alpha \to \beta} f(\alpha).$$

An equivalent definition is the following: $b = \lim_{\alpha \to \beta} f(\alpha)$ if, for every positive number ϵ, there is a positive number $\delta(\epsilon)$ such that

$$(2) \qquad |f(\alpha) - b| < \epsilon \quad \text{whenever} \quad 0 < \|\alpha - \beta\| < \delta(\epsilon), \ \alpha \text{ in } \mathcal{D}.$$

Let us prove that these two definitions are equivalent. Suppose that (1) holds according to the first definition, but we cannot find for every $\epsilon > 0$ a number

$\delta(\epsilon) > 0$ such that (2) holds. This means that for some $\epsilon > 0$ and for every $\delta > 0$ it is possible to find some α such that

$$|f(\alpha) - b| \geq \epsilon > 0 \quad \text{while} \quad 0 < \|\alpha - \beta\| < \delta.$$

Let δ take on in succession the values $\left\{\dfrac{1}{i}\right\}$. We obtain a corresponding sequence $\{\alpha_i\}$ such that

$$|f(\alpha_i) - b| \geq \epsilon > 0 \quad \text{while} \quad 0 < \|\alpha_i - \beta\| < 1/i.$$

The sequence $\{\alpha_i\}$ converges to β while $\{f(\alpha_i)\}$ does not converge to b. This contradiction with our assumption assures us that $b = \lim\limits_{\alpha \to \beta} f(\alpha)$ according to the second definition. To show the converse, we assume that for every $\epsilon > 0$ there exists a $\delta(\epsilon) > 0$ such that (2) holds. Let $\{\alpha_i\}$ be any sequence converging to β, $\alpha_i \neq \beta$. For fixed ϵ, there is an integer $N = N(\epsilon)$ such that if $i > N$, then $0 < \|\alpha_i - \beta\| < \delta(\epsilon)$. Using (2), we now have for each $\epsilon > 0$, an integer $N(\epsilon)$ such that

$$|f(\alpha_i) - b| < \epsilon \quad \text{whenever} \quad i > N.$$

Hence $\{f(\alpha_i)\}$ converges to b.

The function f is said to be **continuous at** β if β is in the domain $\mathscr{D}$ and $\{f(\alpha_i)\}$ converges to $f(\beta)$ whenever $\{\alpha_i\}$ is a sequence of points in $\mathscr{D}$ converging to β.

It is readily seen that f is continuous at each point of $\mathscr{D}$ which is not an accumulation point and f is continuous at an accumulation point β of $\mathscr{D}$ if and only if $\lim\limits_{\alpha \to \beta} f(\alpha) = f(\beta)$.

In terms of inequalities, f is continuous at β if for every $\epsilon > 0$ there exists $\delta(\epsilon, \beta) > 0$ such that

$$(3) \qquad |f(\alpha) - f(\beta)| < \epsilon \quad \text{whenever} \quad \|\alpha - \beta\| < \delta, \ \alpha \text{ in } \mathscr{D}.$$

If f is continuous for every point of a set $\mathscr{S}$, then f is said to be **continuous on** $\mathscr{S}$.

Continuity at an accumulation point β may also be written

$$(4) \qquad \lim_{\sigma \to \theta} f(\beta + \sigma) = f(\beta)$$

since the relation

$$|f(\alpha) - f(\beta)| < \epsilon \quad \text{whenever} \quad \|\alpha - \beta\| < \delta(\epsilon)$$

is equivalent, when $\sigma = \alpha - \beta$, to

$$|f(\beta + \sigma) - f(\beta)| < \epsilon \quad \text{whenever} \quad \|\sigma\| < \delta(\epsilon).$$

THEOREM 3.2A   If $\lim\limits_{\alpha \to \beta} f(\alpha) = b$, $\lim\limits_{\alpha \to \beta} g(\alpha) = c$ then

a. $\lim\limits_{\alpha \to \beta} [f(\alpha) + g(\alpha)] = b + c$.

b. $\lim\limits_{\alpha \to \beta} f(\alpha)\, g(\alpha) = b \cdot c$.

c. $\lim\limits_{\alpha \to \beta} f(\alpha)/g(\alpha) = b/c$ if $c \neq 0$.

Proof   These results are an immediate consequence of the inequalities

a. $|f(\alpha) + g(\alpha) - (b + c)| \leq |f(\alpha) - b| + |g(\alpha) - c|$.

b. $|f(\alpha)\, g(\alpha) - bc| \leq |f(\alpha) - b|\, |g(\alpha) - c| + |b||g(\alpha) - c|$
$$+ |c||f(\alpha) - b|.$$

c. $\left| \dfrac{f(\alpha)}{g(\alpha)} - \dfrac{b}{c} \right| = \left| \dfrac{c(f(\alpha) - b) - b(g(\alpha) - c)}{\bar{c}(g(\alpha) - c) + |c|^2} \right| \leq \dfrac{2\,|c||f(\alpha) - b|}{|c|^2}$

$$+ \dfrac{2|b||g(\alpha) - c|}{|c|^2}$$

when α is chosen close enough to β so that $|g(\alpha) - c| < |c|/2$, for then

$$|\bar{c}(g(\alpha) - c) + |c|^2| \geq |c|^2 - |\bar{c}(g(\alpha) - c)| \geq |c|^2 - |c|^2/2 = |c|^2/2. \quad \bigstar$$

By the sum $f + g$, product fg, quotient f/g of two functions f and g with the same domain we mean those functions whose values at α are $f(\alpha) + g(\alpha)$, $f(\alpha)\, g(\alpha)$ and $\dfrac{f(\alpha)}{g(\alpha)}$ respectively. The quotient is not defined at points where $g(\alpha) = 0$.

In speaking of particular functions it is convenient to denote the function by its functional values. Thus, the statement "the function f in $\mathcal{E}_2$ whose value at (x, y) is $\sin x \cos y$" is replaced by "the function $f(x, y) = \sin x \cos y$".

Corollary 1

The sum and product of two functions f and g continuous at β are also continuous at β. The quotient f/g is continuous at β if $g(\beta) \neq 0$.

When a function f is continuous at β the values $f(\alpha)$ must be within ϵ of $f(\beta)$ when α is sufficiently near β. Hence we obtain

THEOREM 3.2 B   If the real valued function f is continuous at β and $f(\beta) > 0$, then $f(\alpha) > 0$ for all α in some sphere about β and in $\mathcal{D}$.

A similar theorem holds with $>$ replaced by $<$.

The function f is said to be **bounded** on a set $\mathscr{S}$ if there is a positive number b such that $|f(\alpha)| < b$ for every α in $\mathscr{S}$.

The next few examples illustrate the concepts of continuity and boundedness.

EXAMPLE 1 Let f be a real valued function with domain $\mathscr{E}_1$. Suppose f is continuous for $x = a$ and that for all x and y in $\mathscr{E}_1$, the relation

$$(5) \qquad\qquad f(x + y) = f(x) + f(y)$$

is valid. Show that $f(x) = kx$ for some constant k and all x.

First we shall show that f is continuous for all x. With $x = a$ in (5), we see $|f(y)| = |f(a + y) - f(a)|$ approaches 0 as y approaches 0. Using (5) again, $|f(x + y) - f(x)| = |f(y)|$ approaches 0 as y approaches 0. Hence f is continuous for every x. Using the values $x, 2x, \ldots$ successively for y in (5), we get

$$f(2x) = 2f(x),\ f(3x) = f(x) + f(2x) = 3f(x),\ \ldots,\ f(nx) = nf(x),\ \ldots$$

where n is a positive integer. In the last equation put $x = \dfrac{1}{q},\ n = p$ and then $x = \dfrac{1}{q},\ n = q$ for positive integers p and q to obtain

$$f(p/q) = pf\left(\frac{1}{q}\right),\quad f(1) = qf\left(\frac{1}{q}\right)$$

or

$$f(p/q) = f(1)\,(p/q)\,.$$

With $k = f(1)$, we have shown $f(r) = kr$ for every positive rational. If x is any positive real number, we can find a sequence r_n of positive rationals approaching x. The continuity of f and the relation

$$|f(x) - kx| = |f(x) - f(r_n) + kr_n - kx| \le |f(x) - f(r_n)| + |k|\,|r_n - x|$$

now show that $f(x) = kx$ for every positive real x. Putting $y = 0$ and then $y = -x$ in (5), we find $f(0) = 0$, $f(-x) = -f(x)$. Thus when x is negative, $f(x) = -f(-x) = -k(-x) = kx$, proving the desired result for all x.

EXAMPLE 2 Let f be a real valued function of a single variable which is bounded on some finite interval $a \le x \le b$ and for all x and y in $\mathscr{E}_1$ satisfies (5). Show that $f(x) = kx$ for a constant k.

Let

$$(6) \qquad\qquad g(x) = f(x) - \frac{xf(b - a)}{b - a}\,.$$

Then it is easily seen that $g(b - a) = 0$ and

(7) $$g(x + y) = g(x) + g(y).$$

The function g is periodic with period $b - a$ in the sense that

$$g(x + b - a) = g(x) + g(b - a) = g(x).$$

Thus, $g(x)$ is bounded for all x, since it is bounded on the interval $a \leq x \leq b$ and has the same set of values on every interval of length $b - a$. We shall now show that $g(x)$ is identically zero, thus obtaining $f(x) = \dfrac{f(b - a)}{b - a} x$. Suppose $g(z) \neq 0$ for some z. In view of (7) we obtain, as in Example 1, $g(nz) = ng(z)$ which can be made as large in absolute value as we please by choosing a suitable value of the positive integer n. This contradicts the boundedness of g.

EXAMPLE 3   Let f be a polynomial function of a single real variable. Show that f is continuous.

A polynomial function f of one variable is a function whose value at x is

$$f(x) = a_n x^n + a_{n-1} x^{n-1} + \cdots + a_1 x + a_0$$

for scalars a_n and nonnegative integers n.

Now consider the function $g(x) = x$. This is continuous for all x, since

$$|g(x) - g(y)| = |x - y| < \epsilon \quad \text{whenever} \quad |x - y| < \delta = \epsilon.$$

Similarly, the function $h(x) = k$, for constant k, is continuous. By the corollary to Theorem 3.2A, we see that any function of the form kx^n and any sum of such functions is also continuous.

EXAMPLE 4   Show that if the real valued functions $f_i, \ldots, f_m$ are continuous on an open set $\mathscr{D}$, then the set $\{\alpha \mid f_i(\alpha) > 0, \ i = 1, 2, \ldots, m\}$ is open.

Consider first the case of one function f. If β is a point of the set $\{\alpha \mid f(\alpha) > 0\}$, Theorem 3.2B shows that β is an interior point of the set so that the set is open. Since

$$\{\alpha \mid f_i(\alpha) > 0, \ i = 1, \ldots, m\} = \bigcap_i \{\alpha \mid f_i(\alpha) > 0\},$$

it follows that the set on the left of the equality is also open.

Our primary concern is with functions of n real variables. In the remainder of this section we restrict our attention to a function f whose domain $\mathscr{D}$ is a point set in $\mathscr{E}_n$. We shall first show that a continuous function defined over a bounded closed set has additional interesting properties.

Recall that a function f is continuous on $\mathscr{D}$ if it is continuous at each point of $\mathscr{D}$, that is, if for given $\epsilon > 0$ and for given β in $\mathscr{D}$ there is a $\delta > 0$ depending on ϵ and β such that

(8) $$|f(\alpha) - f(\beta)| < \epsilon \quad \text{whenever} \quad \|\alpha - \beta\| < \delta, \ \alpha \text{ in } \mathscr{D}.$$

If for each ϵ one can choose the same δ for every β in $\mathscr{D}$, then f is said to be **uniformly continuous on** $\mathscr{D}$. Notice that this is a property which depends on the point set as well as on the function.

THEOREM 3.2C   A function continuous on a bounded closed set in $\mathscr{E}_n$ is uniformly continuous on that set.

Proof   If it were not true that for every $\epsilon > 0$ one could find $\delta = \delta(\epsilon) > 0$ such that (8) held for every β in $\mathscr{D}$, then for some $\epsilon > 0$ and for $\delta = 1/i$, $i = 1, 2, \ldots$, there would be some β_i and a corresponding α_i such that

(9) $$|f(\alpha_i) - f(\beta_i)| \geq \epsilon \quad \text{while} \quad \|\alpha_i - \beta_i\| \leq \frac{1}{i}.$$

In view of Theorem 3.1B, there is no loss in generality in assuming that the sequence $\{\alpha_i\}$ converges to α, a point in $\mathscr{D}$ since $\mathscr{D}$ is closed. The inequality

$$\|\beta_i - \alpha\| \leq \|\beta_i - \alpha_i\| + \|\alpha_i - \alpha\|$$

then shows that $\{\beta_i\}$ converges to α. By continuity of f, we have $\{f(\alpha_i)\}$ and $\{f(\beta_i)\}$ both converging to $f(\alpha)$. This contradicts (9) since for sufficiently large i we have

$$|f(\alpha_i) - f(\beta_i)| \leq |f(\alpha_i) - f(\alpha)| + |f(\alpha) - f(\beta_i)| < \epsilon/4 + \epsilon/4 = \epsilon/2. \quad \star$$

Another useful result is

THEOREM 3.2D   A function f continuous on a bounded closed set $\mathscr{D}$ in $\mathscr{E}_n$ is bounded on $\mathscr{D}$. If f is real valued, it assumes its maximum and minimum values on $\mathscr{D}$.

Proof   To say that f is not bounded on $\mathscr{D}$ is to say that for each integer i there is an α_i such that $|f(\alpha_i)| > i$. Using Theorem 3.1B we may assume without loss of generality that the sequence $\{\alpha_i\}$ converges to a limit α which must be in $\mathscr{D}$ since $\mathscr{D}$ is closed. For sufficiently large i, we have $|f(\alpha_i)| < |f(\alpha)| + \epsilon$ by the continuity of f, and this contradicts the fact that $|f(\alpha_i)| > i$.

When f is real valued, let $b = $ l.u.b. $\{f(\alpha) \mid \alpha \text{ in } \mathcal{D}\}$. Then there exist α_i in $\mathcal{D}$ such that $b \geq f(\alpha_i) > b - \dfrac{1}{i}$. We may again assume $\{\alpha_i\}$ converges to α in $\mathcal{D}$. By continuity, $\{f(\alpha_i)\}$ converges to $f(\alpha)$ but the inequalities show $\{f(\alpha_i)\}$ converges to b. Therefore $f(\alpha) = b$, that is, f assumes its least upper bound. A similar proof shows f assumes its minimum value. $\star$

In connection with sequences of functions there arises the concept of uniform convergence. The sequence of functions $\{f_i\}$, $i = 1, 2, \ldots$, defined over a point set $\mathcal{D}$ in $\mathcal{E}_n$ is said to **converge uniformly on** $\mathcal{D}$ to a function g defined on $\mathcal{D}$ if for $\epsilon > 0$ there is an integer $N(\epsilon)$ such that

$$(9) \qquad |f_i(\alpha) - g(\alpha)| < \epsilon \quad \text{whenever} \quad i > N \text{ and } \alpha \text{ is in } \mathcal{D}.$$

The uniformity occurs in the independence of N on α. Uniform convergence is a property of the point set $\mathcal{D}$ and the sequence $\{f_i\}$. For each fixed α in $\mathcal{D}$, the sequence $\{f_i(\alpha)\}$ may converge and yet the sequence $\{f_i\}$ may not converge uniformly on $\mathcal{D}$. The next theorem, called the **Cauchy criterion for uniform convergence**, gives a necessary and sufficient condition that a sequence converge uniformly on $\mathcal{D}$.

THEOREM 3.2E The sequence $\{f_i\}$ converges uniformly on $\mathcal{D}$ if and only if for every $\epsilon > 0$ there is an integer $N(\epsilon)$ such that

$$(10) \qquad |f_i(\alpha) - f_j(\alpha)| < \epsilon \quad \text{for} \quad i > N, j > N, \alpha \text{ in } \mathcal{D}.$$

Proof If the sequence converges uniformly there is an integer $N(\epsilon)$ such that (9) holds. Then if $i > N(\epsilon/2), j > N(\epsilon/2)$ we have

$$|f_i(\alpha) - f_j(\alpha)| \leq |f_i(\alpha) - g(\alpha)| + |g(\alpha) - f_j(\alpha)| < \epsilon/2 + \epsilon/2 = \epsilon.$$

To show the converse, suppose that there is an integer $N(\epsilon)$ such that (10) holds. By the Cauchy criterion for convergence, Theorem 3.1C, for each α there is a number $g(\alpha)$ such that

$$|f_j(\alpha) - g(\alpha)| < \epsilon \quad \text{if} \quad j > M(\epsilon, \alpha).$$

Write, for each α,

$$|f_i(\alpha) - g(\alpha)| \leq |f_i(\alpha) - f_j(\alpha)| + |f_j(\alpha) - g(\alpha)|$$

and select $j > M(\epsilon/2, \alpha), j > N(\epsilon/2)$. Then, for $i > N(\epsilon/2)$ and for every α in $\mathcal{D}$, we have

$$|f_i(\alpha) - g(\alpha)| < \epsilon/2 + \epsilon/2 = \epsilon$$

proving that $\{f_i\}$ converges uniformly to g on $\mathcal{D}$. $\star$

The property of uniform convergence imposes certain restrictions on the limiting function.

THEOREM 3.2F   Let β be a continuity point of each function f_i of a sequence $\{f_i\}$ converging uniformly on $\mathcal{D}$. Then the limiting function g is also continuous at β.

Proof   We have, for α in $\mathcal{D}$,

$$|g(\alpha) - g(\beta)| \leq |g(\alpha) - f_i(\alpha)| + |f_i(\alpha) - f_i(\beta)| + |f_i(\beta) - g(\beta)|.$$

Choose i so large that

$$|f_i(\sigma) - g(\sigma)| < \epsilon/3 \text{ for } \sigma \text{ in } \mathcal{D}.$$

This can be done since the sequence converges uniformly. For this i, the continuity of f_i implies there exists $\delta(\epsilon)$ such that

$$|f_i(\alpha) - f_i(\beta)| < \epsilon/3 \quad \text{whenever} \quad \|\alpha - \beta\| < \delta.$$

Thus for given $\epsilon > 0$, we have found a $\delta(\epsilon)$ such that whenever $\|\alpha - \beta\| < \delta$,

$$|g(\alpha) - g(\beta)| < \epsilon/3 + \epsilon/3 + \epsilon/3 = \epsilon.$$

This proves that g is continuous at β.   ★

The previous theorem may be thought of as a theorem on the interchange of limits, for it states

$$\lim_{\alpha \to \beta} \lim_{i \to \infty} f_i(\alpha) = \lim_{\alpha \to \beta} g(\alpha) = g(\beta) = \lim_{i = \infty} f_i(\beta) = \lim_{i \to \infty} \lim_{\alpha \to \beta} f_i(\alpha).$$

EXAMPLE 5   Consider the functions $f_i(x) = \dfrac{ix}{ix + 1}$, $0 \leq x \leq a$, $a > 0$. The limiting function is

$$g(x) = \begin{cases} 0, & x = 0 \\ 1, & 0 < x \leq a. \end{cases}$$

In view of the preceding theorem, the sequence $\{f_i\}$ cannot converge uniformly on $0 \leq x \leq a$, since g is not continuous on $0 \leq x \leq a$. Note that

$$\lim_{x \to 0} \lim_{i \to \infty} \frac{ix}{ix + 1} = 1, \quad \lim_{i \to \infty} \lim_{x \to 0} \frac{ix}{ix + 1} = 0.$$

EXAMPLE 6 Consider the functions $f_i(x) = \dfrac{ix}{1 + i^2 x^2}$, $0 \leq x \leq a$,

$a > 0$. The limiting function is $g(x) = 0$, $0 \leq x \leq a$. In this case

$$\lim_{x \to 0} \lim_{i \to \infty} \frac{ix}{1 + i^2 x^2} = 0 = \lim_{i \to \infty} \lim_{x \to 0} \frac{ix}{1 + i^2 x^2}.$$

Nevertheless, the sequence $\{f_i\}$ does not converge uniformly on $0 \leq x \leq a$. If it did we would have

$$|f_i(x) - 0| = \frac{ix}{1 + i^2 x^2} < \epsilon \text{ for } i > N(\epsilon), \, 0 \leq x \leq a.$$

Fixing $\epsilon = \frac{1}{4}$, taking $i > N(\frac{1}{4})$, and i so large that $\dfrac{1}{i} < a$, and choosing

$x = \dfrac{1}{i}$, we obtain $\frac{1}{2} < \frac{1}{4}$, a contradiction.

Example 6 illustrates that a sequence of continuous functions may converge to a continuous function on a closed interval without converging uniformly on that interval. Such a situation is not possible when a condition of monotonicity is imposed.

THEOREM 3.2G Let f_i be continuous real valued functions defined on a bounded closed set $\mathscr{D}$ in $\mathscr{E}_n$, converging to a continuous function g on $\mathscr{D}$. If also $f_i(\alpha) \geq f_{i+1}(\alpha)$ for each α in $\mathscr{D}$, then $\lim\limits_{i \to \infty} f_i(\alpha) = g(\alpha)$ uniformly on $\mathscr{D}$. The theorem is also valid when f_i are monotone increasing instead of monotone decreasing.

Proof We may assume $g = 0$ for otherwise we could consider the sequence $f_i - g$. If the theorem were false, there would exist a positive ϵ such that for every integer N one could find an α in $\mathscr{D}$ and an integer $j > N$ such that $f_j(\alpha) > \epsilon$. It is therefore possible to find an increasing subsequence of integers $i_1 < i_2 < i_3 \ldots$, and a sequence of points $\{\alpha_{i_j}\}$ such that $f_{i_j}(\alpha_{i_j}) \geq \epsilon$. In view of Theorem 3.1B we may suppose $\{\alpha_{i_j}\}$ converges to β which must be in $\mathscr{D}$ since $\mathscr{D}$ is closed. There is an integer $m(\epsilon)$ such that $f_m(\beta) < \epsilon/4$. By choosing $i_j > m$ we obtain

$$f_{i_j}(\alpha_{i_j}) \leq f_m(\alpha_{i_j}) \leq |f_m(\alpha_{i_j}) - f_m(\beta)| + f_m(\beta).$$

The function f_m being continuous at β, we need only choose i_j sufficiently large to get $|f_m(\alpha_{i_j}) - f_m(\beta)| < \epsilon/4$. Then $f_{i_j}(\alpha_{i_j}) < \epsilon/2$ contradicting the fact that $f_{i_j}(\alpha_{i_j}) \geq \epsilon$. $\star$

An important theorem due to Ascoli permits us to extract from a sufficiently restricted sequence of continuous functions a subsequence which converges uniformly.

Let $\{f_i\}$ be a sequence of functions defined on a set $\mathscr{D}$ in $\mathscr{E}_n$. The sequence is said to be **uniformly bounded** if there is an integer M such that

$$|f_i(\alpha)| < M \text{ for } \alpha \text{ in } \mathscr{D} \text{ and } i = 1, 2, \ldots.$$

The sequence is said to be **equicontinuous** on $\mathscr{D}$ if for given $\epsilon > 0$, there exists a $\delta(\epsilon) > 0$ such that

(11) $|f_i(\alpha) - f_i(\beta)| < \epsilon$ for α and β in $\mathscr{D}$ and $\|\alpha - \beta\| < \delta$.

Using this terminology, **Ascoli's Theorem** may be stated as follows:

THEOREM 3.2H   If $\{f_i\}$ is a uniformly bounded equicontinuous sequence of functions defined on a bounded set $\mathscr{D}$ in $\mathscr{E}_n$, then there is a subsequence $\{f_{i_j}\}$ converging uniformly on $\mathscr{D}$.

Proof   Let $\alpha_1, \alpha_2, \ldots$ be a sequence of points in $\mathscr{D}$ with the following property: For each $\delta > 0$ it is possible to find an integer $N(\delta)$ such that for any α in $\mathscr{D}$ there is an integer $p = p(\alpha) < N$ with $\|\alpha - \alpha_p\| < \delta$. We first indicate how such a sequence may be obtained. The bounded domain $\mathscr{D}$ lies within an n dimensional "cube" of side length $2a$,

$$-a \leq x_1 \leq a, \quad -a \leq x_2 \leq a, \quad \ldots, \quad -a \leq x_n \leq a.$$

By bisection of these intervals we obtain 2^n cubes with each side having length a. Choose a point of $\mathscr{D}$ in each such cube (if there is one). These will form the first 2^n points of the desired sequence. By dividing each of the original intervals into quarters we obtain 4^n cubes with each side having length $a/2$. Choose a point of $\mathscr{D}$ in each such cube. These will form the next 4^n points of the desired sequence. Continuing in this fashion, we obtain the desired sequence.

The sequence $\{f_i(\alpha_1)\}$ is a bounded sequence and there exists a convergent subsequence. We shall denote this subsequence by $\{f_i^1(\alpha_1)\}$. The sequence $\{f_i^1(\alpha_2)\}$ similarly has a convergent subsequence, denoted by $\{f_i^2(\alpha_2)\}$. The sequence $\{f_i^2(\alpha_3)\}$ in its turn has a convergent subsequence denoted by $\{f_i^3(\alpha_3)\}$. Continue in this fashion to obtain for each integer j, a subsequence $\{f_i^j(\alpha)\}$ such that $\{f_i^j(\alpha_j)\}$ converges. Define $g_1 = f_1^1$, $g_2 = f_2^2, \ldots$, $g_k = f_k^k, \ldots$ thus forming a subsequence of the original sequence $\{f_i\}$ by choosing the first function in the first subsequence, the second function in the second subsequence, etc. The sequence $\{g_i(\alpha_j)\}$ converges for each $j = 1, 2, \ldots$

since all its elements, from the jth on, belong to $\{f_i^j(\alpha_j)\}$. By the Cauchy criterion we have

(12) $\lim_{i,k \to \infty} |g_i(\alpha_j) - g_k(\alpha_j)| = 0$ for $j = 1, 2, \ldots$.

Now let us apply the property of equicontinuity. For $\epsilon > 0$, we can find $\delta > 0$ such that (11) holds. In particular, (11) holds with f_i replaced by g_i. By our choice of the set α_i, there is an integer $N(\delta)$ such that for every α in $\mathcal{D}$ there is an integer $p < N$ with $\|\alpha - \alpha_p\| < \delta$. Using (12) for the N points $\alpha_1, \ldots, \alpha_N$, we can say there is an integer $M > N$ such that

(13) $|g_i(\alpha_j) - g_k(\alpha_j)| < \epsilon$ for $i > M$, $k > M$, $j = 1, \ldots N$.

With the aid of (11) and (13) it follows that for $i > M, k > M$,

$$|g_i(\alpha) - g_k(\alpha)| \leq |g_i(\alpha) - g_i(\alpha_p)| + |g_i(\alpha_p) - g_k(\alpha_p)| + |g_k(\alpha_p) - g_k(\alpha)| < 3\epsilon,$$

proving, by the Cauchy criterion, that $\{g_i\}$ converges uniformly on $\mathcal{D}$.   ★

   In the next section we shall see that simple sufficient conditions for term by term integration and differentiation of sequences may be stated in terms of uniform convergence.

   For the present, we remind the reader that any convergence theorem for sequences implies a corresponding theorem for series. For, if $\{f_i\}$ is defined on $\mathcal{D}$, and α is in $\mathcal{D}$, the **sum of the series**

(14) $f_1(\alpha) + f_2(\alpha) + \ldots + f_n(\alpha) + \ldots$

is defined to be

$$\sum_{i=1}^{\infty} f_i(\alpha) = \lim_{m \to \infty} \sum_{i=1}^{m} f_i(\alpha)$$

if the limit exists. The sum of the first m terms of the series (14), $\sum_{i=1}^{m} f_i(\alpha)$, is called the mth **partial sum.** The series (14) is said to **converge uniformly** on $\mathcal{D}$ if the sequence of partial sums, $\left\{ \sum_{i=1}^{m} f_i \right\}$, converges uniformly on $\mathcal{D}$. When stated as a theorem on series, Theorem 3.2F becomes

   THEOREM 3.2 I   If the series (14) converges uniformly on $\mathcal{D}$, and f_i are continuous on $\mathcal{D}$, then the sum of the series is a continuous function on $\mathcal{D}$.

A theorem on series corresponding to Theorem 3.2G is

THEOREM 3.2J Let f_i be continuous real valued functions defined on a bounded closed set $\mathscr{D}$ in $\mathscr{E}_n$. If $f_i(\alpha) \geq 0$ for α in $\mathscr{D}$ and the series $\sum\limits_{i=1}^{\infty} f_i(\alpha)$ converges to the continuous function $g(\alpha)$ on $\mathscr{D}$, then the series converges uniformly on $\mathscr{D}$.

The Cauchy criterion for convergence (Theorem 3.1C) and the Cauchy criterion for uniform convergence (Theorem 3.2E) may also be rephrased for series.

THEOREM 3.2K The series (14) converges if and only if for every $\epsilon > 0$ there is an integer $N(\alpha, \epsilon)$ such that

$$(15) \qquad \left| \sum_{i=p}^{q} f_i(\alpha) \right| < \epsilon \quad \text{for} \quad q > p > N.$$

The series (14) converges uniformly on $\mathscr{D}$ if and only if there is an integer $N(\epsilon)$, independent of α, such that (15) holds.

We recall that the series (14) is said to **converge absolutely** if the series

$$(16) \qquad |f_1(\alpha)| + \ldots + |f_n(\alpha)| + \ldots$$

converges. A series which converges absolutely must also converge, in view of the Cauchy criterion, since

$$(17) \qquad \left| \sum_{i=p}^{q} f_i(\alpha) \right| \leq \sum_{i=p}^{q} \left| f_i(\alpha) \right|.$$

If the series (16) converges uniformly on $\mathscr{D}$ then the series (14) is said to **converge absolutely-uniformly** on $\mathscr{D}$. The relation (17) and Theorem 3.2K assure that a series which converges absolutely-uniformly converges uniformly.

The simplest and most often used test for absolute-uniform convergence is called the **Weierstrass M-test**.

THEOREM 3.2L (*M* test) Let $|f_i(\alpha)| \leq M_i$ for α in $\mathscr{D}$ and suppose $\sum\limits_{i=1}^{\infty} M_i$ converges. Then $\sum\limits_{i=1}^{\infty} f_i(\alpha)$ converges absolutely-uniformly on $\mathscr{D}$.

Proof The desired result is an immediate consequence of Theorem 3.2K since

$$\sum_{i=p}^{q} \left| f_i(\alpha) \right| \leq \sum_{i=p}^{q} M_i. \quad \bigstar$$

Exercise 3.2

1. Let f be a real valued function of a single real variable.
    (a) Suppose f is continuous at $x = a$ and satisfies $f(x + y) = f(x)f(y)$
         for all x and y. Show that $f(x) = k^x$ for all x and some constant k,
         using the method of Example 1. *Hint:* $f(x) = f\left(\dfrac{x}{2}\right)^2 \geq 0$. If f is zero for
         one value of x, it is zero for all values.
    (b) Suppose f is bounded on $a \leq x \leq b$ and satisfies $f(x + y) = f(x)f(y)$
         for all x and y. Show that $f(x) = k^x$ for all x and some constant k.
         Hint: See the hint in part (a). Consider $g(x) = \log f(x)$.

2. Let f be a real valued function of a single real variable defined for positive x.
    (a) Suppose f is continuous at a and satisfies $f(xy) = f(x) + f(y)$. Show that
         $f(x) = k \log x$ for some constant k and all x. *Hint:* Define $g(x) = f(e^x)$
         and reduce to Example 1.
    (b) Suppose f is bounded on the interval $1 \leq x \leq b$ and satisfies $f(xy)$
         $= f(x) + f(y)$. Use the method of Example 2 to prove $f(x) = k \log x$.
         Hint: Put $g(x) = f(x) - f(b) \log x/\log b$ so that $g(bx) = g(x)$, proving g
         has the same bound on each interval $1 \leq x \leq b$, $b \leq x \leq b^2$, etc. Then
         show that g is equal to zero by considering $g(x^n)$.

3. Let f_i and g_i, $i = 1, 2, \ldots$ be continuous real valued functions defined over
    the whole space $\mathscr{E}$. Show that the set $\{\alpha \mid f_i(\alpha) \geq 0, g_i(\alpha) = 0\}$ is a closed set.
    Hint: Note that the set $\{\alpha \mid f(\alpha) \geq 0\}$ is the complement of the set $\{\alpha \mid f(\alpha)$
    $< 0\}$. See Example 4.

4. Let $f(x, y) = y^2 - x^2(x - 2)$ be defined on $\mathscr{E}_2$. Show that the closure of the
    set $\{(x, y) \mid f(x, y) < 0\}$ is not $\{(x, y) \mid f(x, y) \leq 0\}$.

5. (a) Using the result of Exercise 3 show that the set in $\mathscr{E}_2$, $\{(x, y) \mid x^2 + y^2$
         $= 1\}$, is a closed set.
    (b) Hence prove that if α is not on the circle $x^2 + y^2 = 1$ there is a point β
         on the circle such that the distance from α to β is less than or equal to
         the distance from α to any other point of the circle.

6. (a) Show that for fixed β, the function $d(\alpha, \beta) = \|\alpha - \beta\|$ is a continuous
         function of α.
    (b) Let the distance from β to a set $\mathscr{S}$ be defined as $d(\mathscr{S}, \beta) = \text{g.l.b.}\{d(\alpha,$
         $\beta) \mid \alpha \text{ in } \mathscr{S}\}$. If $\mathscr{S}$ is a bounded closed set in $\mathscr{E}_n$, show that there is a σ
         in $\mathscr{S}$ such that $d(\mathscr{S}, \beta) = d(\sigma, \beta)$.

7. Show that as (x, y) approaches $(0, 0)$ along a straight line, the values $\dfrac{xy^2}{x^2 + y^4}$
    approach 0. Show however that $\lim\limits_{(x, y) \to (0, 0)} \dfrac{xy^2}{x^2 + y^4}$ does not exist.

8. Find $\delta(\epsilon)$ such that $0 < (x^2 + y^2)^{1/2} < \delta$ implies $\dfrac{x^2y^2}{x^2 + y^2} < \epsilon$. Write the
    implication using the word limit.

9. Let f be a real valued function of a single real variable continuous on the
    interval $a \leq x \leq b$.
    (a) If $f(a) \leq 0$ and $f(b) \geq 0$, show that there is a value c, $a \leq c \leq b$, such
         that $f(c) = 0$. *Hint:* We may suppose $f(a) < 0$. Consider l.u.b. $\{x \mid f(x)$
         $< 0\}$.

(b) If $f(a) \le k \le f(b)$, show that there is a value c such that $f(c) = k$. *Hint:* Consider $f(x) - k$ and use the result of (a).

(c) Show that f assumes every value between its greatest lower bound and least upper bound.

10. Let the real valued function f have a derivative f' in $a < x < b$ and a relative maximum at c, $a < c < b$ (i.e., $f(c) \ge f(x)$ for all x in some interval about c). Use the definition of derivative to show that $f'(c) = 0$. The same result is valid for a relative minimum.

11. Prove Rolle's theorem: If f is real and continuous on $a \le x \le b$, f' exists on $a < x < b$, $f(a) = f(b) = 0$, then there is a value c, $a < c < b$, such that $f'(c) = 0$. *Hint:* The result is true when $f(x) = 0$ for all x. Otherwise f has a maximum or minimum not zero. Use Theorem 3.2D and Exercise 10.

12. Prove the mean value theorem: If f is real and continuous on $a \le x \le b$, f' exists on $a < x < b$, then there is a value c, $a < c < b$, such that

$$f(b) - f(a) = f'(c)(b - a).$$

Hint: Apply Rolle's theorem to the function

$$h(x) = f(b) - f(x) - (b - x)\frac{f(b) - f(a)}{b - a}.$$

13. (a) Use the mean value theorem to show that if f is continuous and $f' > 0$ on $a \le x \le b$, then f is strictly increasing on $a \le x \le b$.

(b) Use the mean value theorem to show that if $f' = 0$ on an interval, then f is constant on that interval.

14. Let f be a polynomial in the real variable x with real coefficients. The highest power of x is its **degree**.

(a) If the degree is odd, show that $f(x) = 0$ for some x.

(b) If the degree is even, and $\lim_{x \to \infty} f(x) = \infty$, show that there is a value x satisfying $f(x) = b$ if and only if $b \ge$ g.l.b. $\{f(x)\}$.

15. Consider the sequence $f_n(x) = \begin{cases} \sin (n!\pi x), & x \text{ rational,} \\ 0, & x \text{ irrational.} \end{cases}$

(a) Show that $\lim_{n \to \infty} f_n(x) = 0$.

(b) Show that the sequence does not converge uniformly on any interval. *Hint:* If it did converge uniformly on $a \le x \le b$, we would have, with $\epsilon = 1/8$, an integer N (we may suppose $N!\pi(b - a) > 1$) such that

$$|\sin n!\pi x| < 1/8, \quad n > N, \quad a \le x \le b.$$

This yields $|\sin n!\pi b - \sin n!\pi a| < 1/4$. By the mean value theorem, $\sin n!\pi b - \sin n!\pi a = (\cos n!\pi y) \, n!\pi$ $(b - a)$ where $a < y < b$. Show that we would have $|\sin n!\pi y| < 1/4$, $|\cos n!\pi y| < 1/4$ and that this cannot be.

16. Let a_{ij}, $i, j = 1, 2, \ldots$, be complex numbers satisfying $|a_{ij}| \le A$ for some constant A. Show that there is a sequence j_k of integers and a sequence b_i of complex numbers such that $\lim_{k \to \infty} a_{ij_k} = b_i$ for $i = 1, 2, \ldots$

17. Let y_i, $i = 1, \ldots n$ be defined as functions of the variables $x_1, \ldots, x_m$ in some set $\mathscr{D}$ in $\mathscr{E}_m$, and suppose each y_i is continuous at the point β in $\mathscr{D}$. If the function $f(y_1, \ldots, y_n)$ is continuous at $\sigma = (y_1(\beta), \ldots, y_n(\beta))$, then show that

$$g(x_1, \ldots, x_n) = f(y_1(x_1, \ldots, x_m), \ldots, y_n(x_1, \ldots, x_m))$$

is continuous at β.
Hint: Use the sequence definition of continuity.

18. Show the necessity of the hypotheses in Theorem 3.2G by considering the following examples:

(a) $$f_n(t) = \begin{cases} 1, & 0 < t < \dfrac{1}{n}, \\ 0, & t = 0 \quad \text{or} \quad \dfrac{1}{n} \le t \le 1. \end{cases}$$

(b) $f_n(t) = e^{-\hbar t}$, $0 \le t \le 1$.

19. Let $f_n(t) = \displaystyle\int_a^b \sin^3(t + nu)\psi(u)du$, $a \le t \le b$, $n = 1, 2, \ldots$ where $\psi(u)$ is continuous on $a \le u \le b$. Show that a subsequence of $\{f_n\}$ converges uniformly on $a \le t \le b$. (By methods considered later, it can be shown that the entire sequence converges uniformly.)

20. (a) Use the M test to show that the geometric series

$$1 + x + x^2 + \ldots + x^n + \ldots$$

converges uniformly for $|x| \le r < 1$.

(b) Show that the series $\displaystyle\sum_{n=1}^{\infty} \dfrac{x^n}{n^2(1 + x^n)}$ converges uniformly for all x outside the interval $|x + 1| \le a$, where $a > 0$.

21. Show that the sequence $\left\{f_n(x)\right\} = \left\{\dfrac{1 + nx^2}{1 + nx}\right\}$ is not uniformly convergent in any interval including the origin.

22. Let $f_n(x) = (-1)^n x^n (1 - x)$, $0 \le x \le 1$. Show that the series $\displaystyle\sum_1^{\infty} f_n(x)$ converges absolutely for each x on $0 \le x \le 1$ and uniformly on $0 \le x \le 1$ but does not converge absolutely-uniformly on $0 \le x \le 1$.

Hint: To show the uniform convergence, note that, for each x, $\displaystyle\sum_1^{\infty} f_n(x)$ is an alternating series, with $|f_n(x)| \ge |f_{n+1}(x)|$, and $\displaystyle\lim_{n \to \infty} f_n(x) = 0$. Hence, by a known result on alternating series, $\displaystyle\sum_1^{\infty} f_n(x)$ converges for each x and $\left| \displaystyle\sum_1^{\infty} f_n(x) \right.$
$- \displaystyle\sum_{n=1}^N f_n(x) \left| = \right| \displaystyle\sum_{N+1}^{\infty} f_n(x) \left| \le |f_N(x)| \right.$ which converges uniformly to zero as N approaches infinity.

23. Consider the series $\displaystyle\sum_{n=1}^{\infty} \dfrac{(-1)^n x^n}{n}$, $0 < x < 1$. Show that the series converges absolutely and uniformly on $0 < x < 1$ but not absolutely-uniformly.

Hint: See *Hint* for Exercise 22. If there exists $p(\epsilon)$ such that $\displaystyle\sum_{n=p}^{2p} \dfrac{x^n}{n} < \epsilon$, $0 < x < 1$, $\epsilon < \dfrac{1}{4}$, then $\dfrac{1}{2p} \displaystyle\sum_{n=p}^{2p} x^{2p} < \epsilon$ or $x^{2p} < 2\epsilon$ which cannot hold for x sufficiently close to 1.

24. Consider the series $\sum\limits_{n=1}^{\infty} \dfrac{(-1)^n x^2}{(1 + x^2)^n}$, $0 \leq x \leq 1$. Show that the series converges
absolutely and uniformly but not absolutely-uniformly on $0 \leq x \leq 1$.

25. Let f be a real valued monotone increasing bounded function on $a \leq x \leq b$.
Define
$$f(c+) = \lim_{x \to c} f(x), \; x \text{ restricted to be greater than } c.$$
$$f(c-) = \lim_{x \to c} f(x), \; x \text{ restricted to be less than } c.$$

(a) Show that $f(c+)$ and $f(c-)$ exist for every c on $a < c < b$. Also
$f(a+)$ and $f(b-)$ exist.

(b) Show that f is continuous at c if $f(c+) = f(c-)$, $a < c < b$. Show that
f is continuous at a if $f(a+) = f(a)$.

(c) The difference $f(c+) - f(c-)$ is called the "jump" at c. Show that f
cannot have more than a finite number of jumps of value greater than 1.
Show that f cannot have more than a finite number of jumps of value
d, $\dfrac{1}{n+1} < d \leq \dfrac{1}{n}$.
Hence show that f has at most a countable number of discontinuities.

26. Let f be a real valued increasing function on $-\infty < x < \infty$. Show that f has
at most a countable number of discontinuities.

27. Let $\{f_i\}$ be a uniformly bounded equicontinuous sequence of functions defined
on a bounded closed set $\mathscr{D}$ in $\mathscr{E}_n$. Suppose $\{f_i\}$ converges to f. Show that
$\{f_i\}$ converges uniformly on $\mathscr{D}$.

28. Let $\{f_i\}$ be a sequence of continuous functions converging uniformly on a
bounded closed set $\mathscr{D}$ in $\mathscr{E}_n$. Show that $\{f_i\}$ is equicontinuous on $\mathscr{D}$.

29. Let $\{f_i\}$ be a sequence of real valued functions defined on $a \leq x \leq b$. Suppose
f_i', $i = 1, 2, \ldots$ exist and $|f_i'| \leq M$, where M is a constant independent of i.
Show that $\{f_i\}$ is equicontinuous on $a \leq x \leq b$.

3.3

INTEGRATION

Our survey of concepts needed for the next chapter will be completed by a
brief review of some of the fundamentals of integration theory.

3.3.1   Part I

First we consider the definition of an integral over an n dimensional **closed
interval** $\mathscr{I}$ of $\mathscr{E}_n$, defined by

$$\mathscr{I} = \left\{ (x_1, \ldots, x_n) \mid a_i \leq x_i \leq b_i, i = 1, \ldots, n \right\}.$$

The **volume** $|\mathscr{I}|$ of $\mathscr{I}$ is $\overset{n}{\underset{i=1}{\Pi}} b_i - a_i$.

By inserting $q_i - 1$ numbers y_{ij} (**subdivision points**) between a_i and b_i so as to obtain

$$a_i = y_{i0} < y_{i1} < \ldots < y_{iq_i} = b_i,$$

the interval $\mathscr{I}$ may be considered as dividend into $\overset{n}{\underset{i=1}{\Pi}} q_i$ nonoverlapping closed intervals $\mathscr{I}_j$. In this way we form a **partition** P of $\mathscr{I}$. If we associate with each subinterval $\mathscr{I}_j$ of the partition P a point α_j in $\mathscr{I}_j$ we shall say we have an **augmented partition** P. We shall assume without proof that $\sum_j |\mathscr{I}_j| = |\mathscr{I}|$.

The **norm** $|P|$ of a partition P is the length of the largest diagonal of any of the subintervals $\mathscr{I}_j$. That is, if

$$d_j = \text{l.u.b.} \{\|\alpha - \beta\| \mid \alpha \text{ and } \beta \text{ in } \mathscr{I}_j\}$$

then

$$|P| = \text{l.u.b.} \{d_j\}.$$

If f is a bounded real-valued function with domain $\mathscr{I}$, and P is an augmented partition, form the sum

$$S(P) = \sum_j f(\alpha_j) |\mathscr{I}_j|.$$

The numbers $S(P)$ are said to converge to a limit L as the norm $|P|$ approaches zero if for every $\epsilon > 0$ there is a $\delta(\epsilon) > 0$ such that

(1) $|S(P) - L| < \epsilon$ whenever $|P| < \delta$.

When the condition (1) holds, we write

$$L = \lim_{|P| \to 0} S(P) = \int_{\mathscr{I}} f(\alpha) \, d\alpha$$

and say that f is **integrable** on $\mathscr{I}$, and $\int_{\mathscr{I}} f(\alpha) \, d\alpha$ is the **definite integral** of f on $\mathscr{I}$.

Note that $S(P)$ is not a single valued function of the norm $|P|$. For one value of $|P|$, it may be possible to have many values of $S(P)$, for example by choosing different points α_j in $\mathscr{I}_j$ for the same partition.

There is another useful equivalent definition. If f is bounded on $\mathscr{I}$, P is a partition with subintervals $\mathscr{I}_j$,

$$M_j = \text{l.u.b.} \{f(\alpha) \mid \alpha \text{ in } \mathscr{I}_j\}, \quad m_j = \text{g.l.b.} \{f(\alpha) \mid \alpha \text{ in } \mathscr{I}_j\}$$

$$\bar{S}(P) = \sum_j M_j |\mathscr{I}_j|, \quad \underline{S}(P) = \sum_j m_j |\mathscr{I}_j|,$$

then it is clear that

(2) $\underline{S}(P) \le S(P) \le \bar{S}(P)$.

When P_1 and P_2 are any two partitions we always have

(3) $$\underline{S}(P_1) \leq \bar{S}(P_2).$$

To see this first note that if P' is formed from P by addition of one sub-division point, then $\underline{S}(P) \leq \underline{S}(P') \leq \bar{S}(P') \leq \bar{S}(P)$. The same result is then valid when P' is obtained from P by addition of a finite number of sub-division points. Now let P_3 be a partition containing the subdivision points of P_1 and P_2. Then

$$\underline{S}(P_1) \leq \underline{S}(P_3) \leq \bar{S}(P_3) \leq \bar{S}(P_2).$$

This proves (3), and from it we obtain

(4) $$\text{l.u.b. } \underline{S}(P) \leq \text{g.l.b. } \bar{S}(P).$$

The left side of (4) is called the **lower integral** of f on $\mathscr{I}$ and the right side is called the **upper integral** of f on $\mathscr{I}$. We shall see that f is integrable if and only if the upper and lower integrals are equal. First let us prove

(5) $$\text{l.u.b. } \underline{S}(P) = \lim_{|P| \to 0} \underline{S}(P), \quad \text{g.l.b. } \bar{S}(P) = \lim_{|P| \to 0} \bar{S}(P).$$

To verify the first equality, one must exhibit $\delta(\epsilon)$ such that whenever $|P| < \delta$, we have $L - \underline{S}(P) < \epsilon$ where $L = \text{l.u.b. } \underline{S}(P)$. Let P_1 be a partition for which $\underline{S}(P_1) > L - \epsilon/2$. Let the number of subdivision points of P_1 between a_i and b_i be $q_i - 1$ and $Q = \text{l.u.b. } \{q_i + 1\}$. Let $B = \text{l.u.b. } \{|f(\alpha)| \mid \alpha \text{ in } \mathscr{I}\}$ and

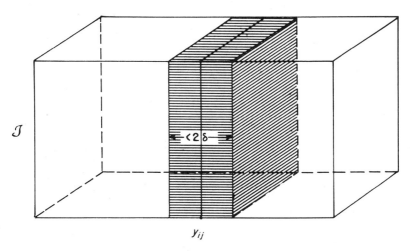

$$\mathscr{I}$$

$$\Leftarrow\langle 2|\delta\Rightarrow$$

$$y_{ij}$$

Volume of all subintervals of P_2 with corner point
whose ith coordinate is y_{ij} is not more than $2\delta r$.

$r = \text{l.u.b.} \{\Pi_{i \neq k} (b_i - a_i) \mid k = 1, \dots n\}$. Here r may be thought of as an upper bound to the "areas" of the "sides" of $\mathcal{I}$. Choose $\delta < \epsilon/8nBQr$. If P is any partition with $|P| < \delta$, let P_2 be a partition containing the subdivision points of P and P_1. In considering the difference $\underline{S}(P_2) - \underline{S}(P)$ we may think of every subinterval $\mathcal{I}_j$ of P as decomposed into the subintervals of P_2 within $\mathcal{I}_j$. Then for any subinterval of P_2 formed only by subdivision points of P, the contribution to $\underline{S}(P_2) - \underline{S}(P)$ is zero. The total volume of all subintervals of P_2 having a corner point whose i^{th} coordinate is a fixed subdivision point y_{ij} of P_1 is at most $2\delta r$ so that the contribution of such intervals to $\underline{S}(P_2) - \underline{S}(P)$ is at most $2B(2\delta r)$.

There are at most nQ subdivision points of P_1 and hence

$$\underline{S}(P_2) - \underline{S}(P) \leq nQ4B\delta r < \epsilon/2.$$

This inequality, together with the inequalities $\underline{S}(P_2) \geq \underline{S}(P_1)$, $\underline{S}(P_1) > L - \epsilon/2$, now yields

$$L - \underline{S}(P) \leq L - \left(\underline{S}(P_2) - \frac{\epsilon}{2}\right) \leq L - \underline{S}(P_1) + \frac{\epsilon}{2} < \epsilon.$$

The second inequality in (5) is proved in the same manner.

THEOREM 3.3A   A necessary and sufficient condition that f be integrable on $\mathcal{I}$ is that the upper and lower integrals be equal. The common value is the integral.

Proof   When f is integrable, we use the inequality (2). By adding partition points, $S(P)$ converges to the value of the integral while $\bar{S}(P)$ decreases. Hence $\int_{\mathcal{I}} f(\alpha) \, d\alpha \leq \bar{S}(P)$ and so

(6) $$\int_{\mathcal{I}} f(\alpha) \, d\alpha \leq \text{g.l.b. } \bar{S}(P).$$

But if we choose a partition P with norm sufficiently small and α_j in $\mathcal{I}_j$ such that $f(\alpha_j) > M_j - \epsilon/|\mathcal{I}|$, we obtain

$$\int_{\mathcal{I}} f(\alpha) \, d\alpha > S(P) - \epsilon \text{ and } S(P) > \bar{S}(P) - \epsilon.$$

Therefore

$$\int_{\mathcal{I}} f(\alpha) d\alpha \geq \bar{S}(P) - 2\epsilon \geq \text{g.l.b. } \bar{S}(P) - 2\epsilon.$$

This inequality for arbitrary ϵ, together with (6), shows that

(7) $$\int_{\mathscr{I}} f(\alpha)d\alpha = \text{g.l.b. } \bar{S}(P)$$

In a similar fashion we can show that the integral is equal to the lower integral.

To prove the converse, suppose the upper and lower integrals equal L. By (5) and (2) there is a $\delta(\epsilon)$ such that if $|P| < \delta$, then

$$L - \epsilon < \underline{S}(P) \le S(P) \le \bar{S}(P) < L + \epsilon$$

or

$$|S(P) - L| < \epsilon. \quad \star$$

Corollary 1

The bounded function f is integrable if and only if for every $\epsilon > 0$ there is a partition P such that $\bar{S}(P) - \underline{S}(P) < \epsilon$.

THEOREM 3.3B If f is continuous on $\mathscr{I}$, then f is integrable on $\mathscr{I}$.

Proof By the uniform continuity of f (Theorem 3.2C) and Theorem 3.2D, for every $\epsilon > 0$ there is a partition P such that on each interval $\mathscr{I}_j$, we have $M_j - m_j < \epsilon/|\mathscr{I}|$. Hence $\bar{S}(P) - \underline{S}(P) < \epsilon$ and the preceding corollary yields the desired result. $\star$

Certain discontinuous functions are also integrable. The connection between integrability and continuity is given by the following important theorem.

THEOREM 3.3C The bounded function f is integrable on $\mathscr{I}$ if and only if for each $\epsilon > 0$ there is a countable number of intervals with total volume less than ϵ containing all the points of discontinuity of f.

We shall not prove this theorem now. The details are given in Exercises 3.3-9 and 3.3-10. We prefer instead to consider some applications.

A set of points in $\mathscr{E}_n$ which for every $\epsilon > 0$ can be covered by a countable number of n dimensional intervals with total volume less than ϵ is said to have **n-dimensional measure zero.** It is clear that any subset of a set of measure zero has measure zero and that the sum of a finite number of sets of measure zero has measure zero. The method of Example 2 below can be used to prove that the union of a countable collection of sets of measure zero has measure zero.

EXAMPLE 1 If f and g are integrable on $\mathscr{I}$, so are $f + g$, fg, $|f|$, and cf for any real number c.

Indeed cf and $|f|$ are continuous whenever f is, and $f + g$ and fg are continuous whenever f and g are. Thus the set of points of discontinuity of $f + g$, fg, $|f|$, cf is contained in the sum of the set of discontinuities of f and the set of discontinuities of g, each of which has measure zero by Theorem 3.3C. Using Theorem 3.3C again yields the desired result.

EXAMPLE 2   Let f be discontinuous only at a countable number of points in $\mathcal{I}$. Show that f is integrable on $\mathcal{I}$.

Surround the ith point by an interval with volume less than $\epsilon/2^i$. Then the total volume is less than $\epsilon \sum\limits_{i=1}^{\infty} \dfrac{1}{2^i} = \epsilon$.

EXAMPLE 3   Let $f(x, y)$ be a continuous function defined over a 2-dimensional closed set $\mathcal{D}$ in a rectangle $\mathcal{I}$. Show that, for $\epsilon > 0$, the 3-dimensional set of points $\mathcal{S} = \{(x, y, f(x, y)) \mid (x, y) \text{ in } \mathcal{D}\}$ can be covered by a finite number of 3-dimensional intervals (rectangular parallelopipeds) with total volume less than ϵ.

Since f is uniformly continuous on $\mathcal{D}$, $\mathcal{I}$ can be subdivided into a finite number of 2-dimensional intervals (rectangles) $\mathcal{I}_j$ such that

$$|f(\alpha) - f(\beta)| < \epsilon/|\mathcal{I}| \text{ for } \alpha \text{ and } \beta \text{ in } \mathcal{I}_j \cap \mathcal{D}.$$

Hence the part of the surface $\mathcal{S}$ whose projection on the x, y plane is within the rectangle $\mathcal{I}_j$ lies within a rectangular parallelopiped of total volume $|\mathcal{I}_j| \cdot \dfrac{\epsilon}{|\mathcal{I}|}$ and the total surface is contained in a finite number of rectangular parallelopipeds with total volume less than $\epsilon \cdot \sum\limits_{j} |\mathcal{I}_j|/|\mathcal{I}| = \epsilon$.

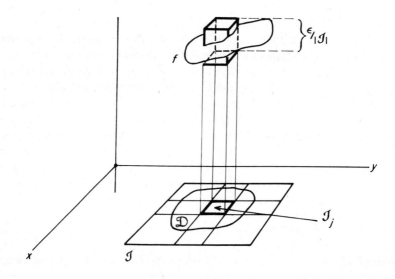

We are now going to define an integral over a bounded set of points $\mathscr{D}$ which is not necessarily an interval. The **boundary** of $\mathscr{D}$ is the set of points β such that every sphere about β contains a point of $\mathscr{D}$ and a point of $C(\mathscr{D})$. *We shall assume that the boundary of $\mathscr{D}$ has measure zero.* If f is originally defined only on $\mathscr{D}$ we define $f = 0$ outside of $\mathscr{D}$. Thus we may assume f is defined on an n dimensional interval $\mathscr{I}$ containing $\mathscr{D}$.

Let the **characteristic function** $\phi(\mathscr{D})$ of $\mathscr{D}$ be defined by

$$(8) \qquad \phi(\mathscr{D}, \alpha) = \begin{cases} 1 & \text{for } \alpha \text{ in } \mathscr{D}, \\ 0 & \text{for } \alpha \text{ not in } \mathscr{D}. \end{cases}$$

Note that $f(\alpha)\phi(\mathscr{D}, \alpha) = f(\alpha)$ for α in $\mathscr{D}$ and $f(\alpha)\phi(\mathscr{D}, \alpha) = 0$ for α outside of $\mathscr{D}$.

Then, the integral of f on $\mathscr{D}$ is defined by

$$(9) \qquad \int_{\mathscr{D}} f(\alpha) \, d\alpha = \int_{\mathscr{I}} f(\alpha)\phi(\mathscr{D}, \alpha) \, d\alpha.$$

The definition states that f is integrable on $\mathscr{D}$ if and only if $f\phi(\mathscr{D})$ is integrable on $\mathscr{I}$, that is, if and only if the discontinuities of $f\phi(\mathscr{D})$ on $\mathscr{I}$ form a set of measure zero. The boundary of $\mathscr{D}$ has been assumed to be a set of measure zero, and $f\phi(\mathscr{D})$ is continuous at a point α not an interior point or boundary point of $\mathscr{D}$, being equal to zero in a sphere about α. Hence f is integrable on $\mathscr{D}$ if and only if the discontinuities of $f\phi(\mathscr{D})$ at interior points of $\mathscr{D}$ form a set of measure zero. An interior point is a point of continuity of $f\phi(\mathscr{D})$ if and only if it is a point of continuity of f. We have therefore shown that f is integrable on $\mathscr{D}$ if and only if the set of discontinuity points within $\mathscr{D}$ of f form a set of measure zero. In particular, if f is integrable on $\mathscr{I}$ it is integrable on $\mathscr{D}$.

For example, if f is a bounded continuous function on a bounded set $\mathscr{D}$ in $\mathscr{E}_3$ whose boundary is composed of a finite number of surfaces each of which may be represented by a continuous function of the form $z = z(x, y)$ for some orientation of the axes, then f is integrable on $\mathscr{D}$. For, by Example 3, the boundary has three-dimensional measure zero.

EXAMPLE 4 If f and g are integrable on $\mathscr{D}$, so are cf for a real constant $c, f + g, fg, |f|$.

This is verified using the method of Example 1.

Another procedure is to note that f integrable on $\mathscr{D}$ means $f\phi(\mathscr{D})$ integrable on $\mathscr{I}$ and hence, by Example 1, $cf\phi(\mathscr{D})$ is integrable on $\mathscr{I}$, implying cf integrable on $\mathscr{D}$.

We can now define the n **dimensional volume** $|\mathscr{D}|$ of a bounded set $\mathscr{D}$ in $\mathscr{E}_n$ whose boundary has measure zero by the formula

(10) $$|\mathscr{D}| = \int_{\mathscr{D}} 1 \, d\alpha = \int_{\mathscr{I}} \phi(\mathscr{D}, \, \alpha) d\alpha.$$

By considering the definition of the integral as a limit, as given by (1), the reader will see that the definition of volume as given by (10) amounts to the following: Divide $\mathscr{I}$ into intervals by a partition P, select all those intervals within $\mathscr{D}$, select or do not select any intervals which contain a point of $\mathscr{D}$ and a point of $C(\mathscr{D})$, and form the sum $S(P)$ of the volumes of all intervals selected. If $\lim_{|P| \to 0} S(P) = L$, then L is the volume of $\mathscr{D}$.

Exercise 3.3 (Part I)

1. Let L be a curve of finite length $|L|$ within an interval $\mathscr{I}$ in $\mathscr{E}_2$. If f is continuous on $\mathscr{I}$ except on L, show that f is integrable on $\mathscr{I}$. *Hint:* Divide the curve into i parts of equal length $\dfrac{|L|}{i}$ by at most $i + 1$ points and describe an interval of side length $\dfrac{2|L|}{i}$ about each point.

2. Let the boundary of a bounded set $\mathscr{D}$ in $\mathscr{E}_2$ be composed of a finite number of curves each of which is represented by a continuous function of the form $y = y(x)$ or $x = x(y)$. Show that if f is a bounded continuous function on $\mathscr{D}$ then f is integrable on $\mathscr{D}$.

3. Let $y_i, \, i = 1, \ldots, n$ be integrable functions on an interval $\mathscr{I}$ in $\mathscr{E}_m$. Suppose $f(y_1, \ldots, y_n)$ is a continuous function on $\mathscr{E}_n$. Show that

   $$g(x_1, \ldots, x_m) = f(y_1(x_1, \ldots, x_m), \ldots, y_n(x_1, \ldots, x_m))$$

   is integrable on $\mathscr{I}$. *Hint:* Use Theorem 3.3C and Exercise 3,2–17.

4. Define f on $0 \le x \le 1$ by taking $f(x) = 0$ if x is irrational, $f(x) = 1/q$ if x is rational and is expressed as a fraction p/q where p and q are integers with no common divisor. Show that f is integrable on $0 \le x \le 1$.

5. By considering the definition of integral, find

   (a) $\displaystyle \lim_{n \to \infty} \frac{1^2 + 2^2 + \ldots + n^2}{n^3}$.

   (b) $\displaystyle \lim_{n \to \infty} \sum_{j=0}^{n-1} \frac{n}{n^2 + j^2}$.

6. The **Cantor set** is obtained from the closed interval $0 \le x \le 1$ by removing the open interval $\dfrac{1}{3} < x < \dfrac{2}{3}$, then removing the middle third open interval from each of the two remaining intervals $0 \le x \le \dfrac{1}{3}$ and $\dfrac{2}{3} \le x \le 1$, and continuing in this fashion removing the middle third open interval from each closed interval remaining. The points remaining constitute the Cantor set. Show that for each $\epsilon > 0$, the Cantor set can be covered by a finite number of intervals of length less than ϵ. *Hint:* At the nth step the amount removed is $2^{n-1} \left(\dfrac{1}{3} \right)^n$. What is the amount remaining after the $n - 1^{\text{st}}$ step?

7. Show that a monotone bounded function is integrable. *Hint:* Exercise 3.2–25.

8. Prove that a necessary and sufficient condition that f be integrable on $\mathscr{I}$ is that for every $\epsilon > 0$ there is a $\delta(\epsilon) > 0$ such that

(*) $|S(P_1) - S(P_2)| < \epsilon$ whenever $|P_1| < \delta, |P_2| < \delta,$

for augmented partitions P_1 and P_2. *Hint:* For a sequence P_i with norms approaching zero, the condition (*) is the Cauchy criterion for existence of a limit L. Hence there is an integer $M(\epsilon)$ such that

$$|S(P_i) - L| < \epsilon \quad \text{for } i > M(\epsilon).$$

When $|P| < \delta$, we have

$$|S(P) - L| = |S(P) - S(P_i)| + |S(P_i) - L|.$$

9. Let f be a bounded function on $\mathscr{I}$. Let α in $\mathscr{I}$ be an interior point of a sequence of intervals $\mathscr{F}_j$ with $\mathscr{F}_{j+1}$ in $\mathscr{F}_j$ such that the diameters of $\mathscr{F}_j$ approach 0 as j approaches ∞. The **oscillation** of f on $\mathscr{F}_j$ is defined by

$$\omega(f, \mathscr{F}_j) = \text{l.u.b.} \ \{f(\alpha) \mid \alpha \text{ in } \mathscr{I} \cap \mathscr{F}_j\} - \text{g.l.b.} \ \{f(\alpha) \mid \alpha \text{ in } \mathscr{I} \cap \mathscr{F}_j\}.$$

(a) Show that $\omega(f, \mathscr{F}_j)$ is a bounded decreasing function of j so that $\omega(\alpha)$ $= \omega(f, \alpha) = \lim\limits_{j \to \infty} \omega(f, \mathscr{F}_j)$ exists. This is called the **oscillation of f at** α. Show that $\omega(\alpha)$ is independent of the sequence $\mathscr{F}_j$ chosen.

(b) Show that f is continuous at α if and only if $\omega(\alpha) = 0$.

(c) Define $\mathscr{D}_n = \{\alpha \mid \omega(\alpha) \geq 1/n\}$. Show that $\mathscr{D}_n$ is contained in $\mathscr{D}_{n+1}$. Show that $\mathscr{D}_n$ is a closed set.

(d) Show that $\cup \mathscr{D}_n$ is the set of points where f is discontinuous.

(e) Let $\mathscr{F}$ be a closed set in $\mathscr{I}$ such that $\omega(\alpha) < \epsilon$ for every α in $\mathscr{F}$. Show that there is a number $\delta > 0$ such that $\omega(\mathscr{G}) < \epsilon$ whenever $\mathscr{G}$ is a subinterval of $\mathscr{F}$ with maximum diameter less than δ. *Hint:* For each α in $\mathscr{F}$ there is a $\delta(\alpha) > 0$ such that the oscillation in an n-dimensional cube with α as center and side length $8\delta(\alpha)$ is less than ϵ. Use the Heine-Borel Theorem (Exercise 3.1–17) on the set of open spheres $\|\beta - \alpha\| < \delta(\alpha)$ to obtain a finite covering of $\mathscr{F}$, and let δ be the smallest radius of the spheres in the finite covering.

10. Prove Theorem 3.3C. *Hint:* Suppose $\cup \mathscr{D}_n$ can be covered by a countable number of intervals with total volume less than ϵ. By enlarging the kth interval by less than $\epsilon/2^k$ the intervals may be enlarged into open parallelopipeds with total volume less than 2ϵ. By the Heine-Borel Theorem the set $\mathscr{D}_n$ is covered by a finite number of these parallelopipeds, $\mathscr{T}_1, \mathscr{T}_2, \ldots, \mathscr{T}_r$. In view of Exercise 9e there is a number δ such that $\omega(\mathscr{G}) < 1/n$ whenever $\mathscr{G}$ is a subinterval of $\mathscr{I} \cap C(\underset{i=1}{\overset{r}{\cup}} \mathscr{T}_i)$ with maximum diameter less than δ. Let P be a partition of $\mathscr{I}$ with norm less than δ such that the corner points of the parallelopipeds $\mathscr{I} \cap \mathscr{T}_i$ are lattice points of the partition P, i.e., are corner points of subintervals $\mathscr{I}_j$ of P. If $M \geq f \geq m$ on $\mathscr{I}$, then

$$\bar{S}(P) - \underline{S}(P) = \Sigma'(M_j - m_j)|\mathscr{I}_j| + \Sigma''(M_j - m_j)|\mathscr{I}_j|$$
$$\leq \frac{1}{n}|\mathscr{I}| + (M - m)2\epsilon$$

where Σ' refers to the sum taken over subintervals $\mathscr{I}_j$ lying in $\mathscr{I} \cap C(\cup \mathscr{T}_i)$ and Σ'' refers to the sum taken over subintervals in $\mathscr{I} \cap \cup \mathscr{T}_i$. Then f is integrable by Corollary 1 of Theorem 3.3A.

To prove the converse, let f be integrable and P_i a sequence of partitions with norm approaching zero. For n fixed and each i, we have

$$\bar{S}(P_i) - \underline{S}(P_i) = {\sum}' (M_j - m_j) |\mathscr{I}_j| + {\sum}'' (M_j - m_j) |\mathscr{I}_j| \geq \frac{1}{n} {\sum}' |\mathscr{I}_j|$$

where Σ' refers to the sum taken over subintervals where the oscillation is $\geq \frac{1}{n}$ and Σ'' refers to the sum taken over subintervals where the oscillation is $< \frac{1}{n}$. The set $\mathscr{D}_n$ is covered by $\Sigma' \mathscr{I}_j$ and the inequality shows (since the left side approaches zero as i increases) that $\Sigma' |\mathscr{I}_j|$ can be made $< \epsilon/2^n$. Hence $\cup \mathscr{D}_n$ can be covered by intervals with total volume less than ϵ.

11.   Let f be integrable in $\mathscr{I}$ and $f(\alpha) = 0$ except for a set of measure zero. Show that $\int_{\mathscr{I}} f(\alpha) d\alpha = 0$. *Hint:* Every interval contains a point α such that $f(\alpha) = 0$.

3.3.2   Part II

The fundamental properties of the integral are easily proved. The next theorem shows that the integral is a linear operator on the vector space of integrable functions defined over a rectangle $\mathscr{I}$ in $\mathscr{E}_n$.

THEOREM 3.3D   If f and g are integrable on $\mathscr{I}$ and a and b are real numbers, then

$$\int_{\mathscr{I}} \left(a f(\alpha) + b g(\alpha) \right) d\alpha = a \int_{\mathscr{I}} f(\alpha) d\alpha + b \int_{\mathscr{I}} g(\alpha) d\alpha.$$

Proof   The function $af + bg$ was proved to be integrable on $\mathscr{I}$ in Example 1. The sum $S(P)$ for any augmented partition for the function $af + bg$ may be written

$$(11) \quad S(P) = \sum_j (a f(\alpha_j) + bg(\alpha_j)) |\mathscr{I}_j| = a \sum_j f(\alpha_j) |\mathscr{I}_j| + b \sum_j g(\alpha_j) |\mathscr{I}_j|.$$

There exists $\delta(\epsilon) > 0$ such that, whenever $|P| < \delta$, the right side of (11), and hence the left side, differs from

$$a \int_{\mathscr{I}} f(\alpha) d\alpha + b \int_{\mathscr{I}} g(\alpha) d\alpha$$

by less than ϵ. This proves the theorem.   ★

THEOREM 3.3E   If f and g are integrable on $\mathscr{I}$ and $f(\alpha) \leq g(\alpha)$ for α in $\mathscr{I}$ then

$$\int_{\mathscr{I}} f(\alpha) d\alpha \leq \int_{\mathscr{I}} g(\alpha) d\alpha.$$

Proof It is clear from the definition of integral that if $h(\alpha) \geq 0$, then $\int_{\mathscr{I}} h(\alpha) d\alpha \geq 0$. It follows that

$$\int_{\mathscr{I}} (g(\alpha) - f(\alpha)) \, d\alpha \geq 0.$$

Use of Theorem 3.3D now shows that

$$\int_{\mathscr{I}} g(\alpha) d\alpha - \int_{\mathscr{I}} f(\alpha) d\alpha \geq 0. \quad \star$$

The previous results can be extended to integrals over a bounded set $\mathscr{D}$ in an interval $\mathscr{I}$ in $\mathscr{E}_n$ when the boundary of $\mathscr{D}$ has n-dimensional measure zero.

THEOREM 3.3F Let f and g be integrable on $\mathscr{D}$, and a and b be real numbers.

a. $\displaystyle\int_{\mathscr{D}} (a f(\alpha) + b g(\alpha)) \, d\alpha = a \int_{\mathscr{D}} f(\alpha) d\alpha + b \int_{\mathscr{D}} g(\alpha) d\alpha,$

b. If $f(\alpha) \leq g(\alpha)$ for α in $\mathscr{D}$, then $\displaystyle\int_{\mathscr{D}} f(\alpha) d\alpha \leq \int_{\mathscr{D}} g(\alpha) d\alpha.$

c. $\displaystyle\left| \int_{\mathscr{D}} f(\alpha) d\alpha \right| \leq \int_{\mathscr{D}} |f(\alpha)| \, d\alpha,$

d. If $m \leq f(\alpha) \leq M$ for α in $\mathscr{D}$, then $m \, |\mathscr{D}| \leq \displaystyle\int_{\mathscr{D}} f(\alpha) d\alpha \leq M \, |\mathscr{D}|.$

Proof We have

$$\int_{\mathscr{D}} (a f(\alpha) + b g(\alpha)) d\alpha = \int_{\mathscr{I}} (a f(\alpha) + b g(\alpha)) \, \phi \, (\mathscr{D}, \alpha) d\alpha$$

$$= a \int_{\mathscr{I}} f(\alpha) \phi(\mathscr{D}, \alpha) d\alpha + b \int_{\mathscr{I}} g(\alpha) \phi(\mathscr{D}, \alpha) d\alpha = a \int_{\mathscr{D}} f(\alpha) d\alpha + b \int_{\mathscr{D}} g(\alpha) d\alpha.$$

The second result is proved similarly, for if $f(\alpha) \leq g(\alpha)$, α in $\mathscr{D}$, then $f(\alpha)\phi(\mathscr{D}, \alpha) \leq g(\alpha)\phi(\mathscr{D}, \alpha)$ for α in $\mathscr{I}$. The third and fourth results follow from the second since

$$- |f(\alpha)| \leq f(\alpha) \leq |f(\alpha)| \quad \text{and} \quad m \leq f(\alpha) \leq M$$

imply

$$- \int_{\mathscr{D}} |f(\alpha)| \, d\alpha \leq \int_{\mathscr{D}} f(\alpha) d\alpha \leq \int_{\mathscr{D}} |f(\alpha)| \, d\alpha$$

and

$$m \int_{\mathscr{D}} 1 \, d\alpha \leq \int_{\mathscr{D}} f(\alpha) d\alpha \leq M \int_{\mathscr{D}} 1 \, d\alpha. \quad \star$$

For the following theorem we shall assume that the sets $\mathscr{D}$, $\mathscr{D}_1$, $\mathscr{D}_2$ are all in an interval $\mathscr{I}$ in $\mathscr{E}_n$ and that their boundaries have n-dimensional measure zero. Two sets $\mathscr{D}_1$ and $\mathscr{D}_2$ are called **disjoint** if they have no points in common, that is, if $\mathscr{D}_1 \cap \mathscr{D}_2$ is the empty set.

THEOREM 3.3G

a.   If $\mathscr{D}_1$ and $\mathscr{D}_2$ are disjoint and f is integrable on $\mathscr{D}_1$ and on $\mathscr{D}_2$, then f is integrable on $\mathscr{D} = \mathscr{D}_1 \cup \mathscr{D}_2$ and

$$\int_{\mathscr{D}} f(\alpha)d\alpha = \int_{\mathscr{D}_1} f(\alpha)d\alpha + \int_{\mathscr{D}_2} f(\alpha)d\alpha,$$

b.   If f is integrable on $\mathscr{D}_1$, and $\mathscr{D}_2$ is contained in $\mathscr{D}_1$ then f is integrable on $\mathscr{D}_2$.

c.   If $\mathscr{D}$ has measure zero, and f is a bounded function then $\int_{\mathscr{D}} f(\alpha)d\alpha = 0$.

d.   If f and g are integrable on $\mathscr{D}$ and differ only on a set $\mathscr{D}_1$ (in $\mathscr{D}$) which has measure zero, then

$$\int_{\mathscr{D}} f(\alpha)d\alpha = \int_{\mathscr{D}} g(\alpha)d\alpha.$$

e.   If $f \geq 0$ is integrable on $\mathscr{D}$ and $\int_{\mathscr{D}} f(\alpha)d\alpha = 0$, then $f = 0$ on $\mathscr{D}$, with the possible exception of a set of measure zero.

Proof

a.   It is clear, when $\mathscr{D}_1$ and $\mathscr{D}_2$ are disjoint and $\mathscr{D} = \mathscr{D}_1 \cup \mathscr{D}_2$, that

$$\phi(\mathscr{D}, \alpha) = \phi(\mathscr{D}_1, \alpha) + \phi(\mathscr{D}_2, \alpha).$$

The function f is integrable on $\mathscr{D}$ since the set of points of discontinuity on $\mathscr{D}$ has measure zero. Write

$$\int_{\mathscr{D}} f(\alpha)d\alpha = \int_{\mathscr{J}} f(\alpha)\, \phi(\mathscr{D}, \alpha)d\alpha = \int_{\mathscr{J}} f(\alpha)\, \phi(\mathscr{D}_1, \alpha)d\alpha$$

$$+ \int_{\mathscr{J}} f(\alpha)\, \phi(\mathscr{D}_2, \alpha)d\alpha = \int_{\mathscr{D}_1} f(\alpha)d\alpha + \int_{\mathscr{D}_2} f(\alpha)d\alpha.$$

b.   To prove the second part, merely note that the points of discontinuity of f interior to $\mathscr{D}_2$ are contained in the set of points of discontinuity of f on $\mathscr{D}_1$.

c.   The third part follows from Theorem 3.3F **d**. Note that f is integrable on $\mathscr{D}$ since the set of points of discontinuity of f on $\mathscr{D}$ has measure zero.

d. Let f and g be integrable on $\mathscr{D}$ and differ on a set $\mathscr{D}_1$ of measure zero. Then

$$\int_{\mathscr{D}} (f-g)d\alpha = \int_{\mathscr{I}} (f-g)\phi(\mathscr{D})d\alpha = \int_{\mathscr{I}} (f-g)\phi(\mathscr{D}_1)d\alpha = \int_{\mathscr{D}_1} (f-g)d\alpha.$$

The last integral is zero by part **c**, yielding

$$\int_{\mathscr{D}} f(\alpha)d\alpha - \int_{\mathscr{D}} g(\alpha)d\alpha = 0.$$

e. The set of interior points of $\mathscr{D}$ which are discontinuity points of f form a set of measure zero. If $f(\alpha) = 0$ at all interior points which are points of continuity, then the desired result is true. Suppose then that $f(\alpha) = k \neq 0$ at some interior point α of $\mathscr{D}$ which is a continuity point of f. By continuity, there is an interval $\mathscr{I}_1$ in $\mathscr{D}$ containing α in which $f(\alpha) > k/2$. If $\mathscr{D}_1$ is the set of points in $\mathscr{D}$ not in $\mathscr{I}_1$, then, using **b** and **a**,

$$0 = \int_{\mathscr{D}} f(\alpha)d\alpha = \int_{\mathscr{I}_1} f(\alpha)d\alpha + \int_{\mathscr{D}_1} f(\alpha)d\alpha \geq \frac{k}{2}|\mathscr{I}_1|$$

since $\int_{\mathscr{D}_1} f(\alpha)d\alpha \geq 0$. This contradiction proves that $f = 0$ at all interior points which are points of continuity.   ★

A word of caution is in order. Part **d** of the theorem does not state that if f is integrable on $\mathscr{D}$ and $g(\alpha) = f(\alpha)$ except for a set $\mathscr{D}_1$ of measure zero, then $\int_{\mathscr{D}} g(\alpha)\,d\alpha = \int_{\mathscr{D}} f(\alpha)\,d\alpha$. For g may not be integrable on $\mathscr{D}$ if the boundary of $\mathscr{D}_1$ does not have measure zero. For example, let $\mathscr{I}$ be the one-dimensional interval $0 \leq x \leq 1$ and $\mathscr{D}_1$ be the set of rationals on $0 \leq x \leq 1$. $\mathscr{D}_1$ is countable and by Example 2, $\mathscr{D}_1$ has measure 0. However, the boundary of $\mathscr{D}_1$ is $\mathscr{I}$ itself. If $f = 1$ on $\mathscr{I}$, and we define

$$g(\alpha) = \begin{cases} 0 & \text{if } \alpha \text{ is in } \mathscr{D}_1, \\ 1 & \text{if } \alpha \text{ is not in } \mathscr{D}_1, \end{cases}$$

then g, although differing from f only on a set of measure zero, is not integrable on $\mathscr{I}$, since the set of points of discontinuity of g is $\mathscr{I}$ which does not have measure zero.

Let us now consider the special case of a one-dimensional interval $\mathscr{I} = \{x \mid a \leq x \leq b\}$. Define

(12) $$\int_a^b f(x)dx = \int_{\mathscr{I}} f(x)dx.$$

When $a \leq b$, define

(13)
$$\begin{cases} \int_b^a f(x)dx = -\int_a^b f(x)dx. \\ \int_a^a f(x)dx = 0. \end{cases}$$

THEOREM 3.3H   If r, s, t are any three points in $\mathscr{I}$ and f is integrable on $\mathscr{I}$, then

$$\int_r^s f(x)dx + \int_s^t f(x)dx = \int_r^t f(x)dx.$$

Proof   Suppose first that $r < s < t$.

Let $\mathscr{D}_1 = \{x \mid r \leq x \leq s\}$, $\mathscr{D}_2 = \{x \mid s < x \leq t\}$, $\mathscr{D}_3 = \{x \mid x = s\}$. By parts **(b)** and **(a)** of Theorem 3.3G, f is integrable on $\mathscr{D}_1$, $\mathscr{D}_2$, and $\mathscr{D}_3$ and

$$\int_r^t f(x)dx = \int_{\mathscr{D}_1} f(x)dx + \int_{\mathscr{D}_2} f(x)dx = \int_r^s f(x)dx + \int_{\mathscr{D}_2} f(x)dx + \int_{\mathscr{D}_3} f(x)dx$$

since $\int_{\mathscr{D}_3} f(x)dx = 0$, $\mathscr{D}_3$ being of measure zero. By part **(a)** of Theorem 3.3G, the sum of the last two integrals is just $\int_s^t f(x)dx$. Suppose next $s < r < t$. By what has just been proved

$$\int_s^r f(x)dx + \int_r^t f(x)dx = \int_s^t f(x)dx$$

so that

$$\int_r^t f(x)dx = \int_s^t f(x)dx - \int_s^r f(x)dx = \int_s^t f(x)dx + \int_r^s f(x)dx.$$

The other cases are handled in a similar fashion.   ★

When f is integrable on $\mathscr{I}$, the function g given by

(14)
$$g(y) = \int_a^y f(x)dx$$

is defined on $\mathscr{I}$ and is called an **indefinite integral** of f. The next theorem shows that differentiation is an operation inverse to integration.

THEOREM 3.3I   The function g defined by (14) is continuous. At each point of continuity of f, g has a derivative given by $g'(t) = f(t)$. (At the points a and b, the derivative is one-sided.)

Proof The equality

$$g(y) - g(t) = \int_a^y f(x)dx - \int_a^t f(x)dx = \int_t^y f(x)dx$$

and Theorem 3.3F yield

$$|g(y) - g(t)| \leq \left| \int_t^y |f(x)| \, dx \right| \leq M \, |y - t|$$

where $|f(x)| \leq M$ on $\mathscr{I}$. The continuity is a direct consequence of this last inequality.

Suppose now that f is continuous at t so that for given $\epsilon > 0$ there is a $\delta(\epsilon)$ such that

$$\bullet \quad |f(x) - f(t)| < \epsilon \quad \text{when} \quad |x - t| < \delta.$$

Then, when $0 < |y - t| < \delta$,

$$\left| \frac{g(y) - g(t)}{y - t} - f(t) \right| = \left| \frac{1}{y - t} \left(\int_t^y f(x)dx - \int_t^y f(t)dx \right) \right|$$

$$\leq \frac{1}{|y - t|} \left| \int_t^y |f(x) - f(t)| \, dx \right| \leq \frac{1}{|y - t|} \left| \int_t^y \epsilon \, dx \right| = \epsilon.$$

This proves $g'(t) = \lim\limits_{y \to t} \dfrac{g(y) - g(t)}{y - t} = f(t)$. ★

As yet we have not given a method for the evaluation of the definite integral. For a continuous function, this is provided by

THEOREM 3.3J If g has an integrable derivative g' on $a \leq x \leq b$ then

$$\int_a^b g'(x) \, dx = g(b) - g(a).$$

Proof For any partition $a = y_0 < y_1 \cdots < y_n = b$, apply the mean value theorem and write

$$g(b) - g(a) = \sum_{i=1}^n g(y_i) - g(y_{i-1}) = \sum_{i=1}^n g'(z_i)(y_i - y_{i-1})$$

where $y_{i-1} < z_i < y_i$. Using a sequence of partitions with norm approaching zero, we obtain a sequence of such equalities with the right sides converging to $\int_a^b g'(x) \, dx$. ★

When f is continuous on $a \le x \le b$, the function g given by (14) satisfies $g' = f$, so that

$$\int_a^b f(x)dx = g(b) - g(a).$$

The evaluation of an n-dimensional integral is usually reduced to the evaluation of an iterated integral, which is a totally different concept. Let us consider the two-dimensional case. The **iterated integral**

(15)
$$\int_c^d \left(\int_a^b f(x, y) \, dx \right) dy$$

(the parentheses are usually omitted) stands for a combination of two single integrals. It is just

$$\int_c^d w(y) \, dy$$

where

(16)
$$w(y) = \int_a^b f(x, y) \, dx.$$

EXAMPLE 5

Let $f(x, y) = \begin{cases} 0, & y \text{ rational, } 0 \le y \le 1, \\ 1, & y \text{ irrational, } 0 < y < 1, 0 \le x < \frac{1}{2}, \\ -1, & y \text{ irrational, } 0 < y < 1, \frac{1}{2} \le x \le 1. \end{cases}$

Then for each y we have $\int_0^1 f(x, y) \, dx = 0$ and

$$\int_0^1 \int_0^1 f(x, y) \, dx \, dy = 0.$$

However, the two-dimensional integral $\int_{\mathscr{I}} f(\alpha)d\alpha$, where

$$\mathscr{I} = \{(x, y) \mid 0 \le x \le 1, 0 \le y \le 1\}$$

does not exist, since f is discontinuous at every point.

THEOREM 3.3K   Let $\mathscr{I} = \{(x, y) \mid a \le x \le b, c \le y \le d\}$. If $\int_{\mathscr{I}} f(\alpha)d\alpha$ and $\int_c^d \int_a^b f(x, y)dx \, dy$ both exist, they must be equal. In fact, the conclusion holds if $\int_{\mathscr{I}} f(\alpha)d\alpha$ exists and $\int_a^b f(x,y)dx$ exists for every y, $c \le y \le d$.

Proof The existence of $\int_{\mathscr{I}} f(\alpha)d\alpha$ implies the existence of $\delta(\epsilon)$ such that

$$\left| \int_{\mathscr{I}} f(\alpha)d\alpha - \sum_j f(\alpha_j) \, |\mathscr{I}_j| \right| < \epsilon/2$$

for every augmented partition with norm $|P| < \delta$. Let $w(y)$ be defined by (16), and let $c = y_0 < y_1 < \cdots < y_n = d$ be a partition of $c \leq y \leq d$ with norm $|P_1| < \delta/2$. Let y'_j be a point in the interval $y_{j-1} \leq y \leq y_j$ of length $\Delta y_j = y_j - y_{j-1}$ and form the sum

$$\sum_j w(y'_j) \, \Delta y_j = \sum_j \int_a^b f(x, y'_j)dx \, \Delta y_j.$$

There exists $\delta_1 < \delta/2$ such that, for every j,

$$\left| \int_a^b f(x, y'_j)dx - \sum_i f(x'_i, y'_j)\Delta x_i \right| < \epsilon/2(d - c)$$

whenever $a = x_0 < x_1 < \cdots < x_m = b$ is a partition of $a \leq x \leq b$ with norm $|P_2| < \delta_1$ and x'_i is in the interval $x_{i-1} \leq x \leq x_i$, whose length is $\Delta x_i = x_i - x_{i-1}$. The partitions P_1 and P_2 and the points (x'_i, y'_j) form an augmented partition P of $\mathscr{I}$ with $|P| < \delta$.

We have

$$\left| \sum_j w(y'_j)\Delta y_j - \int_{\mathscr{I}} f(\alpha)d\alpha \right| \leq$$

$$\left| \sum_j \left(\int_a^b f(x, y'_j)dx - \sum_i f(x'_i, y'_j)\Delta x_i \right)\Delta y_j \right| + \left| \sum_j \sum_i f(x'_i, y'_j)\Delta x_i\Delta y_j \right.$$

$$\left. - \int_{\mathscr{I}} f(\alpha)d\alpha \right| \leq \frac{\epsilon}{2(d - c)} \left| \sum_j \Delta y_j \right| + \frac{\epsilon}{2} = \epsilon.$$

This proves that $\int_c^d \int_a^b f(x, y)dx \, dy$ exists and is equal to $\int_{\mathscr{I}} f(\alpha)d\alpha$. ★

From Theorem 3.3K we obtain a theorem on interchange of order of integration of an iterated integral.

Corollary

If $\int_{\mathscr{I}} f(\alpha)d\alpha, \int_c^d \int_a^b f(x, y)dx \, dy, \int_a^b \int_c^d f(x,y)dy \, dx$ all exist, then they are all equal.

EXAMPLE 6 Evaluate

$$\int_0^a \int_0^{\frac{b}{a}x} \sin\left((a - \frac{a}{b}y)^2\right) dy\, dx.$$

The iterated integral may also be written as

$$\int_0^a \int_0^{\frac{b}{a}x} \sin\left((a - \frac{a}{b}y)^2\right)\phi(\mathcal{D})\, dy\, dx = \int_0^a \int_0^b \sin\left((a - \frac{a}{b}y)^2\right)\phi(\mathcal{D})\, dy\, dx$$

where $\mathcal{D} = \left\{(x, y) \mid 0 \le y \le \frac{b}{a}x, 0 \le x \le a\right\}$. By Theorem 3.3K the iterated integral may also be considered as a double integral over the set $\mathcal{D}$.

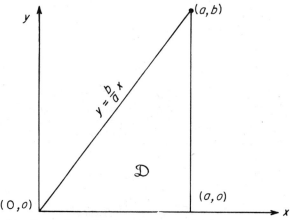

Interchanging the order of integration we obtain

$$\int_0^b \int_0^a \sin\left((a - \frac{a}{b}y)^2\right)\phi(\mathcal{D})\, dx\, dy = \int_0^b \int_{\frac{a}{b}y}^a \sin\left((a - \frac{a}{b}y)^2\right) dx\, dy$$

$$= \int_0^b (a - \frac{a}{b}y) \sin\left((a - \frac{a}{b}y)^2\right) dy = \frac{b}{2a} \cos\left((a - \frac{a}{b}y)^2\right)\Big|_0^b = \frac{b}{2a}(1 - \cos a^2).$$

The limits on the iterated integral taken first with respect to x and then with respect to y may be taken from the sketch of $\mathcal{D}$ or may be derived analytically. It is only necessary to note that the pairs (x, y) satisfying $0 \le y \le \frac{b}{a}x, 0 \le x \le a$ are exactly those satisfying $\frac{a}{b}y \le x \le a, 0 \le y \le b$.

The method of Theorem 3.3K may be used to obtain the following result: Let $\mathcal{I} = \{(x_1, \ldots x_n) \mid a_i \le x_i \le b_i, i = 1, \ldots, n\}$, and suppose $\int_{\mathcal{I}} f(\alpha)d\alpha$ exists. Then

(17) $$\int_{a_n}^{b_n} \ldots \int_{a_1}^{b_1} f(x_1, \ldots, x_n)dx_1 \ldots dx_n = \int_{\mathcal{I}} f(\alpha)d\alpha$$

if the integral on the left of (17) exists.

The last two theorems in this section are concerned with sequences of functions. Theorem 3.3L is not the most general result of its type available, but will suffice for our immediate purpose.

THEOREM 3.3L   If $\{f_n\}$ converges uniformly to f on the bounded set $\mathcal{D}$ in $\mathcal{E}_n$, and f_n are integrable on $\mathcal{D}$, then

$$\lim_{n\to\infty} \int_{\mathcal{D}} f_n(\alpha)d\alpha = \int_{\mathcal{D}} f(\alpha)d\alpha = \int_{\mathcal{D}} \lim_{n=\infty} f_n(\alpha)d\alpha.$$

Proof   We must show that f is integrable. By covering the set of points of discontinuity of f_n by a sequence of intervals with total volume less than $\dfrac{\epsilon}{2^n}$, it is seen that we may cover the set of points which are points of discontinuity for any f_n by a sequence of intervals of volume less than $\sum_n \dfrac{\epsilon}{2^n} = \epsilon$. Every other point is a point of continuity of all f_n and hence of f by Theorem 3.2F. Therefore the discontinuity points of f form a set of measure zero and f is integrable.

For $n > N(\epsilon)$, we have $|f_n(\alpha) - f(\alpha)| < \epsilon/|\mathcal{D}|$. Using Theorem 3.3F **d**, we obtain

$$\left| \int_{\mathcal{D}} f_n(\alpha)d\alpha - \int_{\mathcal{D}} f(\alpha)d\alpha \right| \le \int_{\mathcal{D}} |f_n(\alpha) - f(\alpha)|d\alpha < \epsilon.$$

This yields the theorem.   ★

Corollary

If g_n are integrable on $\mathcal{D}$ and $\sum_n g_n$ converges uniformly to g on $\mathcal{D}$, then $\int_{\mathcal{D}} g(\alpha)d\alpha = \sum_n \int_{\mathcal{D}} g_n(\alpha)d\alpha$.

THEOREM 3.3M   Let f_n have continuous derivatives f_n' on the interval $\mathcal{I} = \{x \mid a \le x \le b\}$. If $\{f_n'\}$ converges uniformly on $\mathcal{I}$, and $\{f_n\}$ converges to f on $\mathcal{I}$, then f is differentiable on $\mathcal{I}$ and $f' = \lim_{n\to\infty} f_n'$.

Proof   Let $g = \lim_{n\to\infty} f_n'$. By Theorem 3.3L, for $a \le y \le b$,

$$\int_a^y g(x)dx = \lim_{n\to\infty} \int_a^y f_n'(x)dx = \lim_{n\to\infty} f_n(y) - f_n(a) = f(y) - f(a).$$

The derivative of the left side, and hence of the right, is $g(y) = f'(y)$.   ★

Corollary

If g_n have continuous derivatives on $a \leq x \leq b$, $\sum\limits_{n=1}^{\infty} g_n$ converges to g, and $\sum\limits_{n=1}^{\infty} g_n'$ converges uniformly on the interval, then $g' = \sum\limits_{n=1}^{\infty} g_n'$.

Up to now we have been considering real valued functions. The extension to complex functions on $\mathscr{E}_n^*$ is readily made. If $f = u + iv$, where $i^2 = -1$ and u and v are real valued, then

$$\int_{\mathscr{D}} f(\alpha)d\alpha = \int_{\mathscr{D}} u(\alpha)d\alpha + i \int_{\mathscr{D}} v(\alpha)d\alpha$$

whenever the right side exists. It is then possible to prove, for complex functions, Theorems 3.3F **a** and **c**; 3.3G **a, b, c, d**; 3.3H; 3.3I, 3.3J, 3.3K, 3.3L and 3.3M. Most of the proofs follow directly from the corresponding theorems for real functions. Theorem 3.3F **c** presents some difficulties, and is left as Exercise 3.3–23.

The integral defined in this section is called the **Riemann Integral**, named after G. F. B. Riemann (1826–66) who gave the theory its definitive form. It is to be noted that it is defined for a bounded function on a bounded set. In fact, if the function is unbounded, the sums $S(P)$ in the definition can be made arbitrarily large and the integral cannot exist. It is possible to define an integral when the function is unbounded. For example if f is bounded and integrable on $a \leq x \leq c < b$ we define

$$\int_a^b f(x)dx = \lim_{c \to b} \int_a^c f(x)dx.$$

Similarly it is possible to define

$$\int_a^{\infty} f(x)dx = \lim_{N \to \infty} \int_a^N f(x)dx$$

when f is bounded and integrable on $a \leq x \leq N$ for every N. Such integrals are referred to as **improper** integrals.

In modern mathematics, Riemann's definition has been superseded by a more general one due to H. L. Lebesgue (1875–1941). The latter has the following advantages: (a) The class of Lebesgue integrable functions is larger than the class of Riemann integrable functions. The Lebesgue integral of any Riemann integrable function is equal to its Riemann integral. The Lebesgue integral may be defined directly for unbounded functions and for unbounded sets. (b) The Lebesgue integral is better adapted to formal procedures. For example, values of an integrable function may be changed on any set of measure zero without changing the value of its integral. It is not necessary to impose restrictions on the boundary of the set where the integral is defined. In certain theorems on term by term integration, the integrability of the limit function is assured and need not be hypothesized.

For the purposes of this book it is not necessary to use the Lebesgue integral. However the generalizations of the theory to be given in the next chapter (and these generalizations are needed for many important physical applications) demand a knowledge of Lebesgue integration. The reader is encouraged to become acquainted with the modern theory of integration, a subject of considerable elegance and usefulness.

Exercise 3.3 (Part II)

12. Show that if f is continuous on $a \le x \le b$ and $f(x) \ge 0$, then $\int_a^b f(x)dx = 0$ implies $f(x) = 0$ for all x on $a \le x \le b$.

13. Explain the paradox,

$$0 < \int_0^\pi \sec^2 x \, dx = \tan x \Big|_0^\pi = 0.$$

14. (a) Prove that $\dfrac{1}{2^a} \le \displaystyle\int_0^1 \dfrac{dx}{(x^p + 1)^a} \le 1$,   if $p \ge 0$, $a \ge 0$.

    (b) Prove that $\frac{1}{2} < \displaystyle\int_0^1 \dfrac{dx}{(4 - x^2 + x^3)^{1/2}} < \pi/6$.

15. Use Theorem 3.3F**d** and Exercise 3.2–9(c) to show that if f is continuous on $a \le x \le b$, then there is a value y on $a \le x \le b$ such that

$$\int_a^b f(x)dx = f(y)(b - a).$$

Now show that we may choose y so that $a < y < b$. *Hint:* If, say, $\int_a^b f(x)dx$
$= f(a)(b - a)$, then $\int_a^b \Big(f(x) - f(a)\Big)dx = 0$. If $f(x) = f(a)$ for all x, the desired result is true. Otherwise, by Exercise 12, $f(x) - f(a)$ is positive for some x and negative for others, yielding a value y, $a < y < b$, such that $f(y) - f(a) = 0$.

16. Prove: If f is continuous on $a \le x \le b$, if g has a continuous derivative on $c \le y \le d$, $g(c) = a$, $g(d) = b$, and $a \le g(y) \le b$ when $c \le y \le d$, then

$$\int_a^b f(x)dx = \int_c^d f(g(y))\, g'(y)dy.$$

Hint: Let $h(z) = \displaystyle\int_a^z f(x)dx$. Then $\displaystyle\int_a^b f(x)dx = h(b) - h(a) = h(g(d)) - h(g(c))$.
Find the derivative of $h(g(y))$.

17. Prove: If f is integrable on $a \le x \le b$, if g is strictly monotone increasing and has a continuous derivative on $c \le y \le d$, $g(c) = a$, $g(d) = b$, then the formula given in Exercise 16 is valid. *Hint:* Show that $f(g(y)) g'(y)$ is integrable by considering the possible discontinuities. Then write

$$\Sigma f(\alpha_i)\Delta x_i = \Sigma f(g(\beta_i))g'(\sigma_i)\Delta y_i, \quad y_{i-1} \le \sigma_i \le y_i,$$

using the mean value theorem. Let the norm of the partition on the left approach 0. Show that the right side does not differ much from

$$\Sigma f(g(\beta_i))g'(\beta_i)\Delta y_i.$$

18. Explain the paradox

$$\int_{-1}^{1} \frac{dx}{1 + x^2} = \left. \text{arc tan } x \right|_{-1}^{1} = \frac{\pi}{2}$$

while the change of variable $x = 1/y$ yields

$$\int_{-1}^{1} \frac{dx}{1 + x^2} = -\int_{-1}^{1} \frac{dy}{1 + y^2} = -\frac{\pi}{2}.$$

19. (a) If f is integrable on $a \le x \le b$, show that

$$\int_{a}^{b} f(x)dx = \int_{a}^{b} f(a + b - x)dx,$$

   (b) If f is continuous on $0 \le x \le 1$, show that

$$\int_{0}^{\pi/2} f(\sin x)dx = \int_{0}^{\pi/2} f(\cos x)dx.$$

20. (a) If $f(x) = -f(-x)$ for all x, f is called an **odd function**. Show that for an integrable odd function,

$$\int_{-a}^{0} f(x)dx = -\int_{0}^{a} f(x)dx \text{ and } \int_{-a}^{a} f(x)dx = 0.$$

   (b) If $f(x) = f(-x)$ for all x, f is called an **even function**. Show that for an integrable even function,

$$\int_{-a}^{0} f(x)dx = \int_{0}^{a} f(x)dx = \tfrac{1}{2}\int_{-a}^{a} f(x)dx.$$

21. If f and g have integrable derivatives on $a \le x \le b$, then

$$\int_{a}^{b} fg' \, dx = \left. fg \right|_{a}^{b} - \int_{a}^{b} f'g \, dx.$$

Prove this by beginning with the formula

$$\frac{d}{dx}(fg) = fg' + f'g.$$

22.   Consider the function defined by

$$f(x, y) = \begin{cases} \dfrac{x - y}{(x + y)^3} & \text{when } 0 \le x \le 1,\, 0 \le y \le 1, \text{ but } (x, y) \ne (0, 0), \\ 0 & \text{when } (x, y) = (0, 0). \end{cases}$$

(a)   By integration by parts, show, when $x \ne 0$, that

$$\int_0^1 f(x, y)dy = \frac{1}{(1 + x)^2}. \text{ Hence } \lim_{x \to 0} \int_0^1 f(x, y)dy \ne \int_0^1 \lim_{x \to 0} f(x, y)dy.$$

(b)   Show that $\displaystyle\int_0^1 \int_0^1 f(x, y)dy\, dx = \tfrac{1}{2}$, while $\displaystyle\int_0^1 \int_0^1 f(x, y)dx\, dy = -\tfrac{1}{2}.$

Does this contradict the corollary to Theorem 3.3K?

23.   Prove that $\left| \int_{\mathscr{D}} f(\alpha)d\alpha \right| \le \int_{\mathscr{D}} |f(\alpha)|\,d\alpha$ when f is complex valued. *Hint:* Consider first the integral over an interval $\mathscr{I}$.

$$\left| \int_{\mathscr{I}} f(\alpha)d\alpha \right| = \left| \lim_{|P| \to 0} \sum_j u(\alpha_j)\,|\mathscr{I}_j| + i \lim_{|P| \to 0} \sum_j v(\alpha_j)\,|\mathscr{I}_j| \right|$$

$$= \lim_{|P| \to 0} \left| \sum_j f(\alpha_j)|\mathscr{I}_j| \right| \le \lim_{|P| \to 0} \sum_j |f(\alpha_j)|\,|\mathscr{I}_j| = \int_{\mathscr{I}} |f(\alpha)|\, d\alpha.$$

24.   Can a sufficiently differentiable function always be written as a definite integral? Show that it is not possible to find a constant a such that $e^x = \int_a^x f(t)dt$ for a continuous function f.

25.   Write down five equivalent forms of

$$\int_0^a \int_0^y \int_0^x f(x, y, z)dz\, dx\, dy$$

obtained by changing the order of integration.

26.   Integrate

$$\int_0^a \int_0^x \frac{1}{b^2 + (y - a)^2}\, dy\, dx$$

by changing the order of integration. Obtain the same result by direct integration.

27.   Show that $\displaystyle\lim_{n \to \infty} \int_0^2 (\sin^{2n} x)(\cos^2 7x)x^4\, dx = 0.$

28. Let $f_n(x) = \dfrac{1}{n} e^{-n^2 x^2}$. Show that $\{f_n\}$ converges uniformly on $-\infty < x < \infty$ to a function f with continuous derivatives. Show that $\lim\limits_{n \to \infty} f_n' = f'$ but $\{f_n'\}$ does not converge uniformly on $-1 \leq x \leq 1$.

29. Show that

(a) $\displaystyle \int_0^1 \int_y^1 e^{y/x}\, dx\, dy = \dfrac{e-1}{2}.$

(b) $\displaystyle \int_1^2 \int_{2/x}^2 y\, e^{xy}\, dy\, dx = \dfrac{e^4 - 3e^2}{2}.$

CHAPTER
4

An Integral
Operator

4.1

THE KERNEL OF AN
INTEGRAL OPERATOR

For an introduction to some of the concepts involved in the study of linear transformations whose domain is an infinite dimensional Euclidean vector space, it is preferable to restrict the discussion to a particular vector space and a particular linear transformation.

Let $\mathscr{R} = \mathscr{R}\{a, b\}$ be the set of real valued Riemann integrable functions on the finite interval $a \leq x \leq b$. These functions will be the elements of our vector space and therefore, in conformity with our original notation, will be denoted by Greek letters. If α and β are in $\mathscr{R}$, we define $\alpha + \beta$, $c\alpha$ for real c, and (α, β) by

$$(\alpha + \beta)(x) = \alpha(x) + \beta(x),$$
$$(c\alpha)(x) = c\alpha(x),$$
$$(\alpha, \beta) = \int_a^b \alpha(x)\beta(x)dx.$$

Then $\mathscr{R}$ satisfies all of the axioms for a Euclidean vector space except positivity of the inner product. We may overcome this difficulty by introducing a new relation, **equivalence** $\cong$, between the vectors. Define

$\alpha \cong \beta$ if α and β differ at most on a set of zero measure.

This may be rephrased as

$$\alpha \cong \beta \text{ if } \int_a^b |\alpha - \beta|^2 \, dx = 0$$

in view of Theorem 3.3G. We proceed as in Example 4 of Section 1.1. If $\alpha \cong \beta$, then we have $\alpha \cong \alpha$, $\beta \cong \alpha$, and $\alpha \cong \mu$ whenever $\beta \cong \mu$. For any vector μ, if $\alpha \cong \beta$, we have $\alpha + \mu \cong \beta + \mu$, $c\alpha \cong c\beta$, $(\alpha, \mu) = (\beta, \mu)$. Moreover, we have $(\alpha, \alpha) = 0$ if and only if $\alpha \cong \theta$. In this way we obtain a Euclidean vector space with the relation $=$ between vectors replaced by $\cong$. However, we shall replace the symbol $\cong$ by $=$, keeping in mind that $\alpha = \beta$ means α and β differ at most on a set of measure zero.

The theory to be developed could have been restricted to the class of continuous functions or the class $\mathscr{P}$ of piecewise continuous functions (see

Section 1.1). Since the formal manipulations are not changed, we may as well develop the theory for the class $\mathscr{R}$.

Let $K(x, y)$ be a real continuous function defined on the square $a \leq x \leq b$, $a \leq y \leq b$. It induces a linear transformation K on $\mathscr{R}$ to $\mathscr{R}$ by means of the formula

(1)
$$\beta(x) = \int_a^b K(x, y) \, \alpha(y) dy, \qquad a \leq x \leq b,$$

which we abbreviate $\beta = K\alpha$. The function $K(x, y)$ is called the **kernel** of the integral transformation K.

The range of K is not all of $\mathscr{R}$. In fact K carries every α into a continuous function. To see this, recall that the function $K(x, y)$, continuous on a bounded closed set, is uniformly continuous. Therefore, for $\epsilon > 0$, there is a $\delta(\epsilon) > 0$ such that, if x_1, x_2, y_1, y_2 lie in $a \leq x \leq b$, then

(2) $|K(x_1, y_1) - K(x_2, y_2)| < \epsilon$ whenever $|x_1 - x_2| < \delta, |y_1 - y_2| < \delta$.

It follows that

$$|K\alpha(x) - K\alpha(t)| = |\int_a^b [K(x, y) - K(t, y)]\alpha(y)dy|$$

$$\leq \int_a^b |K(x, y) - K(t, y)| \, |\alpha(y)| \, dy \leq \epsilon \int_a^b |\alpha(y)| \, dy$$

whenever $|x - t| < \delta$. This proves that $\lim_{x \to t} K\alpha(x) = K\alpha(t)$.

The continuity of $K\alpha$ indicates that if $K\alpha$ is equal (actually equivalent) to the zero vector, then $K\alpha$ is identically zero. For, if $K\alpha(t) \neq 0$, then by continuity, $K\alpha(x) \neq 0$ for all x in some interval containing t, and thus $K\alpha$ would be different from zero in a set not of measure zero.

In a similar manner, we could consider the complex Euclidean vector space $\mathscr{R}^* = \mathscr{R}^*\{a, b\}$ of complex valued integrable functions α on $a \leq x \leq b$. Here the inner product is

$$(\alpha, \beta) = \int_a^b \alpha(x) \, \overline{\beta(x)} dx.$$

Again, two functions are called equal when they differ at most on a set of measure zero. The complex valued continuous function $K(x, y)$ defined on $a \leq x \leq b, a \leq y \leq b$ then induces by (1) a linear transformation K on $\mathscr{R}^*$ to $\mathscr{R}^*$. $K\alpha$ is a continuous complex valued function.

For either $\mathscr{R}$ or $\mathscr{R}^*$, the integral transformation K^*, the **adjoint** of K, is defined by

(3)
$$K^*\alpha(x) = \int_a^b \overline{K(y, x)}\, \alpha(y)dy.$$

It is easily verified that

(4)
$$(K\alpha, \beta) = (\alpha, K^*\beta).$$

In fact, by an interchange of order of integration (see Exercise 4.1–1),

$$(K\alpha, \beta) = \int_a^b \int_a^b K(x, y)\, \alpha(y)dy\, \overline{\beta(x)}dx$$

$$= \int_a^b \int_a^b K(x, y)\, \overline{\beta(x)}dx\, \alpha(y)dy = (\alpha, K^*\beta).$$

Equation (4) determines K^*. That is, if $(K\alpha, \beta) = (\alpha, M\beta)$ for a linear transformation M and every α and β in $\mathscr{R}^*$ (or $\mathscr{R}$, if K is defined only on $\mathscr{R}$), then $M = K^*$. For, if $(\alpha,(K^* - M)\beta) = 0$ for every α and β, choose $\alpha = (K^* - M)\beta$ to obtain $K^*\beta = M\beta$ for every β.

The integral transformation has many properties in common with the linear transformation

$$b_i = \sum_{j=1}^n k_{ij}\, a_j, \qquad i = 1, \ldots, n$$

studied in Chapter 2, the variables x and y corresponding to i and j, and integration replacing summation. As a first example, we prove that the integral transformation is a bounded transformation. Recall that a linear transformation T on a Euclidean vector space $\mathscr{E}$ to a Euclidean vector space $\mathscr{F}$ is bounded if l.u.b. $\left\{ \|T\alpha\| \,\middle|\, \|\alpha\| = 1,\ \alpha \text{ in } \mathscr{E} \right\}$ is finite, and the value of this least upper bound is the norm, $\|T\|$.

THEOREM 4.1A

$$\|K\| \leq \left(\int_a^b \int_a^b |K(x, y)|^2\, dx\, dy \right)^{1/2}.$$

Proof   When $\|\alpha\| = 1$,

$$|K\alpha(x)|^2 = \left| \int_a^b K(x, y)\, \alpha(y)dy \right|^2 \leq \int_a^b |K(x, y)|^2\, dy \int_a^b |\alpha(y)|^2\, dy$$

$$= \int_a^b |K(x, y)|^2\, dy$$

so that

$$\|K\alpha\|^2 = \int_a^b |K\alpha(x)|^2 \, dx \le \int_a^b \int_a^b |K(x, y)|^2 \, dy \, dx.$$

Hence

$$\|K\| = \text{l.u.b.} \left\{ \|K\alpha\| \,\Big|\, \|\alpha\| = 1 \right\} \le \left(\int_a^b \int_a^b |K(x, y)|^2 \, dx \, dy \right)^{1/2}. \quad \bigstar$$

This property of boundedness is intimately connected with continuity. The linear transformation T on $\mathscr{E}$ to $\mathscr{F}$ is called **continuous** at α in $\mathscr{E}$ if the sequence $\{T\alpha_n\}$ converges to $T\alpha$ whenever the sequence $\{\alpha_n\}$ in $\mathscr{E}$ converges to α in $\mathscr{E}$. It is not difficult to show that an equivalent statement for continuity is the following: for every $\epsilon > 0$ there is a $\delta(\epsilon, \alpha) > 0$ such that $\|T\beta - T\alpha\| < \epsilon$ whenever $\|\beta - \alpha\| < \delta$.

Now we can see that *T is bounded if and only if it is continuous for all α.* Indeed if T is bounded and $\{\alpha_n\}$ converges to α, then the inequality

$$\|T\alpha_n - T\alpha\| = \|T(\alpha_n - \alpha)\| \le \|T\| \, \|\alpha_n - \alpha\|$$

shows that $\{T\alpha_n\}$ converges to $T\alpha$. Conversely, if T is continuous at $\alpha = \theta$, then for $\epsilon > 0$ there is a $\delta(\epsilon) > 0$ such that

$$\|T\alpha\| < \epsilon \qquad \text{whenever} \quad \|\alpha\| < \delta.$$

If $\beta \ne \theta$ is given, and $\alpha = \dfrac{\delta(1)}{2} \dfrac{\beta}{\|\beta\|}$, we have

$$\|\alpha\| = \frac{\delta(1)}{2} < \delta(1) \quad \text{and} \quad \|T\alpha\| < 1.$$

This means $\|T\beta\| \le \dfrac{2}{\delta(1)} \|\beta\|$, a statement valid even if $\beta = \theta$. Hence T is bounded.

Our integral transformation has an even stronger property, the property of complete continuity. A linear transformation T on $\mathscr{E}$ to $\mathscr{F}$ is **completely continuous** or **compact** if for every sequence $\{\alpha_n\}$ with uniformly bounded norms (that is, with $\|\alpha_n\| \le c$ for some positive c) there exists a subsequence $\{\alpha_{n_j}\}$ and an element β in $\mathscr{F}$ such that $\{T\alpha_{n_j}\}$ converges to β.

Complete continuity actually implies boundedness. Indeed, if T were not bounded, there would exist a sequence $\{\beta_n\}$ such that $\|T\beta_n\| > n \|\beta_n\|$. Putting $\alpha_n = \beta_n/\|\beta_n\|$ we have $\|\alpha_n\| \le 1$ while $\|T\alpha_n\| > n$. No subsequence of $\{T\alpha_n\}$ could then converge.

Previously we did not need to consider this concept since every linear transformation T whose domain is finite dimensional is necessarily completely continuous. In the case when $\mathscr{F} = \mathscr{E}$, T is bounded by Theorem 2.8C, and if $\|\alpha_n\| \leq c$, then

$$\|T\alpha_n\| \leq \|T\| \, \|\alpha_n\| \leq \|T\| c$$

so that $\{T\alpha_n\}$ is also uniformly bounded. A convergent subsequence exists by Theorem 3.1B. For the case when $\mathscr{F}$ is not $\mathscr{E}$, see Exercise 4.1–12.

THEOREM 4.1B   The continuous kernel $K(x, y)$ defines a completely continuous transformation.

Proof   If $\|\alpha_n\| = \left(\int_a^b |\alpha_n|^2 \, dx \right)^{1/2} < c$, the inequality

$$|K\alpha_n| = \left| \int_a^b K(x, y) \, \alpha_n(y) dy \right| \leq \left(\int_a^b |K^2(x, y)| \, dy \right)^{1/2} \left(\int_a^b |\alpha_n(y)|^2 \, dy \right)^{1/2}$$

shows that the functions $K\alpha_n$ are uniformly bounded. Moreover

$$|K\alpha_n(x_2) - K\alpha_n(x_1)| = |\int_a^b [K(x_2, y) - K(x_1, y)] \, \alpha_n(y) dy|$$

$$\leq \left(\int_a^b |K(x_2, y) - K(x_1, y)|^2 dy \right)^{1/2} \left(\int_a^b |\alpha_n(y)|^2 dy \right)^{1/2} \leq \epsilon(b - a)^{1/2} c$$

when $|x_2 - x_1| < \delta(\epsilon)$

by virtue of equation (2). This proves that the sequence $\{K\alpha_n\}$ is equicontinuous. Hence by Ascoli's theorem, Theorem 3.2H, there is a subsequence $\{K\alpha_{n_j}\}$ converging uniformly to a function $\beta(x)$, continuous on $a \leq x \leq b$ by Theorem 3.2F. In view of the uniform convergence,

$$\lim_{j \to \infty} \|K\alpha_{n_j} - \beta\|^2 = \lim_{j \to \infty} \int_a^b |K\alpha_{n_j} - \beta|^2 \, dx$$

$$= \int_a^b \lim_{j \to \infty} |K\alpha_{n_j} - \beta|^2 \, dx = 0. \qquad \bigstar$$

The notion of a symmetric linear transformation is independent of the dimension of the space. The transformation K is called **symmetric** if

$$(K\alpha, \beta) = (\alpha, K\beta) \quad \text{for every } \alpha \text{ and } \beta.$$

Thus K is symmetric if and only if $K = K^*$.

We shall restrict our attention to the symmetric case and develop a theory parallel to that found in Chapter 2. Moreover we shall consider the case when K is defined on $\mathscr{R}$ and leave as exercises the proofs for the case when K is defined on $\mathscr{R}^*$.

A real kernel $K(x, y)$ is called a **symmetric kernel** if $K(x, y) = K(y, x)$ for $a \leq x \leq b, a \leq y \leq b$.

THEOREM 4.1C The integral transformation K is symmetric if and only if it has a symmetric kernel.

Proof We have

$$(K\alpha, \beta) = \int_a^b \int_a^b K(x, y)\, \alpha(y)dy\, \beta(x)dx = \int_a^b \int_a^b K(x, y)\, \alpha(y)\, \beta(x)dy\, dx,$$

$$(\alpha, K\beta) = \int_a^b \alpha(y) \int_a^b K(y, x)\beta(x)\, dx\, dy = \int_a^b \int_a^b K(y, x)\alpha(y)\beta(x)\, dx\, dy.$$

Thus, if $K(x, y) = K(y, x)$, an interchange of order of integration shows that $(K\alpha, \beta) = (\alpha, K\beta)$.

Conversely, if there exist values t and u in the interval $a \leq x \leq b$ for which $K(t, u) < K(u, t)$, then by continuity there would exist closed intervals $\mathscr{I}_1: c_1 \leq x \leq d_1$ and $\mathscr{I}_2: c_2 \leq x \leq d_2$ in $a \leq x \leq b$ such that t is in $\mathscr{I}_1$, u is in $\mathscr{I}_2$ and

$$m = \text{l.u.b.}\, \{K(x, y) \mid x \text{ in } \mathscr{I}_1, y \text{ in } \mathscr{I}_2\} < \text{g.l.b.}\, \{K(x, y) \mid x \text{ in } \mathscr{I}_2, y \text{ in } \mathscr{I}_1\} = M.$$

If $\alpha = \phi(\mathscr{I}_1)$ and $\beta = \phi(\mathscr{I}_2)$ are the characteristic functions of $\mathscr{I}_1$ and $\mathscr{I}_2$ respectively, we note that

$$(K\alpha, \beta) = \int_a^b \int_a^b K(x, y)\, \alpha(y)dy\, \beta(x)\, dx = \int_{c_2}^{d_2} \int_{c_1}^{d_1} K(x, y)\, dy\, dx$$

$$\geq M(d_1 - c_1)(d_2 - c_2),$$

$$(\alpha, K\beta) = \int_a^b \int_a^b K(x, y)\, \beta(y)\, dy\, \alpha(x)\, dx = \int_{c_1}^{d_1} \int_{c_2}^{d_2} K(x, y)\, dy\, dx$$

$$\leq m\, (d_1 - c_1)\, (d_2 - c_2).$$

Hence K could not be a symmetric transformation. $\star$

For symmetric integral transformations, eigenvectors corresponding to distinct eigenvalues are orthogonal.

THEOREM 4.1D   If K is symmetric, $r \neq s$, $K\alpha = s\alpha$, $K\beta = r\beta$ then $(\alpha, \beta) = 0$.

Proof   This is a consequence of

$$s(\alpha, \beta) = (s\alpha, \beta) = (K\alpha, \beta) = (\alpha, K\beta) = (\alpha, r\beta) = r(\alpha, \beta).   \quad \star$$

The simplest type of symmetric kernel is one of the form

(5)
$$K(x, y) = \sum_{i,j=1}^{n} c_{ij}\, \sigma_i(x)\, \sigma_j(y)$$

where $c_{ij} = c_{ji}$ and $\sigma_i(x)$ are continuous functions on $a \leq x \leq b$. Such a kernel is called a **symmetric separable kernel.** As we shall see later, the transformation induced by such a kernel has only a finite number of nonzero eigenvalues and a symmetric integral transformation which has only a finite number of nonzero eigenvalues must arise from a separable kernel.

Information concerning the eigenvectors and eigenvalues of the transformation with a separable kernel can be obtained by using the results of Chapter 2.

THEOREM 4.1E   Let $K(x, y)$, given by (5), be a symmetric separable kernel, not identically zero. Then there exists an orthonormal set of vectors $\alpha_1(x), \ldots, \alpha_m(x)$ and real scalars $s_1, \ldots, s_m$, all different from zero, such that $K\alpha_i = s_i\, \alpha_i$ and such that if β in $\mathscr{R}$ is orthogonal to α_i, $i = 1, \ldots, m$, then $K\beta = \theta$. The scalars s_i are the only nonzero eigenvalues of K. There are only a finite number of linearly independent eigenvectors corresponding to each nonzero eigenvalue.

Proof   Let $\mathscr{V}$ be the collection of all vectors of the form

$$d_1\, \sigma_1 + \ldots + d_n\, \sigma_n.$$

$\mathscr{V}$ is a vector space and its dimension is the number q of linearly independent vectors in the set $\sigma_1, \ldots, \sigma_n$. Since

(6)
$$\int_a^b K(x, y)\, \mu(y)dy = \sum_{i,j=1}^{n} \left(c_{ij} \int_a^b \sigma_j(y)\, \mu(y)dy \right) \sigma_i(x),$$

it is clear that K transforms $\mathscr{V}$ into itself. Thus, by Theorem 2.7D, there exist q orthonormal vectors α_i in $\mathscr{V}$ such that $K\alpha_i = s_i\, \alpha_i$. If $s_i \neq 0$ for $i = 1, \ldots, m$ and $s_i = 0$ for $i = m + 1, \ldots, q$ we obtain the set α_i, $i = 1, \ldots, m$ referred to in the theorem. But if $s_i = 0$ for all i, $i = 1, \ldots, q$, then $K\alpha_i = \theta$ and hence $K\mu = \theta$ for every μ in $\mathscr{V}$ because α_i form a basis for $\mathscr{V}$. For fixed x, $K(x, y)$ given by (5) is a continuous function $\mu(y)$ in $\mathscr{V}$. Thus

$$0 = K\mu = \int_a^b K(x, y)\,\mu(y)dy = \int_a^b |\mu(y)|^2\,dy.$$

We conclude that $\mu(y) = K(x, y) = 0$ for all y. Since x is arbitrary, $K(x, y) = 0$ for all x and y contradicting the hypothesis. Therefore s_i are not all zero.

Now let β in $\mathscr{R}$ be orthogonal to α_i, $i = 1, \ldots, m$ and define

(7)
$$\mu = \beta - \sum_{j=m+1}^q (\beta, \alpha_j)\,\alpha_j.$$

It is easily verified that μ is orthogonal to α_i, $i = 1, \ldots, q$. For,

(8)
$$(\mu, \alpha_i) = (\beta, \alpha_i) - \sum_{j=m+1}^q (\beta, \alpha_j)(\alpha_j, \alpha_i)$$

and the right side is zero when $i \le m$ because $\beta \perp \alpha_i$ and $\alpha_i \perp \alpha_j$, $j = m + 1, \ldots, q$; while if $i > m$ the right side is $(\beta, \alpha_i) - \sum_{j=m+1}^q (\beta, \alpha_j)\,\delta_{ij} = 0$. Consequently μ is orthogonal to σ_i and $K\mu = \theta$ by (6). When $j = m + 1, \ldots, q$ we have $K\alpha_j = \theta$. It follows from (7) that $K\beta = \theta$.

To prove the last part of the theorem observe that (6) implies $K\beta$ is in $\mathscr{V}$ whenever β is in $\mathscr{R}$. If $K\beta = r\beta$, $r \ne 0$, then $\beta = \dfrac{1}{r} K\beta$ is in $\mathscr{V}$ and has a representation

$$\beta = a_1\,\alpha_1 + \ldots + a_q\,\alpha_q$$

for scalars $a_i = (\beta, \alpha_i)$. By Theorem 4.1D, $a_i = 0$ unless α_i is associated with eigenvalue r. This statement yields the desired result.   ★

There is no more generality in considering a kernel of the form

(9)
$$K(x, y) = \sum_{k=1}^p \alpha_k(x)\,\beta_k(y),$$

for such a kernel may always be reduced to the form (5), and we will have $c_{ij} = c_{ji}$ in (5) when $K(x, y)$ is symmetric. We need only express the $2p$ functions $\alpha_k(x)$, $\beta_k(x)$ in terms of a set of q linearly independent (orthonormal, if one so desires) functions $\sigma_k(x)$. Then (9) becomes

$$K(x, y) = \sum_{k=1}^p \sum_{i=1}^q a_{ki}\,\sigma_i(x) \sum_{j=1}^q b_{kj}\,\sigma_j(y) = \sum_{i,j=1}^q c_{ij}\,\sigma_i(x)\,\sigma_j(y)$$

where $c_{ij} = \sum_{k=1}^{p} a_{ki} b_{kj}$, and similarly

$$K(y, x) = \sum_{i,j=1}^{q} c_{ij}\, \sigma_i(y)\, \sigma_j(x) = \sum_{i,j=1}^{q} c_{ji}\, \sigma_i(x)\, \sigma_j(y).$$

When $K(x, y) = K(y, x)$, the linear independence of $\sigma_j(y)$ yields, for fixed x,

$$\sum_{i=1}^{q} c_{ij}\, \sigma_i(x) = \sum_{i=1}^{q} c_{ji}\, \sigma_i(x).$$

From this we obtain $c_{ij} = c_{ji}$.

For the practical determination of the nonzero eigenvalues s, we can use the form (9). Assuming

$$\int_a^b \sum_{k=1}^{p} \alpha_k(x)\, \beta_k(y)\, \alpha(y)\, dy = s\, \alpha(x)$$

and letting

(10)
$$a_k = \int_a^b \beta_k(y)\, \alpha(y)\, dy$$

we get

(11)
$$\alpha(x) = \frac{1}{s} \sum_{k=1}^{p} a_k\, \alpha_k(x).$$

Substituting (11) in (10) yields

(12)
$$s a_k = \sum_{j=1}^{p} a_j \int_a^b \beta_k(y)\, \alpha_j(y)\, dy.$$

(12) is a set of linear equations for the unknowns a_k, with a nonzero solution existing when

$$\det\left[s\delta_{kj} - \int_a^b \beta_k(y)\, \alpha_j(y)\, dy \right] = 0.$$

This yields the nonzero eigenvalues s and the eigenvectors by (11).

EXAMPLE 1 Obtain the nonzero eigenvalues corresponding to the kernel $K(x, y) = 1 + \cos(x - y)$, $\quad -\pi \le x \le \pi, -\pi \le y \le \pi$.

We want to solve

(13)
$$\int_{-\pi}^{\pi} (1 + \cos x \cos y + \sin x \sin y)\, \alpha(y)\, dy = s\alpha(x), \quad s \ne 0.$$

This may be written

$$a_1 + a_2 \cos x + a_3 \sin x = s\alpha(x)$$

where

$$a_1 = \int_{-\pi}^{\pi} \alpha(y) \, dy = \frac{1}{s} \int_{-\pi}^{\pi} (a_1 + a_2 \cos y + a_3 \sin y) \, dy,$$

$$a_2 = \int_{-\pi}^{\pi} \cos y \, \alpha(y) \, dy = \frac{1}{s} \int_{-\pi}^{\pi} \cos y \, (a_1 + a_2 \cos y + a_3 \sin y) dy,$$

$$a_3 = \int_{-\pi}^{\pi} \sin y \, \alpha(y) \, dy = \frac{1}{s} \int_{-\pi}^{\pi} \sin y \, (a_1 + a_2 \cos y + a_3 \sin y) dy.$$

Upon integration, the system of equations reduces to

(14) $s \, a_1 = 2\pi a_1, \quad s \, a_2 = \pi a_2, \quad s \, a_3 = \pi a_3.$

The possible values of s yielding a nonzero solution for α are π and 2π. When $s = \pi$, (14) has a solution $a_1 = 0$, a_2 and a_3 arbitrary, and

$$\alpha(x) = \frac{1}{\pi}\left(a_2 \cos x + a_3 \sin x\right).$$

When $s = 2\pi$, (14) has a solution $a_2 = 0 = a_3$, a_1 arbitrary, and

$$\alpha(x) = \frac{a_1}{2\pi}.$$

It follows that there are three linearly independent solutions of (13),

$$\alpha_1 = \cos x, \quad \alpha_2 = \sin x, \quad \alpha_3 = 1.$$

These happen to be orthogonal eigenvectors and when normalized become

$$\beta_1 = \frac{\alpha_1}{\|\alpha_1\|} = \frac{\cos x}{\sqrt{\pi}}, \quad \beta_2 = \frac{\sin x}{\sqrt{\pi}}, \quad \beta_3 = \frac{1}{\sqrt{2\pi}}.$$

EXAMPLE 2 Apply the same procedure to the kernel $K(x, y)$ $= \sin x \cos y$, $-\pi \le x \le \pi$, $-\pi \le y \le \pi$.
  Here the equation to be solved is

$$\int_{-\pi}^{\pi} \sin x \cos y \, \alpha(y) \, dy = s \, \alpha(x).$$

It may be rewritten
$$a \sin x = s \, \alpha(x)$$
where
$$a = \int_{-\pi}^{\pi} \cos y \, \alpha(y) \, dy = \int_{-\pi}^{\pi} \cos y \left(\frac{1}{s} a \sin y \right) dy = 0.$$

We conclude that the integral transformation corresponding to this kernel has no nonzero eigenvalues. Note that the kernel is not symmetric.

Using the same kernel on the square $0 \le x \le \pi/2$, $0 \le y \le \pi/2$, we would obtain a different result. A nonzero eigenvalue is $s = \frac{1}{2}$.

With appropriate modifications all the results of this section are valid for an integral transformation defined on $\mathcal{R}^*$. A kernel is called **Hermitian** if $K(x, y) = \overline{K(y, x)}$. A **separable Hermitian kernel** is one of the form

$$K(x, y) = \sum_{i,j=1}^{n} c_{ij} \, \sigma_i(x) \, \overline{\sigma_j(y)}$$

where $c_{ij} = \overline{c_{ji}}$. When K is a symmetric operator the eigenvalues are necessarily real, for if $K\alpha = r\alpha$, $\alpha \ne \theta$, then

$$r(\alpha, \alpha) = (r\alpha, \alpha) = (K\alpha, \alpha) = (\alpha, K\alpha) = (\alpha, r\alpha) = \bar{r}(\alpha, \alpha).$$

Theorem 4.1D is valid as stated, and Theorems 4.1C and 4.1E are valid when "symmetric kernel" is replaced by "Hermitian kernel."

Exercise 4.1

1. Let $\alpha(x)$ and $\beta(x)$ be integrable on $a \le x \le b$ and $K(x, y)$ be continuous. Following the steps indicated show that
$$\int_a^b \int_a^b K(x, y) \, \alpha(x) \, \beta(y) \, dx \, dy = \int_a^b \int_a^b K(x, y) \, \alpha(x) \, \beta(y) \, dy \, dx.$$
   (a) Show that $f(x, y) = \alpha(x) \beta(y)$ is continuous at (x_0, y_0) if $\alpha(x)$ is continuous at x_0 and $\beta(y)$ is continuous at y_0.
   (b) By properly selecting a countable number of rectangles, show that the set of points of discontinuity of $f(x, y)$ on $a \le x \le b$, $a \le y \le b$ has two dimensional measure zero. This proves that $f(x, y)$ is integrable.
   (c) $K\alpha$ and $K\beta$ both exist. Now apply Theorem 3.3K.

2. (a) Show that if $\beta \cong \alpha$, then $\beta(x) = \alpha(x)$ at every point x which is a point of continuity of both α and β.
   (b) Prove the converse, that is, if β and α are Riemann integrable on $a \le x \le b$ and agree at every point which is a point of continuity of both α and β, then $\beta \cong \alpha$.

3. (a) Show that every eigenvector of the integral transformation K with continuous kernel corresponding to a nonzero eigenvalue is continuous.
   (b) Take $K(x, y) = 1$, $-a \le x \le a$, $-a \le y \le a$, and
   $$\alpha(x) = \begin{cases} 1, & 0 \le x \le a \\ -1, & -a \le x < 0 \end{cases}.$$
   Show that α is an eigenvector with eigenvalue zero which is not equivalent to a continuous function.

4. Let $K(x, y) = \sin x \sin y$, $-\pi \le x \le \pi$, $-\pi \le y \le \pi$. Show that there are an infinity of linearly independent eigenvectors corresponding to the eigenvalue zero.

5. (a) Let $\alpha(x)$, $\beta(x)$ be real, continuous, and orthogonal on $a \le x \le b$. Define $K(x, y) = \alpha(x) \beta(y)$. Show that the corresponding integral operator has no nonzero eigenvalues.

    (b) Show that a separable symmetric transformation always has zero as an eigenvalue. *Hint:* Consider a function $\alpha(y)$ orthogonal to $\sigma_j(y)$ in (5) of the text.

6. Show that a linear transformation L on a Euclidean vector space $\mathscr{E}$ to a Euclidean vector space $\mathscr{F}$ is bounded if it is continuous at any one point of $\mathscr{E}$.

7. Obtain the nonzero eigenvalues and corresponding eigenvectors for the following kernels on $a \le x \le b$, $a \le y \le b$.

    (a) $K(x, y) = xy$;   (b) $K(x, y) = x + y$;   (c) $K(x, y) = x^2 + y^2$;
    (d) $K(x, y) = e^x e^y$;   (e) $K(x, y) = \sin x \sin y$;
    (f) $K(x, y) = 1 + xy$;   (g) $K(x, y) = xy^2 + yx^2$.

8. Prove that the integral transformation K defined on $\mathscr{R}^*$ is symmetric if and only if the kernel is Hermitian.

9. By writing $\alpha(x) = \sigma(x) + i\mu(x)$, with σ and μ real, $i^2 = -1$, prove that if α is an eigenvector with real eigenvalue r for a transformation K with real kernel defined on $\mathscr{R}^*$, then $\bar{\alpha}$ is also an eigenvector with eigenvalue r.

10. Let $\alpha_1, \ldots, \alpha_n$ be a basis of the linear manifold of eigenvectors with eigenvalue r for a symmetric integral transformation K with real kernel defined on $\mathscr{R}^*$. When $\alpha_j = \sigma_j + i\mu_j$, $i^2 = -1$, σ_j and μ_j real, show that $K\sigma = r\sigma$, $K\mu = r\mu$, and that exactly n of the functions σ_j, μ_j are linearly independent. In this way, when $K(x, y)$ is real, we can replace $\alpha_1, \ldots, \alpha_n$ by a set of linearly independent real eigenvectors.

11. (a) Assume that $K(x, y) = K(-x, y)$. Show that the eigenvectors corresponding to nonzero eigenvalues are even.

     (b) Assume that $K(x, y) = K(-x, -y)$, $-a \le x \le a$, $-a \le y \le a$. Assume also that s is a nonzero eigenvalue to which there corresponds only one linearly independent real eigenvector α. Show that α is either even or odd.

12. Let L be a linear transformation on $\mathscr{E}$ to $\mathscr{F}$ with $\mathscr{E}$ of finite dimension. Show that L is bounded. *Hint:* The range of L is finite dimensional by Theorem 1.4A. Use Exercise 2.1–17 and carry through a proof like that of Theorem 2.8C.

13. Show that the identity transformation I on $\mathscr{E}_\infty$ to $\mathscr{E}_\infty$ is linear and bounded but is not completely continuous. *Hint:* Consider the sequence $\{\alpha_n\}$ where α_n has all coordinates 0 except the nth, which is 1.

14. (a) Let M be the larger of l.u.b. $\left\{ \int_a^b |K(x, y)|\, dy \,\middle|\, a \le x \le b \right\}$ and l.u.b. $\left\{ \int_a^b |K(x, y)|\, dx \mid a \le y \le b \right\}$. Make a proof similar to that of Theorem 2.8C to show that $\|K\| \le M$.

     (b) Make a proof similar to Theorem 4.1A to show that if the linear transformation A on a finite dimensional space $\mathscr{E}$ has a representation $[a_{ij}]$ in an orthonormal basis, then $\|A\|^2 \le \sum_i \sum_j |a_{ij}|^2$.

15. Show that the class of completely continuous transformations on a Euclidean vector space $\mathscr{E}$ to $\mathscr{E}$ forms a vector space.

4.2

EIGENVALUES OF A SYMMETRIC INTEGRAL OPERATOR

We consider a symmetric integral transformation K with real continuous kernel defined on the real Euclidean vector space $\mathcal{R}$ of integrable functions on $a \leq x \leq b$. Again we leave the proofs for the space $\mathcal{R}^*$ to the reader.

THEOREM 4.2A   The number of distinct nonzero eigenvalues of a symmetric integral transformation K is countable. For each nonzero eigenvalue there corresponds at most a finite number of linearly independent eigenvectors.

Proof   Eigenvectors corresponding to distinct eigenvalues are orthogonal. A finite set of linearly independent eigenvectors corresponding to the same eigenvalue may be replaced by orthonormal eigenvectors. Hence when speaking of a finite set of linearly independent eigenvectors we may assume they are orthonormal. Let α_i, $i = 1, \ldots, m$, be a finite set of orthonormal eigenvectors, corresponding to eigenvalues s_i, which need not be distinct. For fixed x, $\beta(y) = K(x, y)$ is a function in $\mathcal{R}$ and

$$(\beta, \alpha_i) = \int_a^b K(x, y)\, \alpha_i(y) dy = s_i\, \alpha_i(x).$$

By Bessel's inequality, Theorem 1.3E, Corollary 1,

$$(1) \qquad \sum_{i=1}^m s_i^2\, |\alpha_i(x)|^2 \leq \int_a^b |K(x, y)|^2\, dy.$$

Integrating with respect to x, we obtain

$$(2) \qquad \sum_{i=1}^m s_i^2 \leq \int_a^b \int_a^b |K(x, y)|^2\, dy\, dx.$$

The right side is independent of m. It follows that there can be at most a finite number of linearly independent eigenvectors for the same nonzero eigenvalue. Similarly (2) implies that there can be at most a finite number of linearly independent eigenvectors with eigenvalues greater in absolute value than 1, or with eigenvalues whose absolute values lie in the range $\dfrac{1}{2n} < x \leq \dfrac{1}{n}, n = 1, 2, \ldots$. The distinct eigenvalues can now be counted. First we count those whose absolute value is greater than 1, then those whose absolute value is in the range $\frac{1}{2} < x \leq 1$, etc. Every nonzero eigenvalue will then be taken into account.   ★

It will be convenient to display the eigenvalues as a set

$$s_{-1} \leq s_{-2} \leq \cdots < 0 < \cdots s_2 \leq s_1$$

obtained by ordering the eigenvalues according to absolute value, separating them according to sign, and repeating each eigenvalue a number of times equal to the number of linearly independent eigenvectors associated with it. The set of eigenvalues so displayed is called the **spectrum** of K. If zero is an eigenvalue it is included in the spectrum but will not be designated by the symbol s_j.

We may summarize the results as

Corollary 1

If K has at least one nonzero eigenvalue, then there exist nonnegative integers M and N, not both zero, possibly infinite, and an orthonormal set $\alpha_i, -\infty \leq -M \leq i \leq N \leq \infty, i \neq 0$, such that $K\alpha_i = s_i \alpha_i$ with

$$(3) \qquad\qquad s_{-1} \leq s_{-2} \leq \cdots < 0 < \cdots \leq s_2 \leq s_1.$$

The set of numbers s_i includes every nonzero eigenvalue of K, and every eigenvector of K corresponding to a nonzero eigenvalue r is a finite linear combination of eigenvectors α_i associated with eigenvalue r. Moreover

$$(4) \qquad\qquad \sum_i s_i^2 \, |\alpha_i(x)|^2 \leq \int_a^b |K(x, y)|^2 \, dy,$$

$$(5) \qquad\qquad \sum_i s_i^2 \leq \int_a^b \int_a^b |K(x, y)|^2 \, dy \, dx.$$

Equations (4) and (5) follow directly from (1) and (2). It is clear from (5) that if $N = \infty$, then $\lim_{i \to \infty} s_i = 0$ and if $M = \infty$, then $\lim_{i \to \infty} s_{-i} = 0$.

As yet we have not indicated any conditions insuring the existence of a nonzero eigenvalue. Let us recall some of the facts derived for a linear transformation T on a finite dimensional Euclidean vector space. The largest eigenvalue was given by Theorem 2.8A as

$$s_1 = \text{l.u.b.} \left\{ (T\alpha, \alpha) \mid \|\alpha\| = 1 \right\}$$

and the smallest (see Exercise 2.8–10) as

$$s_n = \text{g.l.b.} \left\{ (T\alpha, \alpha) \mid \|\alpha\| = 1 \right\}.$$

We shall see that similar results can be derived for the integral transformation K.

THEOREM 4.2B Let $p = \text{l.u.b} \left\{ (K\alpha, \alpha) \mid \|\alpha\| = 1 \right\}$, $q = \text{g.l.b.} \left\{ (K\alpha, \alpha) \mid \|\alpha\| = 1 \right\}$. Then if $p > 0$, it is the largest nonzero eigenvalue, and if $q < 0$, it is the smallest nonzero eigenvalue.

Proof We need only prove the statement regarding p, for the statement regarding q will then follow by consideration of the transformation $-K$, whose eigenvalues are the negatives of those of K. Indeed if

$$p' = \text{l.u.b.} \left\{ (-K\alpha, \alpha) \mid \|\alpha\| = 1 \right\} = \text{l.u.b.} \left\{ - (K\alpha, \alpha) \mid \|\alpha\| = 1 \right\}$$

is the largest eigenvalue of $-K$, then $-p'$ is the smallest eigenvalue of K and it is easily seen that $-p' = q$.

If $K\alpha = r\alpha$ for $\|\alpha\| = 1$, then

$$r = r(\alpha, \alpha) = (K\alpha, \alpha) \leq p.$$

It follows that if p is an eigenvalue, it is the largest.

We shall prove the theorem first for the case when the kernel is separable. When $p > 0$, the kernel cannot be identically zero, and Theorem 4.1D implies the existence of m orthonormal eigenvectors α_i and nonzero eigenvalues $s_1 \geq s_2 \geq \cdots \geq s_m$ such that $K\beta = \theta$ whenever $\beta \perp \alpha_i$, $i = 1, \ldots, m$. Let $\mathscr{V}$ be the linear manifold of dimension m spanned by α_i. If $\sigma = \sum_{i=1}^{m} a_i \alpha_i$ is in $\mathscr{V}$, so is $K\sigma$ since $K\alpha_i = s_i \alpha_i$. We have

$$(6) \quad s_1 = \text{l.u.b.} \left\{ (K\sigma, \sigma) \mid \|\sigma\| = 1, \sigma \text{ in } \mathscr{V} \right\} \leq \text{l.u.b.} \left\{ (K\alpha, \alpha) \mid \|\alpha\| = 1, \alpha \text{ in } \mathscr{R} \right\} = p.$$

We shall show the reverse inequality is also valid, proving $p = s_1$, an eigenvalue of K. When α is in $\mathscr{R}$ and $\|\alpha\| = 1$ we may write

$$\alpha = \sigma + \beta, \qquad \sigma \text{ in } \mathscr{V}, \qquad \beta \perp \mathscr{V},$$

as shown in Theorem 1.3E. Hence $K\beta = \theta$, $K\alpha = K\sigma$ is in $\mathscr{V}$, and

(7)
$$(K\alpha, \alpha) = (K\sigma, \sigma + \beta) = (K\sigma, \sigma)$$

since $\beta \perp K\sigma$. Moreover

$$(\alpha, \alpha) = (\sigma + \beta, \sigma + \beta) = (\sigma, \sigma) + (\beta, \beta)$$

where $0 \leq \|\sigma\| \leq \|\alpha\| = 1$. Remembering $p > 0$ and restricting α so that $(K\alpha, \alpha) > 0$ we see from (7) that $\|\sigma\| \neq 0$, $(K\sigma, \sigma) > 0$, and

$$(K\alpha, \alpha) = \|\sigma\|^2 (K\mu, \mu) \leq (K\mu, \mu)$$

where $\mu = \sigma/\|\sigma\|$ is in $\mathscr{V}$. It follows that

$$\text{l.u.b.} \Big\{ (K\alpha, \alpha) \Big| \|\alpha\| = 1, \alpha \text{ in } \mathscr{R} \Big\} \leq \text{l.u.b.} \Big\{ (K\mu, \mu) \Big| \|\mu\| = 1, \mu \text{ in } \mathscr{V} \Big\}$$

proving $p \leq s_1$. This, together with the previous inequality (6), yields $p = s_1$.

Next, consider the case where $K(x, y)$ is any continuous symmetric kernel. Later, in Section 5.2, we shall show that for every $\epsilon > 0$, there is a symmetric separable kernel $H(x, y)$ such that

$$\int_a^b \int_a^b |K(x, y) - H(x, y)|^2 \, dx \, dy \leq \epsilon.$$

This means that we can find a sequence $K_n(x, y)$ of separable symmetric kernels such that (see Theorem 4.1A)

$$\|K - K_n\|^2 \leq \int_a^b \int_a^b |K(x, y) - K_n(x, y)|^2 \, dx \, dy \leq \frac{1}{n^2}.$$

We assert $p = \lim_{n \to \infty} p_n$, where

$$p_n = \text{l.u.b.} \Big\{ (K_n\alpha, \alpha) \Big| \|\alpha\| = 1 \Big\}.$$

In fact, if $\|\alpha\| = 1$,

$$|(K\alpha, \alpha) - (K_n\alpha, \alpha)|$$
$$= |((K - K_n)\alpha, \alpha)| \leq \|(K - K_n)\alpha\| \, \|\alpha\| \leq \|K - K_n\| \leq \frac{1}{n}.$$

Therefore

$$(K\alpha,\ \alpha) \leq (K_n\alpha,\ \alpha) + \frac{1}{n} \leq p_n + \frac{1}{n},$$

$$p \leq p_n + \frac{1}{n}.$$

Similarly $p_n \leq p + 1/n$ whence $|p - p_n| \leq 1/n$.

This proves our assertion. Since $p > 0$, we may now restrict our sequence so that $p_n > 0$.

Let α_n be normalized eigenvectors of K_n corresponding to eigenvalues p_n. We have $K_n\alpha_n = p_n\ \alpha_n$, $\|\alpha_n\| = 1$, and we will show that

(8) $$\lim_{n\to\infty} \|K\alpha_n - p\alpha_n\| = 0.$$

This follows from

$$\|K\alpha_n - p\alpha_n\| \leq \|K\alpha_n - K_n\alpha_n\| + \|p_n\ \alpha_n - p\alpha_n\|$$

$$\leq \|K - K_n\| + |p_n - p|.$$

In view of the complete continuity, there is a μ in $\mathscr{R}$ and a subsequence $\{\alpha_{n_j}\}$ such that

(9) $$\lim_{j\to\infty} \|K\alpha_{n_j} - \mu\| = 0.$$

The inequality

$$\|\mu - p\alpha_{n_j}\| \leq \|\mu - K\alpha_{n_j}\| + \|K\alpha_{n_j} - p\alpha_{n_j}\|$$

together with (8) and (9) proves

(10) $$\lim_{j\to\infty} \|\mu - p\alpha_{n_j}\| = 0.$$

It follows that $\|\mu\| = \lim\limits_{j\to\infty} \|p\alpha_{n_j}\| = |p| \neq 0$.

The proof of the theorem will be completed by showing that μ is an eigenvector of K with eigenvalue p. The desired result is a consequence of (9), (10) and

$$\|K\mu - p\mu\| \leq \|K\mu - Kp\alpha_{n_j}\| + \|pK\alpha_{n_j} - p\mu\|$$

$$\leq \|K\|\ \|\mu - p\alpha_{n_j}\| + |p|\ \|K\alpha_{n_j} - \mu\|. \quad \bigstar$$

One interesting aspect of the proof is the equation $p = \lim\limits_{n\to\infty} p_n$, where p_n, being the largest eigenvalues of certain transformations with separable kernels, may be obtained as in Section 4.1. This leads to a method of getting an approximate value for p.

In Exercise 4.2–1 it is indicated that

$$(11) \qquad \|K\| = \text{l.u.b.} \left\{ |(K\alpha, \alpha)| \,\Big|\, \|\alpha\| = 1, \alpha \text{ in } \mathscr{R} \right\}.$$

Thus Theorem 4.2B states that whenever $\|K\| \neq 0$, the transformation K has a nonzero eigenvalue equal to $\pm \|K\|$. The next result shows that a nonzero eigenvalue always exists unless the kernel is identically zero.

THEOREM 4.2C   If $K(x, y)$ is continuous and symmetric, then $(K\alpha, \alpha) = 0$ for all α if and only if $K(x, y) = 0$.

Proof $(K\alpha, \alpha) = 0$ for all α implies $(K\alpha, \beta) = 0$ for all α and β. This follows from the identity

$$(12) \qquad (K\alpha, \beta) = \tfrac{1}{2}\Big((K(\alpha + \beta), \alpha + \beta) - (K\alpha, \alpha) - (K\beta, \beta)\Big).$$

Taking $\beta = K\alpha$, we have $0 = (K\alpha, K\alpha)$ or

$$\int_a^b K(x, y)\,\alpha(y)\,dy = 0, \quad a \le x \le b, \quad \alpha \text{ in } \mathscr{R}.$$

For fixed x, $K(x, y) = \sigma(y)$ is in $\mathscr{R}$. Choosing $\alpha = \sigma$, we obtain

$$\int_a^b |\sigma(y)|^2\,dy = 0$$

or

$$K(x, y) = 0, \quad a \le y \le b, \quad a \le x \le b. \quad \star$$

We shall see that a simple change in the kernel makes it possible to eliminate any eigenvalue. In this way we can get at each eigenvalue in turn.

THEOREM 4.2D   Let $K\alpha_j = r_j\,\alpha_j$ where $\alpha_j, j = 1, \ldots, m$, are orthonormal eigenvectors of K. Then β is an eigenvector of K with nonzero eigenvalue r and orthogonal to $\alpha_j, j = 1, \ldots, m$, if and only if β is an eigenvector with nonzero eigenvalue r of the operator H whose kernel is

$$(13) \qquad H(x, y) = K(x, y) - \sum_{j=1}^{m} r_j\,\alpha_j(x)\,\alpha_j(y).$$

Proof Suppose $H\beta = r\beta$ where $r \neq 0$, $\beta \neq \theta$. We have

$$H\alpha_i = K\alpha_i - \sum_{j=1}^{m} r_j \, \alpha_j(x) \, (\alpha_i, \alpha_j) = K\alpha_i - r_i \, \alpha_i = 0 \, \alpha_i.$$

Therefore Theorem 4.1D implies β is orthogonal to $\alpha_1, \ldots, \alpha_m$. Then

$$r\beta = H\beta = K\beta - \sum_{j=1}^{m} r_j \, \alpha_j(x) \, (\beta, \alpha_j) = K\beta$$

so that β is an eigenvector of K with eigenvalue r.

Conversely, if β is orthogonal to $\alpha_1, \ldots, \alpha_m$ and $K\beta = r\beta$, then $H\beta = K\beta = r\beta$. ★

As an immediate consequence, we can prove the comment made in Section 4.1 that a symmetric integral transformation with a finite number of nonzero eigenvalues must arise from a separable kernel.

THEOREM 4.2E Let $\alpha_1, \ldots, \alpha_m$ constitute a basis of orthonormal eigenvectors of K corresponding to nonzero eigenvalues $r_1, \ldots, r_m$. If K has no other nonzero eigenvalue, then

$$(14) \qquad\qquad K(x, y) = \sum_{j=1}^{m} r_j \, \alpha_j(x) \, \alpha_j(y).$$

Proof The operator H corresponding to the kernel given by (13) has no nonzero eigenvalues in view of Theorem 4.2D, and hence by Theorem 4.2C, $H(x, y)$ is identically zero. This yields (14). ★

As mentioned in Corollary 1 of Theorem 4.2A, we order the nonzero eigenvalues, listing each one a number of times equal to the number of linearly independent eigenvectors corresponding to it, so that we have

$$K\alpha_i = s_i \, \alpha_i, \quad (\alpha_i, \alpha_j) = \delta_{ij}, \quad -\infty \leq -M \leq i \leq N \leq +\infty, \qquad i \neq 0,$$

$$s_{-1} \leq s_{-2} \leq \cdots < 0 < \cdots \leq s_2 \leq s_1.$$

With this notation we prove

THEOREM 4.2F

(a) If $i < N$, $\quad s_{i+1} = $ l.u.b. $\{(K\alpha, \alpha) \mid \|\alpha\| = 1, \quad \alpha \perp \alpha_1, \ldots, \alpha_i\}$.

(b) If $-i > -M$, $\quad s_{-i-1} = $ g.l.b. $\{(K\alpha, \alpha) \mid \|\alpha\| = 1, \quad \alpha \perp \alpha_{-1}, \ldots, \alpha_{-i}\}$.

Proof   When $N > 0$, Theorem 4.2B states that

$$\text{l.u.b. } \{(K\alpha, \alpha) \mid \|\alpha\| = 1\} = s_1.$$

If $N > i$, let

(15)
$$K_i(x, y) = K(x, y) - \sum_{j=1}^{i} s_j \, \alpha_j(x) \, \alpha_j(y).$$

Then, in view of Theorem 4.2D, the integral transformation K_i has exactly $s_{i+1}, s_{i+2}, \ldots$ as positive eigenvalues, with $\alpha_{i+1}, \alpha_{i+2}, \ldots$ as corresponding eigenvectors. It follows that

(16)
$$s_{i+1} = \text{l.u.b. } \left\{ (K_i\alpha, \alpha) \,\middle|\, \|\alpha\| = 1 \right\}.$$

But

$$K_i\alpha = K\alpha \text{ when } \alpha \perp \alpha_j, \quad j = 1, \ldots, i.$$

Therefore

$$s_{i+1} \geq \text{l.u.b. } \left\{ (K_i\alpha, \alpha) \,\middle|\, \|\alpha\| = 1, \, \alpha \perp \alpha_j, \quad j = 1, \ldots, i \right\}$$

$$= \text{l.u.b. } \left\{ (K\alpha, \alpha) \,\middle|\, \|\alpha\| = 1, \, \alpha \perp \alpha_j, \quad j = 1, \ldots, i \right\}$$

$$\geq (K\alpha_{i+1}, \alpha_{i+1}) = s_{i+1}.$$

The inequalities become equalities and the proof of the first part of the theorem is complete. The result about negative eigenvalues may be obtained by considering $-K$.   ★

By observing that the proof of Theorem 2.8B applies, we obtain

Corollary 1

If $i < N$,

$$s_{i+1} = \underset{\beta}{\text{g.l.b.}} \left[\underset{\alpha}{\text{l.u.b.}} \left\{ (K\alpha, \alpha) \,\middle|\, \|\alpha\| = 1, \, \alpha \perp \beta_j, \quad j = 1, \ldots, i \right\} \right]$$

and a similar proof yields

Corollary 2

If $-i > -M$,

$$s_{-i-1} = \underset{\beta}{\text{l.u.b.}} \left[\underset{\alpha}{\text{g.l.b.}} \left\{ (K\alpha, \alpha) \,\middle|\, \|\alpha\| = 1, \quad \alpha \perp \beta_j, \quad j = 1, \ldots, i \right\} \right].$$

With only a few slight changes, the results of this section may be developed for the corresponding integral transformation over $\mathscr{R}^*$. The only changes in the theorems are in Equation (13) which becomes

$$H(x, y) = K(x, y) - \sum_{j=1}^{m} r_j \, \alpha_j(x) \, \overline{\alpha_j(y)},$$

and in Equation (14) which becomes

$$K(x, y) = \sum_{j=1}^{m} r_j \, \alpha_j(x) \, \overline{\alpha_j(y)}.$$

Except for a few conjugate signs, and a modification of (12) (see Exercise 4.2–4), the proofs are the same.

Exercise 4.2

1. (a) Show that $\|K\| = $ l.u.b. $\{|(K\alpha, \beta)| \mid \|\alpha\| = 1, \|\beta\| = 1, \alpha \text{ and } \beta \text{ in } \mathscr{R}\}$. This is Exercise 2.8–2.

   (b) Show that $\|K\| = $ l.u.b. $\{|(K\alpha, \alpha)| \mid \|\alpha\| = 1, \alpha \text{ in } \mathscr{R}\}$. *Hint:* Denote the right side by c. In view of part (a), we have $c \le \|K\|$. We will have $\|K\| \le c$ if we can show $|(K\alpha, \beta)| \le c$ whenever $\|\alpha\| = \|\beta\| = 1$. Use

   $$(A) \quad (K\alpha, \beta) = \left(K\left(\frac{\alpha + \beta}{2}\right), \frac{\alpha + \beta}{2}\right) - \left(K\left(\frac{\alpha - \beta}{2}\right), \frac{\alpha - \beta}{2}\right)$$

   to obtain

   $$|(K\alpha, \beta)| \le c \left\|\frac{\alpha + \beta}{2}\right\|^2 + c \left\|\frac{\alpha - \beta}{2}\right\|^2 = c.$$

   [(A) was obtained with symmetry of K and reality of $(K\alpha, \beta)$. The same proof however applies for $\mathscr{R}^*$ for if $(K\alpha, \beta) = re^{it}$, r and t real, define $\mu = e^{-it}\alpha$. Then $(K\mu, \beta)$ is real and $|(K\mu, \beta)| \le c$ implies $|(K\alpha, \beta)| \le c$.]

2. This exercise yields a proof that the symmetric integral operator K with $\|K\| \ne 0$ has a nonzero eigenvalue without approximating by symmetric separable kernels. Let $\{\alpha_n\}$ have the property that $\|\alpha_n\| = 1$ and $\lim_{n \to \infty} |(K\alpha_n, \alpha_n)| = \|K\|$. (See Exercise 1(b).) Choose the sequence so that $(K\alpha_n, \alpha_n)$ converges to r, where $r = \|K\|$ or $-\|K\|$. Use

   $$0 \le \|K\alpha_n - r\alpha_n\|^2 = \|K\alpha_n\|^2 - 2r(K\alpha_n, \alpha_n) + r^2 \|\alpha_n\|^2$$

   to show that $\lim_{n \to \infty} \|K\alpha_n - r\alpha_n\| = 0$. The rest of the proof follows Theorem 4.2B after Equation (8).

3. (a) In Section 5.2 we shall prove that if $K(x, y)$ is a continuous symmetric function on $a \leq x \leq b, a \leq y \leq b$, then for $\epsilon > 0$, there is a symmetric polynomial in x and y, $p(x, y)$, such that $|K(x, y) - p(x, y)| < \epsilon$ for $a \leq x \leq b, a \leq y \leq b$. Show that this implies the existence of a sequence of symmetric separable kernels $K_n(x, y)$ and a constant D such that

$$\int_a^b \int_a^b |K(x, y) - K_n(x, y)|^2 \, dx \, dy \leq \frac{1}{n^2},$$

$$\int_a^b |K(x, y) - K_n(x, y)|^2 \, dy \leq \frac{1}{n^2} \text{ for } a \leq x \leq b,$$

$$\int_a^b |K_n(x, y)|^2 \, dy \leq D^2.$$

(b) Using the kernels in part (a) to form the integral transformations K_n in the proof of Theorem 4.2B, and the relation $K_n \alpha_n = p_n \alpha_n$ there derived, show that α_n form a uniformly bounded equicontinuous set on $a \leq x \leq b$ and hence that there exists a continuous function σ and a subsequence $\{\alpha_{n_j}\}$ converging uniformly to σ on $a \leq x \leq b$.

(c) Prove $\|\sigma\| = 1$ and $K\sigma = p\sigma$.

4. (a) Prove Theorem 4.2C when $K(x, y)$ is a complex kernel and the transformation K is defined over $\mathscr{R}^*$. *Hint:* By Equation (12), $(K\alpha, \beta) = 0$ whenever $(K\alpha, \beta)$ is real. If $(K\alpha, \beta)$ is complex and is equal to re^{it}, r and t real, let $\mu = e^{-it}\alpha$ so $(K\mu, \beta)$ is real.

(b) Accomplish the same result by use of

$$(K(\alpha + i\beta), a + i\beta) - i(K(\alpha + \beta), \alpha + \beta) - (1 - i)((K\alpha, \alpha) + (K\beta, \beta))$$
$$= -2i(K\alpha, \beta).$$

5. Make a proof of Theorem 4.2C using the method of proof in Theorem 4.1C.

6. Prove Corollary 2 of Theorem 4.2E.

7. (a) Arrange the eigenvalues in order of decreasing absolute value, repeating each nonzero eigenvalue a number of times equal to the number of linearly independent eigenvectors associated with it, so that

$$K\sigma_i = r_i \sigma_i, \quad (\sigma_i, \sigma_j) = \delta_{ij}, \quad i = 1, 2, \ldots, N \leq \infty,$$
$$|r_1| \geq |r_2| \geq \cdots > 0.$$

Use Exercise 1 and a proof similar to that of Theorem 4.2F to show that, if $i < N$,

$$|r_{i+1}| = \text{l.u.b.} \{|(K\alpha, \alpha)| \mid \|\alpha\| = 1, \alpha \perp \sigma_1, \ldots \sigma_i\}.$$

(b) Show also that

$$|r_{i+1}| = \text{l.u.b.} \{\|K\alpha\| \mid \|\alpha\| = 1, \alpha \perp \sigma_1, \ldots \sigma_i\}.$$

Hint: When K_i is defined by

$$K_i(x, y) = K(x, y) - \sum_{j=1}^{i} r_i \sigma_i(x) \sigma_i(y)$$

and $\alpha \perp \sigma_1, \ldots, \sigma_i, \|\alpha\| = 1$, then

$$\|K\alpha\| = \|K_i \alpha\| \leq \|K_i\| = |r_{i+1}|.$$

8. Let P and Q be two integral operators such that $P\alpha = Q\alpha$ for every continuous α. Show that the kernels of P and Q are identical.

9. Show that l.u.b. $\{(K\alpha, \alpha) \mid \|\alpha\| = 1, \alpha \text{ in } \mathscr{R}\} \geq 0$. *Hint:* If the value is less than 0, K must have only a finite number of eigenvalues. Then use Theorem 4.2E and Exercise 4.1–5(b) to obtain a contradiction.

10. (a) Show that if zero is not an eigenvalue of K then the only vector orthogonal to all the eigenvectors α_i is the zero vector.
    Hint: Use Problem 7(b).

    (b) Prove the converse of (a).

4.3

EXPANSION THEOREMS

Let us recall some of the results obtained for a symmetric transformation T on an n-dimensional Euclidean vector space $\mathscr{E}$. We found n orthonormal vectors $\alpha_1, \ldots, \alpha_n$ satisfying $T\alpha_i = r_i \alpha_i$ such that if β is in $\mathscr{E}$, then

$$\text{(1)} \qquad \beta = \sum_{i=1}^{n} (\beta, \alpha_i)\, \alpha_i.$$

$$\text{(2)} \qquad T\beta = \sum_{i=1}^{n} r_i\, (\beta, \alpha_i)\, \alpha_i.$$

Is it possible to obtain similar results for the symmetric integral transformation K on $\mathscr{R}$?

Consider Example (1) of Section 4.1. For the kernel

$$\text{(3)} \quad K(x, y) = 1 + \cos x \cos y + \sin x \sin y, \quad -\pi \leq x \leq \pi, \ -\pi \leq y \leq \pi,$$

we found only three orthogonal solutions of $K\alpha = s\alpha$, $s \neq 0$. These were 1, $\cos x$, and $\sin x$. Any linear combination of these three is continuous and so 1, $\cos x$, $\sin x$ do not span $\mathscr{R}$. Nor can every continuous function be expressed linearly in terms of 1, $\sin x$, $\cos x$, for the vector space of continuous functions has infinite dimension. Suppose, for example, that

$$\text{(4)} \qquad \cos 2x = a + b \cos x + c \sin x.$$

Integrating both sides of (4) over $-\pi \leq x \leq \pi$, we obtain $a = 0$. Multiplying (4) by $\cos x$ and integrating, we obtain $b = 0$. Multiplying (4) by $\sin x$

and integrating yields $c = 0$. Thus (4) cannot hold. This conclusion is not surprising. After all, we have discarded all eigenvectors with eigenvalue zero. Let us seek them.

The identities

(5) $\qquad \cos px \cos qx = \tfrac{1}{2}(\cos (p + q)x + \cos (p - q)x)$,

(6) $\qquad \sin px \sin qx = -\tfrac{1}{2}(\cos (p + q)x - \cos(p - q)x)$,

(7) $\qquad \sin px \cos qx = \tfrac{1}{2}(\sin(p + q)x + \sin(p - q)x)$,

yield, when p and q are integers,

(8) $\qquad \displaystyle\int_{-\pi}^{\pi} \cos px \cos qx \, dx = \int_{-\pi}^{\pi} \sin px \sin qx \, dx$

$$= \begin{cases} 0 & \text{for } p \neq q, \quad p, q = 0, 1, 2, \dots \\ \pi & \text{for } p = q, \quad p = 1, 2, \dots \end{cases}$$

(9) $\qquad \displaystyle\int_{-\pi}^{\pi} \sin px \cos qx \, dx = 0 \qquad \text{for } p = 1, 2, \dots, \quad q = 0, 1, 2, \dots$

It follows that the functions

(10) $\qquad 1, \cos nx, \sin nx, \qquad n = 1, 2, \dots, \qquad -\pi \leq x \leq \pi$,

are orthogonal. As a result, the functions $\cos nx$, $\sin nx$, $n = 2, 3, 4, \dots$ must be eigenvectors with eigenvalue zero for the kernel given by (3). Does there exist another eigenvector β with eigenvalue zero orthogonal to those already found? By Theorem 4.1D β would be orthogonal to 1, $\cos x$, $\sin x$, the eigenvectors with nonzero eigenvalues, and therefore β would be orthogonal to all the vectors listed in (10). We shall see in Chapter 5 that any vector orthogonal to all the vectors in (10) must be the zero vector. Assuming this fact, we conclude that the vectors listed in (10) constitute a maximal set of orthogonal eigenvectors of K. The orthonormalized eigenvectors may be denoted by α_n, $n = 0, 1, 2, \dots$, where

(11) $\alpha_0(x) = \dfrac{1}{\sqrt{2\pi}}, \qquad \alpha_{2j-1}(x) = \dfrac{\cos jx}{\sqrt{\pi}}, \qquad \alpha_{2j}(x) = \dfrac{\sin jx}{\sqrt{\pi}}, \qquad j = 1, 2, \dots.$

Then the desired extension of (1) is the possibility of expressing β in $\mathcal{R}$ as an infinite series

(12) $\qquad \displaystyle\sum_{n=0}^{\infty} (\beta, \alpha_i) \, \alpha_i(x) = \sum_{n=0}^{\infty} \left(\int_{-\pi}^{\pi} \beta(y) \, \alpha_i(y) \, dy \right) \alpha_i(x),$

or

(13) $$\frac{a_0}{2} + \sum_{n=1}^{\infty} \left(a_n \cos nx + b_n \sin nx \right),$$

where

(14) $$a_n = \frac{1}{\pi} \int_{-\pi}^{\pi} \beta(y) \cos ny \, dy, \qquad n = 0, 1, 2, \ldots,$$

(15) $$b_n = \frac{1}{\pi} \int_{-\pi}^{\pi} \beta(y) \sin ny \, dy, \qquad n = 1, 2, \ldots.$$

The series (13) with coefficients a_n, b_n given by (14) and (15) is called the **Fourier series** for β. It is so named in honor of J. B. J. Fourier (1768–1830), who asserted that many functions could be represented by such a series. A more detailed discussion of Fourier series will be given later. For the present, we only wish to mention that not every continuous function on $-\pi \leq x \leq \pi$ can be represented by a convergent Fourier series. Nevertheless, we shall see in Chapter 5 that with a proper interpretation, an extension of (1) is still possible.

The next theorem gives an extension of (2). Note that the eigenvectors corresponding to eigenvalue zero do not enter into the result.

THEOREM 4.3A Let $\{s_i\}$, $-\infty \leq -M \leq i \leq N \leq \infty$, $i \neq 0$, be the spectrum of K with associated orthonormal eigenvectors $\{\alpha_i\}$. If β is in $\mathscr{R}$, then

(16) $$K\beta = \sum_i s_i \, (\beta, \alpha_i)\alpha_i = \sum_i (K\beta, \alpha_i)\alpha_i$$

and the series converges absolutely uniformly on $a \leq x \leq b$.

Proof The series in (16) will converge absolutely uniformly on $a \leq x \leq b$ if, for every $\epsilon > 0$, there is an integer $N_1(\epsilon) > 0$ such that

(17) $$\sum_{i=m}^{n} |s_i \, a_i \, \alpha_i(x)| < \epsilon$$

whenever m and n have the same sign, $|m| > N_1$, $|n| > N_1$, $a_i = (\beta, \alpha_i)$. Let

$$A \geq \text{l.u.b.} \left\{ \int_a^b |K(x, y)|^2 \, dy \,\middle|\, a \leq x \leq b \right\}.$$

By Bessel's inequality, Theorem 1.3E, Corollary 2,

$$\sideset{}{'}\sum_{i} |a_i|^2 \le \|\beta\|^2$$

where the prime (') on the sum indicates i does not take on the value 0. It follows that there exists an integer N_1 such that if m and n have the same sign, $|m| > N_1$, $|n| > N_1$, then

$$\sum_{i=m}^{n} |a_i|^2 \le \frac{\epsilon^2}{A}.$$

An application of Schwarz's inequality and equation 4.2(4) will now yield (17). We have

$$\sum_{i=m}^{n} |s_i\, a_i\, \alpha_i| \le \left(\sum_{i=m}^{n} |a_i|^2 \right)^{1/2} \left(\sum_{i=m}^{n} s_i^2\, |\alpha_i|^2 \right)^{1/2}$$

$$\le \left(\frac{\epsilon}{\sqrt{A}} \right) \left(\int_a^b |K(x, y)|^2\, dy \right)^{1/2} \le \epsilon.$$

It remains to show that the series converges to $K\beta$. If the number of eigenvalues is finite, then

$$K(x, y) = \sum_i s_i\, \alpha_i(x)\, \alpha_i(y)$$

by Theorem 4.2E. From this we derive

$$K\beta = \sum_i s_i(\beta, \alpha_i)\, \alpha_i.$$

Consider next the case when $N = \infty$, $M = \infty$, the other cases being treated similarly. Then $\lim_{i \to \infty} s_i = 0 = \lim_{i \to \infty} s_{-i}$. If σ is any vector orthogonal to $\alpha_1, \ldots, \alpha_j, \alpha_{-1}, \ldots, \alpha_{-j}$, then

$$\|\sigma\|^2\, s_{-j-1} \le (K\sigma, \sigma) \le \|\sigma\|^2\, s_{j+1}$$

as stated in Theorem 4.2F. Therefore, for any sequence $\{\sigma_j\}$ of vectors, with $\sigma_j \perp \alpha_1, \ldots, \alpha_j, \alpha_{-1}, \ldots, \alpha_{-j}$, and with the property that $\|\sigma_j\| \le B$, a constant independent of j, we have

(18) $$\lim_{j \to \infty} |(K\sigma_j, \sigma_j)| = 0.$$

Let $\{\mu_j\}$ be any sequence of vectors with $\|\mu_j\| \le B$ and $\mu_j \perp \alpha_1, \ldots,$ $\alpha_j, \alpha_{-1}, \ldots, \alpha_{-j}$. Then $\sigma_j + \mu_j$ and $\sigma_j - \mu_j$ are $\perp$ to $\alpha_1, \ldots, \alpha_j, \alpha_{-1}, \ldots,$ α_{-j} and $\|\sigma_j + \mu_j\| \le 2B$, $\|\sigma_j - \mu_j\| \le 2B$. Now (18) and the relation

$$(19) \qquad (K\sigma, \mu) = \tfrac{1}{4} \left((K(\sigma + \mu), \sigma + \mu) - (K(\sigma - \mu), \sigma - \mu) \right)$$

show that

$$(20) \qquad \lim_{j \to \infty} |(K\sigma_j, \mu_j)| = 0.$$

The desired objective will be attained by selecting particular sequences $\{\sigma_j\}$ and $\{\mu_j\}$. Let

$$\sigma_j = \beta - \sum_{i=-j}^{j}{}' (\beta, \alpha_i)\, \alpha_i.$$

Then σ_j is orthogonal to $\alpha_1, \ldots, \alpha_j, \alpha_{-1}, \ldots, \alpha_{-j}$ and $\|\sigma_j\| \le \|\beta\|$. The last inequality is a consequence of Corollary 1 of Theorem 1.3F which states that

$$\Big\| \beta - \sum_{i=-j}^{j}{}' (\beta, \alpha_i)\, \alpha_i \Big\| \le \Big\| \beta - \sum_{i=-j}^{j}{}' c_i\, \alpha_i \Big\|$$

for arbitrary c_i, in particular $c_i = 0$.

Similarly, if we let

$$\mu_j = K\sigma_j = K\beta - \sum_{i=-j}^{j}{}' (\beta, \alpha_i)\, s_i\, \alpha_i$$

$$= K\beta - \sum_{i=-j}^{j}{}' (\beta, K\alpha_i)\, \alpha_i = K\beta - \sum_{i=-j}^{j}{}' (K\beta, \alpha_i)\, \alpha_i,$$

then $\mu_j \perp \alpha_1, \ldots, \alpha_j, \alpha_{-1}, \ldots, \alpha_{-j}$ and $\|\mu_j\| \le \|K\beta\|$.

With these choices for σ_j and μ_j in (20), we have

$$(21) \qquad \lim_{j \to \infty} |(K\sigma_j, K\sigma_j)| = 0$$

or

$$\lim_{j \to \infty} \int_a^b \Big| K\beta - \sum_{i=-j}^{j}{}' s_i\, (\beta, \alpha_i)\, \alpha_i \Big|^2 \, dx = 0.$$

In view of the uniform convergence, this may be written

$$\int_a^b \Big| K\beta - \sum_i s_i\, (\beta, \alpha_i)\, \alpha_i \Big|^2 \, dx = 0.$$

The continuity of the integrand now implies

$$KB = \sum_i s_i\,(\beta,\,\alpha_i)\,\alpha_i. \quad \star$$

The previous theorem is an extension of the diagonalization theorem proved in Section 2.7 for symmetric transformations on an n-dimensional Euclidean vector space. We may give it the following interpretation. Suppose that in some sense β is represented by $\sum_i (\beta,\,\alpha_i)\,\alpha_i$, that is, there is a "basis" $\{\alpha_i\}$ in which β has the "coordinate representation" $[(\beta,\,\alpha_i)]$. Then $K\beta$ has the representation $[s_i(\beta,\,\alpha_i)]$ in the same "basis". In other words, in the coordinate system chosen, the operator K is essentially an operation of "multiplication". All these concepts must be made more precise.

For the case when K has only a finite number of eigenvalues, the proof of Theorem 4.3A was a consequence of Theorem 4.2E, an expansion of the kernel $K(x, y)$ in terms of the eigenvectors. In the general case such an expansion is not possible. However, we shall see that the kernel of the operator K^n, $n > 1$, has such an expansion. For this purpose, we introduce the concept of iterated kernels.

Let $P(x, y)$ and $Q(x, y)$ be continuous on $a \le x \le b$, $a \le y \le b$. Define

$$(22) \qquad R(x, y) = \int_a^b P(x, t)\, Q(t, y)dt, \qquad a \le x \le b,\, a \le y \le b.$$

We leave for Exercise 4.3–1 the proof that $R(x, y)$ is continuous on $a \le x \le b$, $a \le y \le b$. $R(x, y)$ need not be symmetric when $P(x, y)$ and $Q(x, y)$ are. However, if we also have

$$(23) \qquad \int_a^b P(x, t)\, Q(t, y)dt = \int_a^b Q(x, t)\, P(t, y)dt$$

then $R(x, y)$ is symmetric, for

$$R(x, y) = \int_a^b P(x, t)\, Q(t, y)dt = \int_a^b Q(x, t)\, P(t, y)dt$$

$$= \int_a^b P(y, t)\, Q(t, x)dt = R(y, x).$$

The kernel given by (22) defines an operator R and

$$R\alpha = \int_a^b \int_a^b P(x, t)\, Q(t, y)dt\, \alpha(y)dy = \int_a^b P(x, t) \int_a^b Q(t, y)\, \alpha(y)dy\, dt$$

$$= \int_a^b P(x, t)\, (Q\alpha)\,(t)dt = P(Q\alpha) = (PQ)\alpha.$$

Therefore, $R(x, y)$ is the kernel of the operator PQ and $R = PQ$. When (23) is valid, $PQ = QP$, and $PR = P(PQ) = P(QP) = (PQ)P = RP$ so that R commutes with P.

In particular, if we define

$$K^n(x, y) = \int_a^b K(x, t)\, K^{n-1}(t, y)dt, \qquad n = 2, 3, \ldots$$

where $K^1(x, y) = K(x, y)$ is symmetric, then $K^n(x, y)$ is symmetric and is the kernel of the integral transformation K^n. The kernel $K^n(x, y)$ is called the nth **iterated kernel** of $K(x, y)$. Since $K^n = K^r K^s$ for $r + s = n$, it follows that

$$(24) \qquad K^n(x, y) = \int_a^b K^r(x, t)\, K^s(t, y)dt, \qquad r + s = n.$$

THEOREM 4.3B If $\{s_i\}, \{\alpha_i\}$ are defined as in Theorem 4.3A, then

$$(25) \qquad K^n(x, y) = \sum_i s_i^n\, \alpha_i(x)\, \alpha_i(y), \qquad n = 2, 3, \ldots$$

and the series converges absolutely uniformly on $a \leq x \leq b, a \leq y \leq b$.

Proof For fixed y, define $\beta(x) = K^{n-1}(x, y)$. Then

$$K\beta(u) = \int_a^b K(u, t)\, \beta(t)dt = \int_a^b K(u, t)\, K^{n-1}(t, y)dt = K^n(u, y).$$

Theorem 4.3A states that every function of the form $K\beta$ has an expansion in eigenvectors,

$$K\beta(x) = \sum_i (K\beta, \alpha_i)\, \alpha_i(x),$$

where $(K\beta, \alpha_i) = \int_a^b K^n(u, y)\, \alpha_i(u)du = K^n \alpha_i(y) = s_i^n\, \alpha_i(y)$.

This yields the series (25), converging uniformly in x for each fixed y. To finish the proof of the theorem we must show that the series converges absolutely uniformly in both x and y. The particular case $n = 2$ for the result just proved shows that

$$K^2(x, x) = \sum_i s_i^2\, |\alpha_i(x)|^2, \qquad a \leq x \leq b.$$

In view of Theorem 3.2J, the last series converges uniformly. Thus there exists an integer $N(\epsilon)$ such that if m and n have the same sign, $|m| > N(\epsilon)$, $|n| > N(\epsilon)$, then

$$\sum_{i=m}^{n} s_i^2 \, |\alpha_i(x)|^2 < \epsilon, \qquad a \leq x \leq b.$$

Furthermore we may suppose $N(\epsilon)$ is so large that $|s_i| \leq 1$ for $|i| > N(\epsilon)$. We apply the Schwarz inequality to obtain

$$\sum_{i=m}^{n} |s_i^n \, \alpha_i(x) \, \alpha_i(y)|^2 \leq \sum_{i=m}^{n} |s_i|^n \, |\alpha_i(x)|^2 \sum_{i=m}^{n} |s_i|^n \, |\alpha_i(y)|^2$$

$$\leq \sum_{i=m}^{n} |s_i|^2 \, |\alpha_i(x)|^2 \sum_{i=m}^{n} |s_i|^2 \, |\alpha_i(y)|^2 \leq \epsilon^2$$

for $a \leq x \leq b$, $a \leq y \leq b$. In view of the Cauchy criterion for convergence, the theorem is proved. ★

Just as in the finite dimensional case, the eigenvalues of K^n are the nth powers of the eigenvalues of K.

THEOREM 4.3C Let $\{s_i\}$, $\{\alpha_i\}$ be defined as in Theorem 4.3A. The nonzero eigenvalues of K^n are s_i^n. If $\mathscr{S}(r)$ is the set of indices i such that $s_i^n = r \neq 0$, then the number of linearly independent eigenvectors of K^n for eigenvalue r is the number of indices in $\mathscr{S}(r)$.

Proof Let $K^n \beta = r\beta$, $r \neq 0$. In view of the uniform convergence furnished by Theorem 4.3B,

(26) $$K^n \beta = \sum_{i} s_i^n \, (\beta, \alpha_i) \, \alpha_i.$$

Every eigenvector of K corresponding to an eigenvalue s_i is also an eigenvector of K^n corresponding to an eigenvalue s_i^n, since $K^n \alpha_i = K^{n-1} K\alpha_i = s_i K^{n-1} \alpha_i$. Therefore, Theorem 4.1D shows that $(\beta, \alpha_i) = 0$ unless i is in $\mathscr{S}(r)$. Equation (26) reduces to

$$r\beta = K^n \beta = \sum_{i \text{ in } \mathscr{S}(r)} s_i^n \, (\beta, \alpha_i) \, \alpha_i.$$

This shows that β is a finite linear combination of eigenvectors of K^n corresponding to eigenvalue s_i^n. Hence $r = s_i^n$ and the number of linearly independent eigenvectors of K^n for eigenvalue r is exactly the number of indices in $\mathscr{S}(r)$. ★

Although the expansion given by (25) is, in general, not valid for $n = 1$, it is possible to prove an expansion theorem of a different type.

THEOREM 4.3D

$$\lim_{n \to \infty} \int_a^b \left| K(x, y) - \sum_{i=-n}^{n}{}' s_i \, \alpha_i(x) \, \alpha_i(y) \right|^2 dx = 0$$

uniformly on $a \leq y \leq b$.

Proof A simple computation gives

$$\int_a^b \left| K(x, y) - \sum_{i=-n}^{n}{}' s_i \, \alpha_i(x) \, \alpha_i(y) \right|^2 dx = K^2(y, y) - \sum_{i=-n}^{n}{}' s_i^2 \, |\alpha_i(y)|^2$$

and the desired result follows from Theorem 4.3B.   ★

The symmetric kernel $K(x, y)$ is called **positive definite** when it defines a positive definite integral transformation, that is, when $(K\alpha, \alpha) > 0$ for α in $\mathscr{R}$ unless $\alpha = \theta$. The symmetric kernel is called **positive semi-definite** when $(K\alpha, \alpha) \geq 0$ for all α in $\mathscr{R}$. It is an immediate consequence of Theorem 4.2F that the kernel is positive semi-definite if and only if all the eigenvalues are nonnegative.

THEOREM 4.3E   If $K(x, y)$ is positive semi-definite, then $K(x, x) \geq 0$ for $a \leq x \leq b$.

Proof If, to suppose the contrary, $K(t, t) < 0$ for some t, then there is an interval $\mathscr{I}$ containing t such that $K(x, y) < 0$ for x in $\mathscr{I}$, y in $\mathscr{I}$. Set $\alpha(x) = 1$ for x in $\mathscr{I}$, $\alpha(x) = 0$ for x not in $\mathscr{I}$ and obtain the contradiction

$$(K\alpha, \alpha), = \int_{\mathscr{I}} \int_{\mathscr{I}} K(x, y) dx \, dy < 0.   \star$$

When $K(x, y)$ is positive semi-definite, the expansion theorem given by (25) is valid even for $n = 1$.

THEOREM 4.3F   Let $K(x, y)$ be positive semi-definite. Then

$$K(x, y) = \sum_{i}{}' s_i \, \alpha_i(x) \, \alpha_i(y)$$

and the series converges absolutely uniformly for $a \leq x \leq b$, $a \leq y \leq b$.

Proof The nonzero eigenvalues of the transformation whose kernel is

$$H(x, y) = K(x, y) - \sum_{i=1}^{n} s_i \, \alpha_i(x) \, \alpha_i(y) \quad \text{are} \quad s_{n+1}, \; s_{n+2}, \ldots \quad \text{which are non-}$$

negative so that $H(x, y)$ is positive semi-definite and

$$K(x, x) - \sum_{i=1}^{n} s_i \, |\alpha_i(x)|^2 \geq 0$$

by Theorem 4.3E. Letting n approach ∞, we obtain

(27)
$$\sum_{i} s_i \, |\alpha_i(x)|^2 \leq K(x, x).$$

Therefore, for fixed x, and $\epsilon > 0$, there is an integer $N(\epsilon)$ such that

$$\sum_{i=m}^{n} s_i \, |\alpha_i(x)|^2 < \epsilon^2 \qquad \text{for } n > m > N.$$

By Schwarz's inequality,

(28)
$$\Big| \sum_{i=m}^{n} s_i \, \alpha_i(x) \, \alpha_i(y) \Big|^2 \leq \sum_{i=m}^{n} s_i \, |\alpha_i(x)|^2 \sum_{i=m}^{n} s_i \, |\alpha_i(y)|^2 \leq \epsilon^2 \, A^2$$

where $A^2 = \text{l.u.b.} \, \{K(y, y) \mid a \leq y \leq b\} \geq \sum_{i} s_i \, |\alpha_i(y)|^2$ by (27).

The inequality (28) and the Cauchy criterion prove that the series in the theorem converges uniformly in y for fixed x (and similarly uniformly in x for fixed y). Write

$$\int_{a}^{b} \Big| K(x, y) - \sum_{i} s_i \, \alpha_i(x) \, \alpha_i(y) \Big|^2 dy$$

$$\leq 2 \int_{a}^{b} \Big| K(x, y) - \sum_{i=1}^{n} s_i \, \alpha_i(x) \, \alpha_i(y) \Big|^2 dy + 2 \int_{a}^{b} \Big| \sum_{i>n} s_i \, \alpha_i(x) \, \alpha_i(y) \Big|^2 dy$$

and apply Theorem 4.3D and the uniform convergence just proved to get

$$\int_{a}^{b} \Big| K(x, y) - \sum_{i} s_i \, \alpha_i(x) \, \alpha_i(y) \Big|^2 dy = 0, \qquad a \leq x \leq b.$$

This shows that

(29)
$$K(x, y) = \sum_{i} s_i \, \alpha_i(x) \, \alpha_i(y).$$

We need only establish the uniformity of convergence in both x and y. Setting $y = x$ in (29), we have

$$K(x, x) = \sum_i s_i \, |\alpha_i(x)|^2.$$

The series converges uniformly in view of Theorem 3.2J. There exists $M(\epsilon)$ such that

$$\sum_{i=m}^n s_i \, |\alpha_i(x)|^2 < \epsilon \qquad \text{for } n > m > M(\epsilon).$$

Now for $a \leq x \leq b, a \leq y \leq b$,

$$\left(\sum_m^n |s_i \, \alpha_i(x) \, \alpha_i(y)| \right)^2 \leq \sum_m^n s_i \, |\alpha_i(x)|^2 \sum_m^n s_i \, |\alpha_i(y)|^2 < \epsilon^2.$$

This proves the desired absolute-uniform convergence. $\star$

Let us now mention the alterations necessary to carry through the results for the space $\mathscr{R}^*$. Theorem 4.3A remains valid. Equation (25) must be replaced by $K^n (x, y) = \sum_i s_i^n \, \alpha_i(x) \, \overline{\alpha_i(y)}$. In Theorem 4.3D we must write

$$\lim_{n \to \infty} \int_a^b \left| K(x, y) - \sum_{i=-n}^n{}' s_i \, \alpha_i(x) \, \overline{\alpha_i(y)} \right|^2 dx = 0,$$

and in Theorem 4.3F, $K(x, y) = \sum_i s_i \, \alpha_i(x) \, \overline{\alpha_i(y)}$. Only simple changes are needed in the proofs.

Exercise 4.3

1. (a) Show that $R(x, y)$ defined in (22) is continuous in both variables.
   (b) Let $P(x, y) = x + y$, $Q(x, y) = xy$, $a \leq x \leq b, a \leq y \leq b$. Show that relation (23) is not satisfied.

2. Prove Exercise 4.2–10 by calculating $(K^2\beta, \beta)$ using Theorem 4.3B.

3. If α_i are the eigenvectors of K as in Theorem 4.3A, zero is not an eigenvalue, β is in $\mathscr{R}$, and $\Sigma(\beta, \alpha_i)\alpha_i$ converges uniformly, then prove $\beta = \sum_i (\beta, \alpha_i)\alpha_i$ (identical except for a set of measure zero).
   Hint: Apply Exercise 2.

4. (a) If σ, μ are in $\mathscr{R}$, show that
   $$\int_a^b \int_a^b K(x, y) \, \sigma(y) \, \mu(x) \, dx \, dy = \sum_i s_i \, (\sigma, \alpha_i) (\mu, \alpha_i).$$
   (b) If all the eigenvalues of K are positive (in particular, zero is not an eigenvalue), then prove K is positive definite.
   (c) Prove the converse of (b).

5. Suppose $\sum_i s_i \alpha_i(x) \alpha_i(y)$ converges uniformly in y for fixed x. Show that it converges to $K(x, y)$.

6. Let $\sigma_i(x)$ be orthonormal and continuous on $a \le x \le b$. Let $H(x, y) = \sum p_i \sigma_i(x) \sigma_i(y)$ converge uniformly in x and y on $a \le x \le b$, $a \le y \le b$. Show that the nonzero eigenvalues of H are exactly p_i with eigenvectors σ_i and there are no other linearly independent eigenvectors with nonzero eigenvalues.

7. Show that if $K(x, y)$ has only a finite number of negative eigenvalues, then $K(x, y) = \sum_i s_i \alpha_i(x) \alpha_i(y)$, the series converging absolutely uniformly in x and y. *Hint:* Consider $H(x, y) = K(x, y) - \sum_{i<0} s_i \alpha_i(x) \alpha_i(y)$.

8. Show that if $K(x, y)$ has only a finite number of negative eigenvalues, then $\sum_i s_i$ converges. *Hint:* Treat first the case where the eigenvalues are non-negative.

9. Show that the converse of Theorem 4.3E is false.

   (a) Try $K(x, y) = x + y$, $0 \le x \le 1$, $0 \le y \le 1$, $\alpha(x) = \left(\dfrac{x^2}{4}\right) - \dfrac{1}{9}$.

   (b) Make up another example, with a different kernel.

10. Let s_i and α_i be the nonzero eigenvalues and associated orthonormal eigenvectors corresponding to the kernel e^{xy} on the square $-a \le x \le a$, $-a \le y \le a$. Show that

$$\sum_i s_i^2 \alpha_i(x) \alpha_i(y) = \frac{2 \sinh(ax + ay)}{x + y}, \qquad x + y \ne 0,$$

and that the series converges uniformly on the square. Can you prove independently of any previous theory that the right side may be extended so as to be continuous in x and y on the square?

11. If $K(x, y) \ge 0$ and $K\alpha = r\alpha$, $r \ne 0$, where $\alpha(x) > 0$ on $a \le x \le b$, then the eigenvalue r has only one linearly independent eigenvector corresponding to it. *Hint:* If β is another eigenvector with eigenvalue r, obtain an equation of the form

$$\int_a^b \int_a^b K(x, y) \Big(\alpha(y) \beta(x) - \beta(y) \alpha(x) \Big) \alpha(y) \beta(x) / \alpha(x) \alpha(y) \, dx \, dy = 0,$$

interchange x and y, and add.

12. Carry through the theory for the integral operator over $\mathscr{R}^*$.
    (a) To prove Theorem 4.3A.
    (b) To prove the theorem corresponding to Theorem 4.3B.

13. The nth *trace* t_n of the kernel $K(x, y)$ is defined by $t_n = \int_a^b K^n(x, x) dx$, $n = 1$, $2, \ldots$. Assume $K(x, y)$ is not identically zero and show that

    (a) For $n \ge 2$, $t_n = \sum_i s_i^n$. If K is positive semi-definite, $t_1 = \sum_i s_i$.

    (b) $t_{2n} = \displaystyle\int_a^b \int_a^b |K^n(x, y)|^2 \, dx \, dy = \int_a^b \int_a^b K^{n-1}(x, t) K^{n+1}(t, x) dt \, dx$.

    (c) $0 < t_{2n}^2 \le t_{2n-2} t_{2n+2}$, and $\dfrac{t_{2n+2}}{t_{2n}} \ge \dfrac{t_4}{t_2}$, $n \ge 2$.

    (d) Each of the series $\displaystyle\sum_{n=1}^{\infty} t_{2n} z^{2n}$ and $\displaystyle\sum_{n=1}^{\infty} t_n z^n$ has a finite radius of convergence.

(e) Let s be the larger of $|s_1|$ and $|s_{-1}|$. Let q be the number of indices i such that $|s_i| = s$ and $\mathcal{Q}$ be the set of indices i such that $|s_i| < s$. Write

$$t_{2n} = qs^{2n}(1 + \epsilon(n)) \text{ where } \epsilon(n) = \frac{1}{q}\sum_{i \text{ in } \mathcal{Q}}\left|\frac{s_i}{s}\right|^{2n}. \text{ If } r = \text{l.u.b. } \left\{|s_i|\middle| i \text{ in } \mathcal{Q}\right\},$$

then $q\epsilon(n) \leq \left(\frac{r}{s}\right)^{2n}\sum_{i \text{ in } \mathcal{Q}}\left(\frac{s_i}{r}\right)^2$. Hence show that $\lim_{n\to\infty}\epsilon(n) = 0$, $\lim_{n\to\infty}\dfrac{t_{2n+2}}{t_{2n}} = s^2$.

This yields a method of calculating s.

(f) Prove that if $a_n > 0$ and $\lim_{n\to\infty}\dfrac{a_{n+1}}{a_n} = L$, then $\lim_{n\to\infty}(a_n)^{1/n} = L$. *Hint:* For some j, the ratios $\dfrac{a_{j+n}}{a_{j+n-1}}$ lie between $L - \epsilon$ and $L + \epsilon$. Hence

$$(L - \epsilon)^n < \frac{a_{j+n}}{a_j} < (L + \epsilon)^n,$$

$$\left(a_j(L - \epsilon)^n\right)^{1/(n+j)} < a_{j+n}\frac{1}{j+n} < \left(a_j(L + \epsilon)^n\right)^{1/(n+j)}.$$

Let $n \to \infty$.

(g) Use (f) to prove $s^2 = \lim_{n\to\infty} n\, (t_{2n})^{1/n}$

14. Let $K(x, y) = (1 - 3xy)/2$, $-1 \leq x \leq 1$, $-1 \leq y \leq 1$. Find $K^n(x, y)$ and the eigenvalues of K^n.

15. For example 1 of Section 4.1, find K^{100}.

16. (a) Let $M = \text{l.u.b. }\{|K(x, y)| \mid a \leq x \leq b, a \leq y \leq b\}$. Show that $|K^n(x, y)| \leq M^n(b - a)^{n-1}$.

(b) Form $G(x, y, z) = \sum_1^\infty \frac{K^n(x, y)}{n!} z^n$, where z is a real number. Show that the series converges uniformly in x, y and z for $|z| \leq c$. Show that $G(x, y, z)$ is continuous for $a \leq x \leq b, a \leq y \leq b$, all z.

(c) Show that

$$\frac{\partial}{\partial z}G(x, y, z) = K(x, y) + \int_a^b K(x, t)\, G(t, y, z)\, dt.$$

4.4

INTEGRAL EQUATIONS

The actual determination of eigenvalues and eigenvectors is difficult. A simple formula giving the solution is not to be expected since there may exist no function $\alpha \neq \theta$ or several such functions satisfying

(1)
$$\int_a^b K(x, y)\, \alpha(y)dy = s\alpha(x)$$

for given s. We shall assume that we have already determined the eigenvalues and eigenvectors and consider the problem of finding α to satisfy

$$(2) \qquad \alpha(x) = \beta(x) + r \int_a^b K(x, y)\, \alpha(y) dy.$$

The problem of determining a function occurring as part of an integrand in an equation involving an integral is referred to as an **integral equation.** The following are examples of integral equations.

EXAMPLE 1   Find α satisfying

$$(3) \qquad \sin x - x = \int_0^x (x - y)^2\, \alpha(y) dy.$$

Assuming a continuous solution exists and differentiating both sides we obtain

$$(4) \qquad \cos x - 1 = \int_0^x 2(x - y)\, \alpha(y) dy.$$

We have here used a theorem on the differentiation of an integral with respect to a parameter occurring in the limits of integration as well as in the integrand. Formally,

$$(5) \qquad \frac{d}{dx} \int_{a(x)}^{b(x)} f(x, y) dy = \int_{a(x)}^{b(x)} \frac{\partial}{\partial x} f(x, y) dy + f(x, b(x)) \frac{db}{dx} - f(x, a(x)) \frac{da}{dx}.$$

A theorem stating sufficient conditions for the validity of (5) will be found in Appendix I.

Two more differentiations applied to (4) yield

$$- \sin x = \int_0^x 2\alpha(y) dy,$$

$$- \cos x = 2\alpha(x),$$

so that the only possible continuous solution is $\alpha(x) = -\frac{1}{2} \cos x$ and this is easily checked to be a solution by substituting in (3) and integrating by parts.

EXAMPLE 2   Find α satisfying

$$(6) \qquad \sin x = \int_0^x (x - y)^2\, \alpha(y) dy.$$

Proceeding as in Example 1, we obtain $\alpha(x) = -\frac{1}{2} \cos x$, which cannot be a solution since it makes the integral equal to $\sin x - x$. Thus (6) has no continuous solutions.

EXAMPLE 3   Find α satisfying

$$(7) \qquad T(u) = \int_0^u \frac{1}{\sqrt{u-y}}\, \alpha(y)dy.$$

The integral in (7) is improper. Proceeding formally, multiply both sides of (7) by $\dfrac{1}{\sqrt{v-u}}$, and integrate with respect to u to obtain

$$(8) \qquad \int_0^v \frac{T(u)}{\sqrt{v-u}}\, du = \int_0^v \int_0^u \frac{1}{\sqrt{v-u}}\, \frac{1}{\sqrt{u-y}}\, \alpha(y)dy\, du$$

$$= \int_0^v \int_y^v \frac{du}{\sqrt{v-u}\,\sqrt{u-y}}\, \alpha(y)dy.$$

The inner integral can be evaluated by the substitution $u = y + (v - y)z$ for it then reduces to

$$\int_0^1 z^{-1/2}(1 - z)^{-1/2}\, dz = \beta(\tfrac{1}{2}, \tfrac{1}{2}) = \pi,$$

where $\beta(p, q)$ is the well known Beta function. From (8),

$$\int_0^v \frac{T(u)}{\sqrt{v-u}}\, du = \pi \int_0^v \alpha(y)dy$$

so that a possible solution of (7) is

$$(9) \qquad \alpha(v) = \frac{1}{\pi}\, \frac{d}{dv} \int_0^v \frac{T(u)}{\sqrt{v-u}}\, du.$$

When $T(u)$ has a continuous derivative, one can show that $\alpha(v)$ given by (9) actually satisfies (7).

The equation (7) was one of the first integral equations considered. It arose in the study of the time needed for a particle to slide under the action of gravity along a given curve between two points in a vertical plane. Assuming the particle starts from rest at time $t = 0$ from the point (x_0, y_0) traveling along the curve $x = x(y)$ to the origin, and $s(t)$ is the distance along the curve from the origin to the position of the particle at time t, then the speed at time t is

$$- \frac{ds}{dt} = \sqrt{2g(y_0 - y)}.$$

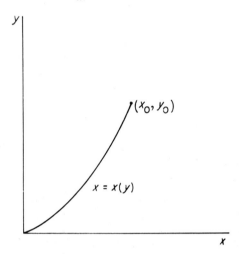

This follows from the fact that the sum of the kinetic and potential energies is a constant, i.e.,

$$\tfrac{1}{2}m \left(\frac{ds}{dt}\right)^2 + mgy = mgy_0$$

where m is the mass of the particle and g is the constant acceleration of gravity. The total time of descent is

$$T(y_0) = \int_0^{y_0} \frac{ds}{dy} \frac{1}{\sqrt{2g(y_0 - y)}} dy.$$

In 1823 Abel solved the inverse problem of finding the curve when $T(y_0)$ is given. Replacing y_0 by u and $\dfrac{1}{\sqrt{2g}} \dfrac{ds}{dy}$ by $\alpha(y)$, Abel's equation is exactly (7), with solution

(10) $$\alpha(y) = \frac{1}{\pi} \frac{d}{dy} \int_0^y \frac{T(u)}{\sqrt{y - u}} du.$$

To obtain the curve in the form $x = x(y)$, write

$$x(v) = \int_0^v \frac{dx}{dy} dy = \int_0^v \left(\left(\frac{ds}{dy}\right)^2 - 1\right)^{1/2} dy.$$

Abel's equation led to a study of integral equations of the types

$$\int_a^x K(x, y)\, \alpha(y)dy = \beta(x),$$

$$\int_a^x K(x, y)\, \alpha(y)dy + \beta(x) = \alpha(x),$$

now known as Volterra equations of types 1 and 2 respectively.

However the study of integral equations came into prominence only after I. Fredholm in 1900 developed the theory of the **Fredholm equation of the second type,**

(11) $$\beta(x) + r \int_a^b K(x, y)\, \alpha(y)dy = \alpha(x),$$

and applied it to solve a famous problem in potential theory. Here the limits on the integral are fixed. Note that the Volterra equation of type 2 is a special case of (11) when the kernel is zero for $y > x$. Fredholm's method gives the solution $\alpha(y)$ as the ratio of two power series in r, the numerator having coefficients which are functions of y. We shall not consider Fredholm's method as we are more interested now in applying what we have learned about integral operators. In fact, this application, developed by D. Hilbert and E. Schmidt in 1906, was the original motivation for the study of integral operators and all our previous work may be called the **Hilbert-Schmidt theory of integral equations with symmetric kernels.**

Let us then restrict ourselves to a discussion of equation (11) where $\beta(x)$ is in $\mathscr{R}$ (or $\mathscr{R}^*$), $K(x, y)$ is continuous on $a \le x \le b$, $a \le y \le b$, and $r \neq 0$ is a parameter.

THEOREM 4.4A   When $1/r$ is not an eigenvalue of the symmetric operator K, there is one and only one solution α of (11). The solution is

(12) $$\alpha = \beta + \sum_i \frac{r\, s_i}{1 - r\, s_i}\, (\beta, \alpha_i)\, \alpha_i$$

where $\{s_i\}$ constitutes the spectrum of K and α_i are the corresponding orthonormal eigenvectors. The series in (12) converges absolutely uniformly.

Proof   When α is a solution of (11),

$$\sigma(x) = \alpha(x) - \beta(x) = \int_a^b K(x, y)\, r\, \alpha(y)dy = K\, r\alpha(x)$$

$$= \sum_i (K\, r\, \alpha, \alpha_i)\, \alpha_i(x) = \sum_i r\, s_i\, (\alpha, \alpha_i)\, \alpha_i(x),$$

in view of Theorem 4.3A, and the series converges absolutely uniformly. Hence

(13)
$$\alpha = \beta + \sigma = \beta + \sum_i r\, s_i\, (\alpha,\, \alpha_i)\, \alpha_i.$$

From (11),

(14)
$$(\beta,\, \alpha_i) = (\alpha,\, \alpha_i) - r(K\alpha,\, \alpha_i) = (\alpha,\, \alpha_i) - r(\alpha,\, K\alpha_i)$$
$$= (\alpha,\, \alpha_i) - r s_i\, (\alpha,\, \alpha_i),$$

so that

(15)
$$(\alpha,\, \alpha_i) = \frac{(\beta,\, \alpha_i)}{1 - r\, s_i}$$

and substitution into (13) yields (12). This shows that if a solution exists it is unique and given by (12).

Next comes a proof that the function α defined by (12) is actually a solution of (11). That the series converges absolutely uniformly is not difficult to verify. In fact, there is a constant $B > 0$ such that

$$\left| \frac{r}{1 - r\, s_i} \right| < B \qquad \text{for all } i,$$

and when m, n have the same sign, we have

(16)
$$\sum_m^n \left| \frac{r}{1 - r\, s_i} (\beta,\, \alpha_i)\, s_i\, \alpha_i(x) \right| \le B \left(\sum_m^n |(\beta,\, \alpha_i)|^2 \sum_m^n |s_i|^2\, |\alpha_i(x)|^2 \right)^{1/2}$$

$$\le BC \left(\sum_m^n |(\beta,\, \alpha_i)|^2 \right)^{1/2}$$

where $C^2 = $ l.u.b. $\left\{ \int_a^b |K(x, y)|^2\, dy \;\middle|\; a \le x \le b \right\}$ by 4.2(4). Bessel's inequality states that $\sum_i |(\beta,\, \alpha_i)|^2$ converges. Therefore we are assured, by the Cauchy criterion, that the right side of (16) is less than ϵ when $|m|$, $|n|$ are sufficiently large. Another application of the Cauchy criterion proves the desired absolute uniform convergence.

From (12) we obtain

$$(\alpha,\, \alpha_j) = (\beta,\, \alpha_j) + \sum_i \frac{r\, s_i}{1 - r\, s_i} (\beta,\, \alpha_i)\, (\alpha_i,\, \alpha_j)$$

showing that

$$(\alpha,\, \alpha_j) = \frac{1}{1 - r\, s_j} (\beta,\, \alpha_j).$$

Thus (12) may be written

$$\alpha(x) = \beta(x) + \sum_i r\, s_i\, (\alpha,\, \alpha_i)\, \alpha_i(x)$$

or, in view of Theorem 4.3A,

$$\alpha(x) = \beta(x) + r \int_a^b K(x,\, y)\, \alpha(y) dy. \quad \star$$

THEOREM 4.4B When $1/r$ is an eigenvalue of K, then (11) has a solution if and only if β is orthogonal to all eigenvectors associated with $1/r$. If this condition is satisfied, then the solution is of the form

(17)
$$\alpha = \beta + \sum_{i\ \mathrm{not\ in}\ \mathscr{2}} \frac{r\, s_i}{1 - r\, s_i}\, (\beta,\, \alpha_i)\, \alpha_i + \sum_{i\ \mathrm{in}\ \mathscr{2}} c_i\, \alpha_i$$

where $\mathscr{2}$ is the set of indices j such that $s_j = 1/r$ and c_i are arbitrary constants.

Proof If there is a solution α of (11), then (14) indicates β must be orthogonal to all eigenvectors α_i such that $s_i = 1/r$. Moreover, when i is not in $\mathscr{2}$, (15) is valid and (13) becomes

$$\alpha = \beta + \sum_{i\ \mathrm{not\ in}\ \mathscr{2}} \frac{r\, s_i}{1 - r\, s_i}\, (\beta,\, \alpha_i)\, \alpha_i + \sum_{i\ \mathrm{in}\ \mathscr{2}} (\alpha,\, \alpha_i)\, \alpha_i$$

which is the form given in (17).

We must now show that if $(\beta,\, \alpha_i) = 0$ whenever $s_i = 1/r$, then the function α defined by (17) for arbitrary c_i is a solution of (11). That the infinite series in (17) converges absolutely uniformly is proved as in Theorem 4.4A. Then, if j is not in $\mathscr{2}$, (17) implies

$$(\alpha,\, \alpha_j) = (\beta,\, \alpha_j) + \frac{r\, s_j}{1 - r\, s_j}\, (\beta,\, \alpha_j) = \frac{1}{1 - r\, s_j}\, (\beta,\, \alpha_j);$$

whereas if j is in $\mathscr{2}$,

$$(\alpha,\, \alpha_j) = c_j.$$

Therefore,

$$\alpha = \beta + \sum_{i\ \mathrm{not\ in}\ \mathscr{2}} r\, s_i\, (\alpha,\, \alpha_i)\, \alpha_i + \sum_{i\ \mathrm{in}\ \mathscr{2}} (\alpha,\, \alpha_i)\, \alpha_i$$

$$= \beta + \sum_i r\, s_i\, (\alpha,\, \alpha_i)\, \alpha_i = \beta + rK\alpha,$$

the last equality following from Theorem 4.3A. $\star$

From the last two theorems we may draw the following conclusion: Either the equation $\alpha = \beta + rK\alpha$ has, for fixed r, a unique solution, or else the equation $\alpha = rK\alpha$ has a nonzero solution. This may be rewritten:

Either $(I - rK)\alpha = \beta$ has, for fixed r, a unique solution, or else the homogeneous equation $(I - rK)\alpha = \theta$ has a nonzero solution. In this form the reader is reminded of Theorem 2.5D, and the question arises as to whether or not a similar result is valid for the nonsymmetric kernel. The answer is yes and we shall state without proof the corresponding either-or condition, called the **Fredholm alternative.**

THEOREM 4.4C Either I: For fixed $r \neq 0$ there is one and only one solution α in $\mathscr{R}$ for each fixed β in $\mathscr{R}$ of

$$\text{(18)} \qquad\qquad\qquad \alpha = \beta + rK\alpha,$$

where K is the operator corresponding to $K(x, y)$, continuous on $a \leq x \leq b$, $a \leq y \leq b$ but not necessarily symmetric. In this case $\alpha = \theta$ if $\beta = \theta$ so that $1/r$ is not an eigenvalue of K. Moreover

$$\alpha = \beta + rK^*\alpha$$

also has a unique solution for each β in $\mathscr{R}$.

or II: The homogeneous equation $\sigma = rK\sigma$ has a finite number $m > 0$ orthonormal solutions $\sigma_1, \ldots, \sigma_m$ and the equation $\mu = rK^*\mu$ also has m orthonormal solutions $\mu_1, \ldots, \mu_m$. In this case a solution for (18) exists if and only if $(\beta, \mu_i) = 0$ for $i = 1, \ldots, m$. The solution of (18) is determined only up to a linear combination of the σ_i.

Let us now consider a technique which may be called the method of successive substitutions. If a solution α exists for

$$\text{(19)} \qquad\qquad\qquad \alpha = \beta + rK\alpha,$$

where K need not be symmetric, we may write

$$\alpha = \beta + rK(\beta + rK\alpha) = \beta + rK\beta + r^2K^2(\beta + rK\alpha)$$
$$= \beta + rK\beta + r^2K^2\beta + r^3K^3(\beta + rK\alpha).$$

Continuing in this fashion, the possibility is suggested that

$$\text{(20)} \qquad\qquad\qquad \alpha = \beta + r\sum_{n=1}^{\infty} r^{n-1} K^n\beta$$

is a solution of (19). Since

$$\sum_{n=1}^{m} r^{n-1} K^n\beta = \int_a^b \sum_{n=1}^{m} r^{n-1} K^n (x, y) \, \beta(y)dy,$$

it may also be of interest to investigate the series

(21)
$$\sum_{n=1}^{\infty} r^{n-1} K^n(x, y).$$

THEOREM 4.4D   Let $M = \text{l.u.b.} \left\{ |K(x, y)| \,\middle|\, a \leq x \leq b,\ a \leq y \leq b \right\}$. Then, if $|r| < 1/M(b - a)$, the series (21) converges absolutely uniformly to a function $R(x, y, r)$, called the **resolvent kernel** of K, and the unique solution of (19) is given by

(22)
$$\alpha(x) = \beta(x) + r \int_a^b R(x, y, r)\,\beta(y)dy.$$

The equation (20) is valid and

(23)
$$-K(x, y) + R(x, y, r) = r \int_a^b R(x, t, r)\,K(t, y)dt$$
$$= r \int_a^b K(x, t)\,R(t, y, r)dt.$$

Proof   The convergence of the series (21) will be demonstrated first. Since

$$|K^2(x, y)| = \left| \int_a^b K(x, t)\,K(t, y)dt \right| \leq M^2(b - a),$$

$$|K^3(x, y)| = \left| \int_a^b K^2(x, t)\,K(t, y)dt \right| \leq M^3(b - a)^2,$$

we obtain

$$|K^n(x, y)| \leq M^n(b - a)^{n-1},$$

$$\sum_1^{\infty} |r^{n-1} K^n(x, y)| \leq M \sum_1^{\infty} (|r|(b - a)M)^{n-1},$$

showing absolute uniform convergence for $|r| < 1/M(b - a)$. Now

$$\sum_{n=2}^{\infty} r^{n-1} K^n(x, y) = \sum_{n=2}^{\infty} r^{n-1} \int_a^b K(x, t)K^{n-1}(t, y)dt$$

$$= r \int_a^b K(x, t) \sum_{j=1}^{\infty} r^{j-1} K^j(t, y)dt = r \int_a^b K(x, t)\,R(t, y, r)dt.$$

Similarly

$$\sum_{n=2}^{\infty} r^{n-1} K^n(x, y) = \sum_{n=2}^{\infty} r^{n-1} \int_a^b K^{n-1}(x, t)\, K(t, y)dt$$

$$= r \int_a^b \sum_{j=1}^{\infty} r^{j-1} K^j(x, t)\, K(t, y)dt = r \int_a^b R(x, t, r)\, K(t, y)dt.$$

These relations show the validity of (23).

Define α by (22). Then, using (22) and (23),

$$\int_a^b K(x, t)\, \alpha(t)dt = \int_a^b K(x, t)\left(\beta(t) + r \int_a^b R(t, y, r)\, \beta(y)dy \right) dt$$

$$= \int_a^b K(x, t)\, \beta(t)dt + \int_a^b \beta(y) \int_a^b rK(x, t)\, R(t, y, r)dt\, dy$$

$$= \int_a^b K(x, t)\, \beta(t)dt + \int_a^b \beta(y)\left(-K(x, y) + R(x, y, r) \right) dy$$

$$= \int_a^b R(x, y, r)\, \beta(y)dy.$$

Substituting this result in (22), we obtain (19), proving that α given by (22) is a solution of (19). It remains to show that the solution is unique. If α is any solution of (19), then

$$\int_a^b R(x, t, r)\, \alpha(t)dt = \int_a^b R(x, t, r)\left(\beta(t) + r \int_a^b K(t, y)\, \alpha(y)dy \right) dt$$

$$= \int_a^b R(x, t, r)\, \beta(t)dt + \int_a^b \left(-K(x, y) + R(x, y, r) \right) \alpha(y)dy,$$

proving that

$$\int_a^b K(x, y)\, \alpha(y)dy = \int_a^b R(x, t, r)\, \beta(t)dt.$$

Therefore (19) becomes (22), determining α uniquely. Clearly (22) implies (20).   ★

By using a finite number of terms of (20), we may obtain an approximation to the solution. Approximation methods are treated in texts on numerical analysis.

It is possible to show, using the Fredholm theory, that a function $R(x, y, r)$ can be defined, when $1/r$ is not an eigenvalue, so as to satisfy (23). Then α defined by (22) is the unique solution of (19).

EXAMPLE 4 Find the resolvent kernel for $K(x, y) = xy$ and solve the equation

(24) $$\alpha(x) = x + r \int_a^b xy \, \alpha(y)dy.$$

We have

$$K^2(x, y) = \int_a^b K(x, t) \, K(t, y)dt = \int_a^b xt^2 \, ydt = xyh,$$

$$K^3(x,y) = \int_a^b K^2(x, t) \, K(t, y)dt = \int_a^b hxt \, ty \, dt = xyh^2,$$

where $h = \dfrac{b^3 - a^3}{3}$, and by induction,

$$K^n(x, y) = xyh^{n-1}.$$

Hence $R(x, y, r) = \displaystyle\sum_{n=1}^{\infty} r^{n-1} K^n(x, y) = xy\left(1 - rh\right)^{-1}$

and

(25) $$\alpha(x) = x + r \int_a^b xy\left(1 - rh\right)^{-1} ydy = x + rhx\left(1 - rh\right)^{-1}.$$

The same result may be obtained by the method given in Section 4.1, since the kernel is separable.

To use Theorem 4.4A, solve

$$\int_a^b xy\alpha(y)dy = s\alpha(x) \quad \text{or} \quad cx = s\alpha(x)$$

where

$$c = \int_a^b y\alpha(y)dy = \int_a^b y\frac{c}{s}y \, dy = \frac{c}{s}\frac{b^3 - a^3}{3} = \frac{c}{s}h,$$

so that $s = h$ and the only orthonormalized eigenvector is

$$\alpha(x) = x/\|x\| = xh^{-1/2}.$$

When $1/r \neq h$, the solution of (24) is given by Theorem 4.4A as

$$\alpha(x) = x + rh(1 - rh)^{-1} \int_a^b y^2 h^{-1/2}dy \, xh^{-1/2},$$

which reduces to (25).

Exercise 4.4

1. Assume $T(u)$ in (9) has a continuous derivative. Integrate by parts before differentiating and show that $\alpha(v)$ in (9) satisfies (1). The integrals are improper, but assume validity of interchange of order of integration.

2. Show that if $T = T(u)$ in (10) is a constant (the time of fall is thus independent of the original position of the particle on the curve), then the curve is a cycloid, $x = r(\phi + \sin \phi)$, $y = r(1 - \cos \phi)$. *Hint:* Find $s'(y)$ and put $y = a \sin^2 w$ where $a = \dfrac{2g}{\pi^2} T^2$.

3. Dividing by $(v - u)^{1-x}$, solve for $\alpha(y)$ in
    $$T(u) = \int_0^u \frac{\alpha(y)dy}{(u - y)^x}, \qquad 0 < x < 1.$$
    Hint: Try $(v - y)t = u - y$.

4. Let T be a symmetric linear transformation on an n dimensional Euclidean vector space $\mathscr{E}$ and
    $$T\alpha_i = s_i\, \alpha_i, \quad i = 1, \ldots n, \quad (\alpha_i, \alpha_j) = \delta_{ij}.$$
    Let β be a given vector in $\mathscr{E}$ and r a constant. Follow through the proofs of Theorem 4.4A and 4.4B to show that the solution of the equation $\alpha = \beta + rT\alpha$ is given by (12) when $1/r$ is not an eigenvalue and, if $(\beta, \alpha_i) = 0$ for all i, by (17) when $1/r$ is an eigenvalue.

5. (a) Let T be a linear transformation on $\mathscr{E}_n$. With respect to an orthonormal basis let α and β in $\mathscr{E}_n$ and T have representations given by $\alpha \leftrightarrow [x_i]$, $\beta \leftrightarrow [y_i]$, $T \leftrightarrow [t_{ij}]$. Show that the Fredholm alternative is valid in the matrix case by considering
    $$[x_i] = [y_i] + r[t_{ij}][x_i]$$
    and using Theorem 2.5D.

    (b) Show that the Fredholm alternative is valid for integral operators with separable kernels by reducing the problem to the matrix case. *Hint:* If $K(x, y) = \sum_{i=1}^{n} \alpha_i(x)\, \beta_i(y)$ then $\alpha = \beta + rK\alpha$ takes the form

    (A) $$\alpha = \beta + r \sum_{i=1}^{n} (\alpha, \beta_i)\, \alpha_i.$$

    We may assume α_i are linearly independent and β_i are linearly independent. If a solution α exists, then
    $$(\alpha, \beta_j) = (\beta, \beta_j) + r \sum_{i=1}^{n} (\alpha, \beta_i)(\alpha_i, \beta_j)$$
    so that the solution is of the form

    (B) $$\alpha = \beta + r \sum_{i=1}^{n} b_i\, \alpha_i$$

    where b_i satisfy

    (C) $$b_j = (\beta, \beta_j) + r \sum_{i=1}^{n} b_i\, (\alpha_i, \beta_j).$$

    Show that (B) is a solution of (A) if and only if $[b_i]$ is a solution of (C). Show also that the number of linearly independent solutions of (A) is equal to the number of linearly independent solutions of (C). Show also that β is orthogonal to solutions of $\mu = rK^*\mu$ if and only if $[b_i]$ is orthogonal to solutions $[c_j]$ of $c_j = r \sum_{i=1}^{n} c_i (\beta_i, \alpha_j)$.

6. When $1/r$ is not an eigenvalue for $K(x, y) = \sin(x + y)$, $-\pi \le x \le \pi$, $-\pi \le y \le \pi$, solve

$$\alpha(x) = x + r \int_{-\pi}^{\pi} \sin(x + y) \, \alpha(y)dy$$

(a) by differentiation, obtaining a differential equation.
(b) as a separable kernel.
(c) by Theorem 4.4A.
(d) by finding the resolvent kernel.

7. Solve by two different methods

$$\alpha(x) = 1 + \int_0^1 e^{x+y} \, \alpha(y)dy.$$

8. Solve

(a) $\alpha(x) = r \int_0^1 \dfrac{(x - y)}{(x + 1)(y + 1)} \, \alpha(y)dy.$

(b) $\alpha(x) = x + r \int_0^1 \dfrac{(x - y)}{(x + 1)(y + 1)} \, \alpha(y)dy.$

9. Define $\|K(t, u)\| = \left(\int_a^b \int_a^b |K(x, y)|^2 \, dx \, dy \right)^{1/2}.$

By using the Schwarz inequality, show that if

$$H(x, y) = \int_a^b K(x, t) \, L(t, y)dt$$

then $\|H(x, y)\| \le \|K(x, y)\| \, \|L(x, y)\|$.
(b) Show that $\|K^n (x, y)\| \le \|K(x, y)\|^n.$
(c) Using the inequality, valid for $n > 2$,

$$|K^n (x, y)| = \left| \int_a^b \int_a^b K(x, t) \, K^{n-2} (t, u) \, K(u, y)du \, dt \right|$$

$$\le \left(\int_a^b \int_a^b |K^{n-2} (t, u)|^2 du \, dt \int_a^b \int_a^b |K(x, t)K(u, y)|^2 du \, dt \right)^{1/2}$$

$$\le \|K(x, y)\|^{n-2}A$$

where A is a suitable constant, show that the condition on r in Theorem 4.4D may be replaced by $|r| < 1/\|K(x, y)\|$.
(d) Why does this imply $\|K(x, y)\|$ is an upper bound for the eigenvalues of K?

10. The proof in Theorem 4.4D shows that if $R(x, y, r)$ is a function satisfying (23), then there exists a unique solution, for fixed β, of (19). Show that this implies there is only one continuous function $R(x, y, r)$ satisfying (23).

11. The equalities (23) may be written in terms of the corresponding operators as
(D) $R = K + rKR = K + rRK.$
Show that if $|r| < 1/\|K(x, y)\|$ (see Exercise 9), then (D) and Theorem 4.1A imply

$$\lim_{n \to \infty} \|R - \sum_{j=1}^{n} r^{j-1} K^j\| = 0.$$

12. Let $K(x, y)$ be real and continuous on $a \le x \le b$, $a \le y \le b$, but not neces-
    sarily symmetric. Define

    $$H(x, y) = \int_a^b K(v, x) K(v, y)dv.$$

    Show that (a) H is symmetric and positive semi-definite over $\mathscr{R}$.
               (b) If also $K(x, y) = -K(y, x)$, then K has no nonzero eigen-
                   value. *Hint:* Investigate the relation between eigenvalues of
                   H and K.
               (c) Assuming the validity of the Fredholm alternative state an exist-
                   ence theorem for solutions of (19) when $K(x, y) = -K(y, x)$.

13. Let $H(x, y) = \rho(y) K(x, y)$ where $K(x, y) = K(y, x)$ and $\rho(y)$ are real and con-
    tinuous on $a \le x \le b$, $a \le y \le b$ and $\rho(y) > 0$ on $a \le y \le b$.
    (a) Let $L(x, y) = \sqrt{\rho(x)} \sqrt{\rho(y)} K(x, y)$. Show that s is an eigenvalue of H
        with eigenvector $\alpha(x)$ if and only if s is an eigenvalue of L with eigen-
        vector $\sqrt{\rho(x)} \alpha(x)$.
    (b) Show that the eigenvectors of H corresponding to different eigenvalues
        are orthogonal with respect to the inner product

    $$(\alpha, \beta)_\rho = \int_a^b \rho(x) \alpha(x) \beta(x)dx.$$

    (c) Show that the number of linearly independent eigenvectors corresponding
        to a nonzero eigenvalue s of H is finite.
    (d) If there is a solution α in $\mathscr{R}$ of $\alpha = \beta + rH\alpha$, obtain a formula for this
        solution in terms of the nonzero eigenvalues s_i and eigenvectors α_i of H,
        when $1/r$ is not an eigenvalue of H. Take α_i to satisfy $(\alpha_i, \alpha_j)_\rho = \delta_{ij}$.

14. For the Volterra equation

    $$\alpha(x) = \beta(x) + r \int_a^x K(x, y) \alpha(y)dy$$

    we define $K^n (x, y) = \int_a^x K(x, t) K^{n-1} (t, y)dt$, $\quad K^1 (x, y) = K(x, y)$.

    Show that $K^{n+m}(x, y) = \int_a^x K^n(x, t) K^m(t, y)dt$. Show also that the series defining
    the corresponding resolvent kernel converges absolutely uniformly for all r.

CHAPTER

5

Orthonormal
Sequences

5.1

GENERALIZED

FOURIER SERIES

When $\mathscr{E}$ is a real or complex Euclidean vector space, we may define the sum of an infinite series of elements of $\mathscr{E}$ as the limit of the sequence of partial sums. More precisely, if $\{\alpha_i\}$ is a sequence of elements in $\mathscr{E}$, we write

(1)
$$\alpha = \sum_{i=1}^{\infty} a_i \alpha_i \quad \text{when} \quad \alpha = \lim_{n \to \infty} \sum_{i=1}^{n} a_i \alpha_i,$$

that is, whenever

$$\lim_{n \to \infty} \left\| \alpha - \sum_{i=1}^{n} a_i \alpha_i \right\| = 0.$$

We shall find it useful to state as a theorem some formal manipulations with limits.

THEOREM 5.1A If $\alpha = \lim\limits_{i \to \infty} \alpha_i$, $\beta = \lim\limits_{i \to \infty} \beta_i$, $\sigma = \sum\limits_{i=1}^{\infty} \sigma_i$ are in $\mathscr{E}$ then

a. $\|\alpha\| = \lim\limits_{i \to \infty} \|\alpha_i\|$.

b. $\lim\limits_{i \to \infty} (\alpha_i, \beta_i) = (\alpha, \beta)$.

c. $\sum\limits_{i=1}^{\infty} (\sigma_i, \mu) = (\sum\limits_{i=1}^{\infty} \sigma_i, \mu)$ for every μ in $\mathscr{E}$.

d. $T(\sum\limits_{i=1}^{\infty} \sigma_i) = \sum\limits_{i=1}^{\infty} T\sigma_i$

for any continuous linear transformation T on $\mathscr{E}$ to $\mathscr{E}$.

Proof The first equality is a consequence of

$$\Big| \|\alpha_i\| - \|\alpha\| \Big| \le \|\alpha_i - \alpha\|.$$

The sequence $\{\|\alpha_i\|\}$ is bounded and the second equality follows from

$$|(\alpha_i, \beta_i) - (\alpha, \beta)| \le |(\alpha_i, \beta_i) - (\alpha_i, \beta)| + |(\alpha_i, \beta) - (\alpha, \beta)|$$
$$\le \|\alpha_i\| \|\beta_i - \beta\| + \|\alpha_i - \alpha\| \|\beta\|.$$

Part (c) follows from (b) by taking $\beta_i = \mu$, $\alpha_i = \sum\limits_{j=1}^{i} \sigma_j$. By continuity of T, $T(\sum\limits_{j=1}^{i} \sigma_j)$ converges to $T(\sigma)$. Hence

$$\sum_{i=1}^{\infty} T\sigma_i = \lim_{i\to\infty} \sum_{j=1}^{i} T\sigma_j = \lim_{i\to\infty} T(\sum_{j=1}^{i} \sigma_j) = T\sigma. \quad \star$$

Even if every finite set of vectors from the sequence $\{\alpha_i\}$ is linearly independent, the representation (1) does not uniquely determine the constants a_i.

EXAMPLE 1   Let $\mathscr{E}$ have infinite dimension so that it is possible to choose a sequence $\{\beta_i\}$ with every finite subset linearly independent and with $\|\beta_i\| \leq 1/i$. Define $\alpha_1 = \beta_1$, $\alpha_2 = \beta_2 - \beta_1, \ldots, \alpha_{n+1} = \beta_{n+1} - \beta_n, \ldots$. Then it is easily verified that every finite subset of the sequence $\{\alpha_i\}$ is linearly independent. Moreover

$$\left\| \sum_{i=1}^{n+1} \alpha_i - \theta \right\| = \|\beta_{n+1}\| < \frac{1}{n+1}.$$

Hence $\sum\limits_{i=1}^{\infty} \alpha_i = \theta = \sum\limits_{i=1}^{\infty} 0\, \alpha_i$ and θ is represented in two ways.

However, when the sequence $\{\alpha_i\}$ is orthornormal the constants a_i in (1) are uniquely determined. We need only note that

$$(\alpha, \alpha_j) = \left(\sum_{i=1}^{\infty} a_i \alpha_i, \alpha_j \right) = \sum_{i=1}^{\infty} a_i (\alpha_i, \alpha_j) = a_j.$$

We have shown that if α can be expanded as an infinite series of the form (1), where $\{\alpha_i\}$ is orthonormal, then

$$(2) \qquad\qquad\qquad \alpha = \sum_{i=1}^{\infty} (\alpha, \alpha_i)\, \alpha_i.$$

This representation is called the **generalized Fourier series** of α relative to the orthonormal sequence $\{\alpha_i\}$. The terms (α, α_i) are called the **generalized Fourier coefficients** of α relative to $\{\alpha_i\}$. The adjective "generalized" is often omitted.

THEOREM 5.1B   Let $\{\alpha_i\}$ be an orthonormal sequence in $\mathscr{E}$. Then the following statements are equivalent:

a. $\alpha = \sum\limits_{i=1}^{\infty} (\alpha, \alpha_i)\, \alpha_i.$

b. $(\alpha, \beta) = \sum\limits_{i=1}^{\infty} (\alpha, \alpha_i)(\alpha_i, \beta)$ for every β in $\mathscr{E}$.

c. $\|\alpha\|^2 = \sum\limits_{i=1}^{\infty} |(\alpha, \alpha_i)|^2$.

Proof Using Theorem 5.1A and assuming **(a)**, we have

$$(\alpha, \beta) = \left(\sum_i (\alpha, \alpha_i)\, \alpha_i, \beta \right) = \sum_i (\alpha, \alpha_i)(\alpha_i, \beta).$$

Then **(c)** can be obtained from **(b)** by letting $\beta = \alpha$. To show that **(c)** implies **(a)**, write

$$\left\| \alpha - \sum_{i=1}^{n} (\alpha, \alpha_i)\, \alpha_i \right\|^2 = \left(\alpha - \sum_{i=1}^{n} (\alpha, \alpha_i)\, \alpha_i, \ \alpha - \sum_{j=1}^{n} (\alpha, \alpha_j)\, \alpha_j \right)$$

$$= \|\alpha\|^2 - \sum_{i=1}^{n} |(\alpha, \alpha_i)|^2$$

which approaches zero as n approaches ∞ in virtue of **(c)**. Hence **(a)** is valid. $\star$

Relations **(b)** and **(c)** of Theorem 5.1B are both called **Parseval's equality.** They are generalizations of Corollaries 1 and 2 of Theorem 1.3D, where α has the representation given in **(a)**.

The preceding discussion indicates that it would be of interest to seek a condition on the orthonormal sequence $\{\alpha_i\}$ which would insure that every element in $\mathscr{E}$ has a representation of the form (2).

When $\mathscr{A}$ and $\mathscr{B}$ are subsets of $\mathscr{E}$, $\mathscr{A}$ is said to be **dense** in $\mathscr{B}$ if every element of $\mathscr{B}$ is the limit of a sequence of elements belonging to $\mathscr{A}$, that is, if $\mathscr{B}$ is contained in $\bar{\mathscr{A}}$. An equivalent statement is the following: $\mathscr{A}$ is dense in $\mathscr{B}$ if for every β in $\mathscr{B}$ and every $\epsilon > 0$ there is an element α in $\mathscr{A}$, depending on ϵ and β, such that $\|\beta - \alpha\| < \epsilon$.

It is left as Exercise 5.1-2 to prove that if $\mathscr{A}$ is dense in $\mathscr{B}$ and $\mathscr{B}$ is dense in $\mathscr{C}$, then $\mathscr{A}$ is dense in $\mathscr{C}$.

A subset $\mathscr{A}$ is **linearly dense** in $\mathscr{B}$ if the linear manifold spanned by $\mathscr{A}$ is dense in $\mathscr{B}$, that is, if every element of $\mathscr{B}$ is a limit of a sequence of elements of $\mathscr{E}$ each of which is a finite linear combination of elements of $\mathscr{A}$.

THEOREM 5.1C Let $\{\alpha_i\}$ be an orthonormal sequence linearly dense in $\mathscr{E}$. Then every α in $\mathscr{E}$ can be written in the form (2).

Proof For $\epsilon > 0$, there exists $\beta = \sum\limits_{i=1}^{N} b_i\, \alpha_i$, where N and b_i depend on α and ϵ, such that

$$\|\alpha - \beta\| = \left\| \alpha - \sum_{i=1}^{N} b_i\, \alpha_i \right\| < \epsilon.$$

Choosing $b_i = 0$ for $i > N$, and using Corollary 1 of Theorem 1.3F, we obtain for $j > N$,

$$\left\| \alpha - \sum_{i=1}^{j} (\alpha, \alpha_i)\alpha_i \right\| \leq \left\| \alpha - \sum_{i=1}^{j} b_i \alpha_i \right\| < \epsilon.$$

This proves that $\alpha = \sum_{i=1}^{\infty} (\alpha, \alpha_i)\alpha_i.$ ★

THEOREM 5.1D   If a set $\mathscr{S}$ is linearly dense in $\mathscr{E}$ and $(\alpha, \sigma) = (\beta, \sigma)$ for every σ in $\mathscr{S}$, then $\alpha = \beta$. In particular, if $(\alpha, \sigma) = 0$ for every σ in $\mathscr{S}$, then $\alpha = \theta$.

Proof   By hypothesis, $(\alpha - \beta, \sigma) = 0$ for σ in $\mathscr{S}$ and hence for every σ which is a finite linear combination of elements of $\mathscr{S}$. Since $\mathscr{S}$ is linearly dense in $\mathscr{E}$, there is a sequence $\{\mu_n\}$ in the linear manifold spanned by $\mathscr{S}$ such that $\alpha - \beta = \lim \mu_n$. Then

$$(\alpha - \beta, \alpha - \beta) = (\alpha - \beta, \lim_{n \to \infty} \mu_n) = \lim_{n \to \infty} (\alpha - \beta, \mu_n) = 0. ★$$

As yet we have made no statement as to whether there exists a linearly dense orthonormal sequence in $\mathscr{E}$. In fact, for some Euclidean vector spaces, no such (countable) sequence exists. The next theorem states that if there is a countable sequence of elements linearly dense in $\mathscr{E}$, then we can always find an orthonormal sequence linearly dense in $\mathscr{E}$. We need only apply the Gram-Schmidt process.

THEOREM 5.1E   If $\{\beta_n\}$ is linearly dense in $\mathscr{E}$, then there is an orthonormal sequence $\{\alpha_n\}$ linearly dense in $\mathscr{E}$.

Proof   We may assume the elements β_n are linearly independent since we may omit any β_j which is linearly dependent on the preceding elements of the sequence. Then the required orthonormal sequence is

$$\alpha_1 = \frac{\beta_1}{\|\beta_1\|}, \quad \alpha_n = \frac{\beta_n - \sum_{j=1}^{n-1} (\beta_n, \alpha_j)\,\alpha_j}{\left\| \beta_n - \sum_{j=1}^{n-1} (\beta_n, \alpha_j)\,\alpha_j \right\|}.$$

In order to show that the elements α_n are well defined we must verify that $\beta_n - \sum_{j=1}^{n-1} (\beta_n, \alpha_j)\,\alpha_j$ is not the zero vector. If it were, then β_n would depend linearly on $\alpha_1, \ldots, \alpha_{n-1}$ and thus on $\beta_1, \ldots, \beta_{n-1}$ since each α_j depends linearly on $\beta_1, \ldots, \beta_j$. This is impossible since $\beta_1, \ldots, \beta_n$ are linearly independent.

It is clear that $\|\alpha_n\| = 1$. That $\alpha_n \perp \alpha_m$, $n \neq m$, will be established by induction. We have

$$(\alpha_1, \beta_2 - (\beta_2, \alpha_1)\, \alpha_1) = (\alpha_1, \beta_2) - (\alpha_1, \beta_2) = 0.$$

If $\alpha_1, \ldots, \alpha_{n-1}$ are assumed orthonormal and $k < n$,

$$\left(\alpha_k, \beta_n - \sum_{j=1}^{n-1} (\beta_n, \alpha_j)\, \alpha_j\right) = (\alpha_k, \beta_n) - (\alpha_k, \beta_n) = 0.$$

This proves that $\{\alpha_i\}$ is orthonormal.

It remains to show that $\{\alpha_i\}$ is linearly dense in $\mathscr{E}$. By definition, β_n is a linear combination of $\alpha_1, \ldots, \alpha_n$. Thus if $\sigma = \lim_{n \to \infty} \mu_n$, where μ_n is a linear combination of the β's, then μ_n is also a linear combination of the α's. This completes the proof. $\star$

A sequence $\{\alpha_i\}$ is called **infinitely linearly independent** whenever $\sum_{i=1}^{\infty} b_i \alpha_i = \theta$ implies $b_i = 0$ for all i. This assures that the coefficients a_i in (1) are uniquely determined whenever α has a representation given by (1). The sequence $\{\alpha_i\}$ is a **basis** for $\mathscr{E}$ when it is infinitely linearly independent and every vector α in $\mathscr{E}$ has a representation of the form (1). We have shown that an orthonormal sequence linearly dense in $\mathscr{E}$ is a basis for $\mathscr{E}$. Special consideration has been given to the case when $\{\alpha_i\}$ is orthonormal. Indeed, it is possible to exhibit an infinitely linearly independent sequence which is linearly dense in $\mathscr{E}$ and does not form a basis for $\mathscr{E}$ (Exercise 5.1–8).

Application will now be made to the Euclidean vector space $\mathscr{R}\{a, b\}$ of real functions integrable on $a \leq x \leq b$, with inner product $(\alpha, \beta) = \int_a^b \alpha(x)\, \beta(x)dx$. We shall assume $\{\alpha_i\}$ is a sequence of orthonormal functions linearly dense in $\mathscr{R}$. This implies that every function α in $\mathscr{R}$ has an expansion of the form (2), that is,

$$(3) \qquad \lim_{n \to \infty} \int_a^b \left| \alpha(x) - \sum_{i=1}^{n} (\alpha, \alpha_i)\, \alpha_i(x) \right|^2 dx = 0.$$

Equation (3) is often expressed by saying that the Fourier series of α (relative to $\{\alpha_i\}$) converges to α in the **mean square**. Of course, this does not mean that the Fourier series converges in the ordinary sense to $\alpha(x)$ at any point x or even converges. Nevertheless (3) is a strong result with many implications.

We shall write

$$(4) \qquad \alpha \sim \sum_{i=1}^{\infty} (\alpha, \alpha_i)\, \alpha_i(x)$$

to indicate that the series on the right is formed from α.

THEOREM 5.1F Let $|\beta|^2$ be integrable on $c \leq x \leq d$, where $a \leq c \leq d \leq b$. Then, whether or not the series in (4) converges, the series obtained by multiplying each term of (4) by $\beta(x)$ and integrating over $c \leq x \leq d$ converges to the integral of $\alpha\beta$ over $c \leq x \leq d$. That is,

$$(5) \qquad \int_c^d \alpha(x)\,\beta(x)dx = \sum_{i=1}^{\infty} (\alpha, \alpha_i) \int_c^d \beta(x)\,\alpha_i(x)dx.$$

Proof One need only note that

$$\left| \int_c^d \alpha(x)\,\beta(x)dx - \sum_{i=1}^{n} \int_c^d (\alpha, \alpha_i)\,\beta(x)\,\alpha_i(x)dx \right|^2$$

$$\leq \int_c^d |\beta(x)|^2\,dx \; \int_c^d \left| \alpha(x) - \sum_{i=1}^{n} (\alpha, \alpha_i)\,\alpha_i(x) \right|^2 dx$$

$$\leq \int_c^d |\beta(x)|^2\,dx \int_a^b \left| \alpha(x) - \sum_{i=1}^{n} (\alpha, \alpha_i)\,\alpha_i(x) \right|^2 dx$$

and apply (3). ★

Corollary 1
The series obtained by integrating (4) term by term over any finite interval $c \leq x \leq d$ in $a \leq x \leq b$ converges to the integral of α over $c \leq x \leq d$.

For, when $\beta(x) = 1$, equation (5) becomes

$$(6) \qquad \int_c^d \alpha(x)dx = \sum_{i=1}^{\infty} (\alpha, \alpha_i) \int_c^d \alpha_i(x)dx.$$

THEOREM 5.1G Assume that α and α_i are continuous on the finite interval $c \leq x \leq d$ and that the series (4) converges uniformly on $c \leq x \leq d$. Then the series must converge to α on $c \leq x \leq d$.

Proof The uniform convergence yields

$$\lim_{n \to \infty} \int_c^d \left| \sigma(x) - \sum_{i=1}^{n} (\alpha, \alpha_i)\,\alpha_i(x) \right|^2 dx = 0$$

where $\sigma(x) = \sum_{i=1}^{\infty} (\alpha, \alpha_i)\,\alpha_i(x)$ is continuous on $c \leq x \leq d$. By the triangle inequality,

$$\left\{ \int_c^d |\alpha(x) - \sigma(x)|^2\,dx \right\}^{1/2} \leq$$

$$\left\{ \int_c^d \left| \alpha(x) - \sum_{i=1}^{n} (\alpha, \alpha_i)\,\alpha_i(x) \right|^2 dx \right\}^{1/2} + \left\{ \int_c^d \left| \sigma(x) - \sum_{i=1}^{n} (\alpha, \alpha_i)\,\alpha_i(x) \right|^2 dx \right\}^{1/2}$$

where both terms on the right approach zero with increasing n. The left side is then equal to zero and the continuity of α and σ assures that $\alpha(x) = \sigma(x)$ on $c \leq x \leq d$. ★

Now let $\mathscr{I}$ represent the finite interval $c \leq x \leq d$ and let $\phi(\mathscr{I})$ be its characteristic function, that is

$$\phi(x) = \phi(\mathscr{I}, x) = \begin{cases} 1, & x \text{ in } \mathscr{I} \\ 0, & x \text{ not in } \mathscr{I}. \end{cases}$$

Replace α in (6) by ϕ to obtain

$$(7) \qquad d - c = \sum_{i=1}^{\infty} \left| \int_c^d \alpha_i(x) dx \right|^2$$

as a necessary condition that the orthonormal sequence $\{\alpha_i\}$ be linearly dense in $\mathscr{R}$. It is in fact true that the validity of (7) for every finite interval $c \leq x \leq d$ in $a \leq x \leq b$ is also a sufficient condition that the orthonormal sequence $\{\alpha_i\}$ be linearly dense in $\mathscr{R}\{a, b\}$. To see that this is so, note first that (7) is exactly Parseval's equality for the function ϕ. From Theorem 5.1B we obtain

$$(8) \qquad \lim_{n \to \infty} \left\| \phi - \sum_{i=1}^{n} (\phi, \alpha_i) \alpha_i \right\| = 0.$$

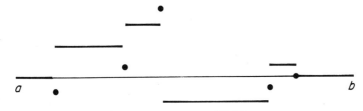

A STEP FUNCTION

We define the linear manifold of **step functions** in $a \leq x \leq b$ to be the linear manifold spanned by characteristic functions of finite intervals in $a \leq x \leq b$ of the form $c \leq x \leq d$ or $c \leq x < d$ or $c < x \leq d$ or $c < x < d$. A member of this linear manifold, a step function, is of the form $\sigma = \sum_{j=1}^{k} c_j \phi_j$ for constants c_j, where ϕ_j are characteristic functions of disjoint intervals of the above described type. From (8) we obtain

$$(9) \qquad \lim_{n \to \infty} \left\| \sigma - \sum_{i=1}^{n} (\sigma, \alpha_i) \alpha_i \right\| = 0.$$

Equation (9) states that the orthonormal sequence $\{\alpha_i\}$ is linearly dense in the linear manifold of step functions. We shall see in the next section that the latter is dense in $\mathscr{R}$. This proves that the sequence $\{\alpha_i\}$ is linearly dense in $\mathscr{R}$.

The preceding discussion has been phrased so as to apply to the case when $a = -\infty$ or $b = \infty$. For that case, the appropriate Euclidean vector space is the space $\mathscr{R}_2\{a, b\}$ of functions integrable on every finite interval and satisfying $\int_a^b |\alpha(x)|^2\, dx < \infty$ (Exercise 5.1–11). If a and b are finite $\mathscr{R}_2\{a, b\}$ is just $\mathscr{R}\{a, b\}$. The theorems are also valid when $\mathscr{R}$ is replaced by $\mathscr{R}^*$.

Exercise 5.1

1. Let $\{\alpha_i\}$ be an orthonormal sequence. Show that there is no vector β such that $\lim\limits_{i\to\infty} \|\alpha_i - \beta\| = 0$.

2. Show that if $\mathscr{A}$ is dense in $\mathscr{B}$ and $\mathscr{B}$ is dense in $\mathscr{C}$ then $\mathscr{A}$ is dense in $\mathscr{C}$.

3. (a)   Let $\{\alpha_i\}$ be an orthonormal sequence in $\mathscr{E}$. Show that the following three statements are equivalent:
    (1)   The only vector orthogonal to every α_i is θ.
    (2)   The sequence α_i is **complete** or **maximal**, that is, we cannot add another orthonormal vector to the set.
    (3)   Every α in $\mathscr{E}$ is uniquely determined by its Fourier coefficients relative to $\{\alpha_i\}$, that is, $(\alpha, \alpha_i) = (\beta, \alpha_i)$ for all i if and only if $\alpha = \beta$.

    (b)   If $\{\alpha_i\}$ is also linearly dense in $\mathscr{E}$, then show that the above statements are valid.

4. In the Euclidean vector space of integrable functions on $0 \le x \le 1$, $\mathscr{R}\{0, 1\}$, define

$$\alpha_{2^n+j}(x) = \begin{cases} 1 & \text{if } \dfrac{j}{2^n} \le x \le \dfrac{j+1}{2^n}, \quad j = 0, 1, \ldots, 2^n - 1, \\ 0 & \text{otherwise.} \end{cases}$$

Show that $\lim\limits_{n\to\infty} \|\alpha_n\| = 0$ so that $\lim\limits_{n\to\infty} \alpha_n = \theta$, but that $\{\alpha_n(x)\}$ does not converge at any point.

5. In $\mathscr{R}\{0, 1\}$ define

$$\alpha_n(x) = \begin{cases} 0, & 0 \le x < \dfrac{1}{n}, \\ n, & \dfrac{1}{n} \le x \le \dfrac{2}{n}, \\ 0, & \dfrac{2}{n} < x \le 1. \end{cases}$$

Show that $\{\alpha_n(x)\}$ converges to zero at each x. Show that $\{\alpha_n(x)\}$ does not converge uniformly on $0 \le x \le 1$. Show that $\|\alpha_n\|$ does not converge to 0.

6. In $\mathcal{R}\{0, \pi\}$ define $\alpha_n(x) = \cos^n x$. Show that $\lim\limits_{n\to\infty} \|\alpha_n\| = 0$. Show that $\{\alpha_n(x)\}$ converges for each x, but $\{\alpha_n(x)\}$ does not converge uniformly on $0 \le x \le \pi$.

7. $\mathcal{E}$ is called **separable** if there is a countable sequence $\{\beta_i\}$ in $\mathcal{E}$ such that for every σ in $\mathcal{E}$ and every $\epsilon > 0$, we can find an element β_k of the sequence with $\|\sigma - \beta_k\| < \epsilon$. Show that separability is equivalent to the fact that there exists a sequence $\{\alpha_i\}$ linearly dense in $\mathcal{E}$. *Hint:* The set of all elements of the form $\sum\limits_{i=1}^{N} c_i \alpha_i$ with c_i rational is a countable set. A complex number $a + bi$, a and b real, is called rational if a and b are rational.

8. Define α_j in $\mathcal{E}_\infty$ by $\alpha_j = (1, 0, 0, \ldots, 0, 1, 0 \ldots)$, $j = 2, 3, \ldots$, where the components of α_j are zero except for 1 in the 1st place and jth place. Show that α_j is infinitely linearly independent. The sequence α_j is linearly dense in $\mathcal{E}_\infty$ for if $\alpha = (x_1, x_2, \ldots)$ with $\Sigma x_i^2 < \infty$ and

$$\beta_n = x_2 \alpha_2 + \cdots + x_n \alpha_n + \frac{a_n}{b_n}(\alpha_{n+1} + \ldots + \alpha_{n+bn})$$

where $a_n = x_1 - x_2 - \cdots - x_n$ and b_n is an integer greater than $n|a_n|^2$, then

$$\|\alpha - \beta_n\| = \left(x_{n+1} - \frac{a_n}{b_n}\right)^2 + \cdots + \left(x_{n+bn} - \frac{a_n}{b_n}\right)^2 + \sum_{i=n+bn+1}^{\infty} x_i^2$$

$$\le 2 \sum_{i=n+1}^{\infty} x_i^2 + 2 b_n \left(\frac{a_n}{b_n}\right)^2 \le 2 \sum_{i=n+1}^{\infty} x_i^2 + \frac{2}{n}$$

so that $\{\beta_n\}$ converges to α. Show that $\{\alpha_j\}$ is not a basis since the element $(1, 0, 0, \ldots)$ cannot be written in the form $\sum\limits_{j=2}^{\infty} a_j \alpha_j$.

9. The situation existing in Exercise 8 cannot hold if the space is finite dimensional. Show that if $\{\alpha_j\}$ is linearly independent and linearly dense in a finite dimensional Euclidean vector space, then $\{\alpha_j\}$ is a basis for the space.

10. (a) Show that if $|\beta|^2$ is in $\mathcal{R}$, the convergence in Theorem 5.1F is uniform with respect to c and d.

(b) Show that when $c = a$, $d = b$, equation (5) is Parseval's equality.

11. Prove that $\mathcal{R}_2\{-\infty, \infty\}$, the set of functions integrable on every finite interval, with $\int_{-\infty}^{\infty} |\alpha(x)|^2 dx < \infty$, with addition, scalar multiplication, and inner product defined in a manner similar to that for $\mathcal{R}\{a, b\}$, is a Euclidean vector space. Here

$$\int_{-\infty}^{\infty} |\alpha(x)|^2 dx = \lim_{M,N\to\infty} \int_{-N}^{M} |\alpha(x)|^2 dx.$$

12. (a) Suppose α_n are integrable on the finite interval $a \le x \le b$ and converge uniformly to α. Show that $\{\alpha_n\}$ converges to α in the mean square, i.e.,

$$\lim_{n\to\infty} \int_a^b |\alpha_n - \alpha|^2 dx = 0. \text{ (Is } \alpha_n - \alpha \text{ integrable?)}$$

(b) Show that the conclusion in (a) is not valid for the interval $-\infty < x < \infty$, by considering

$$\alpha_n(x) = \begin{cases} \dfrac{1}{\sqrt{n}}, & n \le x \le 2n, \\ 0, & \text{otherwise.} \end{cases}$$

13. (a) Consider a Euclidean vector space $\mathscr{E}$ containing an infinite sequence of orthonormal vectors. Show that the identity transformation cannot be completely continuous. (See Exercise 1.)

(b) Let T be a symmetric completely continuous transformation on $\mathscr{E}$ to $\mathscr{E}$. Show that for each nonzero eigenvalue there are at most a finite number of linearly independent eigenvectors. *Hint:* The restriction of T to the linear manifold of eigenvectors associated with a nonzero eigenvalue is a constant times the identity transformation.

(c) Show that for each constant $c > 0$ there are at most a finite number of eigenvalues r of T with $|r| > c$. *Hint:* If $T\alpha_n = r_n \alpha_n$, $(\alpha_n, \alpha_m) = \delta_{nm}$, $|r_n| > c$, then $\|T\alpha_n - T\alpha_m\|^2 > 2c^2$, $n \ne m$.

5.2

APPROXIMATION THEOREMS

In 1885, K. Weierstrass proved a useful theorem, now known as the Weierstrass approximation theorem, which states that for every real continuous function f on the finite interval $a \le x \le b$, and for every $\epsilon > 0$, there exists a polynomial p such that $|f(x) - p(x)| < \epsilon$ for every x on $a \le x \le b$. Thus f is the limit of a uniformly convergent sequence of polynomials. Weierstrass also proved that every function f, continuous on $-\infty < x < \infty$, and periodic of period 2π, can be uniformly approximated by trigonometric sums, that is, by expressions of the form

$$\sum_{n=0}^{k} (a_n \cos nx + b_n \sin nx).$$

The polynomial and trigonometric cases are convertible, one into the other, by a change of variable. We shall begin with the polynomial case.

As a preparation for the Weierstrass theorem, a preliminary result is obtained which is of independent interest. Let $\mathscr{I}$ denote an interval of $\mathscr{E}_n$ defined by $-a_i \le x_i \le a_i$, $a_i > 0$. The interval $\mathscr{I}$ may be infinite in which case certain equality signs are omitted in defining the interval. For given

$\delta > 0$, and for given α in $\mathscr{I}$, let $\mathscr{D} = \{\beta \mid \|\beta - \alpha\| < \delta\}$. Then $\mathscr{I} \cap \mathscr{D}$ is the set of points of $\mathscr{I}$ which lie in the sphere of radius δ with center α and $\mathscr{I} \cap C(\mathscr{D})$ is the set of points in $\mathscr{I}$ not in this sphere. Both sets depend on α and their sum is $\mathscr{I}$. For each point $\alpha = (x_1, \ldots, x_n)$ of $\mathscr{I}$ let $\{K_m(\alpha; \beta)\}$ denote a sequence of real functions of $\beta = (y_1, \ldots, y_n)$ which are integrable on $\mathscr{I}$. We shall consider functions f for which the products $K_m(\alpha; \beta) f(\beta)$ are integrable on $\mathscr{I}$. With this notation we state

THEOREM 5.2A   If, for fixed α and for every δ, $0 < \delta < \delta_1$, the following conditions are satisfied:

(a) $\displaystyle \int_{\mathscr{I} \cap \mathscr{D}} |K_m(\alpha; \beta)| \, d\beta \leq A(\alpha)$, a constant independent of m,

(b) $\displaystyle \lim_{m \to \infty} \int_{\mathscr{I} \cap \mathscr{D}} K_m(\alpha; \beta) \, d\beta = 1$,

(c) $\displaystyle \lim_{m \to \infty} \int_{\mathscr{I} \cap C(\mathscr{D})} K_m(\alpha; \beta) f(\beta) \, d\beta = 0$,

then, whenever α is a point of continuity of f, we have

(1) $$\lim_{m \to \infty} \int_{\mathscr{I}} K_m(\alpha; \beta) f(\beta) \, d\beta = f(\alpha).$$

Moreover, if f is bounded and uniformly continuous on $\mathscr{I}$, and if for every α in a set $\mathscr{B}$ in $\mathscr{I}$, $A(\alpha) \leq A$, a constant, and if the sequences in (b) and (c) converge uniformly on $\mathscr{B}$, then the convergence in (1) is uniform on $\mathscr{B}$.

Proof   Write

$$\left| \int_{\mathscr{I}} K_m(\alpha; \beta) f(\beta) \, d\beta - f(\alpha) \right| \leq \left| \int_{\mathscr{I} \cap \mathscr{D}} K_m(\alpha; \beta)(f(\beta) - f(\alpha)) \, d\beta \right| +$$

$$\left| \left(\int_{\mathscr{I} \cap \mathscr{D}} K_m(\alpha; \beta) \, d\beta - 1 \right) f(\alpha) \right| + \left| \int_{\mathscr{I} \cap C(\mathscr{D})} K_m(\alpha; \beta) f(\beta) \, d\beta \right|.$$

The continuity of f at α assures us that we can choose δ sufficiently small so that $|f(\beta) - f(\alpha)| < \epsilon$ for β in $\mathscr{I} \cap \mathscr{D}$. Then condition (a) of the hypothesis implies that the first term on the right is less than $\epsilon A(\alpha)$. Now use (b) and (c) to find an integer M such that whenever $m > M$, the second and third terms on the right are respectively less than $\epsilon |f(\alpha)|$ and ϵ. Combining these results yields the desired convergence.

When we impose the additional hypotheses stated in the theorem, it is readily seen that we may choose δ and M to be independent of α in $\mathscr{B}$ and the convergence in (1) is uniform on $\mathscr{B}$. $\bigstar$

EXAMPLE 1   Assume f is integrable on every finite interval and bounded on $-\infty < x < \infty$. Show that at every continuity point x of f,

(2) $$\lim_{m \to \infty} \frac{m}{\sqrt{\pi}} \int_{-\infty}^{\infty} e^{-m^2(y-x)^2} f(y)dy = f(x).$$

It is known that $\int_{-\infty}^{\infty} e^{-z^2}\, dz = \sqrt{\pi}$. By a change of variable $z = m(y-x)$ we obtain

$$\int_{-\infty}^{\infty} \frac{m}{\sqrt{\pi}}\, e^{-m^2(y-x)^2}\, dy = \frac{1}{\sqrt{\pi}} \int_{-\infty}^{\infty} e^{-z^2}\, dz = 1.$$

The conditions on f assure us that $e^{-m^2(y-x)^2} f(y)$ will be integrable, since for large $|y|$, we have $|e^{-m^2(y-x)^2} f(y)| \leq F e^{-m^2(y-x)^2}$, where $|f(y)| \leq F$. Then, for $\delta > 0$,

$$\left| m \int_{x+\delta}^{\infty} e^{-m^2(y-x)^2} f(y)dy \right| \leq m F \int_{x+\delta}^{\infty} e^{-m^2(y-x)^2}\, dy = m F \int_{\delta}^{\infty} e^{-m^2 z^2}\, dz$$

$$\leq m F \int_{\delta}^{\infty} \frac{1}{m^2 z^2}\, dz = \frac{F}{m\delta}$$

which approaches 0 as m approaches ∞. A similar statement is valid for the interval $-\infty < y < x - \delta$. In particular, when $f = 1$ we may use $F = 1$. Thus, with $K_m(x; y) = \dfrac{m}{\sqrt{\pi}}\, e^{-m^2(y-x)^2}$, $\mathscr{I} = -\infty < y < \infty$, $\mathscr{D} = \{y \,\big|\, |y - x| < \delta\}$, we have shown that

$$\int_{\mathscr{D}} |K_m(x; y)|\, dy \leq \int_{\mathscr{I}} K_m(x; y)\, dy = 1,$$

$$\left| \int_{\mathscr{I} \cap C(\mathscr{D})} K_m(x; y) f(y)dy \right| \leq \frac{2F}{m\delta\sqrt{\pi}}, \qquad \left| \int_{\mathscr{I} \cap C(\mathscr{D})} K_m(x; y)dy \right| \leq \frac{2}{m\delta\sqrt{\pi}},$$

$$1 \geq \int_{\mathscr{D}} K_m(x; y)dy = \int_{\mathscr{I}} K_m(x; y)dy - \int_{\mathscr{I} \cap C(\mathscr{D})} K_m(x; y)dy \geq 1 - \frac{2}{m\delta\sqrt{\pi}}.$$

Conditions (a), (b), (c) of the theorem are now satisfied (in fact, uniformly for x on $\mathscr{I}$) and the desired result is attained.

A graph of $K_m(x; y)$ for values m_1 and m_2, $m_2 > m_1$ shows that the contribution of the kernel is greatest at x and tends to concentrate at x as m approaches ∞.

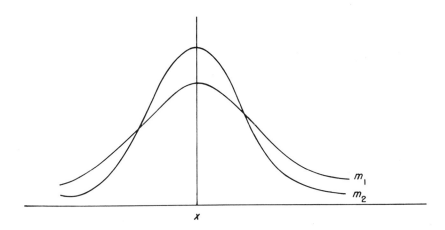

In connection with equation (1), taking $\mathscr{I}$ to be the interval $a \leq x \leq b$ (possibly infinite), we might ask whether there exists a kernel, which we shall denote by $\delta(x, y)$, such that

$$(3) \qquad \int_{\mathscr{I}} \delta(x, y) f(y) dy = f(x)$$

for every f satisfying given continuity conditions. Such a kernel is used formally in quantum mechanics and is called the **Dirac δ function.** Heuristically, it is thought of as a function satisfying equation (3) together with

$$\delta(x, y) = \begin{cases} 0, & y \neq x, \\ \infty, & y = x, \end{cases}$$

although no such combination is possible as the left side of (3) would then be zero. From another point of view, we are asking whether the identity operator acting on a linear manifold of functions can be represented as an integral operator.

Actually no kernel $\delta(x, y)$ satisfying (3) can exist, even for the class of infinitely differentiable functions. Suppose we take $f = 1$. Then (3) becomes

$$(4) \qquad \int_{\mathscr{I}} \delta(x, y) dy = 1.$$

Now choose f_n so that $0 \leq f_n(y) \leq 1$, $a \leq y \leq b$, and

$$f_n(y) = \begin{cases} 1, & |y - x| > 1/n, \\ 0, & y = x. \end{cases}$$

(We shall see later in this section that there exist infinitely differentiable functions satisfying these conditions). Then (3) becomes

$$\int_{|y-x| \leq 1/n} \delta(x, y) f_n(y) dy + \int_{|y-x| > 1/n} \delta(x, y) f_n(y) dy = 0.$$

This leads to a contradiction, since the second integral approaches 1 as n increases, in view of (4), while the first is less in absolute value than $\int_{|y-x| \leq 1/n} |\delta(x, y)| dy$ which approaches 0 as n increases.

However, it is possible to work with $\delta(x, y)$ in an entirely consistent manner to obtain valid results. Different approaches justifying the use of $\delta(x, y)$ are given in the books by Lighthill, Schwartz, and Erdelyi listed in the bibliography. We shall not make much use of the δ function here. Note however that (1) suggests that results obtained by using the δ function may possibly be verified by recourse to appropriate limiting processes.

To prove the Weierstrass theorem, we now select a particular sequence $K_m(\alpha; \beta)$ such that $\int_{\mathcal{I}} K_m(\alpha; \beta) f(\beta) \, d\beta$ are polynomials. In this way we obtain a sequence of polynomials converging to $f(\alpha)$.

THEOREM 5.2B Let f be a real valued continuous function on a bounded closed interval $\mathcal{B}$ in $\mathcal{E}_n$. For given $\epsilon > 0$, there is a polynomial $p(\alpha)$ such that $|f(\alpha) - p(\alpha)| < \epsilon$ for all α in $\mathcal{B}$.

Proof We may assume that the interval $\mathcal{B}$ given by $-b_i \leq x_i \leq b_i$ lies in the interior of the interval $\mathcal{I}: -c_i \leq x_i \leq c_i$ where $c_i > 0$ and $\sum_{i=1}^{n} c_i^2 \leq 1/4$ since this may always be accomplished by a linear change of variables. The function f is defined only on $\mathcal{B}$ but we may extend it so as to be bounded and uniformly continuous on all of $\mathcal{E}_n$ as follows: If $\alpha = (x_1, \ldots, x_n)$, define $x_j' = b_j$ if $x_j > b_j$, $x_j' = -b_j$ if $x_j < -b_j$ and $x_j' = x_j$ if $-b_j \leq x_j \leq b_j$. Then set $\alpha' = (x_1', \ldots, x_n')$ and define $f(\alpha) = f(\alpha')$. In this way $f(\alpha)$ is defined when α is outside $\mathcal{B}$ to have a value corresponding to the value of f at a boundary point of $\mathcal{B}$. We leave for Exercise 5.2–5 the verification that f is bounded and uniformly continuous on $\mathcal{E}_n$.

For $\alpha = (x_1, \ldots, x_n)$, $\beta = (y_1, \ldots, y_n)$ in $\mathscr{I}$, define

$$\frac{1}{h_m} = \int_{\mathscr{I}} \left(1 - \|\beta\|^2\right)^m d\beta,$$

$$K_m(\alpha; \beta) = \left(1 - \|\beta - \alpha\|^2\right)^m h_m,$$

$$g_m(\alpha) = \int_{\mathscr{I}} K_m(\alpha; \beta) f(\beta)\, d\beta.$$

It is readily verified that $K_m(\alpha; \beta) \geq 0$ and that g_m are polynomials in the variables $x_1, \ldots, x_n$. Choose δ less than the minimum distance from the interval $\mathscr{B}$ to the boundary of $\mathscr{I}$. Then for every point α in $\mathscr{B}$ the set $\mathscr{D} = \left\{\beta \,\middle|\, \|\beta - \alpha\| < \delta\right\}$ lies in $\mathscr{I}$. With $\mathscr{C} = \left\{\beta \,\middle|\, \|\beta\| < \frac{1}{\sqrt{m}}\right\}$, we have for large integral m,

$$\frac{1}{h_m} \geq \int_{\mathscr{C}} \left(1 - \|\beta\|^2\right)^m d\beta \geq \int_{\mathscr{C}} \left(1 - \frac{1}{m}\right)^m d\beta = q_1\,(m)^{-n/2} \left(1 - \frac{1}{m}\right)^m$$

where q_1 is a positive constant, since the volume of a sphere of radius r in $\mathscr{E}_n$ is proportional to r^n. Using $\lim_{m \to \infty} (1 + x/m)^m = e^x$, we have, for some constant q_2,

(5) $$\frac{1}{h_m} \geq q_2\, m^{-n/2}.$$

When α is in $\mathscr{B}$ and β is in $\mathscr{I} \cap C(\mathscr{D})$ (so that $\|\beta - \alpha\| \geqslant \delta$), we get

(6) $$0 \leq K_m(\alpha; \beta) \leq (1 - \delta^2)^m h_m \leq (1 - \delta^2)^m m^{n/2} q_2^{-1} \leq q_3\, m^{-n}$$

for constant q_3. Indeed, when $r < 1$, and j is given we can always find a constant q_4 such that $r^m < q_4\, m^{-j}$.

Equation (6) proves that $\lim_{m \to \infty} K_m(\alpha; \beta) = 0$ uniformly for α in $\mathscr{B}$ and β in $\mathscr{I} \cap C(\mathscr{D})$. Then the boundedness of f shows that

$$\lim_{m \to \infty} \int_{\mathscr{I} \cap C(\mathscr{D})} K_m(\alpha; \beta) f(\beta) d\beta = 0 \qquad \text{uniformly for } \alpha \text{ in } \mathscr{B}.$$

In particular, the result applies to $\alpha = \theta$. When $\mathscr{R} = \{\beta \,|\, \|\beta\| < \delta\}$ and α is in $\mathscr{B}$,

$$\int_{\mathscr{D}} K_m(\alpha; \beta)\, d\beta = \int_{\mathscr{D}} \left(1 - \|\beta - \alpha\|^2\right)^m d\beta\, h_m = \int_{\mathscr{R}} \left(1 - \|\beta\|^2\right)^m d\beta\, h_m$$

$$= \int_{\mathscr{I}} \left(1 - \|\beta\|^2\right)^m d\beta\, h_m - \int_{\mathscr{I} \cap C(\mathscr{R})} \left(1 - \|\beta\|^2\right)^m d\beta\, h_m.$$

Therefore

(7) $$\left| \int_{\mathscr{D}} K_m(\alpha; \beta)d\beta - 1 \right| \le \int_{\mathscr{I} \cap C(\mathscr{R})} K_m(\theta; \beta)d\beta \le q_3\, m^{-n} |\mathscr{I}|$$

which approaches zero uniformly for α in $\mathscr{B}$.

In this way the conditions of Theorem 5.2A are satisfied and we can conclude that $\{g_m\}$ converges uniformly to f on $\mathscr{B}$.   ★

It is possible to show that the theorem is true when $\mathscr{B}$ is any bounded closed set. The method above applies after using the known result (a proof of which is not trivial) that a continuous function defined on a bounded closed set can be extended to be continuous on all of $\mathscr{E}_n$.

As a corollary, we obtain a result already used in Theorem 4.2B and Exercise 4.2–3.

Corollary

If $K(x, y)$ is symmetric and continuous on $a \le x \le b$, $a \le y \le b$, then, for every $\epsilon > 0$ there is a symmetric polynomial $P(x, y)$ such that $|K(x, y) - P(x, y)| < \epsilon$ for $a \le x \le b$, $a \le y \le b$.

Proof. By the theorem there is a polynomial

$$G(x, y) = \sum_{i,j=0}^{n} g_{ij}\, x^i\, y^j$$

such that

$$|K(x, y) - G(x, y)| < \epsilon.$$

Define

$$P(x, y) = \frac{1}{2}\left(G(x, y) + G(y, x) \right) = \sum_{i,j=0}^{n} p_{ij}\, x^i\, y^j.$$

Then

$$p_{ij} = \frac{1}{2}\left(g_{ij} + g_{ji} \right) = p_{ji}$$

and

$$|K(x, y) - P(x, y)| \le \frac{1}{2}|K(x, y) - G(x, y)| + \frac{1}{2}|K(x, y) - G(y, x)|$$

$$= \frac{1}{2}|K(x, y) - G(x, y)| + \frac{1}{2}|K(y, x) - G(y, x)| < \epsilon/2 + \epsilon/2 = \epsilon.   ★$$

In view of the fact that our applications will be made to functions of a single variable, and to preserve simplicity of presentation, the remainder of this section will be devoted to the one-dimensional case.

Closely related to polynomial approximation is the concept of approximation by trigonometric sums. By a trigonometric sum of order at most m in the variable x is meant an expression of the form

$$T(x) = \sum_{n=0}^{m} a_n \cos nx + b_n \sin nx.$$

THEOREM 5.2C Let f be continuous for all x and periodic of period 2π. Then for $\epsilon > 0$ there is a trigonometric sum T such that $|f(x) - T(x)| < \epsilon$ for all x.

Proof We shall prove the theorem first for the case when $f(x)$ is an even function, that is, when $f(x) = f(-x)$. Define

$$g(t) = f(\text{Arc } \cos t), \qquad -1 \le t \le 1.$$

For given $\epsilon > 0$, there is a polynomial p, such that

$$|g(t) - p(t)| < \epsilon, \qquad -1 \le t \le 1.$$

Replace t by $\cos x$ to obtain

$$|f(x) - p(\cos x)| < \epsilon, \qquad 0 \le x \le \pi.$$

This inequality subsists also for $-\pi \le x \le 0$ since $f(x)$ and $p(\cos x)$ are even. Then, in view of the periodicity, it is true for all x. The truth of the theorem for even $f(x)$ will be complete when it is shown that $p(\cos x)$ is a trigonometric sum. This is apparent from the identities

$$p(\cos x) = \sum_{j=0}^{n} a_j (\cos x)^j, \qquad (\cos x)^j = \frac{1}{2^j} \sum_{r=0}^{j} \binom{j}{r} \cos(j - 2r)x$$

where

$$\binom{j}{r} = \frac{j!}{r!(j - r)!}.$$

The last formula is obtained from

$$(\cos x)^j = \left(\frac{e^{ix} + e^{-ix}}{2} \right)^j = \frac{1}{2^j} \sum_{r=0}^{j} \binom{j}{r} (e^{ix})^{j-r}(e^{-ix})^r$$

$$= \frac{1}{2^j} \sum_{r=0}^{j} \binom{j}{r} e^{ix(j-2r)} = \frac{1}{2^j} \sum_{r=0}^{j} \binom{j}{r}\left(\cos(j - 2r)x + i \sin(j - 2r)x \right).$$

Next, permit $f(x)$ to be any continuous function with period 2π and write

$$f(x) \sin x = \frac{f(x) + f(-x)}{2} \sin x + \frac{f(x) - f(-x)}{2} \sin x.$$

The functions $\dfrac{f(x) + f(-x)}{2}$ and $\dfrac{f(x) - f(-x)}{2}$ $\sin x$ are even and the above proof implies the existence of trigonometric sums $p(x)$ and $q(x)$ such that

$$\left| \frac{f(x) + f(-x)}{2} \sin x - p(x) \sin x \right| \le \left| \frac{f(x) + f(-x)}{2} - p(x) \right| < \epsilon/2,$$

$$\left| \frac{f(x) - f(-x)}{2} \sin x - q(x) \right| < \epsilon/2.$$

It follows that

$$\left| f(x) \sin x - \left(p(x) \sin x + q(x) \right) \right| < \epsilon,$$

establishing the theorem for the function $f(x) \sin x$.

Then the theorem is also valid for the function $f\left(\dfrac{\pi}{2} - x\right) \sin x$. That is, there is a trigonometric sum $p(x)$ such that

$$\left| f\left(\frac{\pi}{2} - x\right) \sin x - p(x) \right| < \epsilon \qquad \text{for all } x.$$

Replace $\dfrac{\pi}{2} - x$ by t to obtain

$$\left| f(t) \cos t - p\left(\frac{\pi}{2} - t\right) \right| < \epsilon \qquad \text{for all } t$$

proving the theorem for the function $f(x) \cos x$.

Consequently, the theorem is true for the functions $f(x) \sin x \sin x$ and $f(x) \cos x \cos x$ and hence for their sum $f(x)$.   ★

In many cases one can dispense with pointwise approximation and consider approximation in the mean.

THEOREM 5.2D If f is integrable on the finite interval $a \le x \le b$, then for each $\epsilon > 0$ there are infinitely differentiable functions g and h

defined on $a \leq x \leq b$ which are zero outside of an interval $a < c \leq x \leq d < b$, depending on ϵ, and satisfy

(a) $|g(x)| \leq |f(x)|,\ a \leq x \leq b,$ and $\displaystyle\int_a^b |f(x) - g(x)|dx < \epsilon,$

(b) $|h(x)| \leq |f(x)|,\ a \leq x \leq b,$ and $\displaystyle\int_a^b |f(x) - h(x)|^2 dx < \epsilon.$

Proof We need prove only **(a)**. Indeed, if $M = \text{l.u.b.}\left\{|f(x)|\,\Big|\, a \leq x \leq b\right\}$ then

$$\int_a^b |f(x) - g(x)|^2\, dx \leq 2M \int_a^b |f(x) - g(x)|dx$$

when $|g(x) \leq |f(x)|$, so that the existence for each ϵ of a function g satisfying **(a)** implies the existence for each ϵ of a function h satisfying **(b)**. The proof of the theorem for part **(a)** will be divided into four cases.

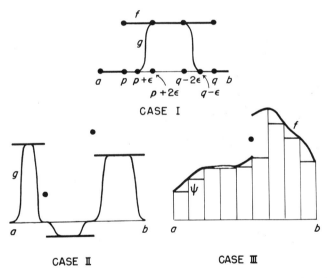

CASE I

CASE II   CASE III

Case I. Suppose first that f is the characteristic function of an interval $\mathscr{I}$ of the form $p \leq x \leq q$ or $p \leq x < q$ or $p < x \leq q$ or $p < x < q$ within $a \leq x \leq b$. That is

$$f(x) = \begin{cases} 1 & \text{if } x \text{ is in } \mathscr{I}, \\ 0 & \text{if } x \text{ is not in } \mathscr{I}. \end{cases}$$

We may suppose $p \neq q$ for then $g = 0$ would suffice. Restrict $\epsilon < \dfrac{q - p}{4}$
and form g as follows (figure for Case I):

$$
g(x) = \begin{cases}
0, & x < p + \epsilon, \\
u(x), & p + \epsilon \leq x \leq p + 2\epsilon, \\
1, & p + 2\epsilon < x < q - 2\epsilon, \\
v(x), & q - 2\epsilon \leq x \leq q - \epsilon, \\
0, & q - \epsilon < x,
\end{cases}
$$

where $u(x)$ is an infinitely differentiable function on $p + \epsilon < x < p + 2\epsilon$
satisfying $0 \leq u(x) \leq 1$, $u(p + \epsilon) = 0$, $u(p + 2\epsilon) = 1$, and having all right
hand derivatives at $p + \epsilon$ and all left hand derivatives at $p + 2\epsilon$ equal to zero;
and where $v(x)$ is an infinitely differentiable function on $q - 2\epsilon < x < q - \epsilon$
satisfying $0 \leq v(x) \leq 1$, $v(q - 2\epsilon) = 1$, $v(q - \epsilon) = 0$, and having all right
hand derivatives at $q - 2\epsilon$ and all left hand derivatives at $q - \epsilon$ equal to
zero. Assuming for the moment that such functions u and v can be constructed, we see that g is infinitely differentiable, satisfies $0 \leq g(x) \leq f(x)$
on $a \leq x \leq b$, vanishes outside of $a < p + \epsilon \leq x \leq q - \epsilon < b$, and that

$$
\int_a^b |f(x) - g(x)| dx = \int_p^{p+\varepsilon} dx + \int_{p+\varepsilon}^{p+2\varepsilon} |1 - g(x)| dx + \int_{q-2\varepsilon}^{q-\varepsilon} |1 - g(x)| dx
$$

$$
+ \int_{q-\varepsilon}^q dx < 4\epsilon.
$$

For the construction of u and v we use the fact that the nonnegative
function

(8)
$$
w(x) = \begin{cases}
e^{\frac{1}{(x-r)(s-x)}}, & r < x < s, \\
\\
0, & x = r, x = s,
\end{cases}
$$

is continuous on $r \leq x \leq s$ and has all right hand derivatives at r and left
hand derivatives at s equal to zero. (Exercise 5.2–9.) Then

$$
z(x) = \int_r^x w(x) dx \Big/ \int_r^s w(x) dx, \qquad r \leq x \leq s,
$$

satisfies $z(r) = 0$, $z(s) = 1$, $0 \leq z(x) \leq 1$, and all one sided derivatives of
z at r and s are zero. In this way we form the function u, when $r = p + \epsilon$,

$s = p + 2\epsilon$. A similar consideration of the function $1 - z(x)$ shows how to form the function v.

   Case II.   Suppose next that f is a step function on $a \le x \le b$; that is, a function which is zero except on a finite number of disjoint intervals of the form $p \le x \le q$, or $p \le x < q$, or $p < x \le q$, or $p < x < q$, and which is constant on these intervals. If we denote these intervals by $\mathcal{I}_j$ and their characteristic functions by $\phi_j(x) = \phi(\mathcal{I}_j, x)$ then f is of the form

$$f(x) = \sum_{j=1}^{n} c_j \, \phi_j(x), \qquad c_j \text{ constant, } a \le x \le b.$$

Corresponding to each ϕ_j we form a function g_j as constructed in Case I ($g_j = 0$ if $p \le x \le q$ is a point) and define

$$g(x) = \sum_{j=1}^{n} c_j \, g_j(x).$$

Since g_j vanishes outside of $\mathcal{I}_j$, it is readily seen that $|g(x)| \le |f(x)|$, that g is infinitely differentiable, that g is zero in intervals (of positive length) containing a and b, and that

$$\int_a^b |f(x) - g(x)| dx = \sum_j \int_{\mathcal{I}_j} |f(x) - g(x)| dx = \sum_j \int_{\mathcal{I}_j} |c_j \, \phi_j(x) - c_j \, g_j(x)| dx$$

$$= \sum_j |c_j| \int_{\mathcal{I}_j} |\phi_j(x) - g_j(x)| dx \le \epsilon \sum_j |c_j|.$$

   Case III.   For this case we will assume that f is a nonnegative integrable function. Consider a partition $P: a = y_0 < y_1 \cdots < y_n = b$ of the interval $a \le x \le b$ and define

$$\mathcal{I}_j: y_{j-1} \le x \le y_j, \quad m_j = \text{g.l.b.} \left\{ f(x) \;\middle|\; x \text{ in } \mathcal{I}_j \right\}, \quad S(p) = \sum_j m_j |\mathcal{I}_j|.$$

We can find a partition P such that

(9) $$0 \le \int_a^b f(x) dx - \underline{S}(P) < \epsilon.$$

If we let ϕ_j be the characteristic function of the interval $y_{j-1} \leq x < y_j$, it is clear that

$$\underline{S}(P) = \sum_j m_j \int_{\mathscr{I}_j} \phi_j(x)dx = \int_a^b \sum_j m_j \, \phi_j(x) \, dx = \int_a^b \psi(x)dx,$$

where $\psi(x) = \sum_j m_j \phi_j(x)$ is a step function satisfying $0 \leq \psi(x) \leq f(x)$. (See figure for Case III.) Then (9) becomes

(10) $$0 \leq \int_a^b \left(f(x) - \psi(x) \right)dx < \epsilon.$$

By Case II, we can obtain a function g, $0 \leq g(x) \leq \psi(x) \leq f(x)$, infinitely differentiable and vanishing on intervals (of positive length) containing a and b, such that

(11) $$0 \leq \int_a^b \left(\psi(x) - g(x) \right)dx < \epsilon.$$

From (10) and (11) we obtain

(12) $$\int_a^b |f(x) - g(x)|dx < 2\epsilon$$

as desired.

Case IV. Let f be any function integrable on $a \leq x \leq b$. Write $f = f^+ - f^-$ where

$$f^+(x) = \max\{f(x), 0\} = \begin{cases} f(x), & \text{if } f(x) \geq 0, \\ 0, & \text{if } f(x) < 0, \end{cases}$$

and

$$f^-(x) = \max\{-f(x), 0\} = \begin{cases} -f(x), & \text{if } f(x) \leq 0, \\ 0, & \text{if } f(x) > 0. \end{cases}$$

Clearly f^+ and f^- are nonnegative. They are also integrable since every common point of continuity of two functions u and v is a point of continuity of

$$\max(u, v) = \frac{u + v + |u - v|}{2}$$

proving that $\max(f, 0)$ and $\max(-f, 0)$ are continuous wherever f is.

By (12) we can find infinitely differentiable functions g_1 and g_2, vanishing in intervals (of positive length) containing a and b, such that $|g_1(x)| \le f^+(x)$, $|g_2(x)| \le f^-(x)$ and

$$\int_a^b |f^+(x) - g_1(x)|dx < \epsilon, \qquad \int_a^b |f^-(x) - g_2(x)|dx < \epsilon.$$

Then $g(x) = g_1(x) - g_2(x)$ is of the required form, for

$$|g(x)| \le |g_1(x)| + |g_2(x)| \le f^+(x) + f^-(x) = |f(x)|$$

and

$$\int_a^b |f(x) - g(x)|dx \le \int_a^b \Big(|f^+(x) \quad g_1(x)| + |f^-(x) - g_2(x)|\Big)dx < 2\epsilon. \quad \bigstar$$

By using equation (10) instead of (12) in Case III, we can derive

Corollary 1
If f is integrable on the finite interval $a \le x \le b$, then for each $\epsilon > 0$ there are step functions g and h on $a \le x \le b$ such that **(a)** and **(b)** of Theorem 5.2D hold.

A similar result for the infinite interval is given by

Corollary 2
(a) If $\int_{-\infty}^{\infty} |f(x)|dx < \infty$, then for each $\epsilon > 0$ there is an infinitely differentiable function g, zero outside a finite closed interval (or a step function g), such that $|g(x)| \le |f(x)|$ for all x and $\int_{-\infty}^{\infty} |f(x) - g(x)|dx < \epsilon$.

(b) If $\int_{-\infty}^{\infty} |f(x)|^2 dx < \infty$, then for each $\epsilon > 0$ there is an infinitely differentiable function h, zero outside a finite closed interval (or a step function h), such that $|h(x)| \le |f(x)|$ for all x and $\int_{-\infty}^{\infty} |f(x) - h(x)|^2 dx < \epsilon$.

Indeed, since we have defined $\int_{-\infty}^{\infty} |f(x)|dx = \lim_{M, N \to \infty} \int_{-M}^{N} |f(x)|dx$, it is possible to find an integer N such that

$$0 \le \int_{-\infty}^{\infty} |f(x)|dx - \int_{-N}^{N} |f(x)|dx < \epsilon/2.$$

Then there is a function g of the type desired, defined on $-N \le x \le N$ such that

$$\int_{-N}^{N} |f(x) - g(x)|dx < \epsilon/2.$$

Define $g(x) = 0$ for $|x| > N$ and obtain

$$\int_{-\infty}^{\infty} |f(x) - g(x)| dx = \int_{|x| > N} |f(x)| dx + \int_{-N}^{N} |f(x) - g(x)| dx < \epsilon.$$

In an analogous fashion part (b) is established.

The above conclusions can be rephrased in the terminology of Section 5.1. The linear manifold of infinitely differentiable functions vanishing outside an interval $a < c \le x \le d < b$ (the interval depends on the function) is dense in $\mathcal{R}\{a, b\}$. The linear manifold of step functions on $a \le x \le b$ is dense in $\mathcal{R}\{a, b\}$. The results for the infinite interval have a corresponding interpretation in $\mathcal{R}_2\{a, b\}$.

The usefulness of approximation theories is evident. First a theorem is proved for functions with sufficient continuity properties. Then, by approximating a less well-behaved function by functions for which the theorem is true, it may be possible to establish the result for the more general case. This was the procedure employed in Theorem 4.2B. The same method will be used later.

Exercise 5.2

1. Show that $\lim\limits_{n \to \infty} \displaystyle\int_{-2}^{3} \frac{1}{\pi n^2 \left(x^2 + \dfrac{1}{n^4} \right)} e \sin x^5 \, dx = 1.$

2. (a) Show that $\lim\limits_{\epsilon \to 0} \dfrac{1}{\epsilon \sqrt{\pi}} \displaystyle\int_{-\infty}^{\infty} e^{-(y-x)^2/\epsilon^2} f(y) dy = f(x)$ at every point of continuity of the function f bounded on $-\infty < x < \infty$ and integrable on every finite interval.

    (b) Show that this implies $\lim\limits_{n \to \infty} \left(\dfrac{n}{\pi} \right)^{1/2} \displaystyle\int_{-\infty}^{\infty} e^{-n(y-x)^2} f(y) dy = f(x).$

3. Let $K_m(x, y) = \dfrac{m}{\sqrt{\pi}} e^{-m^2(y-x)^2}$ and let f and its derivative f' be bounded and continuous on $-\infty < y < \infty$. In view of equation (2) we assign the symbol $\delta(x, y)$ to the sequence $\{K_m(x, y)\}$ and write $\displaystyle\int_{-\infty}^{\infty} \delta(x, y) f(y) dy = f(x)$. Show, using integration by parts, that

    $$\lim_{m \to \infty} \int_{-\infty}^{\infty} \left\{ \frac{\partial}{\partial y} K_m(x, y) \right\} f(y) dy = -f'(x).$$

    We therefore assign the symbol $\delta'(x, y)$ to the sequence $\left\{ \dfrac{\partial}{\partial y} K_m(x, y) \right\}$ and write $\displaystyle\int_{-\infty}^{\infty} \delta'(x, y) f(y) dy = -f'(x).$

4. A "generalized" function can be defined as follows: Let $\mathcal{G}$ be the class of all functions f infinitely differentiable on $-\infty < y < \infty$ and for any N satisfying $|f(y)| < \dfrac{c}{|y|^N}$ when $|y|$ is sufficiently large. Let $\{\phi_n\}$ be a sequence of functions

in $\mathscr{G}$ such that $\lim\limits_{n\to\infty} \int_{-\infty}^{\infty} \phi_n(y)\, f(y)dy$ exists for every f in $\mathscr{G}$. Corresponding to the sequence $\{\phi_n\}$ we assign the symbol ϕ and call it a "generalized function." We write $\phi \leftrightarrow \{\phi_n\}$. If ψ_n is another such sequence in $\mathscr{G}$ with

$$\lim_{n\to\infty} \int_{-\infty}^{\infty} \phi_n(y)\, f(y)dy = \lim_{n\to\infty} \int_{-\infty}^{\infty} \psi_n(y)\, f(y)dy$$

for every f in $\mathscr{G}$, then the same symbol is assigned to both sequences.
Show that $\delta(x, y)$ is, for each x, a generalized function.

5. Show that the extension to $\mathscr{E}_n$ of the continuous function f on $\mathscr{B}$ in Theorem 5.2B is bounded and uniformly continuous on all of $\mathscr{E}_n$. *Hint:* With α' related to α as indicated when forming the extension, note $\|\alpha - \beta\| \geq \|\alpha' - \beta'\|$.

6. The one-dimensional form of Theorem 5.2B states that if f is continuous on a closed interval $\mathscr{B}$ in the interior of $-\frac{1}{2} \leq x \leq \frac{1}{2}$, then

$$\lim_{m\to\infty} \int_{-\frac{1}{2}}^{\frac{1}{2}} \left(1 - |y - x|^2\right)^m f(y)dy \Big/ \int_{-\frac{1}{2}}^{\frac{1}{2}} \left(1 - |y|^2\right)^m dy = f(x)$$

uniformly on $\mathscr{B}$. Make the change of variable $z = (b - a)y + \dfrac{b + a}{2}$, $t = (b - a)x + \dfrac{b + a}{2}$ to show that if v is continuous on a closed interval $\mathscr{B}$ in the interior of $a \leq x \leq b$, then

$$\lim_{m\to\infty} \int_a^b \left((b - a)^2 - |z - t|^2\right)^m v(z)dz \Big/ \int_a^b \left((b - a)^2 - \left|z - \frac{a + b}{2}\right|^2\right)^m dz = v(t)$$

uniformly on $\mathscr{B}$.

7. Use Exercise 6 with $a = 0$, $b = 1$, to approximate $\sqrt{t}$ at $t = \frac{1}{2}$. Take $m = 1, 2, 3$.

8. (a) Prove Leibnitz's rule for the differentiation of a product:

$$\frac{d^n(uv)}{dx^n} = \sum_{r=0}^{n} \binom{n}{r} \frac{d^{n-r}u}{dx^{n-r}} \frac{d^r v}{dx^r} \quad \text{where} \quad \binom{n}{r} = \frac{n!}{r!(n - r)!}.$$

(b) Apply (a) to obtain the nth derivative of $\dfrac{x + 2}{x - 1}$; of $\dfrac{x + 2}{x^2 - 1}$.

9. (a) Let ϕ be continuous on $r \leq x \leq s$ and have a derivative ϕ' for $r < x < s$. Suppose $\lim\limits_{x\to r+} \phi'(x)$ exists. Use the mean value theorem to show that ϕ has a right hand derivative $\phi'_+(r)$ equal to $\lim\limits_{x\to r+} \phi'(x)$.

(b) Use the Maclaurin expansion for e^x to show that

$$0 < e^{-\frac{1}{(x-r)(s-x)}} < n!(x - r)^n (s - x)^n \text{ for every } n,$$

$r < x < s$, and hence $\lim\limits_{x\to r+} \dfrac{e^{-\frac{1}{(x-r)(s-x)}}}{(x - r)^n} = 0$ for every n.

(c) Show that the function $w(x)$ defined by (8) in the text is continuous on $r \leq x \leq s$ and has all right hand derivatives at r and left hand derivatives at s equal to zero. *Hint:* Let $v = \dfrac{1}{(x - r)(s - x)}$, note that $w^n(x)$ is equal to e^{-v} multiplied by a polynomial in the first n derivatives of v, and apply Leibnitz's rule (Exercise 8) to find the derivatives of v.

10. Note that Case II of Theorem 5.2E proves that the linear manifold of infinitely differentiable functions vanishing outside an interval $a < c \leq x \leq d < b$ is dense in the linear manifold of step functions on $a \leq x \leq b$. Hence show that the manifold of continuous functions is dense in the manifold of step functions. Show that the linear manifold of polynomials on $a \leq x \leq b$ is dense in the set of step functions on $a \leq x \leq b$. Show that the linear manifold of polynomials on $a \leq x \leq b$ is dense in $\mathscr{R}\{a, b\}$.

11. Let f be integrable on $a - 1 \leq x \leq b + 1$ and let $w(t) = \int_a^b |f(t + x) - f(x)| dx$,
    $-1 \leq t \leq 1$. Show that $w(t)$ is continuous at $t = 0$. *Hint:* Show that there is a continuous function g on $a - 1 \leq x \leq b + 1$ such that $\int_{a-1}^{b+1} |f(x) - g(x)| dx < \epsilon$. Write

    $$w(t) \leq \int_a^b |f(x + t) - g(x + t)| dx + \int_a^b |g(x + t) - g(x)| dx.$$
    $$+ \int_a^b |g(x) - f(x)| dx.$$

12. Prove the following extension of Theorem 5.2D. Let f and $\rho \geq 0$ be integrable on the finite interval $a \leq x \leq b$. Then for each $\epsilon > 0$, there are infinitely differentiable functions g and h which are zero outside of an interval $a < c \leq x \leq d < b$ and satisfy

    (a) $|g(x)| \leq |f(x)|$, $a \leq x \leq b$, and $\int_a^b \rho(x)|f(x) - g(x)| dx < \epsilon$.

    (b) $|h(x)| \leq |f(x)|$, $a \leq x \leq b$, and $\int_a^b \rho(x)|f(x) - g(x)|^2 dx < \epsilon$.

    Hint: $\int_a^b \rho(x)|f(x) - g(x)| dx \leq \left(\int_a^b \rho^2 dx \int_a^b |f(x) - g(x)|^2 dx \right)^{1/2}$.

13. Prove that a continuous function f on a closed interval may be approximated uniformly by a sequence of monotone decreasing polynomials. *Hint:* Let
    $g_n = f + \dfrac{1}{n}$ and let p_n be polynomials such that $|g_n - p_n| < \dfrac{1}{2(n + 1)^2}$.

14. State and prove the extension of the corollary to Theorem 5.2B to the case when $K(x, y)$ is Hermitian.

5.3

LEGENDRE

POLYNOMIALS

The simplest case of an orthonormal sequence of functions in $\mathscr{R}\{a, b\}$, the vector space of real integrable functions on the finite interval $a \leq x \leq b$, is obtained by applying the orthonormalization process to the polynomials x^n, $n = 0, 1, 2, \ldots$. Let us restrict our attention to the interval $-1 \leq x \leq 1$.

THEOREM 5.3A Any finite set of the functions $f_n(x) = x^n$, $n = 0, 1, 2, \ldots$, is a linearly independent set in $\mathscr{R}\{-1, 1\}$. Application of the Gram-Schmidt process yields an orthonormal sequence

$$(1) \quad \pi_n = \pi_n(x) = \sqrt{\frac{2n+1}{2}} \frac{1}{2^n n!} \frac{d^n}{dx^n} (x^2 - 1)^n, \quad n = 0, 1, 2, \ldots,$$

called the **normalized Legendre polynomials**. The sequence $\{\pi_n\}$ is linearly dense in $\mathscr{R}\{-1, 1\}$.

Proof. If $\displaystyle\sum_{i=0}^{k} a_i x^i$ is equal to the zero vector, it must be identically zero since it is continuous. This implies all a_i are zero, since a polynomial of degree $k > 0$ has at most k zeros. Now apply the Gram-Schmidt process. The procedure used in Theorem 5.1E shows that the orthonormal sequence $\{\phi_n\}$ so formed will have ϕ_n of degree n and the coefficient of x^n in ϕ_n will be a positive number.

We shall show in the next paragraph that the sequence π_n in (1) is also an orthonormal sequence in $\mathscr{R}\{-1, 1\}$ with π_n of degree n and the coefficient of x^n in π_n a positive number. We claim that this will prove $\pi_n = \phi_n$, and we shall establish this claim by an inductive proof. First note that ϕ_0, a constant, must satisfy $\displaystyle\int_{-1}^{1} \phi_0^2 \, dx = 1$ and hence $\phi_0 = 1/\sqrt{2} = \pi_0$. Now suppose $\phi_j = \pi_j, j = 0, 1, \ldots, k$. Then, since both $\{\pi_i\}$ and $\{\phi_i\}, i = 0, 1, \ldots, k+1$ are bases in the linear manifold spanned by $1, x, \ldots, x^{k+1}$, we may write

$$\pi_{k+1} = a_0 \phi_0 + a_1 \phi_1 + \cdots + a_{k+1} \phi_{k+1}$$

with

$$0 = (\pi_{k+1}, \pi_j) = (\pi_{k+1}, \phi_j) = a_j$$

for $j \leq k$. Therefore

$$\pi_{k+1} = a_{k+1} \phi_{k+1},$$

$$1 = \|\pi_{k+1}\| = |a_{k+1}| \, \|\phi_{k+1}\| = |a_{k+1}|,$$

and we conclude that $a_{k+1} = 1$, since the coefficients of x^{k+1} in π_{k+1} and ϕ_{k+1} are positive numbers. This shows that $\pi_{k+1} = \phi_{k+1}$ and completes the induction.

Here is a proof that $\{\pi_n\}$ is an orthonormal sequence. Suppose σ is any polynomial of degree $m < n, n \geq 1$. An integration by parts yields

$$\int_{-1}^{1} \frac{d^n}{dx^n} (x^2 - 1)^n \sigma(x) dx = \left(\frac{d^{n-1}}{dx^{n-1}} (x^2 - 1)^n \right) \sigma(x) \Big|_{-1}^{1}$$

$$- \int_{-1}^{1} \left(\frac{d^{n-1}}{dx^{n-1}} (x^2 - 1)^n \right) \frac{d\sigma}{dx} dx = - \int_{-1}^{1} \left(\frac{d^{n-1}}{dx^{n-1}} (x^2 - 1)^n \right) \frac{d\sigma}{dx} dx$$

because the jth derivative of $(x^2 - 1)^n$, $j < n$, contains $(x^2 - 1)^{n-j}$ as a factor. Thus if $m < n$, m partial integrations will yield

$$\int_{-1}^{1} \left(\frac{d^n}{dx^n} (x^2 - 1)^n \right) \sigma(x) \, dx = c \, (-1)^m \int_{-1}^{1} \frac{d^{n-m}}{dx^{n-m}} (x^2 - 1)^n \, dx$$

$$= c(-1)^m \frac{d^{n-m-1}}{dx^{n-m-1}} (x^2 - 1)^n \bigg|_{-1}^{1} = 0$$

where c is the constant obtained by differentiating σ m times. We have therefore shown that π_n is orthogonal to every polynomial of degree less than n, in particular to π_m, $m < n$.

By n partial integrations we get

$$\int_{-1}^{1} \frac{d^n}{dx^n} (x^2 - 1)^n \frac{d^n}{dx^n} (x^2 - 1)^n \, dx = (-1)^n \int_{-1}^{1} (x^2 - 1)^n \frac{d^{2n}}{dx^{2n}} (x^2 - 1)^n \, dx$$

$$= (-1)^n (2n)! \int_{-1}^{1} (x^2 - 1)^n \, dx = 2 \cdot (2n)! \int_{0}^{1} (1 - x^2)^n \, dx$$

$$= 2 \cdot (2n)! \int_{0}^{\pi/2} \cos^{2n+1} y \, dy = 2 \cdot (2n)! \frac{2 \cdot 4 \cdots (2n)}{3 \cdot 5 \cdots (2n + 1)} = \frac{2}{(2n + 1)} (2n \cdot n!)^2.$$

This implies that π_n as defined in (1) has norm equal to 1.

For the proof that $\{\pi_n\}$ is linearly dense in $\mathscr{R} \{-1, 1\}$, we need only show that the linear manifold spanned by $1, x, x^2 \ldots$ is dense in $\mathscr{R}\{-1, 1\}$. When α is in $\mathscr{R}$, we appeal to Theorem 5.2D to yield a function β, continuous on $-1 \leq x \leq 1$, such that $\|\alpha - \beta\| < \epsilon/2$. For this β, we choose a polynomial σ, using Theorem 5.2B, such that $|\beta(x) - \sigma(x)| < \epsilon/2\sqrt{2}$ and hence $\|\beta - \sigma\| < \epsilon/2$. Now we have $\|\alpha - \sigma\| < \epsilon$ and the manifold of polynomials is dense in $\mathscr{R}$. This completes the proof of the theorem.   ★

The conclusions attained in Section 5.1 are now applicable. For example, Theorem 5.1D indicates that if $(\alpha, \pi_n) = 0$ for every n, then α is the zero vector. This condition may be rephrased in terms of the sequence $\{x^n\}$ as follows:

Corollary 1

If $\int_{-1}^{1} \alpha(x) \, x^n \, dx = 0$ for $n = 0, 1, 2, \ldots$ and α is in $\mathscr{R} \{-1, 1\}$ then α is the zero vector. In particular, if α is continuous, it is identically zero.

For, when α is orthogonal to x^n for each n, then α is orthogonal to each π_n. For every α in $\mathscr{R} \{-1, 1\}$, we have, by Theorem 5.1C,

$$(2) \qquad\qquad\qquad \alpha = \sum_{n=0}^{\infty} (\alpha, \pi_n) \, \pi_n$$

in the sense of mean square convergence. This expansion theorem is usually phrased in terms of the functions

(3) $\quad P_n = P_n(x) = \dfrac{1}{2^n\, n!} \dfrac{d^n}{dx^n} (x^2 - 1)^n = \sqrt{\dfrac{2}{2n + 1}}\, \pi_n(x), \quad n = 0, 1, 2, \ldots$

called the **Legendre Polynomials.** Thus we have

(4) $\quad \displaystyle\lim_{n \to \infty} \int_{-1}^{1} \left| \alpha(x) - \sum_{j=0}^{n} \dfrac{2j + 1}{2} \int_{-1}^{1} \alpha(t)\, P_j(t)\, dt\, P_j(x) \right|^2 dx = 0.$

The series

(5) $\quad \displaystyle\sum_{0}^{\infty} \dfrac{2j + 1}{2} \int_{-1}^{1} \alpha(t)\, P_j(t)\, dt\, P_j(x)$

is called the **Legendre Series** for α. Equation (4) states that the Legendre series for α converges to α in the mean square sense.

The Parseval equality (see Theorem 5.1B) in terms of Legendre polynomials is

(6) $\quad \displaystyle\int_{-1}^{1} \alpha^2(x)\, dx = \sum_{n=0}^{\infty} \dfrac{2n + 1}{2} \left| \int_{-1}^{1} \alpha(x)\, P_n(x)\, dx \right|^2.$

The Legendre polynomials were introduced in 1784 by Legendre in connection with a problem in potential theory. Let a unit positive charge be placed at Q, distant d' from the origin O, and let point P be distant r from Q and d from O. Then the potential at P is

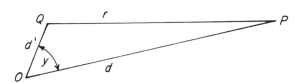

$$\frac{1}{r} = \left(d^2 - 2d\, d' \cos y + (d')^2 \right)^{-1/2} = d^{-1} \left(1 - 2vx + v^2 \right)^{-1/2}$$

where y is the angle POQ, $x = \cos y$, $v = d'/d$. If we develop d/r as a power series in v, it is possible to show that

$$\frac{d}{r} = \left(1 - 2vx + v^2 \right)^{-1/2} = \sum_{j=0}^{\infty} P_j(x)\, v^j$$

where $P_j(x)$ are the Legendre polynomials and the series converges absolutely for sufficiently small v. (See Exercise 5.3–15.)

We know that $P_n(x)$ is a polynomial of degree n and

(7) $$\int_{-1}^{1} P_n(x)\, P_m(x)\, dx = \frac{2}{2n+1}\, \delta_{nm}.$$

The next theorem exhibits further properties.

THEOREM 5.3B The Legendre Polynomials $P_n(x)$ satisfy

1. (a) $P_n'(x) = xP_{n-1}'(x) + n\, P_{n-1}(x)$,

    (b) $P_n(x) = \dfrac{x^2-1}{n} P_{n-1}'(x) + x\, P_{n-1}(x)$, $n \geq 1$,

2. $((1-x^2)\, P_n'(x))' + n(n+1)\, P_n(x) = 0$,

3. $P_{n+1}(x) = \dfrac{(2n+1)x\, P_n(x) - n\, P_{n-1}(x)}{n+1}$, $n \geq 1$,

4. $P_{n+1}'(x) - P_{n-1}'(x) = (2n+1)\, P_n(x)$, $n \geq 1$,

5. $P_n(1) = 1$, $P_n(-1) = (-1)^n$,

6. $P_{2n}(x)$ is even, $P_{2n+1}(x)$ is odd,

7. (a) $\dfrac{1-x^2}{n^2} (P_n'(x))^2 + (P_n(x))^2 = \dfrac{1-x^2}{n^2} (P_{n-1}'(x))^2$
    $$+ (P_{n-1}(x))^2,   n \geq 1,$$

    (b) $\dfrac{1-x^2}{n^2} (P_n'(x))^2 + (P_n(x))^2 \leq 1$, $n \geq 1,\ |x| \leq 1$,

    (c) $P_n(x)^2 \leq 1$, $|x| \leq 1$.

Proof We shall prove only **1**, leaving the rest as exercises. Leibnitz's rule for the nth derivative of a product

$$\frac{d^n fg}{dx^n} = \sum_{r=0}^{n} \binom{n}{r} \frac{d^{n-r}f}{dx^{n-r}} \frac{d^r g}{dx^r}, \qquad \binom{n}{r} = \frac{n!}{r!(n-r)!},$$

(see Exercise 5.2–8), yields

$$\frac{d}{dx} P_n(x) = \frac{1}{2^n\, n!} \frac{d^n}{dx^n} (n(x^2-1)^{n-1} \cdot 2x)$$

$$= \frac{1}{2^{n-1}} (n-1)! \left(x \frac{d^n}{dx^n} (x^2-1)^{n-1} + n \frac{d^{n-1}}{dx^{n-1}} (x^2-1)^{n-1} \right)$$

$$= x\, P_{n-1}'(x) + n\, P_{n-1}(x).$$

Next, let $f(x) = x^2 - 1$ and write $P_n(x)$ in two forms

(8)
$$P_n(x) = \frac{1}{2^n \, n!} \frac{d^n}{dx^n} (f^{n-1} \cdot f)$$

$$= \frac{1}{2^n \, n!} \left(f \frac{d^n}{dx^n} f^{n-1} + n \cdot 2x \frac{d^{n-1}}{dx^{n-1}} f^{n-1} + n(n-1) \frac{d^{n-2}}{dx^{n-2}} f^{n-1} \right)$$

and also

(9) $$P_n(x) = \frac{1}{2^n \, n!} \frac{d^{n-1}}{dx^{n-1}} (2x \, n \, f^{n-1}) = \frac{1}{2^{n-1}(n-1)!} \left(x \frac{d^{n-1}}{dx^{n-1}} f^{n-1} \right.$$

$$\left. + (n-1) \frac{d^{n-2}}{dx^{n-2}} f^{n-1} \right).$$

Multiplying (8) by 2 and subtracting (9), we obtain

$$P_n(x) = \frac{f}{n} \frac{d}{dx} P_{n-1}(x) + x \, P_{n-1}(x).$$

This proves part **1** of the theorem. The other parts can be deduced from this.   ★

A theorem of a different nature follows.

THEOREM 5.3C   The zeros of $P_n(x)$ are all real, distinct, and interior to the interval $-1 < x < 1$.

Proof For $n \geq 1$, we have

(10)
$$\int_{-1}^{1} P_n(x)dx = 0$$

since $P_n(x)$ is orthogonal to any polynomial of lower degree, in particular to $P_0(x) = 1$. Equation (10) implies that $P_n(x)$ must change sign at least once in $-1 < x < 1$. Suppose it changes sign at exactly q points

$$-1 < x_1 < x_2 \cdots < x_q < 1, \quad q < n.$$

Then the polynomial $\sigma(x) = (x - x_1)(x - x_2) \cdots (x - x_q)$ is of degree $q < n$ and we must have

$$\int_{-1}^{1} P_n(x) \, \sigma(x)dx = 0.$$

This is a contradiction since $P_n(x) \, \sigma(x)$ does not change sign in $-1 < x < 1$. Hence q cannot be less than n. It must be exactly n, since $P_n(x)$ cannot have more than n zeros.   ★

For the purpose of investigating the behavior of a polynomial for large values of x, it will be useful to obtain an integral representation of $P_n(x)$ due to Laplace.

Theorem 5.3D

(11) $$P_n(x) = \frac{1}{\pi} \int_0^\pi \left(x + \sqrt{x^2 - 1} \, \cos t \right)^n dt,$$

Proof The right side is seen to be a polynomial in x of degree n, for, upon expansion of the integrand by the binomial theorem, each odd power of $\sqrt{x^2 - 1}$ is multiplied by an odd power of $\cos t$ and the integral of an odd power of $\cos t$ over the range 0 to π vanishes. The integral may be written

(12) $$I_n(x) = \frac{1}{\pi} \int_0^\pi \left(x + i \sqrt{1 - x^2} \, \cos t \right)^n dt$$

but, of course, all odd powers of i disappear upon integration.

By letting $n = 0$ and 1 we find $I_0(x) = 1 = P_0(x)$, $I_1(x) = x = P_1(x)$. We shall show that $I_n(x)$ satisfies the same recurrence relation that $P_n(x)$ does (see relation **3** of Theorem 5.3B) and it will follow that $I_n(x) = P_n(x)$. Let $y = x + \sqrt{x^2 - 1} \, \cos t$. Then

$$I_{n+1}(x) = \frac{1}{\pi} \int_0^\pi y^{n+1} \, dt = \frac{x}{\pi} \int_0^\pi y^n \, dt + \frac{\sqrt{x^2 - 1}}{\pi} \int_0^\pi y^n \cos t \, dt$$

so that

$$(n + 1) I_{n+1}(x) - (2n + 1)x I_n(x) = \frac{-nx}{\pi} \int_0^\pi y^n \, dt$$

$$+ (n + 1) \frac{\sqrt{x^2 - 1}}{\pi} \int_0^\pi y^n \cos t \, dt$$

$$= \frac{-n}{\pi} \int_0^\pi y^{n-1} (x + \sqrt{x^2 - 1} \, \cos t) (x - \sqrt{x^2 - 1} \, \cos t) dt$$

$$+ \frac{\sqrt{x^2 - 1}}{\pi} \int_0^\pi y^n \cos t \, dt.$$

By integration by parts, it is verified that

$$\sqrt{x^2 - 1} \int_0^\pi y^n \cos t \, dt = n(x^2 - 1) \int_0^\pi y^{n-1} \sin^2 t \, dt.$$

Therefore

$$(n + 1) I_{n+1}(x) - (2n + 1)x I_n(x) = \frac{-n}{\pi} \int_0^{\pi} y^{n-1} (x^2 - (x^2 - 1) \cos^2 t$$
$$- (x^2 - 1) \sin^2 t) dt$$
$$= -n I_{n-1}(x).$$

This is the desired recurrence relation.   ★

Corollary 1

Let $\sigma(x)$ be a polynomial of degree $n \geq 1$ and let $M = \text{l.u.b.}\{|\sigma(x)| \mid -c \leq x \leq c\}$. Then for $|x| \geq c$, we have

(13) $$|\sigma(x)| \leq 4M \, n^2 \left|\frac{2x}{c}\right|^n.$$

To validate (13), write $\beta(x) = \sigma(cx)$ and note that

$$\text{l.u.b.}\{\beta(x)| -1 \leq x \leq 1\} = M.$$

Expand the polynomial $\beta(x)$ in terms of Legendre polynomials,

(14) $$\beta(x) = a_0 P_0(x) + a_1 P_1(x) + \cdots + a_n P_n(x),$$

where

$$a_j = \frac{2j + 1}{2} \int_{-1}^{1} \beta(y) P_j(y) \, dy$$

are computed by multiplying (14) by $P_j(x)$ and integrating. We have

$$|a_j| \leq (2j + 1) M.$$

From the integral representation (11) and the fact that

$$|\sqrt{x^2 - 1} \cos t| \leq |x| \qquad \text{for } |x| \geq 1$$

we find

$$|P_n(x)| \leq |2x|^n \qquad \text{for } |x| \geq 1.$$

Therefore, for $|x| \geq 1$,

$$|\beta(x)| \leq M \sum_{j=0}^{n} (2j + 1) |2x|^j \leq M |2x|^n \sum_{j=0}^{n} 2j + 1 = (n + 1)^2 M |2x|^n$$

$$\leq 4n^2 M |2x|^n.$$

Finally

$$|\sigma(x)| = \left|\beta\left(\frac{x}{c}\right)\right| \le 4n^2 M\left|\frac{2x}{c}\right|^n.$$

A natural question to ask is whether the Legendre series (5) for α actually converges to $\alpha(x)$, or rather, what conditions must be imposed on α in order that the series (5) converge to $\alpha(x)$. We already know, by Theorem 5.1G, that if α is continuous and the series (5) converges uniformly, then the series converges uniformly to α on $-1 \le x \le 1$. It is not our intention to develop the most general conditions under which convergence takes place, but we indicate in the next theorem that the desired conclusion is valid when α is sufficiently restricted.

THEOREM 5.3E If α has a continuous second derivative on $-1 \le x \le 1$, then the Legendre series for α converges uniformly to α on $-1 \le x \le 1$.

Proof The Legendre series is

(15) $$\sum_{0}^{\infty} a_j P_j(x), \qquad a_j = \frac{2j+1}{2}\int_{-1}^{1} \alpha(t)P_j(t)dt.$$

Using property **4** of Theorem 5.3B, and integrating by parts, we obtain, for $j \ge 1$,

$$2a_j = (2j+1)\int_{-1}^{1} \alpha(t)\,P_j(t)\,dt = \int_{-1}^{1} \alpha(t)\left(P'_{j+1}(t) - P'_{j-1}(t)\right)dt$$

$$= \alpha(t)\left(P_{j+1}(t) - P_{j-1}(t)\right)\Big|_{-1}^{1} - \int_{-1}^{1} \alpha'(t)\left(P_{j+1}(t) - P_{j-1}(t)\right)dt.$$

The first part on the right side of the equation is zero in view of property **5** of Theorem 5.3B. Another integration by parts yields, for $j \ge 2$,

(16) $$2a_j = \int_{-1}^{1} \alpha''(t)\left(\frac{P_{j+2}(t) - P_j(t)}{2j+3} - \frac{P_j(t) - P_{j-2}(t)}{2j-1}\right)dt.$$

Upon application of the Schwarz inequality,

$$2|a_j| \le \frac{1}{2j-1}\left(\int_{-1}^{1} |\alpha''(t)||P_{j+2}(t)|dt + 2\int_{-1}^{1} |\alpha''(t)||P_j(t)|dt\right.$$

$$\left. + \int_{-1}^{1} |\alpha''(t)||P_{j-2}(t)|dt\right)$$

$$\le \frac{1}{2j-1}\left(\left(\int_{-1}^{1}|\alpha''(t)|^2 dt\int_{-1}^{1}|P_{j+2}(t)|^2 dt\right)^{1/2} + 2\left(\int_{-1}^{1}|\alpha''(t)|^2 dt\int_{-1}^{1}|P_j(t)|^2 dt\right)^{1/2}\right.$$

$$\left. + \left(\int_{-1}^{1}|\alpha''(t)|^2\,dt\int_{-1}^{1}|P_{j-2}(t)|^2\,dt\right)^{1/2}\right).$$

Therefore

(17) $$|a_j| \le \frac{2}{2j-1} \sqrt{\frac{2}{2j-3}} \, \|\alpha''\|,$$

the last inequality being a consequence of $\|P_n\| = \sqrt{\dfrac{2}{2n+1}}$.

Applying this result together with $|P_j| \le 1$ shows that the series $\sum\limits_{j=2}^{\infty} a_j P_j(x)$ is dominated by the convergent series $\sum\limits_{j=2}^{\infty} \dfrac{2\sqrt{2}\,\|\alpha''\|}{(2j-3)^{3/2}}$ and hence converges uniformly by the M test.

The comments preceding the theorem now imply that the series (15) converges uniformly to α on $-1 \le x \le 1$. ★

The method of proof can be used to estimate how well α can be approximated by the first $n + 1$ terms of the Legendre series. We therefore obtain a statement regarding the closeness of approximation to a function by a polynomial of given degree. For, when α satisfies the conditions of the theorem, and $n \ge 2$,

$$\left|\alpha(x) - \sum_{j=0}^{n} a_j P_j(x)\right| \le \sum_{j=n+1}^{\infty} |a_j(x)|\,|P_j(x)| \le \sum_{j=n+1}^{\infty} \frac{2}{(2j-1)} \sqrt{\frac{2}{2j-3}} \, \|\alpha''\|$$

in virtue of (17). If c is a constant such that $\dfrac{2}{2j-1} \sqrt{\dfrac{2}{2j-3}} < \dfrac{c}{j^{3/2}}$ we apply $\sum\limits_{j=n+1}^{\infty} \dfrac{1}{j^{3/2}} \le \displaystyle\int_{n}^{\infty} \dfrac{dx}{x^{3/2}} = 2n^{-1/2}$ to obtain

$$\left|\alpha(x) - \sum_{j=0}^{n} a_j P_j(x)\right| \le \sum_{j=n+1}^{\infty} \frac{c}{j^{3/2}} \|\alpha''\| \le 2c \, \|\alpha''\| \, n^{-1/2}.$$

We have proved that the error obtained by using the first $n + 1$ terms of the Legendre series as an approximation to α is less, in absolute value, than a constant divided by $n^{1/2}$.

It is clear that if α has more derivatives, a better estimate can be obtained. Assume for example that α has four continuous derivatives. Continuing the procedure which led to equation (16) we have, after two more steps,

$$|a_j| \le \frac{k}{j^2 j^{3/2}} \|\alpha^{(4)}\|, \qquad j \ge 4,$$

where the constant k does not depend on x, j, or α. It follows that

$$\left|\alpha(x) - \sum_{j=0}^{n} a_j P_j(x)\right| \leq \frac{k \, \|\alpha^{(4)}\|}{n^2} \sum_{j=n+1}^{\infty} \frac{1}{j^{3/2}}.$$

We shall use this in the following corollary.

Corollary 1

Let α be defined on $a \leq x \leq b$ and have four continuous derivatives. Then for $n \geq 4$, there is a polynomial β of degree n such that

$$|\alpha(x) - \beta(x)| \leq M \frac{(b-a)^{7/2}}{n^2} \left(\int_a^b |\alpha^{(4)}(x)|^2 \, dx\right)^{1/2}, \qquad a \leq x \leq b,$$

where M is independent of n, x, α and the interval.

To prove the corollary, use the fact that the interval $-1 \leq t \leq 1$ is carried into $a \leq x \leq b$ by $x = \dfrac{b-a}{2} t + \dfrac{b+a}{2}$.

Define

$$\sigma(t) = \alpha\left(\frac{b-a}{2} t + \frac{b+a}{2}\right), \qquad -1 \leq t \leq 1.$$

In view of the previous discussion there is a polynomial $\mu(t)$ of degree $n \geq 4$ such that

$$|\sigma(t) - \mu(t)| \leq \frac{c_1}{n^2}\left(\int_{-1}^{1} |\sigma^{(4)}(t)|^2 \, dt\right)^{1/2}, \qquad -1 \leq t \leq 1.$$

Since

$$\sigma^{(4)}(t) = \alpha^{(4)}(x)\left(\frac{b-a}{2}\right)^4,$$

it is readily verified that

$$\left(\int_{-1}^{1} |\sigma^{(4)}(t)|^2 \, dt\right)^{1/2} = \left(\int_a^b |\alpha^{(4)}(x)|^2 \, dx\right)^{1/2}\left(\frac{b-a}{2}\right)^{7/2}.$$

Now define

$$\beta(x) = \mu\left(\frac{2}{b-a}\left(x - \frac{b+a}{2}\right)\right), \qquad a \leq x \leq b,$$

and obtain

$$|\alpha(x) - \beta(x)| \leq \left(\frac{b-a}{2}\right)^{7/2} \frac{c_1}{n^2}\left(\int_a^b |\alpha^{(4)}(x)|^2 \, dx\right)^{1/2}. \qquad \bigstar$$

It is possible to define Legendre polynomials for any interval, although it is convenient to use $-1 \leq x \leq 1$. By the transformation $u = \dfrac{(b-a)}{2} x + \dfrac{b+a}{2}$ the interval $-1 \leq x \leq 1$ is carried into $a \leq u \leq b$.

Then
$$x^2 - 1 = \frac{4}{(b-a)^2}(u-a)(u-b),$$

$$\frac{d^n}{dx^n}(x^2 - 1)^n = \left(\frac{2}{b-a}\right)^n \frac{d^n}{du^n}\left((u-a)(u-b)\right)^n,$$

and $Q_n(u) = P_n(x) = \dfrac{1}{n!\,(b-a)^n} \dfrac{d^n}{du^n}\left((u-a)(u-b)\right)^n.$

Here $\delta_{jk} = \dfrac{2j+1}{2} \displaystyle\int_{-1}^{1} P_j(x)\,P_k(x)dx = \dfrac{2j+1}{b-a} \displaystyle\int_{a}^{b} Q_j(u)\,Q_k(u)du$ and the differential equation satisfied by $Q_n(u)$ is

$$-\frac{d}{du}\left((u-a)(u-b)\frac{dQ_n}{du}\right) + n(n+1)\,Q_n = 0.$$

The first two of the following examples point out interesting differences between finite and infinite dimensional spaces.

EXAMPLE 1. When we consider the sequence of Legendre polynomials with P_k omitted, the resulting sequence is no longer linearly dense in $\mathscr{R}\{-1, 1\}$. Indeed, if it were, Theorem 5.1D and $(P_k, P_n) = 0$ for $n \neq k$ would show that $P_k = 0$, a contradiction. However, we shall now show that the omission of the first k elements from the set $1, x, x^2, \ldots$ still leaves a linearly dense set.

If α is in $\mathscr{R}\{-1, 1\}$, define

$$\beta(x) = \begin{cases} 0 & \text{for } -1 < -c < x < c < 1, \\ \alpha(x) & \text{for } -1 \leq x \leq -c < 0 \ \text{ or } \ c \leq x \leq 1, \end{cases}$$

where c is chosen so that $\|\alpha - \beta\| < \epsilon/2$. Then μ defined by

$$\mu(x) = \begin{cases} \beta/x^k, & x \neq 0, \\ 0, & x = 0, \end{cases}$$

is in $\mathscr{R}\{-1, 1\}$ and there exists a polynomial σ such that $\|\mu - \sigma\| < \epsilon/2$. (Exercise 5.2–10). Therefore

$$\|\beta - x^k \sigma\|^2 = \int_{-1}^{1} x^{2k}\left(\frac{\beta(x)}{x^k} - \sigma(x)\right)^2 dx \leq \int_{-1}^{1}\left(\mu(x) - \sigma(x)\right)^2 dx < \epsilon^2/4.$$

Finally,

$$\|\alpha - x^k \sigma\| \le \|\alpha - \beta\| + \|\beta - x^k \sigma\| < \epsilon.$$

This proves that α is the limit, in $\mathscr{R}\{-1, 1\}$, of a sequence of polynomials, each being a finite linear combination of the functions $x^k, x^{k+1}, x^{k+2}, \cdots$.

As a consequence, we obtain directly from Theorem 5.1D the following result:

If $\int_{-1}^{1} \alpha(x)\, x^n\, dx = 0$ for $n = k, k + 1, \cdots$ and α in $\mathscr{R}\{-1, 1\}$, then α is the zero vector.

EXAMPLE 2.   The converse of Theorem 5.1D is not necessarily valid. Let π_{2n} be the even normalized Legendre polynomials on $-1 \le x \le 1$.

Let $\alpha(x) = \displaystyle\sum_{n=0}^{\infty} \frac{\cdot\, 1}{(n + 1)^4}\, \pi_{2n}(x)$. The series defining α converges uniformly on $-1 \le x \le 1$ since $|\pi_{2n}| \le \sqrt{\dfrac{4n + 1}{2}}$. Let $\mathscr{E}$ be the linear manifold in $\mathscr{R}\{-1, 1\}$ spanned by the elements π_{2n} together with the element $\pi_1 + \alpha$. That is, every element in $\mathscr{E}$ is of the form

(18)
$$\beta = \sum_{n=0}^{N} b_n \pi_{2n} + a\left(\pi_1 + \alpha\right)$$

where b_n and a are scalars.

We shall show that $(\beta, \pi_{2n}) = 0$ for $n = 0, 1, 2, \ldots$ implies $\beta = 0$, yet nevertheless the sequence $\{\pi_{2n}\}$ is not linearly dense in $\mathscr{E}$.

In fact, if β has the form (18), $(\beta, \pi_{2n}) = 0$, and $j > N$, we obtain

$$0 = (\beta, \pi_{2j}) = a(\alpha, \pi_{2j}) = \frac{a}{(j + 1)^4}$$

so that $a = 0$. Then, taking $j \le N$, we obtain

$$0 = (\beta, \pi_{2j}) = b_j.$$

Thus $\beta = 0$. Nevertheless, the element $\pi_1 + \alpha$ in $\mathscr{E}$ does not satisfy Parseval's equality, since

$$\|\pi_1 + \alpha\|^2 = \left(\pi_1 + \sum_{n=0}^{\infty} \frac{\pi_{2n}}{(n + 1)^4},\ \pi_1 + \sum_{n=0}^{\infty} \frac{\pi_{2n}}{(n + 1)^4}\right)$$

$$= (\pi_1, \pi_1) + \sum_{n=0}^{\infty} \frac{1}{(n + 1)^8}$$

while

$$\sum_{n=0}^{\infty} |(\pi_1 + \alpha, \pi_{2n})|^2 = \sum_{n=0}^{\infty} |(\alpha, \pi_{2n})|^2 = \sum_{n=0}^{\infty} \frac{1}{(n+1)^8}.$$

Theorems 5.1C and 5.1B imply that $\{\pi_{2n}\}$ is not linearly dense in $\mathscr{E}$.

EXAMPLE 3 Show that the integral operator defined by the symmetric kernel $K(x, y) = e^{xy}$, $a \leq x \leq b$, $a \leq y \leq b$, does not have zero as eigenvalue.

Suppose $\int_a^b e^{xy} \alpha(y) \, dy = 0$ for α in $\mathscr{R} \{a, b\}$. Expand e^{xy} as a power series in y, converging absolutely uniformly on $a \leq y \leq b$, multiply by the bounded function $\alpha(y)$, and integrate term by term, to obtain

$$0 = \int_a^b \alpha(y)dy + x \int_a^b y \, \alpha(y)dy + \frac{x^2}{2!}\int_a^b y^2 \, \alpha(y) \, dy + \cdots.$$

The validity of this equation for all x on $a \leq x \leq b$ implies that the coefficient of x^n is zero, that is $\int_a^b y^n \, \alpha(y) \, dy = 0$, and hence $\alpha = 0$, so that α is not an eigenvector.

Exercise 5.3

1. From **1** of Theorem 5.3B, obtain for $n \geq 1$,
$$P'_{n-1}(x) = x \, P'_n(x) - n \, P_n(x) \text{ and } P_{n-1}(x) = \frac{1 - x^2}{n} P'_n(x) + x \, P_n(x).$$

2. Using Exercise 1 and **1** of Theorem 5.3B, obtain relations **2, 3, 4, 7** of that theorem.

3. Using **1** and **3** of Theorem 5.3B and $P_0(x) = 1$, obtain **5** and **6**.

4. Sketch the first five Legendre polynomials.

5. (a) From **7(b)** of Theorem 5.3B obtain
$$|P'_n(x)| \leq \frac{n}{\sqrt{1 - x^2}}, \quad -1 < x < 1.$$

   (b) Use **2** and **7(b)** of Theorem 5.3B to obtain
$$\left| \int_{-1}^x P_n(x)dx \right| \leq \frac{\sqrt{1 - x^2}}{n + 1}, \, |x| \leq 1, \quad \text{and} \quad \left| \int_a^b P_n(x)dx \right| \leq \frac{2}{n + 1},$$
$$-1 \leq a \leq b \leq 1.$$

6. Show that
$$\int_{-1}^1 (1 - x^2) \, P'_n(x) \, P'_m(x)dx = \frac{2n(n + 1)}{2n + 1} \delta_{nm}.$$

7. Use the recurrence formula **3** of Theorem 5.3B to show that $P_n(0) = 0$ for n odd, and $P_n(0) = (-1)^{n/2} \frac{1 \cdot 3 \cdot 5 \cdots (n - 1)}{2 \cdot 4 \cdots n}$ for n even.

8. Prove that

$$(2n + 1) (1 - x^2) P_n'(x) = n(n + 1) (P_{n-1}(x) - P_{n+1}(x)).$$

9. Show that $P_n'(1) = \dfrac{n(n + 1)}{2}$, $P_n'(-1) = (-1)^{n+1} \dfrac{n(n + 1)}{2}$.

10. Show that if $m \le n$, m and n both even or both odd, then $\int_{-1}^{1} P_n'(x) P_m'(x)dx$
    $= m(m + 1)$. What is the value if one of m and n is even, the other odd?

11. (a) Since $|x + i \sqrt{1 - x^2} \cos t| = (x^2 + (1 - x^2) \cos^2 t)^{1/2}$ for $|x| \le 1$,
         obtain $|P_n(x)| \le 1$ for $|x| \le 1$ from the integral representation (11).
    (b) This integral representation can be used to give a different type of bound
         for $|P_n|$. Show that for $|x| \le 1$,

$$|P_n(x)| \le \frac{2}{\pi} \int_0^{\pi/2} \left(1 - (1 - x^2) \sin^2 t \right)^{n/2} dt \le \frac{2}{\pi} \int_0^{\pi/2} \left(1 - a^2 t^2 \right)^{n/2} dt,$$

    where $a = \dfrac{2}{\pi} \sqrt{1 - x^2}$, using the substitution $z = \pi - t$ and the

    inequality $\dfrac{\sin t}{t} \ge 2/\pi$, $0 \le t \le \pi/2$. (Prove the inequality.) Now prove

    that $1 - z \le e^{-z}$ for all real z, and so obtain

$$|P_n(x)| \le \frac{2}{\pi} \int_0^{\pi/2} e^{-n a^2 t^2/2} dt \le \frac{2}{\pi} \int_0^{\infty} e^{-n a^2 t^2/2} dt = \frac{2^{3/2}}{a\pi \sqrt{n}} \int_0^{\infty} e^{-t^2}dt.$$

    Show then that $|P_n(x)| \le \dfrac{c}{\sqrt{n} \sqrt{1 - x^2}}$ on $|x| < 1$ for some constant c.
    This implies that for fixed x on $|x| < 1$ the normalized Legendre
    polynomials are uniformly bounded with respect to n.

12. Show that the orthogonality property of the Legendre polynomials follows
    directly from the differential equation (2) of Theorem 5.3B. *Hint:* Write the
    equation satisfied by P_n, the equation satisfied by P_m, multiply the first by
    P_m, the second by P_n, subtract, and integrate by parts over $-1 \le x \le 1$.

13. Expand $(x^2 - 1)^n$ by the binomial theorem and differentiate n times to obtain

$$P_n(x) = \sum_{k=0}^{N} (-1)^k \frac{(2n - 2k)!}{2^n k!(n - k)! (n - 2k)!} x^{n-2k}$$

    where $N = n/2$ when n is even and $(n - 1)/2$ when n is odd.

14. Let $H(x, v) = (1 - 2v x + v^2)^{-1/2}$. For v sufficiently small, $z = 2v x - v^2$
    satisfies $|z| < 1$ for $-1 \le x \le 1$, and so

$$(1 - z)^{-1/2} = 1 + \sum_{j=1}^{\infty} \frac{1 \cdot 3 \cdot 5 \cdots (2j - 1)}{2 \cdot 4 \cdots (2j)} z^r = 1 + \sum_{r=1}^{\infty} \frac{(2j)!}{2^{2j}(j!)^2} z^r$$

    by the binomial theorem. Expand $(2v x - v^2)^r$ by the binomial theorem and
    show that $H(x, v) = \sum_{j=0}^{\infty} P_j(x) v^j$, using the result of Exercise 13. It can be
    shown that this expansion is valid for $|x| \le 1$, $|v| < 1$ in view of the fact that
    the first zero for $1 - 2v x + v^2$ occurs when $v = x \pm i \sqrt{1 - x^2}$, that is,
    when $|v| = 1$.

15. Assuming the expansion

$$H(x, v) = (1 - 2xv + v^2)^{-1/2} = \sum_{j=0}^{\infty} Q_j(x) \, v^j$$

it can be shown that $Q_j(x) = \dfrac{1}{j!} \dfrac{\partial^j}{\partial v^j} H(x, v)\Big|_{v=0}$. Hence show that $Q_j(x)$ is a polynomial of degree j. Show also that $Q_0(x) = 1$, $Q_1(x) = x$. Prove that

$$(1 - 2xv + v^2) \frac{\partial H}{\partial v} = (x - v) H(x, v).$$

Substitute $H(x, v) = \sum\limits_{j=0}^{\infty} Q_j(x) \, v^j$ in this last relation, and equate coefficients of like powers of v to obtain the recurrence relation for Legendre polynomials. State why this proves that $Q_j(x)$ are the Legendre polynomials.

16. Using **4** of Theorem 5.3B, show that

$$P_n'(x) = (2n - 1) P_{n-1} + (2n - 5) P_{n-3} + (2n - 9) P_{n-5} + \dots$$

ending with $3 P_1$ if n is even and with P_0 if n is odd. Hence, using the fact that $|P_n| \le 1$, show that

$$|P_n'(x)| \le \frac{n(n + 1)}{2}, \quad |x| \le |.$$

The value $n(n + 1)/2$ is assumed when $x = 1$.

17. Prove Theorem 5.3C directly from the formula for $P_n(x)$ and Rolle's Theorem. *Hint:* $(x^2 - 1)^n$ and its first $n - 1$ derivatives vanish at $x = \pm 1$.

18. Let β be a function in $\mathscr{R}\{-1, 1\}$. Then show that the nth degree polynomial α which is the best approximation to β in the sense of least squares (that is, which minimizes $\int_{-1}^{1} |\beta - \alpha|^2 \, dx$) is given by

$$\alpha = a_0 P_0 + \dots + a_n P_n$$

where $a_j = \dfrac{2j + 1}{2} \int_{-1}^{1} \beta(x) P_j(x) \, dx$.

Hint: Reread Section 1.3.

19. If α is a polynomial of degree n such that

$$\int_{-1}^{1} x^j \, \alpha(x) dx = 0 \text{ for } j = 1, \dots, n - 1, \text{ then } \alpha(x) = c \, P_n(x)$$

for some constant c.

20. (a) Between two consecutive zeros of P_n, $n \ge 2$, lies one and only zero of P_{n+1} and of P_{n-1}. *Hint:* Use **1(b)** of Theorem 5.3B. If x_0 and x_1 are consecutive zeros of P_{n-1} what can you say about the signs of P_n at x_0 and x_1?

(b) Between two consecutive zeros of P_n lies one and only one zero of P_n'.

21. Suppose $\alpha(x)$ is a nonzero solution of $\dfrac{d}{dx}\left((1 - x^2)\dfrac{d\alpha}{dx}\right) + r \, \alpha = 0$, $-1 \le x \le 1$, for constant r. Show that r must be $n(n + 1)$. *Hint:* If r were not one of the numbers $n(n + 1)$, then α would be orthogonal to all the Legendre polynomials. See Exercise 12.

22. Show that the only polynomial solutions of the Legendre differential equation are constant multiples of the Legendre polynomials.

23. Prove that the expansion in Legendre series of an odd function contains only odd Legendre polynomials. *Hint:* Consider the coefficients in (5).

24. Evaluate $\int_{-1}^{1} P_n(x) P'_m(x)dx$.

25. Suppose it were known, independent of the work of this section, that the Legendre series of every function α having k continuous derivatives (where k is some fixed integer) converges uniformly to α on $-1 \le x \le 1$. Using this fact and Theorem 5.2D, obtain a proof that the Legendre polynomials are linearly dense in $\mathscr{R}\{-1, 1\}$.

5.4

POLYNOMIALS ORTHONORMAL

WITH RESPECT TO

A WEIGHT FUNCTION

The results of the previous section may be generalized. Let ρ be a non-negative integrable function on the finite interval $a \le x \le b$, with $\rho(x) > 0$ for $a < x < b$.

For $n = 0, 1, 2, \ldots$ let α_n be a polynomial of degree n such that the coefficient of x^n is positive. If

(1) $$\int_a^b \rho(x)\, \alpha_n(x)\, \alpha_m(x)dx = \delta_{nm}, \quad n, m = 0, 1, 2, \ldots,$$

then the polynomials α_n are said to be **orthonormal with respect to the weight function** ρ **on** $a \le x \le b$.

It is clear that (1) is equivalent to the condition that $\sqrt{\rho}\, \alpha_n$ are orthonormal on $a \le x \le b$. The proof given in Theorem 5.3A in connection with Legendre polynomials can be used here to show that orthonormalization of $\sqrt{\rho}, x\sqrt{\rho}, x^2\sqrt{\rho}, \ldots$ yields the sequence $\{\sqrt{\rho}\, \alpha_n\}$. Thus there is a unique set of polynomials α_n orthonormal with respect to the weight function ρ such that α_n is of degree n and has coefficient of x^n positive.

There is another manner of considering (1). Consider the space $\mathscr{R}\{a, b; \rho\}$ of integrable functions on $a \leq x \leq b$ with inner product defined by

$$(2) \qquad\qquad (\alpha, \beta)_\rho = \int_a^b \rho(t)\, \alpha(t)\, \beta(t)\, dt.$$

Then (1) states that $(\alpha_n, \alpha_m)_\rho = \delta_{nm}$. The sequence α_n is obtained by ortho-normalizing $1, x, x^2, \ldots$ using this new inner product.

THEOREM 5.4A   The sequence $\{\alpha_n\}$ is linearly dense in $\mathscr{R}\{a, b; \rho\}$. If $\rho(x) \geq c > 0$ on $a \leq x \leq b$, then the sequence $\{\sqrt{\rho}\,\alpha_n\}$ is linearly dense in $\mathscr{R}\{a, b\}$.

Proof   We need here an extension of Theorem 5.2D as provided by Exercise 5.2–12. When σ is in $\mathscr{R}\{a, b; \rho\}$, there is a continuous function μ such that

$$\|\sigma - \mu\|_{\bar\varrho}^2 = \int_a^b \rho(x)\,(\sigma(x) - \mu(x)\,)^2\, dx < \epsilon^2.$$

By the Weierstrass approximation theorem there is a polynomial

$\beta = \displaystyle\sum_{i=0}^{N} a_i\,\alpha_i$ such that $|\mu(x) - \beta(x)| < \epsilon$, $a \leq x \leq b$, and

$$\|\mu - \beta\|_{\bar\varrho}^2 = \int_a^b \rho(x)\,(\mu(x) - \beta(x)\,)^2\, dx < \epsilon^2 \int_a^b \rho(x)\,dx.$$

Then

$$\|\sigma - \beta\|_{\bar\varrho}^2 \leq (\|\sigma - \mu\|_\varrho + \|\mu - \beta\|_\varrho)^2 \leq \epsilon^2 \left(1 + \left(\int_a^b \rho(x)dx\right)^{1/2}\right)^2 = \epsilon_1.$$

This shows that $\{\alpha_n\}$ is linearly dense in $\mathscr{R}\{a, b; \rho\}$.

When $\rho(x) \geq c > 0$ on $a \leq x \leq b$, then every integrable function λ can be written as $\lambda = \sqrt{\rho}\,\sigma$ for some integrable σ. The inequality obtained above,

$$\int_a^b \rho(x)\left(\sigma(x) - \sum_{i=0}^{N} a_i\,\alpha_i(x)\right)^2 dx \leq \epsilon_1,$$

is equivalent to

$$\int_a^b \left(\lambda(x) - \sum_{i=0}^{N} a_i\,\sqrt{\rho(x)}\,\alpha_i(x)\right)^2 dx \leq \epsilon_1$$

which shows that $\{\sqrt{\rho}\,\alpha_n\}$ is linearly dense in $\mathscr{R}\{a, b\}$.   ★

The formal Fourier expansion of an integrable function σ on $a \leq x \leq b$ may therefore be written as

$$(3) \qquad \sigma \sim \sum_{n=0}^{\infty} \left(\int_a^b \rho(t)\, \sigma(t)\, \alpha_n(t)dt \right) \alpha_n$$

when considered as a vector in $\mathscr{R}\{a, b; \rho\}$, or, when $\rho(x) \geq c > 0$ on $a \leq x \leq b$,

$$(4) \qquad \sigma \sim \sum_{n=0}^{\infty} \left(\int_a^b \sigma(t)\, \sqrt{\rho(t)}\, \alpha_n(t)dt \right) \sqrt{\rho}\, \alpha_n$$

when considered as a vector in $\mathscr{R}\{a, b\}$. The theory for (4) may be obtained from (3) by the substitution $\lambda = \sqrt{\rho}\, \sigma$.

When σ is a polynomial of degree m, the series given by (3) is just a finite sum and is exactly equal to $\sigma(x)$. Indeed we may write

$$\sigma(x) = \sum_{n=0}^{m} c_n\, \alpha_n(x)$$

and obtain the coefficients c_j by multiplying by $\rho(x)\, \alpha_j(x)$ and integrating. We obtain $c_j = \int_a^b \rho(x)\, \sigma(x)\, \alpha_j(x)dx$.

If β_n are polynomials of degree n satisfying

$$(5) \qquad \int_a^b \rho(x)\, \beta_n(x)\, \beta_m(x)dx = 0, \quad m \neq n,$$

then β_n are orthogonal with respect to the weight function ρ. They are determined except for a constant factor. To obtain the orthonormal polynomials we specify that the coefficient of the highest power of x be positive and that the integral in (5) shall equal 1 when $m = n$. However, the constant may be determined by other requirements. For example, we may fix the value of the polynomial at some given value of x. In the case of Legendre polynomials, we have $P_n(1) = 1$. This condition assures us that the Legendre polynomials are uniformly bounded on $-1 \leq x \leq 1$.

Since $a \leq x \leq b$ is a finite interval, the study of the polynomials can be simplified by taking a and b to be particular values, since we may pass from one interval to another by a linear change of variable. For example, taking $a = -1$, $b = 1$ and letting $\sigma_n(t)$ be orthonormal with respect to the weight function $\rho(t)$ on $-1 \leq t \leq 1$, the transformation $x = \dfrac{b-a}{2} t + \dfrac{b+a}{2}$

implies

$$\delta_{nm} = \int_{-1}^{1} \rho(t)\, \sigma_n(t)\, \sigma_m(t)dt = \frac{2}{b-a} \int_a^b \rho(t(x))\, \sigma_n(t(x))\, \sigma_m(t(x))\, dx,$$

so that $\sqrt{\dfrac{2}{b-a}}\,\sigma_n(t(x)\,)$ are orthonormal on $a \leq x \leq b$ with respect to the weight function $\rho(t(x)\,)$.

We have just seen that for each ρ on $a \leq x \leq b$ with the properties specified in the first paragraph of this section, there is a unique (up to a constant factor) set of polynomials β_n of degree n orthogonal with respect to the weight function ρ. An important class of such polynomials, the **Jacobi polynomials,** is obtained when $a = -1$, $b = 1$, $\rho(x) = (1 - x)^r$ $(1 + x)^s$, $r \geq 0$, $s \geq 0$. (See, however, Exercise 5.4–4.) The Jacobi polynomials are defined explicitly by

$$P_n(x; r, s) = \frac{(-1)^n}{2^n\, n!}\, (1 - x)^{-r}\, (1 + x)^{-s}\, \frac{d^n}{dx^n}\!\left((1 - x)^{r+n}\, (1 + x)^{s+n} \right)$$

for $n = 0, 1, 2, \ldots$. (See Exercise 5.4–1.) When $r = s$, the Jacobi polynomials are called the **ultra spherical polynomials.** When $r = s = 0$ we have the Legendre polynomials.

Many of the properties possessed by Legendre polynomials can be proved for arbitrary polynomials β_n orthogonal with respect to a weight function. For example, all the roots of β_n are real, distinct, and interior to the interval $a < x < b$. The proof is that given in Theorem 5.3C, the only modification being that we start with $\displaystyle\int_a^b \rho(x)\, \beta_n(x)dx = 0$ for $n \geq 1$. The next theorem indicates further similarities.

THEOREM 5.4 B   The polynomials α_n, orthonormal with respect to the weight function ρ on $a \leq x \leq b$, satisfy a recurrence relation

$$(6) \qquad x\alpha_n(x) = a_{n,n+1}\, \alpha_{n+1}(x) + a_{nn}\, \alpha_n(x) + a_{n,n-1}\, \alpha_{n-1}(x)$$

where $n \geq 1$ and

$$(7) \qquad a_{nk} = \int_a^b x\rho(x)\, \alpha_n(x)\, \alpha_k(x)dx = a_{kn}.$$

When $a = -b$ and ρ is even then $\alpha_{2n}(x)$ are even, $\alpha_{2n+1}(x)$ are odd, and the recurrence relation (6) is

$$(8) \qquad x\alpha_n(x) = a_{n,n+1}\, \alpha_{n+1}(x) + a_{n,n-1}\, \alpha_{n-1}(x).$$

Proof   Since $x\alpha_n$ is a polynomial of degree $n + 1$ it is expressible in the form

$$(9) \qquad x\alpha_n(x) = \sum_{j=0}^{n+1} a_{nj}\, \alpha_j(x).$$

Multiplying both sides of (9) by $\rho(x)\,\alpha_k(x)$ and integrating from a to b yields (7). Since

$$(10) \qquad \int_a^b \rho(x)\,\alpha_n(x)\,\sigma(x)dx = 0$$

whenever $\sigma(x)$ is a polynomial of degree less than n, relation (7) shows that $a_{nk} = 0$ whenever $k < n - 1$. Therefore (9) reduces to (6).

Now suppose ρ is even and $a = -b$. Then, if $n > m$, the change of variable $y = -x$ shows that

$$\int_{-b}^b \rho(x)\,\alpha_n(-x)\,\alpha_m(-x)dx = \int_{-b}^b \rho(-y)\,\alpha_n(y)\,\alpha_m(y)dy$$

$$= \int_{-b}^b \rho(x)\,\alpha_n(x)\,\alpha_m(x)dx = 0,$$

the last equality being a consequence of (10). It follows that $\alpha_n(-x)$ are orthogonal with respect to the weight function ρ. Furthermore

$$\int_{-b}^b \rho(x)\,\alpha_n(-x)^2dx = \int_{-b}^b \rho(y)\,\alpha_n(y)^2dy = 1,$$

$\alpha_n(-x)$ are polynomials of degree n, and $(-1)^n\,\alpha_n(-x)$ has a positive coefficient for x^n. It follows that $(-1)^n\,\alpha_n(-x) = \alpha_n(x)$. Therefore α_n is even or odd according as n is even or odd. Now (7) implies $a_{nn} = 0$ and (6) reduces to (8).   ★

For the study of the pointwise convergence of the series given by (3), it is necessary to consider

$$\lim_{n\to\infty} \sum_{k=0}^n \left(\int_a^b \rho(t)\,\sigma(t)\,\alpha_k(t)dt \right) \alpha_k(x)$$

or

$$(11) \qquad \lim_{n\to\infty} \int_a^b \rho(t)\,\sigma(t) \sum_{k=0}^n \alpha_k(t)\,\alpha_k(x)dt.$$

For this purpose it is useful to have a condensed representation of $\sum_{k=0}^n \alpha_k(t)$ $\alpha_k(x)$. This is given by the so-called **Christoffel-Darboux identity**,

$$(12) \qquad \sum_{k=0}^n \alpha_k(t)\,\alpha_k(x) = a_{n,n+1} \frac{\alpha_{n+1}(x)\,\alpha_n(t) - \alpha_n(x)\,\alpha_{n+1}(t)}{x - t} = \frac{K_n(x,\,t)}{x - t}$$

where $a_{n,n+1}$ is given by (7). We note that $\dfrac{K_n(x,\,t)}{x - t}$ is a symmetric kernel and that the $n + 1^{st}$ partial sum of the series (3) can be represented as

(13)
$$\int_a^b \rho(t)\, \sigma(t)\, \frac{K_n(t, x)}{t - x}\, dt.$$

For the proof of (12), we use the recurrence relation given by (6). It is valid also when $n = 0$ if we define $a_{0, -1} = 0$. Clearly

$$(x - t)\, \alpha_k(x)\, \alpha_k(t) = x\, \alpha_k(x)\, \alpha_k(t) - t\, \alpha_k(t)\, \alpha_k(x)$$

$$= a_{k, k+1}\, (\alpha_{k+1}(x)\, \alpha_k(t) - \alpha_k(x)\, \alpha_{k+1}(t)\,)$$

$$+ a_{k-1, k}\, (\alpha_{k-1}(x)\, \alpha_k(t) - \alpha_k(x)\, \alpha_{k-1}(t)\,)$$

since $a_{k, k-1} = a_{k-1, k}$. Letting k range from 0 to n and summing yields the desired result

$$(x - t) \sum_{k=0}^n \alpha_k(x)\, \alpha_k(t) = a_{n, n+1}\, (\alpha_{n+1}(x)\, \alpha_n(t) - \alpha_n(x)\, \alpha_{n+1}(t)\,).$$

We shall illustrate the usefulness of the representation given by (13) in

THEOREM 5.4C　Let σ be in $\mathscr{R}\,\{a, b;\, \rho\}$ and consider the case when the orthonormal polynomials $\alpha_n(x)$ are uniformly bounded at the point x. Then the series (3) converges to $\sigma(x)$ at the point x if $\dfrac{\sigma(t) - \sigma(x)}{t - x} = \beta(t)$ is in $\mathscr{R}\,\{a, b;\, \rho\}$.

Proof　First note that

(14)
$$\int_a^b \rho(t)\, \frac{K_n(t, x)}{t - x}\, dt = 1.$$

Indeed, we have seen the series (3) is exactly σ when σ is a polynomial, in particular, when $\sigma = 1$.

It follows that

$$\int_a^b \rho(t)\, \frac{K_n(t, x)}{t - x}\, \sigma(x)\, dt = \sigma(x)$$

and then by (13), the difference D between the $n + 1^{st}$ partial sum and $\sigma(x)$ is

$$D = \sum_{k=0}^n \left(\int_a^b \rho(t)\, \sigma(t)\, \alpha_k(t)\, dt \right) \alpha_k(x) - \sigma(x)$$

$$= \int_a^b \rho(t)\, \sigma(t)\, \frac{K_n(t, x)}{t - x}\, dt - \int_a^b \rho(t)\, \frac{K_n(t, x)}{t - x}\, \sigma(x)\, dt$$

$$= \int_a^b \rho(t) \frac{\sigma(t) - \sigma(x)}{t - x} K_n(t, x) dt$$

$$= a_{n,n+1} \left(\alpha_n(x) \int_a^b \rho(t)\, \beta(t)\, \alpha_{n+1}(t) dt - \alpha_{n+1}(x) \int_a^b \rho(t)\, \beta(t)\, \alpha_n(t) dt \right).$$

The integrals appearing in the last expression for D are the Fourier coefficients of β and hence, in view of Bessel's inequality, approach 0 as n approaches ∞. We have assumed $\alpha_n(x)$ are uniformly bounded with respect to n. Hence D will approach zero if we can only show that $a_{n,n+1}$ is uniformly bounded with respect to n. This, however, follows from (7), for if A is the larger of $|a|$ and $|b|$, then

$$|a_{nk}| \leq A \int_a^b \rho(x)|\alpha_n(x)\, \alpha_k(x)| dx \leq A \left(\int_a^b \rho(x)\alpha_n(x)^2 dx \int_a^b \rho(x)\alpha_k(x)^2 dx \right)^{1/2}$$

$$= A.$$

Thus the theorem is proved. ★

In order that β be in $\mathcal{R}\{a, b; \rho\}$ it suffices to assume $|\sigma(t) - \sigma(x)| \leq B|t - x|$ for some constant B and $a \leq t \leq b$. For then, β is bounded and, except possibly at x, has the same points of continuity as σ.

This proof applies to the Legendre polynomials, for as indicated in Exercise 5.3–11, the normalized Legendre polynomials are uniformly bounded for fixed x with $|x| < 1$.

Exercise 5.4

1. Show that the Jacobi polynomials are actually polynomials and $P_n(x; r, s)$ is of degree n.

2. Show that the Jacobi polynomials are orthogonal polynomials.

3. The function $\cos nt$ can be expressed as a polynomial of degree n in $\cos t$. Prove this by equating real parts of

$$\cos nt + i \sin nt = (\cos t + i \sin t)^n.$$

4. We have restricted the parameters r, s in the definition of Jacobi polynomials by $r \geq 0$, $s \geq 0$. Then $\rho(x) = (1 - x)^r (1 + x)^s$ is Riemann integrable on $-1 \leq x \leq 1$. However if we permit ρ to be improper Riemann integrable, we may take $r > -1$, $s > -1$. Define the polynomial $T_n(x)$ of degree n by

$$T_n(x) = \cos(n \text{ Arc cos } x).$$

This is obtained by substituting x for $\cos t$ in the expansion of $\cos nt$ in terms of $\cos t$. (See problem 3.) Show that the sequence $\{T_n\}$, $n = 0, 1, 2, \ldots$ so formed is a set of polynomials orthogonal with respect to the weight function $(1 - x^2)^{-1/2}$ on $-1 \leq x \leq 1$. These are the **Tchebichef polynomials of the first kind.**

5. Show that $\dfrac{\sin(n+1)t}{\sin t} = U_n(\cos t)$ is a polynomial of degree n in $\cos t$. Show that $\{U_n(x)\}$, $n = 0, 1, 2, \ldots$ form a set of polynomials orthogonal with respect to $(1 - x^2)^{1/2}$ on $-1 \le x \le 1$. These are **Tchebichef polynomials of the second kind.**

6. Using the notation of Theorem 5.4B, write $\alpha_n(x) = \sum\limits_{j=0}^{n} c_{nj}\, x^j$ and equate the coefficients of x^{n+1} and x^n in the recurrence formula (6) to obtain equations relating a_{nn}, $a_{n,n+1}$ and c_{kj}. Hence show that the recurrence relation (6) may be put in the form

$$x\,\alpha_n(x) = \frac{c_{n,n}}{c_{n+1,n+1}}\,\alpha_{n+1}(x) + \left(\frac{c_{n,n-1}}{c_{n,n}} - \frac{c_{n+1,n}}{c_{n+1,n+1}}\right)\alpha_n(x) + \frac{c_{n-1,n-1}}{c_{n,n}}\,\alpha_{n-1}(x)$$

7. Obtain (14) from (12) by multiplying by ρ and integrating.

8. Using (9), show that $a_{n,n+1} > 0$.

5.5

HERMITE

POLYNOMIALS

For many purposes it is necessary to use an infinite interval of integration, which we write as $a \le x \le b$ but agree to delete the equality sign on the left if $a = -\infty$ and the equality sign on the right if $b = \infty$. We shall then assume $\rho(x) > 0$ on $a < x < b$ and $\int_a^b \rho\,\sigma^2\,dx < \infty$ for any polynomial σ. As in Section 5.4 we define orthonormality with respect to the nonnegative weight function ρ on $a \le x \le b$ of polynomials α_n and note there is a unique set of polynomials α_n orthonormal with respect to the weight function such that α_n is of degree n and has coefficient of x^n positive. These polynomials may be considered as obtained by orthonormalization of $\sqrt{\rho}$, $x\sqrt{\rho}$, $x^2\sqrt{\rho}\ldots$ considered as vectors in $\mathscr{R}_2\{a, b\}$ or as obtained by orthonormalization of $1, x, x^2, \ldots$ considered as vectors in $\mathscr{R}_2\{a, b; \rho\}$, the space of functions σ, integrable on every finite interval in $a \le x \le b$, with $\int_a^b \rho\,\sigma^2\,dx < \infty$, and with inner product defined by

$$(\alpha, \beta)_\rho = \int_a^b \rho(t)\,\alpha(t)\,\beta(t)\,dt.$$

As in Section 5.4 we have orthogonality with respect to the weight function ρ of polynomials β_n of degree n when

$$\int_a^b \rho(x)\, \beta_n(x)\, \beta_m(x)\, dx = 0, \quad m \neq n.$$

They are determined by ρ (and the interval) except for a constant factor. All the roots of β_n are real and distinct and interior to $a < x < b$. Theorem 5.4B is valid as stated even for an infinite interval.

Since the Weierstrass theorem is valid only for finite intervals, the proof as given in Theorem 5.4A that α_n is linearly dense can no longer be employed.

As an example of an orthogonal sequence defined over an infinite interval, we propose to discuss the **Hermite polynomials** $H_n(x)$ defined by

(1) $\qquad H_n(x) = (-1)^n\, e^{x^2} \dfrac{d^n}{dx^n}\, e^{-x^2}, \qquad n = 0, 1, 2, \ldots, \quad -\infty < x < \infty.$

Write $\dfrac{d^n}{dx^n}\, e^{-x^2} = (-1)^n\, e^{-x^2}\, H_n(x)$ and differentiate to obtain

$$(-1)^{n+1}\, e^{-x^2}\, H_{n+1}(x) = \frac{d^{n+1}}{dx^{n+1}}\, e^{-x^2} = (-1)^n\, (-2x\, H_n(x) + H_n'(x))\, e^{-x^2}$$

so that

(2) $\qquad\qquad\qquad\qquad H_{n+1}(x) = 2x\, H_n(x) - H_n'(x).$

Since $H_0(x) = 1$, inductive use of formula (2) shows that $H_n(x)$ is a polynomial of degree n with the coefficient of x^n equal to 2^n.

THEOREM 5.5A The Hermite polynomials satisfy

(3) $\quad H_n(x) - 2x\, H_{n-1}(x) + 2(n-1)\, H_{n-2}(x) = 0, \quad n = 2, 3, \ldots$

(4) $\quad H_n''(x) - 2x\, H_n'(x) + 2n\, H_n(x) = 0, \qquad\qquad\quad n = 0, 1, \ldots$

(5) $\quad H_n(-x) = (-1)^n\, H_n(x).$

(6) $\quad \displaystyle\int_{-\infty}^{\infty} e^{-x^2}\, H_n(x)\, H_m(x)\, dx = \delta_{mn}\, \sqrt{\pi}\, 2^n\, n!.$

Proof The function $\beta(x) = e^{-x^2}$ satisfies the differential equation

$$\beta'(x) + 2x\beta(x) = 0.$$

By differentiation we verify

$$\beta''(x) + 2x\beta'(x) + 2\beta(x) = 0,$$

(7) $$\beta^{(n)}(x) + 2x\beta^{(n-1)}(x) + 2(n - 1)\,\beta^{(n-2)}(x) = 0.$$

Multiplying (7) by $(-1)^n\,e^{x^2}$ yields (3). From (2) and (3) we find

(8) $$H_n'(x) = 2n\,H_{n-1}(x).$$

Differentiating (2) and replacing $H_{n+1}'(x)$ by use of (8), we derive (4), the differential equation satisfied by the Hermite polynomial of degree n.

To prove (5) we need only use the recurrence relation (3) together with $H_0(x) = 1$, $H_1(x) = 2x$. Then it is easily seen that $H_n(x)$ contains only even powers of x when n is even and only odd powers of x when n is odd.

It remains to prove (6). Since the product of e^{-x^2} and a polynomial always vanishes as $x \to \pm\infty$, repeated integration by parts, for $m \le n$, shows that

$$\int_{-\infty}^{\infty} e^{-x^2} H_n(x)\,H_m(x)dx = \int_{-\infty}^{\infty} H_m(x)(-1)^n \frac{d^n}{dx^n}\,e^{-x^2}\,dx$$
$$= \int_{-\infty}^{\infty} e^{-x^2} \frac{d^n}{dx^n}\,H_m(x)dx.$$

Thus, if $m < n$, the value of the integral is zero, while if $m = n$, it has the value

$$n!\,d_n \int_{-\infty}^{\infty} e^{-x^2}\,dx = n!\,d_n\,\sqrt{\pi}$$

where d_n is the coefficient of the highest power of x in $H_n(x)$ and is thus 2^n.   ★

For any sufficiently differentiable function f, we have

$$\frac{\partial^n}{\partial t^n}f(t - x)\Big|_{t=0} = \frac{d^n}{dz^n}f(z)\Big|_{z=-x} = (-1)^n \frac{d^n}{dx^n}f(-x).$$

This implies

(9) $$\frac{\partial^n}{\partial t^n}e^{-(t-x)^2}\Big|_{t=0} = (-1)^n \frac{d^n}{dx^n}e^{-x^2}.$$

Therefore, if we expand $G(x, t) = e^{x^2}\,e^{-(t-x)^2}$ in a Maclaurin series in t,

(10) $$G(x, t) = e^{2tx-t^2} = \sum_{n=0}^{\infty} \frac{\partial^n}{\partial t^n}e^{x^2}\,e^{-(t-x)^2}\Big|_{t=0}\frac{t^n}{n!} = \sum_{n=0}^{\infty} \frac{H_n(x)t^n}{n!}.$$

The function e^{2tx-t^2} is called the **generating function** for the Hermite polynomials. Indeed, the entire theory of Hermite polynomials may be based on the relation expressed by (10).

We have seen that the Hermite polynomials are orthogonal with respect to the weight function e^{-x^2} on $-\infty < x < \infty$. We now define the **normalized Hermite functions** by

(11) $E_n(x) = (\sqrt{\pi}\, 2^n\, n!)^{-1/2}\, e^{-x^2/2}\, H_n(x), \quad n = 0, 1, \ldots .$

These are the normalized Hermite polynomials $\eta_n(x) = (\sqrt{\pi}\, 2^n\, n!)^{-1/2}\, H_n(x)$ multiplied by the square root of the weight function.

THEOREM 5.5B   The normalized Hermite functions E_n are linearly dense in $\mathscr{R}_2\{-\infty, \infty\}$.

Proof   We are seeking to prove that whenever α, integrable on every finite interval, satisfies $\int_{-\infty}^{\infty} \alpha(x)^2\, dx < \infty$, and $\epsilon > 0$ is given, there is a linear combination $\sum_{j=0}^{N} a_j\, E_j(x)$ such that

(12) $\displaystyle \int_{-\infty}^{\infty} \left(\alpha(x) - \sum_{j=0}^{N} a_j\, E_j(x)\right)^2 dx < \epsilon.$

In view of the discussion given at the end of Section 5.2 it suffices to prove (12) when α is an infinitely differentiable function vanishing outside a finite interval $a \le x \le b$.

Expressed in terms of Hermite polynomials, we must show that

$$\int_{-\infty}^{\infty} e^{-x^2} \left(\alpha\, e^{x^2/2} - \sum_{j=0}^{N} b_j\, H_j(x)\right)^2 dx < \epsilon$$

or, that there is a polynomial β such that

(13) $\displaystyle \int_{-\infty}^{\infty} e^{-x^2} (\mu - \beta)^2\, dx < \epsilon$

where $\mu = \alpha\, e^{x^2/2}$.

To exhibit such a β, choose $c = 2\sqrt{n}$ where $n > 4$ is sufficiently large so that $-c \le x \le c$ contains $a \le x \le b$ in its interior. $|\mu|$ has an upper bound B on $-c \le x \le c$ which is independent of c, since μ vanishes outside $a \le x \le b$. Similarly $\int_{-c}^{c} |\mu^{(4)}(x)|^2\, dx$ is independent of c. By Corollary 1 of Theorem 5.3E there is a polynomial β of degree at most n such that

(14) $\displaystyle |\mu(x) - \beta(x)| \le \frac{L}{n^2}\, (2c)^{7/2}, \qquad -c \le x \le c,$

where L is independent of c, n, or x.

This implies

$$|\beta(x)| \leq B + \frac{L}{n^2}(2c)^{7/2}, \qquad -c \leq x \leq c,$$

and hence, by Corollary 1 of Theorem 5.3D,

$$|\beta(x)| \leq 4n^2\left(B + \frac{L}{n^2}(2c)^{7/2}\right)\left|\frac{2x}{c}\right|^n, \qquad |x| \geq c.$$

We can now estimate the integral in (13). First, over the interval $-c \leq x \leq c$, we have

$$\int_{-c}^{c} e^{-x^2}(\mu - \beta)^2\, dx \leq \left(\frac{L}{n^2}(2c)^{7/2}\right)^2 \int_{-c}^{c} e^{-x^2}\, dx \leq \frac{L^2}{n^4}(2c)^7 \int_{-\infty}^{\infty} e^{-x^2}\, dx$$

$$= \frac{\sqrt{\pi}\, L^2}{n^4}(2c)^7.$$

Then, over the interval $c \leq x < \infty$,

$$\int_{c}^{\infty} e^{-x^2}(\mu - \beta)^2\, dx$$

$$= \int_{c}^{\infty} e^{-x^2}\beta^2\, dx \leq 16n^4\left(B + \frac{L}{n^2}(2c)^{7/2}\right)^2 \left|\frac{2}{c}\right|^{2n} \int_{c}^{\infty} e^{-x^2} x^{2n}\, dx.$$

Since $c > 1$,

$$\int_{c}^{\infty} e^{-x^2} x^{2n}\, dx \leq \int_{c}^{\infty} e^{-x^2} x^{2n+1}\, dx \leq \int_{0}^{\infty} e^{-x^2} x^{2n+1}\, dx = \frac{1}{2}\int_{0}^{\infty} e^{-y} y^n\, dy$$

$$= \frac{1}{2}\Gamma(n+1) = n!/2.$$

Therefore,

$$\int_{c}^{\infty} e^{-x^2}(\mu - \beta)^2\, dx \leq 8n^4\left(B + \frac{L}{n^2}(2c)^{7/2}\right)^2 \left|\frac{2}{c}\right|^{2n} n!$$

with a similar estimate for $\int_{-\infty}^{-c} e^{-x^2}(\mu - \beta)^2\, dx$. Combining these results,

$$\int_{-\infty}^{\infty} e^{-x^2}(\mu - \beta)^2\, dx \leq \frac{\sqrt{\pi}L^2}{n^4}(2c)^7 + 16n^4\left(B + \frac{L}{n^2}(2c)^{7/2}\right)^2 \left|\frac{2}{c}\right|^{2n} n!.$$

Since $c = 2\sqrt{n}$, the right side can be made less than ϵ for sufficiently large n. One need only note that $n! < n^n e^{-n}(en)$ (see Exercise 5.5–1) and that $\lim_{n\to\infty} \frac{n^k}{e^n} = 0$ for fixed k.   ★

Corollary 1

The normalized Hermite polynomials η_n are linearly dense in $\mathcal{R}_2\{-\infty, \infty; e^{-x^2}\}$.

For, if $\int_{-\infty}^{\infty} e^{-x^2} \sigma(x)^2\, dx < \infty$, then $\alpha(x) = e^{-x^2/2} \sigma(x)$ satisfies $\int_{-\infty}^{\infty} \alpha(x)^2\, dx < \infty$ and there is a linear combination $\sum_{j=0}^{N} a_j E_j(x)$ such that (12) is satisfied. This is equivalent to

$$\int_{-\infty}^{\infty} e^{-x^2} \left(\sigma(x) - \sum_{j=0}^{N} a_j \eta_j(x) \right)^2 dx < \epsilon.$$

Having proved Theorem 5.5B and Corollary 1, we obtain the conclusions given in Section 5.1, which we state here only for $\mathcal{R}_2\{-\infty, \infty; e^{-x^2}\}$.

Corollary 2

Let α be in $\mathcal{R}_2\{-\infty, \infty; e^{-x^2}\}$ and satisfy $\int_{-\infty}^{\infty} e^{-x^2} \alpha(x) H_n(x) dx = 0$, $n = 0, 1, 2, \ldots$. Then $\alpha = \theta$.

Corollary 3

Let α and β be in $\mathcal{R}_2\{-\infty, \infty; e^{-x^2}\}$. Then

$$(15) \quad \int_{-\infty}^{\infty} e^{-x^2} \alpha(x)\, \beta(x) dx$$

$$= \sum_{n=0}^{\infty} \frac{1}{\sqrt{\pi}\, 2^n n!} \int_{-\infty}^{\infty} e^{-x^2} \alpha(x) H_n(x) dx \int_{-\infty}^{\infty} e^{-x^2} \beta(x) H_n(x) dx.$$

The formal Fourier expansion of σ in $\mathcal{R}_2\{-\infty, \infty\}$ is

$$(16) \quad \sigma(x) \sim \sum_{n=0}^{\infty} \left((2^n\, n!\, \sqrt{\pi})^{-1} \int_{-\infty}^{\infty} \sigma(t)\, e^{-t^2/2} H_n(t) dt \right) e^{-x^2/2} H_n(x).$$

The formal Fourier expansion of α in $\mathcal{R}_2\{-\infty, \infty; e^{-x^2}\}$ is

$$(17) \quad \alpha(x) \sim \sum_{n=0}^{\infty} \left((2^n\, n!\, \sqrt{\pi})^{-1} \int_{-\infty}^{\infty} e^{-t^2} \alpha(t) H_n(t) dt \right) H_n(x).$$

By the substitution $\sigma(x)\, e^{x^2/2} = \alpha(x)$ we can pass from (16) to (17). The latter series is called a **Hermite series.** It converges to $\alpha(x)$ in the mean square as indicated in Section 5.1.

A convergence theorem may be based upon equation (15), the Parseval identity.

THEOREM 5.5C Let α have a continuous derivative α' on $-\infty < x < \infty$. Assume $\alpha(x)$ and $2x\alpha(x) - \alpha'(x)$ are in $\mathscr{R}_2\{-\infty, \infty; e^{-x^2}\}$ and $|\alpha(x)| \le c\, e^{kx^2}$ where k and c are constants, $k < \frac{1}{2}$. Then the series given in (17) converges to $\alpha(x)$ for every x.

Proof With $\mu(x) = 2x\alpha(x) - \alpha'(x)$ we have

$$\frac{d}{dx}\left(e^{-x^2}\,\alpha(x)\,\right) = e^{-x^2}\left(\alpha'(x) - 2x\alpha(x)\,\right) = -e^{-x^2}\,\mu(x)$$

and, when $c_n = (\sqrt{\pi}\, 2^n\, n!)^{-1}$, we can apply (8) for $n \ge 1$, to get

$$c_{n-1}\int_{-\infty}^{\infty} e^{-x^2}\,\alpha(x)\,H_{n-1}(x)dx = \frac{c_{n-1}}{2n}\int_{-\infty}^{\infty} e^{-x^2}\,\alpha(x)\,H_n'(x)dx$$

$$= c_n\left(e^{-x^2}\alpha(x)\,H_n(x)\Big|_{-\infty}^{\infty} - \int_{-\infty}^{\infty} \frac{d}{dx}\left(e^{-x^2}\,\alpha(x)\right) H_n(x)dx\right)$$

$$= c_n\int_{-\infty}^{\infty} e^{-x^2}\mu(x)H_n(x)dx.$$

Here $e^{-x^2}\,\alpha(x)\,H_n(x)$ vanishes at $\pm\infty$ because $|\alpha(x)| < c\,e^{kx^2}$, $k < \frac{1}{2}$. Moreover, when $n = 0$, $\int_{-\infty}^{\infty} e^{-x^2}\mu(x)\,H_o(x)dx = -\int_{-\infty}^{\infty}\frac{d}{dx}\left(e^{-x^2}\,\alpha(x)\right)dx = 0$. Thus, when α in (15) is replaced by μ, and β is defined by

$$\beta(x) = \begin{cases} 1, & -\infty < x \le t, \\ 0, & x > t, \end{cases}$$

then (15) becomes

$$\int_{-\infty}^{t} e^{-x^2}\mu(x)dx = \sum_{n=1}^{\infty} c_n \int_{-\infty}^{\infty} e^{-x^2}\,\mu(x)\,H_n(x)dx \int_{-\infty}^{t} e^{-x^2}\,H_n(x)dx,$$

or,

$$-\int_{-\infty}^{t} \frac{d}{dx}\left(e^{-x^2}\,\alpha(x)\,\right)dx$$

$$= \sum_{n=1}^{\infty} c_{n-1} \int_{-\infty}^{\infty} e^{-x^2}\alpha(x)\,H_{n-1}(x)dx \int_{-\infty}^{t} (-1)\frac{d}{dx}\left(e^{-x^2}H_{n-1}(x)\,\right)dx,$$

where we have used

$$\frac{d}{dx}\left(e^{-x^2}\,H_{n-1}\right) = \frac{d}{dx}\left((-1)^{n-1}\frac{d^{n-1}}{dx^{n-1}}e^{-x^2}\right) = -e^{-x^2}\,H_n(x).$$

We conclude that

(18) $\displaystyle e^{-t^2}\,\alpha(t) = \sum_{n=1}^{\infty} \left(c_{n-1} \int_{-\infty}^{\infty} e^{-x^2}\,\alpha(x)\,H_{n-1}(x)dx \right) e^{-t^2}\,H_{n-1}(t)$

$\displaystyle = \sum_{n=0}^{\infty} \left(c_n \int_{-\infty}^{\infty} e^{-x^2}\,\alpha(x)\,H_n(x)dx \right) e^{-t^2}\,H_n(t).$

Dividing by e^{-t^2} yields the desired result.   ★

By paying attention to the bounds of $H_n(t)$, it is possible to show that the series given in (18) converges absolutely uniformly for all t and hence the series (17) converges absolutely uniformly to $\alpha(x)$ on every finite interval.

In Exercise 5.5–13, it is shown that

(19) $|H_n(x)| \le (2^n\,n!)^{1/2}\,e^{x^2/2}$

and in Exercise 6.6–7 it is shown that for some constant B,

(20) $|H_n(x)| \le B(2^n\,n!)^{1/2}\,e^{x^2/2}\,(1 + |x|^{5/2})\,n^{-1/4}, \quad n \ge 1.$

The general term on the right side of (18) is

(21) $\displaystyle \left(c_n \int_{-\infty}^{\infty} e^{-x^2}\alpha(x)\,H_n(x)dx \right) e^{-t^2}\,H_n(t)$

$\displaystyle = \left(c_{n+1} \int_{-\infty}^{\infty} e^{-x^2}\mu(x)H_{n+1}(x)dx \right) e^{-t^2}H_n(t)$

$\displaystyle = (\sqrt{\pi}\,2^{n+1}\,(n+1)!)^{-1/2}\,b_{n+1}\,e^{-t^2}\,H_n(t),$

where

$\displaystyle b_n = (\sqrt{\pi}\,2^n\,n!)^{-1/2} \int_{-\infty}^{\infty} e^{-x^2}\,\mu(x)\,H_n(x)dx$

are the Fourier coefficients of μ and therefore satisfy

(22) $\displaystyle \sum_{0}^{\infty} b_n^2 < \infty.$

Using the inequality (20) and then $|ab| \le \dfrac{1}{2}\,(a^2 + b^2)$, the expression in (21) is less in absolute value than

$\displaystyle k_1\,e^{-t^2/2}\,(1 + |t|)^{5/2}\,(|b_{n+1}|\,n^{-1/4}\,(n+1)^{-1/2})$

$\displaystyle \le k_2\,e^{-rt^2}\,(b_{n+1}^2 + n^{-1/2}\,(n+1)^{-1})$

where k_1, k_2 are constants and $r < 1$. This proves that the series in (18) converges absolutely uniformly.

Exercise 5.5

1. Write $\log n = \int_n^{n+1} \log n \, dx < \int_n^{n+1} \log x \, dx, \quad n = 1, 2 \dots,$

    $\log (n - 1)! = \log 1 + \log 2 + \cdots \log(n - 1) < \int_1^n \log x \, dx,$

    and thus show that $n! < en(n/e)^n$. Compare with Stirling's formula given in Exercise 6.6–7(b).

2. (a) If $\alpha(t) = \dfrac{\sin t}{\sqrt{t}}$, show that $\int_{-\infty}^{\infty} \alpha(t)dt$ converges, but $\int_{-\infty}^{\infty} \alpha^2(t)dt$ does not.

    (b) If $\beta(t) = 0$ for $|t| \le 1$, $\beta(t) = 1/t$ for $|t| > 1$, show that $\int_{-\infty}^{\infty} \beta^2(t)dt$ converges, but $\int_{-\infty}^{\infty} \beta(t)dt$ does not.

3. Find the first five Hermite polynomials and draw their graphs.

4. (a) Using equation (3), prove that $H_{2n}(0) = \dfrac{(-1)^n \, (2n)!}{n!}, \quad H_{2n+1}(0) = 0.$

    (b) With the results of (a), and a formula in the text, show that $H'_{2n}(0) = 0$,
    $$H'_{2n+1}(0) = \frac{2(-1)^n \, (2n + 1)!}{n!}$$

5. Use $G(x, t) = e^{2tx - t^2}$ to get $\dfrac{\partial G}{\partial x} = 2tG$ and $\dfrac{\partial^2 G}{\partial x^2} - 2x \dfrac{\partial G}{\partial x} + 2t \dfrac{\partial G}{\partial t} = 0.$

    With $G(x, t) = \displaystyle\sum_{n=0}^{\infty} \dfrac{H_n(x)}{n!} t^n$, show that these relations yield (8) and (4) of the text.

6. State Corollary 2 and 3 of Theorem 5.5B for $\mathcal{R} \, \{ -\infty, \infty \}$, using the normalized Hermite functions.

7. (a) Let α be in $\mathcal{R}_2 \, \{ -\infty, \infty; e^{-x^2} \}$. Show that $\int_{-\infty}^{\infty} e^{-x^2} \alpha(x) \, x^n \, dx = 0$ for $n = 0, 1, 2, \dots$ implies $\alpha = 0$. *Hint:* Corollary 2 of Theorem 5.5B.

    (b) Let α be integrable on every finite interval and satisfy $|\alpha(x)| \le c \, e^{-kx^2}$ for positive constants k and c. Suppose that $\int_{-\infty}^{\infty} \alpha(x) \, H_n(x) \, dx = 0$ for $n = 0, 1, 2, \dots$. Show that $\int_{-\infty}^{\infty} \alpha(x) \, H_n\!\left(\dfrac{x}{p}\right)dx = 0$ for fixed $p > 0$.

    Hint $\int_{-\infty}^{\infty} \alpha(x) \, x^n \, dx = 0.$

    (c) Now prove that α in (b) is the zero vector. This is clear when $k > \frac{1}{2}$, for then $\alpha(x) = e^{-x^2} \beta(x)$ where β is in $\mathcal{R}_2 \, \{ -\infty, \infty; e^{-x^2} \}$. Otherwise, choose the constant p in part (b) so that $k \, p^2 > \frac{1}{2}$.

8. Let $\alpha(x) = e^{kx^2}, k < \frac{1}{2}$. Then α satisfies the conditions of Theorem 5.5C and has a development
    $$\alpha(x) = \sum_{n=0}^{\infty} \left((2^n \, n! \, \sqrt{\pi})^{-1} \int_{-\infty}^{\infty} e^{-t^2} e^{kt^2} \, H_n(t)dt \right) H_n(x).$$

However the series on the right may be formed whenever $k < 1$. Use formulas (3) and (8) of the text to show that

$$\int_{-\infty}^{\infty} e^{-(1-k)t^2} H_{n+1}(t)dt = \left(\frac{k}{1-k}\right)(2n) \int_{-\infty}^{\infty} e^{-(1-k)t^2} H_{n-1}(t)dt,$$

and hence show that the above series at $x = 0$ is

$$\left(1 + \sum_{n=1}^{\infty} \frac{(-1)^n}{2^n n!} \left((2n-1)(2n-3)\cdots 1\right)\left(\frac{k}{1-k}\right)^n\right)(1-k)^{-\frac{1}{2}}.$$

(Use Exercise 4.)   Prove that the series converges absolutely for $k < \frac{1}{2}$, conditionally for $k = \frac{1}{2}$, and diverges for $k > \frac{1}{2}$. Thus Theorem 5.5C gives the best possible value for k.

9. Show that

(a) $xE_n = \sqrt{2n}\, E_{n-1} - E_n',\quad n \geq 1.$

(b) $E_n - \sqrt{\frac{2}{n}} xE_{n-1} + \sqrt{\frac{n-1}{n}} E_{n-2} = 0,\quad n \geq 2.$

From these deduce that for $n \geq 1$,

(c) $xE_n = \sqrt{\frac{n}{2}} E_{n-1} + \sqrt{\frac{n+1}{2}} E_{n+1}.$

(d) $E_n' = \sqrt{\frac{n}{2}} E_{n-1} - \sqrt{\frac{n+1}{2}} E_{n+1}.$

(e) $\sqrt{2n}\, E_n = xE_{n-1} - E_{n-1}'.$

(f) $\sqrt{2n}\, E_n' = (2n - x^2) E_{n-1} + x E_{n-1}'.$

(g) $\sqrt{2n}\, E_{n-1}' = xE_n' - (2n - x^2) E_n.$

10. A study of the zeros of E_n yields useful information. E_n has the n distinct real zeros of H_n. Show that for $x > 0$, $H_n(x)$, and hence $E_n(x)$, is positive for sufficiently large x. By considering the polynomial part, show that $E_n' = (\sqrt{\pi}\, 2^n n!)^{-1/2} e^{-x^2/2} (H_n' - xH_n)$ is negative for sufficiently large x. Show that E_n' must have $n + 1$ zeros, all real.

11. Use Exercise 9 to obtain

(a) $(2n - x^2)E_n^2 + (E_n')^2 = (2(n-1) - x^2)E_{n-1}^2 + (E_{n-1}')^2 + 2 E_{n-1}^2.$
     Hence

(b) $(2n - x^2) E_n^2 + (E_n')^2 = 2 \sum_{j=0}^{n-1} E_j^2.$

Use this to prove that the zeros of E_n' lie in the interval $|x| < \sqrt{2n}$. Show that the relative maxima and minima of E_n and the zeros of E_n lie in this interval. Show that "sufficiently large" in Exercise 10 may be replaced by $x > \sqrt{2n}$.

12. Show that the differential equation satisfied by E_n is
$$E_n''(x) + (2n + 1 - x^2) E_n(x) = 0.$$

Show that if $x_1 < x_2 < \cdots < x_j$ are the nonnegative zeros of E_n' (n fixed), then
$$|E_n(x_1)| < |E_n(x_2)| < \cdots < |E_n(x_j)|$$
by proving that the derivative of
$$g(x) = E_n^2 + \frac{(E_n')^2}{2n + 1 - x^2}, \qquad |x| < \sqrt{2n + 1},$$
is positive between the zeros of E_n'. This shows that the relative maxima of $|E_n(x)|$, $x > 0$, steadily increase.

13. Use 9(f) and the results of Exercises 10–12 to show that $E_n'(x_0) > 0$ if $x_0 \geq 0$ is the point where E_{n-1} achieves its maximum value. Hence show that if $y_0 \geq 0$ is the point where E_n achieves its maximum then $y_0 > x_0$. Next define (see Exercise 11(a))
$$h(x) = E_n^2 + \frac{(E_n')^2}{2n - x^2} = E_{n-1}^2 + \frac{(E_{n-1}')^2}{2n - x^2}, \qquad x^2 < 2n,$$
and show that
$$h'(x) = \frac{2\sqrt{2n}}{(2n - x^2)^2} E_n' E_{n-1}'.$$

This proves that E_n' has no zero on the interval $x_0 \leq x < y_0$, for if z_0 were the largest such zero, then $h'(x) \leq 0$ on $z_0 \leq x < y_0$ and $E_n^2(z_0) \geq E_n^2(y_0)$, contradicting Exercise 12. Hence show that $h'(x) \leq 0$ on $x_0 \leq x < y_0$ and thus prove that
$$h(x_0) = E_{n-1}^2(x_0) \geq h(y_0) = E_n^2(y_0).$$
Show that this implies $|E_n(x)| \leq \pi^{-1/4}$ and $|H_n(x)| \leq (2^n n!)^{1/2} e^{x^2/2}$.

14. Prove that $\displaystyle\int_{-\infty}^{\infty} \left(E_n'(x)\right)^2 dx = \frac{2n + 1}{2}$.

15. Some statisticians prefer to define Hermite polynomials by
$$h_n(x) = e^{x^2/2} \frac{d^n}{dx^n}(e^{-x^2/2}).$$
Show that
$$H_n(x) = (-2^{1/2})^n h_n(2^{1/2}x).$$

5.6

SIMPLE

HARMONIC FUNCTIONS

One of the first orthonormal sequences studied was the sequence $\{\alpha_n\}$ defined on the interval $-\pi \leq x \leq \pi$ by

(1) $\displaystyle \alpha_0(x) = \frac{1}{\sqrt{2\pi}}, \quad \alpha_{2n-1}(x) = \frac{\cos nx}{\sqrt{\pi}}, \quad \alpha_{2n}(x) = \frac{\sin nx}{\sqrt{\pi}}, \quad n = 1, 2, \ldots.$

That the sequence so defined is orthonormal on $-\pi \le x \le \pi$ was indicated in Section 4.3. The functions $\sin nx$ and $\cos nx$ are called **simple harmonic functions** because the acoustic phenomena of the vibrating string can be interpreted with their use.

THEOREM 5.6A   The sequence $\{\alpha_n\}$ defined by (1) is linearly dense in $\mathscr{R}\{-\pi, \pi\}$.

Proof Suppose first that β is continuous on $-\pi \le x \le \pi$ and $\beta(-\pi) = \beta(\pi)$. Then β can be extended to be periodic over the entire x-axis. By Theorem 5.2C, for given $\epsilon > 0$, there is a trigonometric sum μ such that $|\beta(x) - \mu(x)| < \epsilon/\sqrt{2\pi}$ for all x and hence

$$\|\beta - \mu\|^2 = \int_{-\pi}^{\pi} |\beta(x) - \mu(x)|^2 \, dx < \epsilon^2.$$

When σ is any function in $\mathscr{R}\{-\pi, \pi\}$, we can find, for $\epsilon > 0$, a function β continuous on $-\pi \le x \le \pi$ which vanishes at the end points and satisfies

$$\|\sigma - \beta\| < \epsilon.$$

Using this β in the first part of the proof, we obtain

$$\|\sigma - \mu\| \le \|\sigma - \beta\| + \|\beta - \mu\| < 2\epsilon.$$

In this way we prove that the linear manifold spanned by $\{\alpha_n\}$ is dense in $\mathscr{R}\{-\pi, \pi\}$.   ★

As a result of this theorem, we obtain the conclusions of Section 5.1. They are, however, usually phrased in terms of the functions

(2)   1, $\cos nx$, $\sin nx$.

Thus the series $\sum\limits_{n=0}^{\infty} (\sigma, \alpha_n) \alpha_n(x)$ is written as

(3) $$F(\sigma) = \frac{a_0}{2} + \sum_{n=1}^{\infty} (a_n \cos nx + b_n \sin nx),$$

where

(4) $$a_n = \frac{1}{\pi} \int_{-\pi}^{\pi} \sigma(t) \cos nt \, dt, \qquad n = 0, 1, 2, \ldots,$$

(5) $$b_n = \frac{1}{\pi} \int_{-\pi}^{\pi} \sigma(t) \sin nt \, dt, \qquad n = 1, 2, \ldots.$$

Here a_n and b_n are called the **Fourier coefficients** of σ, and $F(\sigma)$ is called the **Fourier series** for σ. The factor $\frac{1}{2}$ is inserted in the constant term so that formula (4) will apply even in the case $n = 0$.

Early in the eighteenth century it was indicated by d'Alembert, Euler, and Bernoulli that the solution $y(x, t)$ of the partial differential equation

(6)
$$\frac{\partial^2 y}{\partial t^2} = a^2 \frac{\partial^2 y}{\partial x^2}$$

subject to

(7)
$$y(x, 0) = \sigma(x)$$

involved a representation of σ in the form (3). The equation (6) is the equation characterizing the motion of an elastic string stretched on the x axis with ends at $(-\pi, 0)$ and $(\pi, 0)$. When displaced from an initial position given by $\sigma(x)$ at time $t = 0$, it vibrates in such a fashion that the ordinate position of a point on the string is given as a function $y(x, t)$ depending only on the abscissa and the time. It was shown by Euler that if σ could be represented for all x by (3) then the coefficients a_n and b_n must be given by (4) and (5). Fourier in 1807, working on the subject of the transfer of heat in a conducting medium, dealt with the equation

(8)
$$\frac{\partial^2 T}{\partial x^2} = \frac{1}{k} \frac{\partial T}{\partial t}, \quad T(x, 0) = \sigma(x),$$

and represented σ in the form (3) with coefficients given by (4) and (5). Because of his usage of these formulas, the series (3) with coefficients given by (4) and (5) is now called the Fourier series for σ.

For each function σ we can always write down the Fourier series given by (3), (4), (5). If it converges uniformly and σ is continuous, the series must converge to σ. Whether it converges or not, the series obtained by integrating term by term over any interval $c \leq x \leq d$ within $-\pi \leq x \leq \pi$ converges to the integral of σ over $c \leq x \leq d$. Whether the series converges or not, it certainly converges to σ in the mean square. When $\int_{-\pi}^{\pi} \sigma(x) \alpha_n(x)dx = 0$ for every n, that is, when all the Fourier coefficients are zero, then σ is the zero vector. All these results are, according to Section 5.1, consequences of Theorem 5.6A.

Let us write Parseval's equality,

$$\sum_{n=0}^{\infty} |(\sigma, \alpha_n)|^2 = \|\sigma\|^2,$$

in terms of the Fourier coefficients a_n and b_n. It is

(9)
$$\left(\frac{1}{\sqrt{2\pi}} \int_{-\pi}^{\pi} \sigma(t)dt \right)^2 + \sum_{n=1}^{\infty} \left(\left(\frac{1}{\sqrt{\pi}} \int_{-\pi}^{\pi} \sigma(t) \cos nt \, dt \right)^2 \right.$$
$$\left. + \left(\frac{1}{\sqrt{\pi}} \int_{-\pi}^{\pi} \sigma(t) \sin nt \, dt \right)^2 \right) = \pi \left(\frac{a_0^2}{2} + \sum_{n=1}^{\infty} \left(a_n^2 + b_n^2 \right) \right) = \int_{-\pi}^{\pi} |\sigma|^2 \, dx.$$

EXAMPLE 1   Consider Parseval's equality for $\sigma(x) = x$. Since x is an odd function, so is $\sigma(x) \cos nx$ and therefore $a_n = 0$ (see Exercise 3.3–19). However $\sigma(x) \sin nx$ is even so that

$$b_n = \frac{2}{\pi} \int_0^\pi t \sin nt \, dt = \frac{2}{\pi} \left(-t \frac{\cos nt}{n} \Big|_0^\pi - \int_0^\pi - \frac{\cos nt}{n} \, dt \right)$$

$$= \frac{2}{n} (-1)^{n+1}.$$

Also $\int_{-\pi}^\pi t^2 \, dt = 2\pi^3/3$. Then Parseval's equality yields

$$\frac{\pi^2}{6} = \sum_{n=1}^\infty \frac{1}{n^2}.$$

Similar equalities are found in the exercises.

EXAMPLE 2   Consider Parseval's equality for the function

$$\sigma(x) = \begin{cases} 1, & -\pi < c \le x \le d < \pi, \\ 0, & \text{outside } c \le x \le d. \end{cases}$$

This is the characteristic function for the interval $c \le x \le d$. We have

$$a_0 = \frac{1}{\pi} \int_c^d dt = \frac{d - c}{\pi},$$

$$a_n = \frac{1}{\pi} \int_c^d \cos nt \, dt = \frac{1}{n\pi} (\sin nd - \sin nc),$$

$$b_n = \frac{1}{\pi} \int_c^d \sin nt \, dt = \frac{1}{n\pi} (\cos nc - \cos nd),$$

and Parseval's equality is

$$d - c = \frac{(d - c)^2}{2\pi} + \sum_{n=1}^\infty \frac{2}{\pi n^2} (1 - \cos n(d - c)).$$

Replacing $d - c$ by x, we have

(10)
$$\sum_{n=1}^\infty \frac{1 - \cos nx}{n^2} = \frac{\pi x}{2} - \frac{x^2}{4}, \quad 0 < x < 2\pi.$$

This formula is also valid for $x = 0$ and $x = 2\pi$. In view of the discussion in Section 5.1, the validity of (10) is equivalent to Theorem 5.6A. Thus a proof of Theorem 5.6A could be based on (10). (See Exercise 5.6–13.)

EXAMPLE 3 If it were permissible to differentiate (10) term by term, we would have

(11)
$$\sum_{n=1}^{\infty} \frac{\sin nx}{n} = \frac{\pi - x}{2}, \quad 0 < x < 2\pi.$$

We shall show that (11) is valid by proving that the series $\sum_{1}^{\infty} \dfrac{\sin nx}{n}$ con-

verges uniformly on any interval $0 < c \leq x \leq d < 2\pi$, thus permitting term by term differentiation of (10) for $c \leq x \leq d$.

For this purpose it is useful to consider the series in (11)·as the imaginary part of the complex series $\sum_{n=1}^{\infty} \dfrac{e^{inx}}{n}$. For the geometrical progression

$$S(k, x) = \sum_{n=1}^{k} e^{inx} = \frac{e^{ix} - e^{ix}(e^{ix})^k}{1 - e^{ix}}$$

we obtain, for $0 < x < 2\pi$,

$$|S(k, x)| \leq \frac{2}{|1 - e^{ix}|} = \left| \frac{2i}{e^{ix/2} - e^{-ix/2}} \right| = \frac{1}{\sin x/2}.$$

Thus,

$$\sum_{n=j}^{k} \frac{e^{inx}}{n} = \sum_{n=j}^{k} \frac{1}{n}(S(n, x) - S(n - 1, x))$$

$$= \sum_{n=j}^{k} \frac{S(n, x)}{n} - \sum_{n=j}^{k} \frac{S(n, x)}{n + 1} - \frac{S(j - 1, x)}{j} + \frac{S(k, x)}{k + 1}$$

and

(12)
$$\left| \sum_{n=j}^{k} \frac{e^{inx}}{n} \right| \leq \frac{1}{\sin x/2} \left(\sum_{n=j}^{k} \left(\frac{1}{n} - \frac{1}{n + 1} \right) + \frac{1}{j} + \frac{1}{k + 1} \right) = \frac{2}{j \sin x/2}.$$

It follows, by the Cauchy Criterion, that $\sum_{n=1}^{\infty} \dfrac{e^{inx}}{n}$ converges uniformly for

$0 < c \leq x \leq d < 2\pi$. In particular, the real and imaginary parts of the series converge, and (11) is valid.

An important property of the series in (11) is that its partial sums $\sum_{1}^{k} \dfrac{\sin nx}{n}$ are bounded uniformly in x and n, on $0 \leq x \leq 2\pi$. To see this we need only consider x on the range $0 < x < \pi$ (why?) and write

$$\left| \sum_{n=1}^{k} \frac{\sin nx}{n} \right| \leq \left| \sum_{1 \leq n < 1/x} \frac{x \sin nx}{nx} \right| + \left| \sum_{1/x \leq n \leq k} \frac{\sin nx}{n} \right|.$$

By (12) and the inequality $\dfrac{2}{\pi} \leq \dfrac{\sin y}{y} \leq 1$ for $0 < y < \dfrac{\pi}{2}$ we derive

$$(13) \quad \left| \sum_{1}^{k} \frac{\sin nx}{n} \right| \leq \left(\sum_{1 \leq n < 1/x} x \right) + \frac{2}{\dfrac{1}{x} \sin \dfrac{x}{2}} \leq x \cdot \frac{1}{x} + \frac{2}{\dfrac{1}{x} \dfrac{x}{2}} = 1 + 2\pi.$$

In the study of Fourier series, it is convenient to have σ defined over the entire x axis and periodic of period 2π. Of course, if $\sigma(x)$ is defined only on $-\pi \leq x \leq \pi$ we cannot extend it to be periodic of period 2π unless $\sigma(-\pi) = \sigma(\pi)$. However, we recall that vectors in $\mathcal{R}\{-\pi, \pi\}$ are considered as equal when they differ at most on a set of measure zero. Thus we may consider instead of σ, the integrable function σ^* defined by

$$\sigma^*(x) = \sigma(x), \qquad -\pi < x < \pi,$$
$$\sigma^*(\pi) = \sigma^*(-\pi) \qquad \text{arbitrary,}$$

and then extend σ^* to be periodic of period 2π. In any integrand σ^* can be replaced by σ. The Fourier coefficients of σ^* are those of σ and the Fourier series of σ^* is that of σ. The advantage of this procedure of defining the function over the entire x axis is that the Fourier coefficients of a function β periodic of period 2π may be calculated over any interval of length 2π.

Indeed

$$\int_{-\pi+y}^{\pi+y} \beta(x)\sin nx \, dx = \left(\int_{-\pi+y}^{-\pi} + \int_{-\pi}^{\pi} + \int_{\pi}^{\pi+y} \right) \beta(x)\sin nx \, dx$$

$$= \int_{\pi+y}^{\pi} \beta(t)\sin nt \, dt + \int_{-\pi}^{\pi} \beta(x)\sin nx \, dx + \int_{\pi}^{\pi+y} \beta(x) \sin nx \, dx$$

$$= \int_{-\pi}^{\pi} \beta(x)\sin nx \, dx$$

by use of the transformation $x = t - 2\pi$.
Similarly,

$$\int_{-\pi+y}^{\pi+y} \beta(x)\cos nx \, dx = \int_{-\pi}^{\pi} \beta(x)\cos nx \, dx.$$

In view of this it suffices, for functions periodic of period 2π, to give the values of the function on any interval of length 2π. We can form the Fourier series by integration over this interval and the series will converge to L at x_0 in the interval if and only if it converges to L at the point y_0 in $-\pi \leq x \leq \pi$ obtained from x_0 by adding a multiple of 2π. For example, equation (11) indicates that $\displaystyle\sum_{n=1}^{\infty} \frac{\sin nx}{n}$ converges to the periodic function $\sigma(x) = \dfrac{\pi - x}{2}$, $0 < x < 2\pi$. It can be readily verified that this series is the Fourier series of σ.

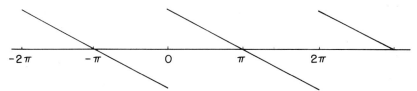

The periodic function $\frac{\pi-x}{2}$, $0 < x < 2\pi$, the values
at $2n\pi$ being all equal (say to 0)

Note, in the above example, that the Fourier series for the periodic function $\sigma(x) = \frac{\pi - x}{2}$, $0 < x < 2\pi$, converges at the points of discontinuity 0 and 2π to the value 0, which is the average, at each discontinuity point, of the left and right hand limits of σ at the discontinuity point. This behaviour is characteristic of a large class of functions.

Since $\alpha_n(x)$, defined by equation (1), satisfy

$$\int_{-\pi+y}^{\pi+y} \alpha_n(x)\, \alpha_m(x)dx = \int_{-\pi}^{\pi} \alpha_n(x)\, \alpha_m(x)dx = \delta_{nm},$$

it is clear that we can consider the Fourier series of a function defined over $\mathscr{R}\{-\pi + y, \pi + y\}$ and that the Fourier series of a periodic function over this interval of length 2π will coincide with the Fourier series of the periodic function considered as a vector in $\mathscr{R}\{-\pi, \pi\}$.

More generally, it is possible to define the Fourier series of a function defined over any interval $a \leq u \leq b$. The transformation $x = \frac{2\pi}{b-a}$ $\left(u - \frac{b+a}{2}\right)$ carries $a \leq u \leq b$ into $-\pi \leq x \leq \pi$ and equation (3), with a_n and b_n given by (4) and (5), and with $\alpha(u) = \sigma(x(u))$, into

(14) $$F(\sigma; -\pi, \pi) = F(\alpha; a, b) = \frac{c_0}{2} + \sum_{n=1}^{\infty} c_n \cos\frac{2n\,\pi u}{b-a} + d_n \sin\frac{2n\,\pi u}{b-a},$$

where

(15) $$c_n = \frac{2}{b-a} \int_a^b \alpha(t) \cos\frac{2n\,\pi t}{b-a}\, dt,$$

(16) $$d_n = \frac{2}{b-a} \int_a^b \alpha(t) \sin\frac{2n\,\pi t}{b-a}\, dt.$$

Here the orthonormal functions on $\mathcal{R}\{a, b\}$ are

(17) $\quad \beta_0(u) = \sqrt{\dfrac{1}{b-a}}, \quad \beta_{2n-1}(u) = \sqrt{\dfrac{2}{b-a}} \cos \dfrac{2n\pi u}{b-a}$,

$$\beta_{2n}(u) = \sqrt{\dfrac{2}{b-a}} \sin \dfrac{2n\pi u}{b-a}.$$

When (15) and (16) are substituted into (14), we obtain the Fourier series for α on $a \leq u \leq b$ represented as

(18) $\qquad \alpha \sim \dfrac{1}{b-a} \displaystyle\int_a^b \alpha(t)dt + \dfrac{2}{b-a} \sum_{n=1}^{\infty} \int_a^b \alpha(t) \cos \dfrac{2n\pi}{b-a}(t-u)dt.$

A more symmetrical form may be obtained with the aid of complex numbers. Recall that

$$e^{ix} = \cos x + i \sin x, \quad e^{-ix} = \cos x - i \sin x,$$

from which we deduce

$$\cos x = \frac{e^{ix} + e^{-ix}}{2}, \quad \sin x = \frac{e^{ix} - e^{-ix}}{2i}.$$

Then (14) may be written

$$\alpha \sim \frac{c_0}{2} + \frac{1}{2} \sum_{n=1}^{\infty} (c_n - id_n)\, e^{\frac{2n\pi u i}{b-a}} + (c_n + id_n)\, e^{-\frac{2n\pi u i}{b-a}}$$

or,

(19) $\qquad\qquad\qquad \alpha \sim \displaystyle\sum_{n=-\infty}^{\infty} q_n\, e^{\frac{2n\pi u i}{b-a}},$

where

(20) $\qquad q_n = \dfrac{1}{b-a} \displaystyle\int_a^b \alpha(t)\, e^{-\frac{2n\pi t i}{b-a}}\, dt, \qquad n = 0, \pm 1, \pm 2, \dots .$

Note that $q_n = \dfrac{c_n - id_n}{2}, \quad q_{-n} = \dfrac{c_n + id_n}{2} = \overline{q_n}, \quad n = 0, 1, 2, \dots ,$

where $d_0 = 0$.

In particular, for the interval $-\pi \leq x \leq \pi$, the complex form is

(21) $\qquad\qquad \alpha \sim \displaystyle\sum_{n=-\infty}^{\infty} q_n\, e^{n x i}, \quad q_n = \dfrac{1}{2\pi} \int_{-\pi}^{\pi} \alpha(t)\, e^{-n t i}\, dt.$

With regard to the theory of convergence of Fourier series we need only concern ourselves with $\mathcal{R}\{-\pi, \pi\}$.

It is natural to be interested in the properties of the Fourier coefficients a_n and b_n given by (4) and (5) for they uniquely determine the Fourier series of σ. Indeed, when two functions σ and μ have the same Fourier coefficients their difference $\sigma - \mu$ has its Fourier coefficients identically zero and so is the zero vector. We see at once, from Parseval's equality, that

$$(22) \qquad \lim_{n \to \infty} a_n = 0, \quad \lim_{n \to \infty} b_n = 0.$$

A very useful strengthening of this result is the next theorem, known as the **Riemann-Lebesgue Theorem.**

THEOREM 5.6B Let σ be integrable on $a \le t \le b$. Then

$$(23) \qquad \lim_{y \to \infty} \int_a^b \sigma(t) \sin yt \, dt = 0, \quad \lim_{y \to \infty} \int_a^b \sigma(t) \cos yt \, dt = 0.$$

Proof It is clear that (23) is valid when σ is constant on the interval, for then

$$\left| \int_a^b \sigma \sin yt \, dt \right| = \left| \sigma \frac{(\cos ya - \cos yb)}{y} \right| \le \frac{2|\sigma|}{y}.$$

The theorem is then seen to be valid when σ is a step function,

$$\sigma = \sum_{k=1}^{n} c_k \, \phi_k,$$

where ϕ_k are characteristic functions of disjoint intervals $\mathscr{I}_k$. We have

$$\lim_{y \to \infty} \int_a^b \sigma(t) \sin yt \, dt = \sum_{k=1}^{n} c_k \lim_{y \to \infty} \int_{\mathscr{I}_k} \phi_k \sin yt \, dt = 0,$$

since ϕ_k is 1 on $\mathscr{I}_k$.

Finally, to prove the theorem when σ is integrable, for given $\epsilon > 0$ let μ be a step function such that $\int_a^b |\sigma - \mu| dt < \epsilon$, and choose y_0 sufficiently large so that $| \int_a^b \mu(t) \sin yt \, dt | < \epsilon$ when $y \ge y_0$. Then, for $y \ge y_0(\epsilon)$,

$$\left| \int_a^b \sigma(t) \sin yt \, dt \right| \le \left| \int_a^b (\sigma(t) - \mu(t)) \sin yt \, dt \right| + \left| \int_a^b \mu(t) \sin yt \, dt \right|$$

$$\le \int_a^b |\sigma - \mu| dt + \epsilon < 2\epsilon.$$

The second part of (23) is similarly proved. ★

The following examples illustrate the concepts already developed.

EXAMPLE 4 Solve the integral equation

$$\int_{-\pi}^{\pi} K(x + y) \, \sigma(y) dy = r\sigma(x), \quad r \ne 0,$$

where $K(t)$ is a real valued continuous function periodic of period 2π.

Assume a solution σ in $\mathcal{R}\{-\pi, \pi\}$ for some fixed r. The Fourier series for σ and K are given by

$$\sigma(x) \sim \frac{a_0}{2} + \sum_1^\infty (a_n \cos nx + b_n \sin nx),$$

$$K(t) \sim \frac{a_0'}{2} + \sum_1^\infty (a_n' \cos nt + b_n' \sin nt),$$

where, making use of the periodicity of $K(t)$,

$$a_n = \frac{1}{\pi} \int_{-\pi}^\pi \frac{1}{r} \int_{-\pi}^\pi K(x + y)\, \sigma(y) dy \cos nx\, dx$$

$$= \frac{1}{r\pi} \int_{-\pi}^\pi \sigma(y) \int_{-\pi}^\pi K(x + y) \cos nx\, dx\, dy$$

$$= \frac{1}{r\pi} \int_{-\pi}^\pi \sigma(y) \int_{-\pi}^\pi K(t) \cos n(t - y) dt\, dy$$

$$= \frac{1}{r\pi} \int_{-\pi}^\pi \sigma(y) \left(\int_{-\pi}^\pi K(t) \cos nt\, dt \cos ny + \int_{-\pi}^\pi K(t) \sin nt\, dt \sin ny \right) dy$$

$$= \frac{1}{r} \int_{-\pi}^\pi \left(a_n' \sigma(y) \cos ny + b_n' \sigma(y) \sin ny \right) dy,$$

or,

(24) $$\frac{r}{\pi} a_n = a_n' a_n + b_n' b_n, \qquad n = 0, 1, \ldots,$$

where $b_0 = 0 = b_0'$. Similarly

(25) $$\frac{r}{\pi} b_n = b_n' a_n - a_n' b_n, \qquad n = 1, 2, \ldots.$$

We are thus led to consider the equation

$$\begin{bmatrix} \dfrac{r}{\pi} - a_n' & -b_n' \\ -b_n' & \dfrac{r}{\pi} + a_n' \end{bmatrix} \begin{bmatrix} a_n \\ b_n \end{bmatrix} = \begin{bmatrix} 0 \\ 0 \end{bmatrix} = 0.$$

For fixed $n = 1, 2, 3, \ldots$ a nonzero solution α_n exists if and only if

(26) $$r = \pm \pi \sqrt{(a_n')^2 + (b_n')^2}.$$

For $n = 0$, a_0 will be different from 0 if and only if

(27) $$r = \pi a_0'$$

since equation (25) is absent. Thus if r is not one of the values listed in (26) or (27), a_n and b_n will be zero for all n and σ will be the zero vector. When r is one of the values listed in (26) or (27), the fact that a_n' and b_n' approach zero as n increases assures that there are only a finite number of nonnegative integers n, say $n_1, n_2, \ldots n_s$, for which (26) or (27) is satisfied; that is, there are only a finite number of values of n for which a_n and b_n are not both zero for the fixed value of r. For each such integer n_j, let $\begin{bmatrix} a_{n_j} \\ b_{n_j} \end{bmatrix}$ be a nonzero solution of the matrix equation, where we may assume $a_{n_j}^2 + b_{n_j}^2 = 1$. Then the general solution of the matrix equation is

$$\alpha_{n_j} = c_{n_j} \begin{bmatrix} a_{n_j} \\ b_{n_j} \end{bmatrix}$$

for arbitrary values of c_{n_j}. The solution of the integral equation for the fixed value of r is

$$\sum_{j=1}^{s} c_{n_j} \left(a_{n_j} \cos n_j x + b_{n_j} \sin n_j x \right)$$

or, if w_{n_j} is chosen so that $\cos w_{n_j} = a_{n_j}$, $\sin w_{n_j} = -b_{n_j}$, the solution σ is

$$\sum_{j=1}^{s} c_{n_j} \cos (n_j x + w_{n_j})$$

where s, n_j, and w_{n_j}, as indicated above, depend on r. All nonzero r of the form (26) or (27) are eigenvalues, and for each eigenvalue r there are $s = s(r)$ linearly independent eigenvectors.

EXAMPLE 5 Let the Fourier expansion for the periodic integrable function σ be given by (3). Show that

(28) $$\sum_{1}^{\infty} \frac{b_n}{n} = \frac{1}{2\pi} \int_{0}^{2\pi} \sigma(x) (\pi - x)\,dx.$$

The convergence of $\sum_{n=j}^{\infty} \dfrac{b_n}{n}$ could be obtained directly from Schwarz's inequality, since

$$\left| \sum_{n=j}^{k} \frac{b_n}{n} \right|^2 \le \sum_{n=1}^{\infty} b_n^2 \sum_{n=j}^{\infty} \frac{1}{n^2}.$$

However formula (28) actually evaluates the series. The result may be obtained by considering the periodic function

$$(29) \qquad \alpha = \frac{\pi - x}{2} \sim \sum_{1}^{\infty} \frac{\sin nx}{n}$$

as a vector in the space $\mathscr{R}\{0, 2\pi\}$ (see Example 3). It is permissible to multiply the Fourier series for α by σ and integrate term by term to obtain

$$\int_{0}^{2\pi} \alpha(x)\, \sigma(x)dx = \sum_{1}^{\infty} \frac{1}{n} \int_{0}^{2\pi} \sigma(x)\, \sin nx\, dx;$$

that is,

$$\frac{1}{2\pi} \int_{0}^{2\pi} \sigma(x)\, (\pi - x)dx = \sum_{1}^{\infty} \frac{b_n}{n}.$$

For example, if σ is given by

$$\sigma(x) = \begin{cases} x, & 0 \le x \le \pi, \\ 0, & \pi < x \le 2\pi, \end{cases}$$

then $b_n = \dfrac{(-1)^{n-1}}{n}$ and (28) yields

$$(30) \qquad \sum_{1}^{\infty} \frac{(-1)^{n-1}}{n^2} = \frac{1}{2\pi} \int_{0}^{\pi} x(\pi - x)dx = \frac{\pi^2}{12}.$$

The Riemann Lebesgue Theorem can be used to show that *the convergence or divergence of the Fourier series for σ at the fixed point x depends only on the values of σ in an arbitrarily small open interval about x.* This is rather surprising considering that a_n and b_n are calculated by integration over an interval of length 2π. To obtain this result we shall find an integral representation of the partial sums. Let

$$(31) \quad S_j(x) = \frac{a_0}{2} + \sum_{n=1}^{j} a_n \cos nx + b_n \sin nx$$

$$= \frac{1}{2\pi} \int_{-\pi}^{\pi} \sigma(t)dt + \frac{1}{\pi} \sum_{1}^{j} \int_{-\pi}^{\pi} \sigma(t)\, (\cos nt \cos nx + \sin nt \sin nx)dt$$

$$= \frac{1}{\pi} \int_{-\pi}^{\pi} \sigma(t) \left(\frac{1}{2} + \sum_{1}^{j} \cos n(x - t) \right)dt.$$

It is easy to verify that

(32) $\dfrac{1}{2} + \cos u + \cos 2u + \cdots + \cos ju = \dfrac{\sin\left(j + \frac{1}{2}\right)u}{2 \sin (u/2)}$, $u \ne 2n\pi$.

Indeed, multiplication of the left side of (32) by $2 \sin (u/2)$ yields

$$\sin \frac{u}{2} + \left(\sin \frac{3u}{2} - \sin \frac{u}{2}\right) + \cdots + \left(\sin \left(j + \frac{1}{2}\right)u - \sin \left(j - \frac{1}{2}\right)u\right)$$

which reduces to $\sin \left(j + \frac{1}{2}\right)u$.

Substitution of (32), with $u = x - t$, into (31) shows that

(33) $S_j(x) = \dfrac{1}{2\pi} \displaystyle\int_{-\pi}^{\pi} \sigma(t) \, \dfrac{\sin \left(j + \dfrac{1}{2}\right)\left(x - t\right)}{\sin \left(\dfrac{x - t}{2}\right)} \, dt.$

We are assuming σ is periodic. Put $t = x + y$ and obtain

$$2\pi S_j(x) = \int_{-\pi-x}^{\pi-x} \frac{\sin \left(j + \frac{1}{2}\right)y}{\sin y/2} \, \sigma(x + y)dy = \int_{-\pi}^{\pi} \frac{\sin \left(j + \frac{1}{2}\right)y}{\sin y/2} \, \sigma(x + y)dy$$

$$= \int_{-\pi}^{0} \frac{\sin \left(j + \frac{1}{2}\right)y}{\sin y/2} \, \sigma(x + y)dy + \int_{0}^{\pi} \frac{\sin \left(j + \frac{1}{2}\right)y}{\sin y/2} \, \sigma(x + y)dy$$

$$= \int_{0}^{\pi} \frac{\sin \left(j + \frac{1}{2}\right)z}{\sin z/2} \, \sigma(x - z)dz + \int_{0}^{\pi} \frac{\sin \left(j + \frac{1}{2}\right)y}{\sin y/2} \, \sigma(x + y)dy$$

and finally

(34) $S_j(x) = \dfrac{1}{2\pi} \displaystyle\int_{0}^{\pi} \dfrac{\sin \left(j + \frac{1}{2}\right)y}{\sin y/2} \left(\sigma(x + y) + \sigma(x - y)\right) dy.$

This is the desired integral representation. When $\delta > 0$,

(35) $S_j(x) = \dfrac{1}{2\pi} \displaystyle\int_{0}^{\delta} \dfrac{\sin \left(j + \frac{1}{2}\right)y}{\sin y/2} \left(\sigma(x + y) + \sigma(x - y)\right) dy$

$$+ \frac{1}{2\pi} \int_{\delta}^{\pi} \sin \left(j + \tfrac{1}{2}\right)y \left(\frac{\sigma(x + y) + \sigma(x - y)}{\sin y/2}\right) dy.$$

The expression in parentheses in the second integral is an integrable function of y, since $0 < \delta \le y \le \pi$. By the Riemann-Lebesgue Theorem, the second integral approaches zero as $j \to \infty$. Then the convergence of $S_j(x)$

depends on whether the first integral in (35) has a limit as $j \to \infty$. This integral however involves only the values of σ on the range $x - \delta \leq t \leq x + \delta$. The convergence depends only on the values of σ in an arbitrarily small interval about x.

Formula (35) indicates that if σ vanishes on $x - \delta \leq t \leq x + \delta$ then $S_j(x)$ converges to zero. Hence if α and β are integrable functions coinciding on any interval, their Fourier series converge or diverge together for each x on the interval, and, if they converge, they converge to the same value.

The next two theorems are devoted to sufficient conditions for the convergence of a Fourier series. Theorem 5.6C states conditions assuring uniform convergence.

THEOREM 5.6C   Let σ be continuous on $-\pi \leq x \leq \pi$ and have a continuous derivative σ'. Suppose $\sigma(\pi) = \sigma(-\pi)$. Then the Fourier series for σ converges to σ absolutely uniformly on $-\pi \leq x \leq \pi$.

Proof   Let a_n' and b_n' be the Fourier coefficients for σ'. Then, for $n \neq 0$,

$$a_n = \frac{1}{\pi} \int_{-\pi}^{\pi} \sigma(x) \cos nx\, dx = \frac{1}{\pi} \left(\frac{\sin nx}{n} \sigma(x) \Big|_{-\pi}^{\pi} - \int_{-\pi}^{\pi} \frac{\sin nx}{n} \sigma'(x) dx \right) = \frac{-b_n'}{n}.$$

Using $\sigma(\pi) = \sigma(-\pi)$, we find also $b_n = \dfrac{a_n'}{n}$. Then

$$\sum_{j}^{k} |a_n \cos nx + b_n \sin nx| \leq \sum_{j}^{k} |a_n| + |b_n| = \sum_{j}^{k} \left| \frac{b_n'}{n} \right| + \left| \frac{a_n'}{n} \right|$$

$$\leq \left(\sum_{j}^{k} \frac{1}{n^2} \sum_{j}^{k} (|b_n'| + |a_n'|)^2 \right)^{1/2} \leq \left(\sum_{j}^{k} \frac{2}{n^2} \sum_{j}^{k} |b_n'|^2 + |a_n'|^2 \right)^{1/2}$$

$$\leq \left(\sum_{j}^{k} \frac{2}{n^2} \right)^{1/2} \left(\frac{1}{\pi} \int_{-\pi}^{\pi} |\sigma'(x)|^2\, dx \right)^{1/2}.$$

The last inequality is an application of Parseval's equality. The uniform convergence follows from the Cauchy criterion, and the theorem from Theorem 5.1G.   ★

It is possible to relax the conditions in the previous theorem slightly by demanding σ' be only piecewise continuous. That is, the interval $-\pi \leq x \leq \pi$ can be divided into a finite number of subintervals in whose interiors σ' is continuous. $\sigma'(x)$ need not exist at the end points of the subintervals but has limits at these end points. If the subdivision is $-\pi = x_0 < x_1 < x_2 \cdots < x_n = \pi$, then

$$a_n = \frac{1}{\pi} \int_{-\pi}^{\pi} \sigma(x) \cos nx \, dx = \frac{1}{\pi} \sum_{i=1}^{n} \int_{x_{i-1}}^{x_i} \sigma(x) \cos n \, dx$$

$$= \sum_{i=1}^{n} \frac{1}{\pi} \left(\frac{\sin nx}{n} \sigma(x) \Big|_{x_{i-1}+}^{x_i-} - \int_{x_{i-1}}^{x_i} \frac{\sin nx}{n} \sigma'(x) dx \right) = \frac{-b_n'}{n}$$

in view of the continuity of σ. Similarly $b_n = \dfrac{a_n'}{n}$ and the proof proceeds as before. We shall use this extension in the next theorem.

THEOREM 5.6D   Let σ and σ' be piecewise continuous on $-\pi \leq x \leq \pi$ and periodic of period 2π. The Fourier series for σ converges to $\dfrac{\sigma(x+) + \sigma(x-)}{2}$, and converges uniformly in every closed interval in which σ is continuous.

Proof   Let $\beta(x) = \dfrac{\sigma(x+) + \sigma(x-)}{2}$. The discontinuity points of β on $-\pi \leq x < \pi$ are those of σ. If they are $u_1 < u_2 < \cdots < u_m$, define $r_j = \beta(u_j +) - \beta(u_j -)$. The series $\sum_{1}^{\infty} \dfrac{\sin n(x - u)}{n\pi}$ converges to the periodic function $H(x, u)$ defined over $u \leq x \leq u + 2\pi$ by

$$H(x, u) = \begin{cases} \dfrac{\pi - (x - u)}{2\pi}, & u < x < u + 2\pi, \\[2mm] 0, & x = u. \end{cases}$$

The convergence is uniform in any closed interval within $u - 2\pi < x < u + 2\pi$ which does not contain u. At $x = u$, the function $H(x, u)$ has a jump of 1, since $H(u -, u) = -\frac{1}{2}$ and $H(u +, u) = \frac{1}{2}$. It follows that

$$(36) \qquad\qquad \alpha(x) = \beta(x) - \sum_{j=1}^{m} r_j H(x, u_j)$$

is continuous over the entire axis and has a piecewise continuous derivative on $-\pi \leq x \leq \pi$. Moreover $\alpha(\pi) = \alpha(-\pi)$ since β and $H(x, u_j)$ are periodic of period 2π. Hence, by the comment following Theorem 5.6C, the series

$$(37) \qquad\qquad F(\alpha(x)) = \frac{a_0}{2} + \sum_{1}^{\infty} (a_n \cos nx + b_n \sin nx),$$

where a_n and b_n are the Fourier coefficients of α, converges uniformly to $\alpha(x)$. It follows that

(38)
$$F(\alpha(x)) + \sum_{j=1}^{m} r_j \sum_{1}^{\infty} \frac{\sin n(x - u_j)}{n\pi}$$

converges to $\beta(x)$ and converges uniformly in every closed interval not containing any $u_j + 2k\pi$, k an integer. Moreover, the Fourier series for β is

$$F(\beta(x)) = F\left(\alpha(x) + \sum_{j=1}^{m} r_j H(x, u_j)\right) = F(\alpha(x)) + \sum_{j=1}^{m} r_j F(H(x, u_j))$$

which is the series given by (37). Hence the Fourier series for β, which is exactly the Fourier series for σ, converges to

$$\beta(x) = \frac{\sigma(x +) + \sigma(x -)}{2}. \quad \star$$

It must be emphasized that many trigonometric series may represent the same function on a given interval. Suppose, for example, that a function α is defined on $0 \le x \le \pi$. Extend the definition of α to the domain $-\pi \le x \le \pi$ by defining $\alpha(-x) = \alpha(x)$, $0 \le x \le \pi$. Then α is an even function and its Fourier series is

$$\frac{1}{\pi} \int_0^\pi \alpha(t)dt + \sum_{n=1}^\infty \left(\frac{2}{\pi} \int_0^\pi \alpha(t) \cos nt \, dt\right) \cos nx.$$

This series is called the **Fourier Cosine series** of α. It represents the extended function on $-\pi \le x \le \pi$ and the original function α on $0 \le x \le \pi$.

Or, we might redefine α to be 0 at $x = 0$ and then extend α to be odd by defining $\alpha(-x) = -\alpha(x)$, $0 \le x \le \pi$. The Fourier series for this odd function is then

$$\sum_{n=1}^\infty \left(\frac{2}{\pi} \int_0^\pi \alpha(t) \sin nt \, dt\right) \sin nx$$

and this series, called the **Fourier Sine series** of α, also represents α on $0 \le x \le \pi$.

Again, we could have made a different type of extension, say $\alpha(x) = 0$, $-\pi \le x \le 0$, and obtained a series containing both sines and cosines.

None of these series may be the Fourier series of α considered as a vector in $\mathcal{R}\{0, \pi\}$, as formula (17) indicates this series will be given in terms of $\cos 2nu$ and $\sin 2nu$.

The Fourier Sine series may also be considered as a representation of α in the vector space $\mathscr{R}\{0, \pi\}$ in terms of the orthonormal sequence $\left\{\sqrt{\dfrac{2}{\pi}} \sin nx\right\}$, and the Fourier Cosine series may be considered as a representation of α in $\mathscr{R}\{0, \pi\}$ in terms of the orthonormal sequence $\left\{\dfrac{1}{\sqrt{\pi}}, \sqrt{\dfrac{2}{\pi}} \cos nx\right\}$. These sequences are linearly dense in $\mathscr{R}\{0, \pi\}$. (Exercise 5.6–25). Of course, the Fourier Sine and Cosine series are just special cases of the Fourier series. However, it is also true that Fourier series may be studied in terms of Fourier Sine and Cosine series. This follows from the fact that any function α on $-\pi \le x \le \pi$ may be written as the sum of an even function σ and an odd function μ,

$$\sigma(x) = \frac{\alpha(x) + \alpha(-x)}{2}, \quad \mu(x) = \frac{\alpha(x) - \alpha(-x)}{2}.$$

Then $F(\alpha) = F(\sigma) + F(\mu)$ indicates that the Fourier series for α is the sum of the Fourier Cosine and Fourier Sine series. Suppose, for example, that the Fourier Cosine series for σ converges to $\sigma(x_0)$ at x_0, and the Fourier Sine series for μ converges to $\mu(x_0)$ at x_0. Then the Fourier series for α converges to $\sigma(x_0) + \mu(x_0) = \alpha(x_0)$.

Indeed, as we shall see, theorems about expansions of functions in terms of the orthonormal sequences just mentioned arise naturally in the study of boundary value problems. On the other hand, many of the results obtained in the theory of Fourier series, a subject which has been studied extensively, can be applied directly to these problems.

Exercise 5.6

1. Show that the Fourier series of an even function contains only cosine terms.
2. Show that if the trigonometric series

$$\frac{c_0}{2} + \sum_{n=1}^{\infty}\left(c_n \cos nt + d_n \sin nt\right)$$

converges uniformly to β on $-\pi \le t \le \pi$, then the series is the Fourier series for β.

3. Assume that α and β have the same Fourier series and are continuous at t_0. Show that $\alpha(t_0) = \beta(t_0)$. *Hint:* Use Theorem 5.1D.

4. (a) Use Exercises 2 and 3 (or Theorem 5.1G) to show that

$$|x| = \frac{\pi}{2} + \sum_{n=1}^{\infty}\frac{2}{\pi}\frac{(-1)^n - 1}{n^2} \cos nx, \quad -\pi \le x \le \pi.$$

(b) Find $\displaystyle\sum_{n=1}^{\infty}\frac{1}{(2n-1)^2}$ using (a).

(c) Solve part (b) by use of the results obtained in Examples 1 and 5.

5. Using the series in 4(a), obtain by integration

$$\frac{\pi}{8}(\pi x - x^2) = \sum_{n=1}^{\infty} \frac{\sin (2n - 1)x}{(2n - 1)^3}.$$

Thus show that

$$\sum_{n=1}^{\infty} \frac{(-1)^{n+1}}{(2n - 1)^3} = \frac{\pi^3}{32}.$$

6. Write out the Fourier series for the following periodic functions over the intervals indicated, each interval indicating the period,
    (a) $x^2, \ -\pi < x \le \pi$ (c) $x - \frac{1}{2}, \ 0 < x \le 1$
    (b) $x, \ -\pi < x \le \pi$ (d) $x/2, \ 0 < x \le 2.$

7. Take $0 < x < \pi, 0 < y < \pi.$
    Prove that

$$H(x, y) = \sum_{n=1}^{\infty} \frac{\sin nx \cos ny}{n} = \begin{cases} \dfrac{\pi - x}{2} & \text{if } x > y \\[2mm] \dfrac{\pi}{4} - \dfrac{x}{2} & \text{if } x = y \\[2mm] -\dfrac{x}{2} & \text{if } x < y. \end{cases}$$

    Hint: Write $\displaystyle\sum_{n=1}^{\infty} \frac{\sin n(x + y)}{n}$ and also $\displaystyle\sum_{n=1}^{\infty} \frac{\sin n(x - y)}{n}$ in terms of $H(x, y)$.

8. Apply Parseval's equation to the Fourier series for x^2 on $-\pi \le x \le \pi$ to obtain $\displaystyle\sum_{n=1}^{\infty} \frac{1}{n^4} = \frac{1}{90}\pi^4.$

9. Show that the series

$$\cos x - \frac{1}{\sqrt{2}}\cos 2x + \frac{1}{\sqrt{3}}\cos 3x - \frac{1}{\sqrt{4}}\cos 4x$$

$$+ \cdots + \frac{1}{\sqrt{n}}(-1)^{n+1}\cos nx + \cdots$$

    cannot be a Fourier series.

10. Write the Fourier series for the function

$$\sigma(x) = \begin{cases} -\dfrac{\pi}{4}, & -\pi < x < 0, \\[2mm] 0, & x = 0, \\[2mm] \dfrac{\pi}{4}, & 0 < x < \pi, \end{cases}$$

    and prove that the series does not converge uniformly on the interval. Integrate from $\dfrac{\pi}{2}$ to x, $0 \le x \le \pi$, and obtain the value of $\displaystyle\sum_{n=1}^{\infty} \frac{\cos(2n - 1)x}{(2n - 1)^2}$. Integrate again from 0 to x, $0 \le x \le \pi$, and obtain the value of $\displaystyle\sum_{n=1}^{\infty} \frac{\sin(2n - 1)x}{(2n - 1)^3}.$

11. (a) Let m be a positive integer. Does $\lim_{m \to \infty} \sin mx$ exist? Show that the limit exists only when $x = n\pi$. *Hint:* Use $\sin 2mx = 2 \sin mx \cos mx$, $\sin^2 mx + \cos^2 mx = 1$, $\sin^2 mx = \dfrac{1 - \cos 2 mx}{2}$, $(\sin (m + 1)x - \sin (m - 1)x)^2 = 4 \cos^2 mx \sin^2 x$.

(b) Does $\lim_{m \to \infty} \cos mx$ exist?

12. By an example, show that the Fourier series of an integrable function on $-\pi \le x \le \pi$ may converge at every point, but the series need not converge uniformly.

13. (a) Show that $\displaystyle\sum_{n=1}^{\infty} \frac{\sin nx}{n} = \frac{\pi - x}{2}$, $0 < x < 2\pi$, in the following way: Integrate equation (32) from π to x obtaining

$$\sum_{n=1}^{j} \frac{\sin nx}{n} - \frac{\pi - x}{2} = \int_{\pi}^{x} \frac{\sin(j + \frac{1}{2})y}{2 \sin(y/2)} dy.$$

Now use the Riemann-Lebesgue Theorem.

(b) Using the uniform convergence proved in Example 3, integrate term by term to establish (10).

14. Establish (10) as follows: Apply Theorem 5.1G in $\mathscr{R}\{0, 2\pi\}$ to show that

$$(\pi - t)^2 = \frac{\pi^2}{3} + \sum_{n=1}^{\infty} \frac{4}{n^2} \cos nt, \quad 0 \le t \le 2\pi.$$

From this, show that $\displaystyle\sum_{1}^{\infty} \frac{1}{n^2} = \frac{\pi^2}{6}$ and (10) holds. (How does this proof of (10) use Theorem 5.6A?)

15. Prove the Riemann-Lebesgue Theorem in the following way: Define $\sigma(x) = 0$ outside of $a \le x \le b$. Write

$$J(y) = \int_{a}^{b} \sigma(t) \sin yt \, dt = \int_{a-\pi/y}^{b-\pi/y} \sigma(t + \pi/y) \sin(yt + \pi)dt$$
$$= -\int_{a-\pi/y}^{b-\pi/y} \sigma(t + \pi/y) \sin yt \, dt.$$

Then $2J = \displaystyle\int_{a}^{b} \sigma(t) \sin yt \, dt - \int_{a-\pi/y}^{b-\pi/y} \sigma(t + \pi/y) \sin yt \, dt$

$= \displaystyle\int_{a}^{a-\pi/y} \sigma(t)\sin yt \, dt + \int_{a-\pi/y}^{b-\pi/y} (\sigma(t) - \sigma(t + \pi/y))\sin yt \, dt$
$$+ \int_{b-\pi/y}^{b} \sigma(t)\sin yt \, dt$$

$= \displaystyle\int_{a}^{a-\pi/y} \sigma(t) \sin yt \, dt + \int_{a}^{b} (\sigma(t - \pi/y) - \sigma(t)) \sin(yt - \pi) \, dt$
$$+ \int_{b-\pi/y}^{b} \sigma(t) \sin yt \, dt.$$

Then

$$|2J| \le \int_{a-\pi/y}^{a} |\sigma(t)| \, dt + \int_{a}^{b} |\sigma(t - \pi/y) - \sigma(t)| \, dt + \int_{b-\pi/y}^{b} |\sigma(t)| \, dt.$$

Now use Exercise 5.2–11.

16. (a) Prove that $\lim\limits_{n\to\infty} \int_a^b |\sin nt|\, dt = \dfrac{2}{\pi}\int_a^b dt$.

Hint: Fix n. If $\mathcal{S}$ is the set of points on the t axis of the form $k\dfrac{\pi}{n}$, $k = 1, 2, 3, \ldots$ and $a_1, a_2, \ldots, a_p$ are the points of $\mathcal{S}$ in the interval $a \le x \le b$, then

$$\int_{a_{j-1}}^{a_j} |\sin nt|\, dt = \frac{2}{n},$$

$$\int_a^b |\sin nt|\, dt = \int_a^{a_1} |\sin nt|\, dt + (p - 1)\frac{2}{\pi}\cdot\frac{\pi}{n} + \int_{a_p}^b |\sin nt|\, dt,$$

$$\int_a^b dt = (p - 1)\frac{\pi}{n} + (a_1 - a) + (b - a_p).$$

(b) Let σ be a step function on $a \le t \le b$. Prove that

$$\lim_{n\to\infty} \int_a^b \sigma(t)|\sin nt|\, dt = \frac{2}{\pi}\int_a^b \sigma(t)dt.$$

(c) Let α be integrable on $a \le t \le b$. Prove that

$$\lim_{n\to\infty} \int_a^b \alpha(t)\,|\sin nt|\, dt = \frac{2}{\pi}\int_a^b \alpha(t)dt,$$

Hint: Choose step function σ so that $\int_a^b |\alpha - \sigma|\, dt < \epsilon$. Write

$$\int_a^b \alpha(t)\,|\sin nt|\, dt - \frac{2}{\pi}\int_a^b \alpha(t)dt$$

$$= \int_a^b (\alpha - \sigma)|\sin nt|\,dt + \int_a^b \sigma|\sin nt|\,dt - \frac{2}{\pi}\int_a^b \sigma\, dt + \frac{2}{\pi}\int_a^b (\sigma - \alpha)dt.$$

17. Verify equation (14) of the text.

18. Show that equation (32),

$$\tfrac{1}{2} + \sum_{n=1}^{j} \cos nu = \frac{\sin(j + \tfrac{1}{2})u}{2\sin u/2}, \qquad u \ne 2n\pi,$$

and also

$$\sum_{n=1}^{j} \sin nu = \frac{\cos u/2 - \cos(j + \tfrac{1}{2})u}{2\sin u/2} = \frac{\sin((j + 1)/2)u \sin ju/2}{\sin u/2}, \qquad u \ne 2n\pi,$$

can be obtained by considering $\sum\limits_{n=1}^{j} e^{inu}$. Use these formulas to show that $\tfrac{1}{2} + \sum\limits_{n=1}^{j} \cos nu$ and $\sum\limits_{n=1}^{j} \sin nu$ are bounded uniformly with respect to n and j in any closed interval within $0 < u < 2\pi$.

19. (a) Prove that $\sum\limits_{n=1}^{\infty} \dfrac{\cos 2nx - \cos 2ny}{n} = \log\sin y - \log\sin x$ for $0 < x < y$ $< \pi$. Hint: Integrate $\sum\limits_{n=1}^{j} \sin 2nu$ between x and y using the result of Exercise 18. Then use the Riemann-Lebesgue Theorem.

(b) Prove (*), $\displaystyle\sum_{n=1}^{\infty} \frac{\cos nx}{n} = -\log\left(2\sin\frac{x}{2}\right), \quad 0 < x < \pi,$

and (**), $\displaystyle\sum_{n=1}^{\infty} \frac{(-1)^n}{n}\cos nx = -\log\left(2\cos\frac{x}{2}\right), \quad 0 < x < \pi.$

Hint: With $c = \displaystyle\sum_{1}^{\infty}\frac{(-1)^n}{n}$, show that $\log\sin y = c - \displaystyle\sum_{1}^{\infty}\frac{\cos 2ny}{n}$,

$\log\sin\dfrac{y}{2} = c - \displaystyle\sum_{1}^{\infty}\frac{\cos ny}{n}, \quad \log\cos\dfrac{x}{2} = c - \displaystyle\sum_{1}^{\infty}\frac{(-1)^n}{n}\cos nx.$ Then

$\log\sin y = \log\sin\dfrac{y}{2} + \log\cos\dfrac{y}{2} + \log 2$ implies

$-2\displaystyle\sum_{1}^{\infty}\frac{\cos 2\,ny}{2n} = -\sum_{1}^{\infty}\frac{\cos ny}{n} - \sum_{1}^{\infty}(-1)^n\frac{\cos ny}{n} + c + \log 2.$

From this, $c = -\log 2$. Finish the proof.

The right side of equation (*) is unbounded on $0 < x < \pi$ and thus is not Riemann integrable. Nevertheless it is "square integrable" in the Lebesgue sense, (*) is valid for $0 < x < 2\pi$, and one can show, using the method of Example 5 and Lebesgue integration theory, that

$$\sum_{1}^{\infty}\frac{a_n}{n} = -\frac{1}{\pi}\int_{0}^{2\pi}\sigma(t)\log\left(2\sin\frac{t}{2}\right)dt, \text{ where } a_n \text{ is given by equation (4).}$$

20. Show that if σ is in $\mathscr{R}\{-\pi, \pi\}$, a_n, b_n are given by (4) and (5), and $c > \dfrac{1}{2}$,

then $\displaystyle\sum_{n=1}^{\infty}\frac{a_n}{n^c}$ and $\displaystyle\sum_{1}^{\infty}\frac{b_n}{n^c}$ are absolutely convergent series.

21. Show that if a trigonometric series converges to σ in $\mathscr{R}\{-\pi, \pi\}$ in the mean square, then the series is the Fourier series for σ.

22. Show that the series $\dfrac{c_0}{2} + \displaystyle\sum_{n=1}^{\infty}(c_n\cos nt + d_n\sin nt)$ is a Fourier series if $\displaystyle\lim_{n\to\infty}n^p c_n$ and $\displaystyle\lim_{n\to\infty}n^p d_n$ are finite for some constant $p > 1$.

23. Use (34) or (32) to show that $\dfrac{1}{\pi}\displaystyle\int_{0}^{\pi}\frac{\sin(j + \frac{1}{2})y}{\sin y/2}dy = 1.$

24. (a) Let σ be continuous and σ' be piecewise continuous on $-\pi \le x \le \pi$ and $\sigma(\pi) = \sigma(-\pi)$. Prove that the Fourier series of σ' can be obtained by differentiating the Fourier series of σ. (No statement is made here concerning the convergence of the differentiated series.)

(b) Show that the series obtained by differentiating the Fourier series of the function $\alpha(x) = x$, $-\pi \le x \le \pi$, never converges.

(c) If, in part (a), σ'' is continuous, will the Fourier series for σ' converge to σ'?

25. Show that the sequence $\{\sin nx\}$ is linearly dense in $\mathscr{R}\{0, \pi\}$. *Hint:* If α is in $\mathscr{R}\{0, \pi\}$, extend it to be odd. Then the Fourier series for α on $-\pi \le x \le \pi$ converges in the mean square to α. Finish the proof.

26. (a) Write the Fourier series for the function $K(t) = \left|\sin\dfrac{t}{2}\right|$, $-\pi \le t \le \pi$.

(b) Solve the integral equation $\displaystyle\int_{-\pi}^{\pi}\left|\sin\frac{x+y}{2}\right|\sigma(y)dy = r\sigma(x)$ by the method of Example 4.

27. Let σ be continuous and σ' piecewise continuous on $-\pi \le x \le \pi$, $\sigma(-\pi)$ $= \sigma(\pi)$. Show that if $\int_{-\pi}^{\pi} \sigma(x)dx = 0$, then $\int_{-\pi}^{\pi} \sigma^2(x)dx \le \int_{-\pi}^{\pi} \sigma'(x)^2 dx$, and the equality holds only if $\sigma = A\cos x + B\sin x$. *Hint:* Use Exercise 24 and the Parseval equality for the Fourier series for σ and σ'.

5.7

COMPLETE

SPACES

A Euclidean vector space $\mathscr{E}$ is said to be **complete** if every Cauchy sequence in $\mathscr{E}$ converges to an element in $\mathscr{E}$. Thus, for every sequence $\{\alpha_i\}$ with $\lim_{i,\,j\to\infty} \|\alpha_i - \alpha_j\| = 0$, there is a β in $\mathscr{E}$ such that $\lim_{i\to\infty} \|\alpha_i - \beta\| = 0$. This property was called the **Cauchy criterion for convergence** in Section 3.1 where it was proved that $\mathscr{E}_n$ and $\mathscr{E}_\infty$ are complete. In particular, both the real and complex number systems are complete. On the other hand, the space $\mathscr{R}\,\{a, b\}$ of real Riemann integrable functions on the interval $a \le x \le b$ is not complete (Exercise 5.7–2).

The intuitive idea of completeness is that the space contains no gaps. If the elements of a sequence "squeeze together" they are converging onto another element of the space. For example, the rational numbers $a_n = 1 + \dfrac{1}{1!} + \dfrac{1}{2!} + \dfrac{1}{3!} + \cdots \dfrac{1}{n!}$ have the property that $\lim_{i,\,j\to\infty} |a_i - a_j| = 0$, but there is no rational number which is the limit of the sequence $\{a_i\}$. The space of rational numbers is not complete. "Completing" the set of rational numbers by adjoining new numbers (irrationals), we obtain the real numbers, a complete space, and we call $\lim_{n\to\infty} a_n = $ e. The addition of these new elements permits us greater ease in formal work. Familiarity with irrational numbers has removed the demand that we check whether or not the answer to a physical problem is rational, for we know that we can approximate an irrational by rationals as closely as we please.

A complete Euclidean vector space is called a **Hilbert space,** named after D. Hilbert who intensively studied $\mathscr{E}_\infty$ in connection with certain problems in integral equations. About 1929, twenty years or so after Hilbert's initial work, it was recognized that the abstract structure of $\mathscr{E}_\infty$, rather than the special character of the elements constituting it, was of major importance.

The idea of completeness of a vector space involves the notion of norm, but not necessarily of inner product. Thus it may be used in vector spaces for which a norm can be defined, although an inner product cannot. A vector space $\mathscr{V}$ is said to be **normed** if we can assign to every element α of $\mathscr{V}$ a real number denoted by $\|\alpha\|$, (**norm** of α), with the properties

1. $\|\alpha\| \geq 0$.

2. $\|\alpha\| = 0$ if and only if $\alpha = \theta$.

3. $\|a\alpha\| = |a| \, \|\alpha\|$ for scalar a.

4. $\|\alpha + \beta\| \leq \|\alpha\| + \|\beta\|$ for every α and β.

In modern mathematics much study has been devoted to complete normed vector spaces, also called **Banach spaces** after S. Banach, who contributed to the initial investigation.

A linear manifold of a complete vector space which is also complete is called a **subspace.** Every subspace of a Banach space is a Banach space. Every subspace of a Hilbert space is a Hilbert space. Every finite dimensional linear manifold of a Banach space is a subspace.

In this section we shall show how to add additional elements, called **ideal elements,** to a normed vector space $\mathscr{V}$ to form a complete normed vector space $\mathscr{B}$, that is, a Banach space. If were $\mathscr{V}$ originally Euclidean, the completed space $\mathscr{B}$ would be a Hilbert space. $\mathscr{V}$ will be dense in $\mathscr{B}$ and hence $\mathscr{B}$ is the closure of $\mathscr{V}$. It is sometimes important to know when an element of $\mathscr{B}$ is also an element of $\mathscr{V}$. But we must also learn to accept conclusions about ideal elements, just as we have learned to accept irrational numbers.

THEOREM 5.7A   Every normed vector space $\mathscr{V}$ can be completed to form a complete normed vector space $\mathscr{B}$ such that $\mathscr{V}$ is dense in $\mathscr{B}$. If $\mathscr{V}$ is Euclidean, $\mathscr{B}$ is a Hilbert space.

Proof   The procedure used is to form a new space $\mathscr{B}$ and show that there is a subset $\mathscr{B}_1$ of $\mathscr{B}$ which has all the properties of $\mathscr{V}$. Then we can identify $\mathscr{B}_1$ with $\mathscr{V}$.

If $\{\alpha_n\}$ and $\{\beta_n\}$ are two Cauchy sequences of elements from $\mathscr{V}$, satisfying $\lim_{n\to\infty} (\alpha_n - \beta_n) = \theta$, then the two sequences $\{\alpha_n\}$ and $\{\beta_n\}$ will be called equivalent. The class of all Cauchy sequences equivalent to $\{\alpha_n\}$ will be denoted by $[\{\alpha_n\}]$. The set of all classes $[\{\alpha_n\}]$ will form the space $\mathscr{B}$. Thus $\mathscr{B}$ is a set of classes of Cauchy sequences.

Let us define the vector operations in $\mathscr{B}$. We define $[\{\alpha_n\}] = [\{\beta_n\}]$ if $\{\alpha_n\}$ is equivalent to $\{\beta_n\}$. For scalar a, we define $a[\{\alpha_n\}] = [\{a\alpha_n\}]$. Addition is defined by $[\{\alpha_n\}] + [\{\beta_n\}] = [\{\alpha_n + \beta_n\}]$. To show that the operations are well defined, it is necessary to show that the definitions are independent of the sequences chosen. Thus, let $[\{\alpha_n\}] = [\{\alpha_n'\}]$ and $[\{\beta_n\}] = [\{\beta_n'\}]$. If

$[\{\alpha_n\}] = [\{\beta_n\}]$, is $[\{\alpha_n'\}] = [\{\beta_n'\}]$? Is $a[\{\alpha_n\}] = a[\{\alpha_n'\}]$? Is $[\{\alpha_n\}] + [\{\beta_n\}]$ $=[\{\alpha_n'\}] + [\{\beta_n'\}]$? These relations are easy to verify.

The zero vector in $\mathscr{B}$ will be denoted by θ, the same notation being used for the zero vector in $\mathscr{V}$. It is defined to be $[\{\theta\}]$ where $\{\theta\}$ is that sequence of vectors in $\mathscr{V}$ all of whose elements are the zero vector.

It is left to the reader to show that the space $\mathscr{B}$ so defined is a vector space.

For every element α in $\mathscr{V}$, the sequence $\{\alpha_n\}$ with $\alpha_n = \alpha$ for every n is a Cauchy sequence. Set up the correspondence

$$(1) \qquad\qquad \alpha \leftrightarrow [\{\alpha_n\}], \qquad \alpha_n = \alpha,$$

and note that this is a one-to-one correspondence between $\mathscr{V}$ and a subset $\mathscr{B}_1$ of $\mathscr{B}$. Moreover this correspondence preserves the operations of scalar multiplication and addition, that is, if also

$$(2) \qquad\qquad \beta \leftrightarrow [\{\beta_n\}], \qquad \beta_n = \beta,$$

then

$$\alpha + \beta \leftrightarrow [\{\alpha_n\}] + [\{\beta_n\}],$$

$$a\beta \leftrightarrow a[\{\beta_n\}].$$

If the norm of $\mathscr{V}$ is defined in terms of an inner product, define the inner product of two elements in $\mathscr{B}$ by

$$(3) \qquad\qquad ([\{\alpha_n\}], [\{\beta_n\}]) = \lim_{n\to\infty} (\alpha_n, \beta_n).$$

To see that this limit exists, write

$$|(\alpha_i, \beta_i) - (\alpha_j, \beta_j)| \le |(\alpha_i, \beta_i - \beta_j)| + |(\alpha_i - \alpha_j, \beta_j)|$$

$$\le \|\alpha_i\| \, \|\beta_i - \beta_j\| + \|\alpha_i - \alpha_j\| \, \|\beta_j\|.$$

The right side approaches zero as i and j approach ∞ since $\{\alpha_n\}$ and $\{\beta_n\}$ are Cauchy sequences, and also are bounded as shown in Section 3.1. The existence of the limit then follows from the Cauchy criterion for scalars. A similar argument establishes the fact that the limit in (3) is independent of the sequences chosen from $[\{\alpha_n\}]$ and $[\{\beta_n\}]$.

The operation of taking the inner product is preserved under the correspondence given by (1). Indeed, if (1) and (2) hold,

$$([\{\alpha_n\}], [\{\beta_n\}]) = \lim_{n\to\infty} (\alpha_n, \beta_n) = (\alpha, \beta).$$

One must verify that the inner product so defined is a true inner product, as defined in Section 1.1.

However, if the norm in $\mathscr{V}$ is not defined by an inner product, define

$$(4) \qquad \|[\{\alpha_n\}]\| = \lim_{n \to \infty} \|\alpha_n\|.$$

This definition agrees with the definition (3) in case the norm is defined by an inner product. The limit in (4) exists since

$$\Big| \|\alpha_n\| - \|\alpha_m\| \Big| \le \|\alpha_n - \alpha_m\|$$

and $\{\alpha_n\}$ is a Cauchy sequence. A similar inequality establishes the fact that the limit in (4) is independent of the sequence chosen from $[\{\alpha_n\}]$. The operation of taking the norm is preserved under (1), since $\alpha_n = \alpha$ implies

$$\|[\{\alpha_n\}]\| = \lim_{n \to \infty} \|\alpha_n\| = \lim_{n \to \infty} \|\alpha\| = \|\alpha\|.$$

One must verify that the norm so defined for $\mathscr{B}$ is a true norm, as defined at the beginning of this section.

It now follows that $\mathscr{B}_1$ has exactly the properties of $\mathscr{V}$. We may identify $\mathscr{B}_1$ and $\mathscr{V}$ and say $\mathscr{V}$ is embedded in $\mathscr{B}$.

We will show that $\mathscr{B}_1$ is dense in $\mathscr{B}$. Let $[\{\alpha_n\}]$ be any element of $\mathscr{B}$. Define $\sigma_{ij} = \alpha_j$ for every i. Thus, for fixed j, $[\{\sigma_{ij}\}]$ is in $\mathscr{B}_1$. We intend to prove

$$[\{\alpha_n\}] = \lim_{j \to \infty} [\{\sigma_{ij}\}].$$

For fixed j, the sequence $\{\alpha_i - \alpha_j\}$ is a Cauchy sequence. We have seen above that the limit of the norms of the elements of a Cauchy sequence exists. Thus there exists

$$\lim_{i \to \infty} \|\alpha_i - \alpha_j\| \le \epsilon, \qquad j \ge N.$$

That is,

$$\lim_{i \to \infty} \|\alpha_i - \sigma_{ij}\| \le \epsilon, \qquad j \ge N.$$

Hence

$$\|[\{\alpha_i\}] - [\{\sigma_{ij}\}]\| = \lim_{i \to \infty} \|\alpha_i - \sigma_{ij}\| \le \epsilon, \qquad j \ge N.$$

This proves $\mathscr{B}_1$ is dense in $\mathscr{B}$.

It remains to show that $\mathscr{B}$ is complete. Let $[\{\alpha_{ni}\}]$, $i = 1, 2, \ldots$, be a Cauchy sequence in $\mathscr{B}$. Thus if $\epsilon > 0$ there is an integer $N = N(\epsilon)$ such that $i \ge N$, $j \ge N$ imply $\|[\{\alpha_{ni}\}] - [\{\alpha_{nj}\}]\| = \lim_{n \to \infty} \|\alpha_{ni} - \alpha_{nj}\| \le \epsilon$. Hence for each i and j, $i \ge N$, $j \ge N$, there is an integer $M(i, j)$ such that

$$\|\alpha_{ni} - \alpha_{nj}\| \le 2\epsilon \qquad \text{when } n \ge M(i, j).$$

Since $\{\alpha_{ni}\}$ is a Cauchy sequence for fixed i, there is an integer $Q(i) > i$ such that

$$\|\alpha_{ni} - \alpha_{mi}\| \leq \epsilon \qquad \text{whenever } n \geq Q, m \geq Q.$$

Note that the sequence $\{\beta_i\} = \{\alpha_{Q(i),i}\}$ is a Cauchy sequence. In fact, whenever $i \geq N, j \geq N$ we need only select $m > \max \{Q(i), Q(j), M(i,j)\}$ and have

$$\|\alpha_{Q(i),i} - \alpha_{Q(j),j}\|$$

$$\leq \|\alpha_{Q(i),i} - \alpha_{mi}\| + \|\alpha_{mi} - \alpha_{mj}\| + \|\alpha_{mj} - \alpha_{Q(j),j}\|$$

$$\leq \epsilon + 2\epsilon + \epsilon.$$

The completeness of $\mathscr{B}$ will be shown when we verify

$$[\{\beta_n\}] = \lim_{i \to \infty} [\{\alpha_{ni}\}],$$

that is, when for $\epsilon > 0$ and for all sufficiently large i,

$$\|[\{\beta_n\}] - [\{\alpha_{ni}\}]\| = \lim_{n \to \infty} \|\beta_n - \alpha_{ni}\| \leq \epsilon.$$

Fix $i \geq N(\epsilon), n > Q(i), j > \max \{Q(n), Q(i), M(n,i)\}$. We have

$$\|\beta_n - \alpha_{ni}\| = \|\alpha_{Q(n),n} - \alpha_{ni}\| \leq$$

$$\|\alpha_{Q(n),n} - \alpha_{jn}\| + \|\alpha_{jn} - \alpha_{ji}\| + \|\alpha_{ji} - \alpha_{ni}\|$$

$$\leq \epsilon + 2\epsilon + \epsilon = 4\epsilon.$$

Therefore for $i \geq N(\epsilon), \lim_{n \to \infty} \|\beta_n - \alpha_{ni}\| \leq 4\epsilon$. This completes the proof of the theorem. $\star$

The next two theorems are valid in Hilbert space, but not in arbitrary Euclidean spaces.

THEOREM 5.7B Let $\{\alpha_n\}$ be an orthonormal sequence in a Hilbert space $\mathscr{H}$. Then $\alpha = \sum_1^\infty a_n \alpha_n$ is an element of $\mathscr{H}$ if and only if $\sum_1^\infty |a_n|^2 < \infty$. In this case, $a_n = (\alpha, \alpha_n)$.

Proof For $n > m$,

$$(5) \qquad \|\sum_{j=1}^n a_j \alpha_j - \sum_{j=1}^m a_j \alpha_j\| = \|\sum_{j=m+1}^n a_j \alpha_j\| = \sum_{j=m+1}^n |a_j|^2.$$

Thus $\{\sum_1^n a_j \alpha_j\}$ is a Cauchy sequence if and only if $\sum_1^n |a_j|^2$ converges. Since a sequence of elements of $\mathscr{H}$ converges if and only if the sequence is a Cauchy sequence, it follows that $\alpha = \lim_{n=\infty} \sum_{j=1}^n a_j \alpha_j$ exists if and only if $\sum_1^\infty |a_j|^2 < \infty$. Then

$$(\alpha, \alpha_n) = \left(\sum_{j=1}^\infty a_j \alpha_j, \alpha_n\right) = \sum_{j=1}^\infty a_j (\alpha_j, \alpha_n) = a_n. \quad \star$$

THEOREM 5.7C   Let $\{\alpha_n\}$ be an orthonormal sequence in a Hilbert space $\mathscr{H}$. Suppose that α is the zero vector whenever $(\alpha, \alpha_n) = 0$ for all n. Then the sequence $\{\alpha_n\}$ is linearly dense in $\mathscr{H}$.

Proof   Let β be any element in $\mathscr{H}$. By Bessel's inequality, $\sum_{n=1}^\infty |(\beta, \alpha_n)|^2$ $< \infty$ and so $\sum_{n=1}^\infty (\beta, \alpha_n) \alpha_n$ is in $\mathscr{H}$ as proved in Theorem 5.7B. We find

$$\left(\beta - \sum_{n=1}^\infty (\beta, \alpha_n) \alpha_n, \alpha_k\right) = 0 \text{ for all } k.$$

By hypothesis, $\beta - \sum_{n=1}^\infty (\beta, \alpha_n) \alpha_n = \theta$. This proves $\{\alpha_n\}$ is linearly dense in $\mathscr{H}$. $\star$

Just as vectors in finite dimensional spaces can be represented as n-tuples of numbers, so vectors in certain infinite dimensional spaces can be represented as infinite sequences of numbers.

THEOREM 5.7D   If $\mathscr{H}$ is a real (or complex) Hilbert space and if there exists a sequence $\{\alpha_n\}$, $n = 1, 2, 3, \ldots$, of orthonormal vectors of $\mathscr{H}$ which is linearly dense in $\mathscr{H}$, then there is a one-to-one correspondence between the elements of $\mathscr{H}$ and of $\mathscr{E}_\infty$ (or $\mathscr{E}_\infty^*$) preserving the operations of addition, multiplication by scalars, and inner product.

Proof   Every vector α in $\mathscr{H}$ may be written uniquely in the form

$$\alpha = \sum_{i=1}^\infty a_i \alpha_i, \quad \sum_{i=1}^\infty |a_i|^2 < \infty, \quad a_i = (\alpha, \alpha_i).$$

We therefore set up the correspondence

$$\alpha \leftrightarrow [a_1, a_2, \ldots]$$

carrying elements of $\mathcal{H}$ into elements of $\mathcal{E}_\infty$ (or $\mathcal{E}_\infty^*$). In view of Theorem 5.7B, the range of the mapping is all of $\mathcal{E}_\infty$ (or $\mathcal{E}_\infty^*$) and also the correspondence is one-to-one.

If $\alpha = \sum a_i \alpha_i$, $\beta = \sum\limits_{i=1}^{\infty} b_i \alpha_i$, and c is a scalar, then

$$\alpha + \beta = \sum_{i=1}^{\infty} (a_i + b_i) \alpha_i \leftrightarrow [a_1 + b_1, a_2 + b_2, \dots]$$

$$= [a_1, a_2, \dots] + [b_1, b_2, \dots],$$

$$c\alpha = \sum_{i=1}^{\infty} ca_i \alpha_i \leftrightarrow [ca_1, ca_2, \dots]$$

$$= c[a_1, a_2, \dots],$$

$$(\alpha, \beta) = \sum_{i=1}^{\infty} (\alpha, \alpha_i)(\alpha_i, \beta) = \sum_{i=1}^{\infty} a_i \bar{b}_i, \text{ the inner product of the representa-}$$

tions of α and β in $\mathcal{E}_\infty$ (or $\mathcal{E}_\infty^*$). ★

Although the previous theorem shows that $\mathcal{E}_\infty$ ($\mathcal{E}_\infty^*$) is the prototype of all separable Hilbert spaces (see Exercise 5.1–7), it is often more convenient to treat such spaces abstractly, rather than consider their representations in $\mathcal{E}_\infty$ ($\mathcal{E}_\infty^*$).

The next theorem indicates that bounded linear transformations defined on normed linear vector spaces may have their domain of definition extended to the completed space.

THEOREM 5.7E Every bounded linear transformation L on a normed vector space $\mathcal{V}$ to another such space $\mathcal{V}_1$ can be uniquely extended onto the completion $\mathcal{B}$ of $\mathcal{V}$ so that it remains linear and bounded. The norm of the extension will be that of L. The range of L will be in the completion $\mathcal{B}_1$ of $\mathcal{V}_1$.

Proof Each element α of $\mathcal{B}$ is a limit of elements α_n in $\mathcal{V}$. Hence $\{\alpha_n\}$ is a Cauchy sequence. Moreover

$$\|L\alpha_n - L\alpha_m\| \le \|L\| \|\alpha_n - \alpha_m\|$$

indicates $\{L\alpha_n\}$ is a Cauchy sequence in $\mathcal{V}_1$ and so has a limit σ in $\mathcal{B}_1$, the completion of $\mathcal{V}_1$. If $\{\beta_n\}$ is another sequence in $\mathcal{V}$ converging to α, then the sequence

$$\alpha_1, \beta_1, \alpha_2, \beta_2, \alpha_3, \beta_3, \dots$$

also converges to α and the above proof shows that

$$L\alpha_1, L\beta_1, L\alpha_2, L\beta_2, \dots$$

also converges, and hence converges to σ. It follows that the transformation $\sigma = L\alpha$ is well defined. It is easily seen to be linear. From the relationship

$$\|L\alpha_n\| \leq \|L\| \, \|\alpha_n\|$$

we obtain $\|L\alpha\| \leq \|L\| \, \|\alpha\|$. To prove L is unique, suppose M is a bounded linear transformation on $\mathscr{B}$ agreeing with L on $\mathscr{V}$. Then, if α is in $\mathscr{B}$ and $\{\alpha_n\}$ in $\mathscr{V}$ converges to α we use the continuity of L and M to show

$$L\alpha = \lim_{n\to\infty} L\alpha_n = \lim_{n\to\infty} M\alpha_n = M\alpha. \quad \star$$

It is a natural question to ask whether an operator T on a Euclidean vector space $\mathscr{V}$ to $\mathscr{V}$, where $\mathscr{V}$ contains an orthonormal basis $\{\alpha_n\}$, can be represented by an infinite matrix. Since

$$T\alpha_i = \sum_{j=1}^{\infty} t_{ji} \, \alpha_j$$

we may, as in the finite dimensional case, set up the correspondence

(6) $$T \overset{\alpha}{\leftrightarrow} [t_{ij}], \qquad t_{ji} = (T\alpha_i, \alpha_j).$$

thus representing T by an infinite matrix in terms of the α basis.

EXAMPLE 1   Consider the linear manifold of real functions α with continuous derivatives on $-\infty < x < \infty$ satisfying

$$\int_{-\infty}^{\infty} \alpha(x)^2 dx < \infty, \qquad \int_{-\infty}^{\infty} \alpha'(x)^2 dx < \infty,$$

and inner product defined by

$$(\alpha, \beta) = \int_{-\infty}^{\infty} \alpha(x) \, \beta(x) \, dx.$$

Define

$$T\,\alpha(x) = \alpha'(x).$$

The normalized Hermite functions $\alpha_n = E_n(x)$, $n = 0, 1, 2, \ldots$ form a linearly dense orthonormal sequence. By Exercise 5.5–9, we find

$$E_0'(x) = -\frac{1}{\sqrt{2}} E_1(x),$$

$$E_n'(x) = \sqrt{\frac{n}{2}} E_{n-1}(x) - \sqrt{\frac{n+1}{2}} E_{n+1}(x), \qquad n \geq 1,$$

so that, if δ_{-1j} is defined to be 0, we may write

$$t_{ji} = (T\alpha_i, \alpha_j) = (E'_i, E_j)$$

$$= \sqrt{\frac{i}{2}} \int_{-\infty}^{\infty} E_{i-1}(x)\, E_j(x)dx - \sqrt{\frac{i+1}{2}} \int_{-\infty}^{\infty} E_{i+1}(x)\, E_j(x)dx$$

$$= \sqrt{\frac{i}{2}}\, \delta_{i-1,j} - \sqrt{\frac{i+1}{2}}\, \delta_{i+1,j}, \qquad i,j = 0, 1, 2, \ldots,$$

and the representation of the differentiation operator in this basis is

$$(7) \quad \frac{d}{dt} \leftrightarrow \frac{1}{\sqrt{2}} \begin{bmatrix} 0 & \sqrt{1} & 0 & 0 & 0 & \ldots \\ -\sqrt{1} & 0 & \sqrt{2} & 0 & 0 & \ldots \\ 0 & -\sqrt{2} & 0 & \sqrt{3} & 0 & \ldots \\ 0 & 0 & -\sqrt{3} & 0 & \sqrt{4} & \ldots \\ 0 & 0 & 0 & -\sqrt{4} & 0 & \ldots \\ \vdots & \vdots & & & & \end{bmatrix}.$$

The transformation (6) associates with each linear transformation an infinite matrix. However not every infinite matrix gives rise, by (6), to a linear transformation. That is, for given $[t_{ij}]$, there may be no linear operator T with $t_{ji} = (T\alpha_i, \alpha_j)$. This may be seen by choosing t_{ji} so that $\sum_{j=1}^{\infty} |t_{ji}|^2$ diverges, yet we know that the sum of the squares of the Fourier coefficients of $T\alpha_i$ must converge. The kind of restrictive conditions needed are indicated by the next theorem.

THEOREM 5.7F Let $\{\alpha_n\}$ be an orthonormal basis in a Hilbert space $\mathscr{H}$. Then the transformation (6) defines a one-to-one correspondence between the class of all bounded linear operators on $\mathscr{H}$ to $\mathscr{H}$ and the class of all infinite matrices $[t_{ij}]$ with the property

$$(8) \qquad \sum_{j=1}^{\infty} \left| \sum_{i=1}^{\infty} t_{ji}\, b_i \right|^2 \le c \sum_{i=1}^{\infty} |b_i|^2$$

for some constant c and all sequences $\{b_i\}$ with $\sum_{i=1}^{\infty} |b_i|^2 < \infty$.

Proof If T is a bounded operator and $\sum\limits_{i=1}^{\infty} |b_i|^2 < \infty$, then $\beta = \sum\limits_{i=1}^{\infty} b_i\,\alpha_i$ is in $\mathscr{H}$ and, by Theorem 5.1A,

$$(T\beta,\,\alpha_j) = \left(T \sum_{i=1}^{\infty} b_i\,\alpha_i,\,\alpha_j\right) = \sum_{i=1}^{\infty} b_i\,(T\alpha_i,\,\alpha_j) = \sum_{i=1}^{\infty} b_i\,t_{ji}.$$

Parseval's equality states

$$\sum_{j=1}^{\infty} \left| \sum_{i=1}^{\infty} t_{ji}\,b_i \right|^2 = \|T\beta\|^2 \le \|T\|^2\,\|\beta\|^2$$

Hence $\|T\|^2$ serves as c.

Conversely, suppose (8) is valid. For fixed k, let $b_i = \delta_{ik}$. We obtain from (8),

$$\sum_{j=1}^{\infty} \left| t_{jk} \right|^2 \le c \qquad \text{for } k = 1, 2, \ldots.$$

Therefore $\sum\limits_{j=1}^{\infty} t_{jk}\,\alpha_j$ is in $\mathscr{H}$. Define the operator T by

$$T\,\alpha_k = \sum_{j=1}^{\infty} t_{jk}\,\alpha_j,$$

$$T\left(\sum_{j=1}^{N} a_j\,\alpha_j\right) = \sum_{j=1}^{N} a_j\,T\alpha_j.$$

This defines a linear operator T on the linear manifold $\mathscr{S}$ generated by $\{\alpha_n\}$. We have

(9) $$(T\alpha_k,\,\alpha_i) = \left(\sum_{j=1}^{\infty} t_{jk}\,\alpha_j,\,\alpha_i\right) = t_{ik}.$$

If $\beta = \sum\limits_{=1}^{N} a_j\,\alpha_j$, then

$$T\beta = \sum_{j=1}^{N} a_j\,T\alpha_j = \sum_{j=1}^{N} a_j \sum_{i=1}^{\infty} t_{ij}\,\alpha_i = \sum_{i=1}^{\infty} \sum_{j=1}^{N} a_j\,t_{ij}\,\alpha_i$$

so that

$$\|T\beta\|^2 = \sum_{i=1}^{\infty} \left| \sum_{j=1}^{N} t_{ij}\,a_j \right|^2 \le c \sum_{j=1}^{N} \left| a_j \right|^2 = c\|\beta\|^2.$$

This proves that T is bounded on $\mathscr{S}$. But $\mathscr{S}$ is dense in $\mathscr{H}$ and so, in view of Theorem 5.7E, T can be extended with the same bound to $\mathscr{H}$. Moreover,

T is the only bounded operator on $\mathcal{H}$ to $\mathcal{H}$ with property (9). For suppose L is another bounded operator with

$$(L\alpha_k, \alpha_i) = (T\alpha_k, \alpha_i), \qquad i, k = 1, 2, 3, \ldots .$$

Then $L\alpha_k = T\alpha_k$ by Theorem 5.1D. Hence for any $\sigma = \sum_{i=1}^{\infty} d_i \alpha_i$ in $\mathcal{H}$, we have

$$L\sigma = \sum_{i=1}^{\infty} d_i L\alpha_i = \sum_{i=1}^{\infty} d_i T\alpha_i = T\sigma. \quad \bigstar$$

THEOREM 5.7G The class of bounded linear operators on the Euclidean vector space $\mathscr{E}$ to $\mathscr{E}$ forms a vector space. If c is a scalar and $[A]$, $[B]$ are the matrix representations, with respect to an orthonormal basis $\{\alpha_n\}$, of the bounded operators A and B, then the matrix representations of cA, $A + B$, and AB in this basis are $c[A]$, $[A] + [B]$, $[A][B]$. If $\beta = \sum_{i=1}^{\infty} b_i \alpha_i$ is in $\mathscr{E}$, and $A \overset{\alpha}{\leftrightarrow} [a_{ij}]$, then $A\beta$ has the representation $[a_{ij}][b_i]$, where multiplication of matrices is defined as in the finite case.

Proof When A, B are bounded linear operators, so are O, I, cA for scalar c, $A + B$, and even AB. Thus the class of linear bounded operators on $\mathscr{E}$ to $\mathscr{E}$ forms a vector space. Let us find the matrix representation of $AB = C$ when

$$A \overset{\alpha}{\leftrightarrow} [a_{ij}], \quad B \overset{\alpha}{\leftrightarrow} [b_{ij}], \quad C \overset{\alpha}{\leftrightarrow} [c_{ij}].$$

Applying Theorem 5.1A,

$$c_{ij} = (AB\,\alpha_j, \alpha_i) = \left(A \sum_{n=1}^{\infty} b_{nj} \alpha_n, \alpha_i \right)$$

$$= \left(\sum_{n=1}^{\infty} b_{nj} A\alpha_n, \alpha_i \right) = \sum_{n=1}^{\infty} b_{nj} (A\alpha_n, \alpha_i) = \sum_{n=1}^{\infty} a_{in} b_{nj}.$$

This proves that $[c_{ij}] = [a_{ij}][b_{ij}]$. Also $A\beta = A(\sum_{i=1}^{\infty} b_i \alpha_i) = \sum_{i=1}^{\infty} b_i A\alpha_i$. If $A\beta = \sum_{i=1}^{\infty} d_i \alpha_i$ we find

$$(A\beta, \alpha_j) = \left(\sum_{i=1}^{\infty} d_i \alpha_i, \alpha_j \right) = d_j$$

and

$$(A\beta, \alpha_j) = \left(\sum_{i=1}^{\infty} b_i A\alpha_i, \alpha_j \right) = \sum_{i=1}^{\infty} b_i (A\alpha_i, \alpha_j) = \sum_{i=1}^{\infty} a_{ji} b_i.$$

This proves that

$$A\beta \leftrightarrow [d_i] = [a_{ij}][b_i]. \quad \bigstar$$

In view of the theorems already proved, it is evident that we may suppose, when discussing bounded linear operators, that the domain is a complete space. A general theory for bounded symmetric operators on a Hilbert space $\mathcal{H}$ to $\mathcal{H}$ has been developed. Many linear transformations, however, are not bounded. Indeed in many situations, the transformation may be defined only for a linear manifold in a Euclidean vector space $\mathcal{E}$. Consider, for example, the operator L defined by

$$L\alpha = \alpha'$$

for the linear manifold of continuously differentiable functions in $\mathcal{R}\{-\pi, \pi\}$. It is not bounded, for if $\alpha_n = \sin nx$, then $\|\alpha_n\| = \sqrt{\pi}$ while $\|L\alpha_n\| = n\sqrt{\pi}$, and there is no constant c such that $\|L\alpha\| \leq c\|\alpha\|$ for all α in the domain of definition of L. In general, it is true that the domain of definition of an unbounded symmetric operator cannot be a complete space for it is possible to prove that a linear symmetric operator defined for all elements of a Hilbert space is bounded.

In the next chapter we shall study some simple unbounded operators.

Exercise 5.7

1. (a) Show that the sequence $\{\alpha_n\}$ defined below is a Cauchy sequence in $\mathcal{C}\{0, 1\}$. (Example 2, Sec. 1.1.)

$$\alpha_n(t) = \begin{cases} 0, & 0 \leq t \leq \dfrac{1}{2} - \dfrac{1}{2n}, \\[2mm] n\left(t - \dfrac{1}{2}\right) + 1, & \dfrac{1}{2} - \dfrac{1}{2n} \leq t \leq \dfrac{1}{2} + \dfrac{1}{2n}, \\[2mm] 1, & \dfrac{1}{2} + \dfrac{1}{2n} \leq t \leq 1. \end{cases}$$

   (b) Show that there is no β in $\mathcal{C}$ such that $\lim \|\alpha_n - \beta\| = 0$. *Hint:* If $r > 0$, $\{\alpha_n\}$ converges uniformly on $0 \leq t \leq \frac{1}{2} - r$, $\frac{1}{2} + r \leq t \leq 1$. If there exists β such that $\lim \|\alpha_n - \beta\| = 0$, show that $\beta(t) = 0$ for $0 \leq t < \frac{1}{2}$ and $\beta(t) = 1$ for $\frac{1}{2} < t \leq 1$. Thus β is not in $\mathcal{C}$.

2. (a) Show that the sequence $\{\alpha_n\}$ defined below is a Cauchy sequence in $\mathcal{R}\{0, 1\}$.

$$\alpha_n(t) = \begin{cases} n^{1/4}, & 0 \leq t \leq \dfrac{1}{n}, \\[2mm] t^{-1/4}, & \dfrac{1}{n} \leq t \leq 1. \end{cases}$$

   (b) Show that there is no β in $\mathcal{R}$ such that $\lim_{n \to \infty} \|\alpha_n - \beta\| = 0$.

3. Show that, in any Euclidean vector space,

$$\|\alpha - \beta\|^2 + \|\alpha + \beta\|^2 = 2\|\alpha\|^2 + 2\|\beta\|^2.$$

Interpret this relation geometrically for vectors in the plane.

4. Consider the space of real continuous functions α defined on $0 \le x \le 1$ with $\|\alpha\| = $ l.u.b. $\{ \, |\alpha(t)| \mid 0 \le t \le 1 \}$. Show that this is a true norm. Show that the space so defined is complete. Show that the property expressed in Exercise 3 does not hold for the norm here defined. We have then an example of a Banach space which is not a Hilbert space having the same norm.

5. Let $\mathscr{E}$ be the space of functions having a continuous derivative on $a \le t \le b$. Define $\|\alpha\|^2 = |\alpha(a)|^2 + \int_a^b |\alpha'(t)|^2 \, dt$. Show that this is a true norm. Show that $\lim_{n \to 0} \|\alpha_n - \beta\| = 0$ implies $\lim_{n \to 0} \alpha_n(t) = \beta(t)$ uniformly on $a \le t \le b$.

6. Let $\mathscr{E}$ be the space of complex numbers $z = x + iy$. Define $\|z\| = |x| + |y|$. Show that this is a true norm. Show that $\mathscr{E}$ is not a Euclidean vector space with this norm.

7. Let $\{ \alpha_n \}$ be a sequence of orthonormal vectors linearly dense in a Euclidean vector space $\mathscr{E}$. Show that $\{ \alpha_n \}$ is linearly dense in the completion of $\mathscr{E}$.

8. (a) Use Theorem 5.7B to show that $\sum\limits_{1}^{\infty} \left(\dfrac{\cos nx}{n^{3/4}} - \dfrac{\sin nx}{n^{5/7}} \right)$ is the Fourier series of an element in the completion of $\mathscr{R}\{ -\pi, \pi \}$.

    (b) Show that $\lim\limits_{j \to \infty} \int_{-\pi}^{\pi} \left(\sum\limits_{n=j}^{j+k} \dfrac{\cos nx}{n^{3/4}} - \dfrac{\sin nx}{n^{5/7}} \right)^2 dx = 0$.

9. Give an example of a subspace of a Hilbert space $\mathscr{H}$ such that the subspace is infinite dimensional but does not contain all elements of $\mathscr{H}$.

10. If L is bounded and symmetric on a Euclidean vector space $\mathscr{E}$, show that its extension to the completion of $\mathscr{E}$ is also symmetric.

11. (a) Using Exercise 5.5–9 and the Hermite functions $\{ E_n \}$ as a basis show that the operator M defined over the linear manifold of functions α in $\mathscr{R}_2\{ -\infty, \infty \}$ with two continuous derivatives and with

$$\int_{-\infty}^{\infty} t^4 \, \alpha^2(t) \, dt < \infty \quad \text{by}$$

$$M\alpha(t) = t\alpha(t)$$

has a representation

$$M \leftrightarrow \frac{1}{\sqrt{2}} \begin{bmatrix} 0 & \sqrt{1} & 0 & 0 & \cdots \\ \sqrt{1} & 0 & \sqrt{2} & 0 & \\ 0 & \sqrt{2} & 0 & \sqrt{3} & \\ 0 & 0 & \sqrt{3} & 0 & \\ & \cdot & & & \\ & \cdot & & & \\ & \cdot & & & \end{bmatrix}.$$

    (b) Show that M and the operator $L = d/dt$ given by equation (7) satisfy $LM - ML = I$, both from their definitions and from their representation as matrices.

(c) Express $t^2 E_n$ and E_n'' in terms of E_n using Exercise 5.5–9, and find the representation of the operators P and Q defined by

$$(P\alpha)(t) = t^2\alpha(t), \qquad (Q\alpha)(t) = \alpha''(t).$$

By addition show that the representation of $-Q + P$ is

$$\begin{bmatrix} 1 & 0 & 0 & 0 & \cdots \\ 0 & 3 & 0 & 0 & \\ 0 & 0 & 5 & 0 & \\ 0 & 0 & 0 & 7 & \\ \cdot & & & & \\ \cdot & & & & \\ \cdot & & & & \end{bmatrix}.$$

Is there any relationship between the above representation and the fact that the Hermite functions satisfy the differential equation

$$\left(-\frac{d^2}{dt^2} + t^2 \right) E_n = (2n + 1)E_n?$$

(d) We have $LM - ML = I$. Can such an equation be true for finite matrices? *Hint:* See Example 3 of Section 2.6.

(e) Show that the operator $-\dfrac{d^2}{dt^2} + t^2$ in part (c) is unbounded.

A Differential Operator

6.1

PHYSICAL

BACKGROUND

Mathematical theories often are generalizations obtained from consideration of specific problems. The advantage of the generalization is that the theory may then be applied to many problems having the same formal structure. However, even when attention is focused upon the mathematical discipline, it is worthwhile to discuss some of the problems whose formulation led to a study of the theory, not only to obtain historical perspective and to motivate the procedure, but also to indicate why interrelationships between various aspects of the theory are to be expected.

In the previous chapter we studied the representation of a given function as an infinite series, whose terms were constant multiples of the members of a special orthonormal sequence. By considering the differential equations associated with particular physical problems, we will show in this section that orthonormal sequences, and the desirability of expansion of a given function in terms of the members of the orthonormal sequences, originate in a natural manner. These examples will serve to introduce us to the study of a differential operator associated with a linear second order differential equation and certain boundary conditions.

6.1.1 The Vibrating String

The phenomenon of the vibrating string was subjected to analysis as early as the sixteenth century. Let us consider a string of finite or infinite length, restricted to move in the x, y plane, whose density per unit length is ρ, and whose displacement from the x axis at time t is represented by $y(x, t)$. Let us suppose that the string is vibrating under tension and there are no external forces. If we assume that the tension vector has constant length τ and is tangent to the string and that $\left(\dfrac{\partial y}{\partial x}\right)^2$ is so small that it may be neglected, we can show, by an application of Newton's laws to an element of the string, that the motion is characterized by the differential equation

(1) $$\frac{\partial^2 y}{\partial x^2} = \frac{1}{c^2}\frac{\partial^2 y}{\partial t^2}, \qquad c = \sqrt{\frac{\tau}{\rho}}.$$

Consider the case when the string is fixed at $x = 0$ and $x = L$ and is released from rest from the initial position $h(x)$. Then the motion is restricted to satisfy (1) and

(2) $$y(0, t) = 0 = y(L, t),$$

(3) $$y(x, 0) = h(x),$$

(4) $$\frac{\partial y}{\partial t}(x, 0) = 0.$$

We shall employ the **method of separation of variables,** that is, we shall seek nonidentically zero functions of the form

(5) $$y(x, t) = X(x)\,T(t)$$

which satisfy (1) and try to obtain a solution of (1), (2), (3), (4) as an infinite series whose terms are of type (5). Substituting (5) into (1), we get

(6) $$\frac{1}{X}\frac{d^2X}{dx^2} = \frac{1}{c^2 T}\frac{d^2 T}{dt^2},$$

where the left side is independent of t, the right side of x. Hence both sides are independent of x and t, and may be set equal to a constant k. Thus we are led to solve

(7) $$\begin{cases} X'' - kX = 0, \\ X(0) = X(L) = 0, \end{cases}$$

and

(8) $$\begin{cases} T'' - kc^2 T = 0, \\ T'(0) = 0, \end{cases}$$

where the boundary conditions in (7) and (8) are obtained by imposing (2) and (4) on (5). If k is zero or positive it is easily seen that a nonzero solution of (7) cannot exist. We therefore write $k = -p^2$ and obtain a solution of (7) as

$$X(x) = A \sin px, \quad p = \frac{n\pi}{L}, \quad n \text{ a positive integer.}$$

We may omit negative values of n since $\sin \dfrac{-n\pi}{L} = -\sin \dfrac{n\pi}{L}$ and the minus

sign can be absorbed in the constant A. Then a solution of (8) is

$$T = B \cos \frac{n\pi ct}{L}, \quad B \text{ constant.}$$

It follows that a solution of (1), (2), (4) is given by

(9) $$y(x, t) = D \sin \frac{n\pi x}{L} \cos \frac{n\pi ct}{L},$$

for every value of D and every positive integral value of n. As a solution for
the motion of the vibrating string we shall try

(10) $$y(x, t) = \sum_{n=1}^{\infty} A_n \sin \frac{n\pi x}{L} \cos \frac{n\pi ct}{L}.$$

This function will satisfy (2) and also (1) and (4) if the series can be differentiated twice term by term. Moreover, (3) will be satisfied if

(11) $$\sum_{n=1}^{\infty} A_n \sin \frac{n\pi x}{L} = h(x),$$

that is, if the left side of (11) is the Fourier Sine series of h. We therefore
expect that (10) will be a solution, representing the motion of the string, if A_n
is chosen as

(12) $$A_n = \frac{2}{L} \int_0^L h(x) \sin \frac{n\pi x}{L} \, dx.$$

To make the analysis rigorous, assume $h(x)$ has continuous second
derivatives on $0 \leq x \leq L$, $h(0) = h(L) = 0$, $h''_+(0) = h''_-(L) = 0$, and extend
$h(x)$ to be an odd periodic function of period $2L$. Then $h(x)$ has continuous
second derivatives on $-\infty < x < \infty$. (Exercise 6.1–1.)

Form the series (10) where A_n is given by (12). When $t = 0$, the series in
(10) is the Fourier series on $-L \leq x \leq L$ for the function h and so converges
absolutely uniformly to h by Theorem 5.6C. Thus (11) is satisfied. Since
$\left| \cos \dfrac{n\pi ct}{L} \right| \leq 1$, the series in (10) converges absolutely uniformly. Since

$$2 \sin \frac{n\pi x}{L} \cos \frac{n\pi ct}{L} = \sin \frac{n\pi}{L}(x - ct) + \sin \frac{n\pi}{L}(x + ct),$$

we can write (10) as

$$y(x, t) = \frac{1}{2} \sum_{n=1}^{\infty} A_n \sin \frac{n\pi}{L} (x - ct) + \frac{1}{2} \sum_{n=1}^{\infty} A_n \sin \frac{n\pi}{L} (x + ct),$$

that is,

(13) $$y(x, t) = \frac{1}{2} h(x - ct) + \frac{1}{2} h(x + ct).$$

Differentiation of (13) shows that (1) and (4) are satisfied. Clearly (2) and (3) are satisfied and (10) is a solution of the problem.

To establish the uniqueness of the solution, we return to a consideration of equation (1). Under the change of variables

$$r = x - ct, \qquad s = x + ct,$$

equation (1) is transformed into

(14) $$\frac{\partial^2 y}{\partial r \partial s} = 0,$$

whose solution is

$$y = f(r) + g(s)$$

for arbitrary functions f and g. Expressed in terms of the original variables, the last equation is

(15) $$y(x, t) = f(x - ct) + g(x + ct).$$

The function $h(x)$ is defined only on $0 \leq x \leq L$, but we may consider it to be defined for all x, the explicit extension being reserved for the moment. In order that (3) and (4) hold for a solution (15) of equation (1), we must have

(16) $$f(x) + g(x) = h(x),$$

(17) $$f'(x) - g'(x) = 0,$$

whence

$$f(x) - g(x) = k, f(x) = \frac{1}{2} (h(x) + k), g(x) = \frac{1}{2} (h(x) - k),$$

and

$$y(x, t) = \frac{1}{2} h(x - ct) + \frac{1}{2} h(x + ct).$$

If (2) is also to be satisfied we must have

$$h(- ct) = -h(ct) \text{ and } h(L - ct) = -h(L + ct).$$

These conditions imply that h must be an odd function periodic with period $2L$. It follows that the series in (10), where A_n is given by (12), or the representation given by (13), furnishes a unique solution for the problem of the vibrating string when $h(x)$ has the differentiability properties specified above.

The restrictions imposed on $h(x)$ are not unnatural if we seek a solution of (1) valid for all x and t, since the partial differential equation presupposes the existence of second partial derivatives for $y(x, t)$. However, there still remains the problem of finding the motion of a vibrating string released from rest when its initial position is $h(x)$, where $h(x)$ is just continuous. Here we may take several viewpoints. We must realize that (1) represents a mathematical idealization of the physical phenomenon and may not describe the true motion if h is not sufficiently smooth. We may claim that for a real string h is necessarily sufficiently smooth. Since differentiation is a local process we may claim that our analysis is correct for points where (13) has continuous second derivatives. Finally we may claim that the true motion is to be obtained as $y(x, t) = \lim_{n \to \infty} y_n(x, t)$ where $y_n(x, t)$ is a solution with h replaced by h_n, sufficiently smooth, where $\lim_{n \to \infty} h_n = h$. We then get (13) as the true solution.

In discussing the question of uniqueness, we obtained (13) as a solution by a method independent of the method of separation of variables, but our main interest is in the latter technique. Notice that (11) gives an expansion of h in terms of solutions of (7), a second order differential equation with two point boundary conditions. The system (7) does not have solutions for all values of k; indeed a solution exists only when $-k = n^2\pi^2/L^2$. The solutions $\sin \dfrac{n\pi x}{L}$ are orthogonal over $0 \le x \le L$. These facts suggest that we may be dealing with an eigenvalue problem.

Before leaving the subject of the vibrating string, we comment briefly on the nature of the solution of (1) given by (15). We have $f(x - ct) = f(x_0 - ct_0)$ when $x - ct = x_0 - ct_0$, that is, when $x - x_0 = c(t - t_0)$. Thus the value f has at position x_0 and time t_0 is propagated to the position x with speed c. The expression $f(x - ct)$ represents the propagation of a disturbance moving in the direction of the positive x-axis with speed $c > 0$. Conversely, every such propagation may be represented analytically as $u(x, t) = f(x - ct)$ where $f(x) = u(x, 0)$. Indeed, if we postulate that $u(x, t)$ has the property that the value of u at position x and time t is the same as the value of u at position $x + s$ and time $t + \dfrac{s}{c}$, that is,

$$u(x, t) = u\left(x + s, t + \frac{s}{c}\right),$$

then, with $w = x - ct$, $s = w - x$, $f(x) = u(x, 0)$, we have

$$u(x, t) = u\left(x + s, t + \frac{s}{c}\right) = u\left(w, t + \frac{w - x}{c}\right) = u(w, 0) = f(w)$$
$$= f(x - ct).$$

In a similar fashion we can show that a disturbance moving in the direction of the negative x axis with speed $c > 0$ is represented by a function of the form $g(x - ct)$. Each of the expressions $f(x + ct)$ and $g(x - ct)$ is a solution of (1) and the solution of (1) is a sum of f and g, as indicated in (15). For this reason, equation (1) is called the **one-dimensional wave equation.** The functions f and g are called **one-dimensional waves.**

In higher dimensions, the **wave equation** is defined by

$$(18) \qquad\qquad\qquad \nabla^2 u = \frac{1}{c^2} \frac{\partial^2 u}{\partial t^2},$$

where, in two dimensions, using rectangular coordinates,

$$(19) \qquad\qquad\qquad \nabla^2 u = \frac{\partial^2 u}{\partial x^2} + \frac{\partial^2 u}{\partial y^2},$$

and, using polar coordinates (r, ϕ),

$$(20) \qquad\qquad\qquad \nabla^2 u = \frac{\partial^2 u}{\partial r^2} + \frac{1}{r} \frac{\partial u}{\partial r} + \frac{1}{r^2} \frac{\partial^2 u}{\partial \phi^2};$$

while, in three dimensions, using rectangular coordinates,

$$(21) \qquad\qquad\qquad \nabla^2 u = \frac{\partial^2 u}{\partial x^2} + \frac{\partial^2 u}{\partial y^2} + \frac{\partial^2 u}{\partial z^2},$$

and, using spherical coordinates, defined by

$$(22) \qquad x = r \sin \theta \cos \phi, \quad y = r \sin \theta \sin \phi, \quad z = r \cos \theta,$$

$$(23) \qquad \nabla^2 u = \frac{1}{r^2 \sin \theta} \left(\sin \theta \frac{\partial}{\partial r} \left(r^2 \frac{\partial u}{\partial r} \right) + \frac{1}{\sin \theta} \frac{\partial^2 u}{\partial \phi^2} + \frac{\partial}{\partial \theta} \left(\sin \theta \frac{\partial u}{\partial \theta} \right) \right).$$

6.1.2   The Potential Due to a Spherical Surface Distribution

The presence of matter in a bounded set $\mathscr{S}$ creates a force field in the sense that a unit mass at $P = (x, y, z)$ is given an acceleration described by a force vector $\vec{F}(x, y, z)$. For example, when $\mathscr{S}$ consists of a single point

$Q = (x_1, y_1, z_1)$ to which a mass m is associated, the force per unit mass at P is $\vec{F} = \dfrac{-m}{r^2} \hat{r}$, where

$$r^2 = (x - x_1)^2 + (y - y_1)^2 + (z - z_1)^2,$$

and

$$\hat{r} = \frac{1}{r}\left((x - x_1)\vec{i} + (y - y_1)\vec{j} + (z - z_1)\vec{k}\right)$$

is the unit vector from Q to P. It is easily verified that $\vec{F} = \nabla u$, where differentiation is taken with respect to the variables x, y, z and where $u = \dfrac{m}{r}$ is called the **potential** at P arising from the mass m at Q.

If we have n point masses m_i at positions $Q_i = (x_i, y_i, z_i)$ respectively, the force at P is $\vec{F} = \sum\limits_{i=1}^{n} \dfrac{-m_i}{r_i^2} \hat{r}_i$ where $r_i^2 = (x - x_i)^2 + (y - y_i)^2 + (z - z_i)^2$ and $\hat{r}_i$ is the unit vector from Q_i to P. It is clear that $\vec{F} = \nabla u$, where $u = \sum\limits_{i=1}^{n} \dfrac{m_i}{r_i}$.

To generalize to the case of a continuous distribution, we shall restrict ourselves to surfaces which are composed of a finite number of bounded two-sided surface elements for each point of which a normal can be assigned which varies continuously along the surface element, and we shall restrict ourselves to volumes which are composed of a finite number of bounded volumes having as boundaries surfaces of the type just described.

Consider first the case of a volume distribution $\mathscr{V}$ and let $\rho(x_1, y_1, z_1)$ be the mass per unit volume at $Q = (x_1, y_1, z_1)$ in $\mathscr{V}$. Define, for $P = (x, y, z)$,

$$(24) \qquad \vec{F}(P) = \iiint\limits_{\mathscr{V}} \frac{-\rho}{r^2} \hat{r}\, dx_1\, dy_1\, dz_1,$$

$$(25) \qquad u(P) = \iiint\limits_{\mathscr{V}} \frac{\rho}{r}\, dx_1\, dy_1\, dz_1,$$

where r is the distance and $\hat{r}$ is the unit vector from Q to P. It can be shown, assuming ρ integrable, that the integrals are defined and continuous at all points P and that $\vec{F} = \nabla u$. For points P not in $\mathscr{V}$, the function u, called the **volume potential**, is infinitely differentiable and may be expanded in a power series about P. Moreover u satisfies **Laplace's equation,**

$$(26) \qquad \nabla^2 u = \frac{\partial^2 u}{\partial x^2} + \frac{\partial^2 u}{\partial y^2} + \frac{\partial^2 u}{\partial z^2} = 0,$$

at all points P not in $\mathscr{V}$, and $\lim\limits_{P \to \infty} u(P) = 0$.

For a surface distribution $\mathscr{S}$, let $\sigma(x_1, y_1, z_1)$ be the mass per unit area at $Q = (x_1, y_1, z_1)$ on $\mathscr{S}$. Define

(27) $$\vec{F}(P) = \iint_{\mathscr{S}} \frac{-\sigma}{r^2} \hat{r} \, dS,$$

(28) $$u(P) = \iint_{\mathscr{S}} \frac{\sigma}{r} \, dS,$$

where dS is the element of surface area and integration is taken with respect to Q on $\mathscr{S}$. Assuming σ integrable on $\mathscr{S}$, it can be shown that the integrals are defined for all P. For points P not on $\mathscr{S}$, the function $u(P)$ given by (28), called the **surface potential**, is infinitely differentiable, may be expanded in a power series about P, satisfies Laplace's equation, satisfies $\lim_{P \to \infty} u(P) = 0$, and $\vec{F} = \nabla u$. For points P on $\mathscr{S}$, $u(P)$ is continuous when the normal to $\mathscr{S}$ varies continuously for all points sufficiently near P.

The fact that the potential satisfies Laplace's equation permits its determination as an infinite series in terms of members of an orthonormal sequence. We shall consider the potential arising from a distribution of mass over a spherical surface of radius a about the origin, under the assumption that the surface density σ, and hence the potential u, is symmetric about an axis. That is, using spherical coordinates given by (22), we shall assume that u depends only on r and θ. With $\nabla^2 u$ given by (23), our problem is to find $u(r, \theta)$ satisfying

(29) $$\nabla^2 u = \frac{\partial^2 u}{\partial r^2} + \frac{2}{r} \frac{\partial u}{\partial r} + \frac{1}{r^2 \sin \theta} \frac{\partial}{\partial \theta} \left(\sin \theta \frac{\partial u}{\partial \theta} \right) = 0.$$

Note that r in (29) is the distance from the origin, and is not the r in (28).

The value of u on the surface of the sphere is determined by (28) as $u(a, \theta) = f(\theta)$. The problem of finding u inside the sphere is called the **interior problem**, while the determination of u outside the sphere is called the **exterior problem**.

To apply the method of separation of variables, set $u(r, \theta) = R(r) S(\theta)$ and substitute in (29), obtaining

(30) $$\frac{r^2}{R} \frac{d^2 R}{dr^2} + \frac{2r}{R} \frac{dR}{dr} = -\frac{1}{S \sin \theta} \left(\cos \theta \frac{dS}{d\theta} + \sin \theta \frac{d^2 S}{d\theta^2} \right) = k,$$

where k is a constant.

The differential equation for R is

(31) $$r^2 \frac{d^2 R}{dr^2} + 2r \frac{dR}{dr} - kR = 0.$$

A solution of the form $R = r^n$ is obtained when n satisfies $n(n + 1) = k$. For each value of k there are two values of n, one of which is $m = (-1 + \sqrt{1 + 4k})/2$; the other is $(-1 - \sqrt{1 + 4k})/2 = -(m + 1)$. The general solution of (31) is therefore

$$(32) \qquad\qquad R(r) = Ar^m + Br^{-(m+1)}.$$

We have $m(m + 1) = k$. Replacing k by $m(m + 1)$ in (30), we find the equation for $S(\theta)$ to be

$$(33) \qquad \sin \theta \, \frac{d^2 S}{d\theta^2} + \cos \theta \, \frac{dS}{d\theta} + m(m + 1)(\sin \theta)S = 0.$$

The change of variable $x = \cos \theta$ transforms (33) into

$$(34) \qquad (1 - x^2)\frac{d^2 S}{dx^2} - 2x\frac{dS}{dx} + m(m + 1)S = 0.$$

This is **Legendre's equation**, and the only solutions with continuous second derivatives on $-1 \le x \le 1$ are the Legendre Polynomials $P_m(x)$, $m = 0, 1, 2, \ldots$. (Exercise 5.3–21.) Therefore m must be chosen as a non-negative integer.

Restricting our attention to the interior problem, we see that B in (32) must be taken as 0, so that R will be finite at $r = 0$. Solutions of (29) of the form $R(r) S(\theta)$ have been determined as

$$(35) \qquad A_m r^m P_m(\cos \theta), \qquad A_m \text{ constant}, \quad m = 0, 1, 2, \ldots .$$

To obtain a solution of (29) satisfying $u(a, \theta) = f(\theta)$, set

$$(36) \qquad\qquad u(r, \theta) = \sum_{m=0}^{\infty} A_m r^m P_m(\cos \theta),$$

and seek A_m so that

$$(37) \qquad\qquad f(\theta) = \sum_{m=0}^{\infty} A_m a^m P_m(\cos \theta), \qquad 0 \le \theta \le \pi.$$

With $x = \cos \theta$, $g(x) = f(\theta)$, (37) becomes

$$(38) \qquad\qquad g(x) = \sum_{m=0}^{\infty} A_m a^m P_m(x), \qquad -1 \le x \le 1,$$

suggesting that

$$(39) \quad A_m a^m = \frac{2m + 1}{2} \int_{-1}^{1} g(x) P_m(x) dx = \frac{2m + 1}{2} \int_{0}^{\pi} f(\theta) P_m(\cos \theta) \sin \theta \, d\theta.$$

Thus a formal solution for the interior problem is given by (36) where A_m is determined by (39).

In particular, when σ, and hence $f(\theta) = f$, is constant over the surface of the sphere, we get

$$A_m a^m = \frac{2m+1}{2} f \int_{-1}^{1} P_m(x)dx = 0, \qquad m = 1, 2, \ldots,$$

$$A_0 = \frac{f}{2} \int_{-1}^{1} P_0(x)dx = f,$$

and (36) reduces to $u(r, \theta) = A_0 P_0(\cos \theta) = f$, $r \leq a$. The potential, in this case, is constant within the sphere.

It is possible to verify that (36) together with (39), is indeed a continuous solution of (29) for $r \leq a$ and satisfies $u(a, \theta) = f(\theta)$ when $f(\theta)$ is sufficiently restricted (Exercise 6.1–15). There remains the problem of uniqueness. How do we know our solution is the potential given by (28)? Let both u and v be continuous solutions of (29) for $r \leq a$, and take on the same values on the boundary, so that $w = u - v$ satisfies (29) and is zero on the boundary. We will prove that w is identically zero, and thus obtain the desired uniqueness.

By a linear change of variables, $x = cx_1 + d$, $y = cy_1$, $z = cz_1$, we can carry the interior of the sphere into a region of space $\mathcal{V}_1$ lying between the planes $x_1 = 0$ and $x_1 = 1$, and $w(x, y, z)$ into a function $w_1(x_1, y_1, z_1)$ satisfying $\dfrac{\partial^2 w_1}{\partial x_1^2} + \dfrac{\partial^2 w_1}{\partial y_1^2} + \dfrac{\partial^2 w_1}{\partial z_1^2} = 0$ in $\mathcal{V}_1$ and vanishing on the boundary of $\mathcal{V}_1$. Since w_1 identically zero implies w identically zero, we may as well assume our original sphere lies between the planes $x = 0$ and $x = 1$. Then $\cos x \neq 0$ and, since $\nabla^2 w = 0$, $t(x, y, z)$ defined by $w(x, y, z) = t(x, y, z) \cos x$ satisfies

$$\text{(40)} \qquad \frac{\partial^2 t}{\partial x^2} + \frac{\partial^2 t}{\partial y^2} + \frac{\partial^2 t}{\partial z^2} - 2\frac{\partial t}{\partial x}\tan x = t,$$

for (x, y, z) within the sphere. If t is positive at an interior point of the sphere, then it has a positive maximum at an interior point, since it is zero on the boundary and is continuous on the closed sphere. At this point we have $t > 0$, $t_x = 0$, $t_y = 0$, $t_z = 0$, $t_{xx} \leq 0$, $t_{yy} \leq 0$, $t_{zz} \leq 0$ making the right side of (40) positive, the left side nonpositive. This contradiction shows that $t \leq 0$ within the sphere. A similar argument shows that $t \geq 0$ and hence $t = 0$ within the sphere. It follows that w is identically zero.

Next we seek a series solution of the exterior problem. Take $A = 0$ in (32) in preparation for the fact that $\lim_{P \to \infty} u(P) = 0$. Solutions of (29) are given by

$$\frac{B_m}{r^{m+1}} P_m(\cos \theta), \quad B_m \text{ constant}, \quad m = 0, 1, 2, \ldots.$$

To obtain a solution of (29) satisfying $u(a, \theta) = f(\theta)$, set

$$(41) \qquad u(r, \theta) = \sum_{m=0}^{\infty} \frac{B_m}{r^{m+1}} P_m(\cos \theta), \qquad r \geq a,$$

and seek B_m so that

$$(42) \qquad f(\theta) = \sum_{m=0}^{\infty} \frac{B_m}{a^{m+1}} P_m(\cos \theta).$$

As above, we expect that

$$(43) \qquad \frac{B_m}{a^{m+1}} = \frac{2m+1}{2} \int_0^{\pi} f(\theta) P_m(\cos \theta) \sin \theta \, d\theta.$$

A formal solution for the exterior problem is (41), where B_m is determined from (43).

In the special case when σ, and hence $u(a, \theta) = f$, is constant on the surface, (41) reduces to $u(r, \theta) = \dfrac{af}{r}$, $r \geq a$. The total mass M on the surface of the sphere can be shown to be af (Exercise 6.1–16), so that $u(r, \theta)$ can be thought of as the potential generated by a particle of mass M at the center of the sphere.

The uniqueness of the solution of the exterior problem is indicated in Exercise 6.1–14.

If we drop the requirement of axial symmetry, so that u depends on ϕ as well as on r and θ, we must solve

$$(44) \qquad \nabla^2 u = \frac{\partial^2 u}{\partial r^2} + \frac{2}{r} \frac{\partial u}{\partial r} + \frac{1}{r^2 \sin^2\theta} \frac{\partial^2 u}{\partial \phi^2} + \frac{1}{r^2 \sin \theta} \frac{\partial}{\partial \theta}\left(\sin \theta \frac{\partial u}{\partial \theta}\right) = 0.$$

Any continuous solution of Laplace's equation is called a **harmonic function.** A solution which is homogeneous of degree l, $l = 0, 1, 2, \ldots$, in x, y, and z, is called a **solid spherical harmonic of degree** l. When a solution is of the form $r^l g(\theta, \phi)$, then $g(\theta, \phi)$ is called a **surface spherical harmonic,** being the value of the solution on the unit sphere, $r = 1$. Substituting $u = r^l g(\theta, \phi)$ in (44) yields

$$(45) \qquad l(l+1)g + \frac{1}{\sin \theta} \frac{\partial}{\partial \theta}\left(\sin \theta \frac{\partial g}{\partial \theta}\right) + \frac{1}{\sin^2 \theta} \frac{\partial^2 g}{\partial \phi^2} = 0$$

as the differential equation of surface spherical harmonics. Replacing $\cos \theta$ by x, (45) reduces to

$$(46) \qquad l(l+1)g + \frac{\partial}{\partial x}\left((1 - x^2) \frac{\partial g}{\partial x}\right) + \frac{1}{1 - x^2} \frac{\partial^2 g}{\partial \phi^2} = 0.$$

Assuming also that $g(\theta, \phi) = S(\theta) T(\phi)$, (46) becomes

(47) $(1 - x^2)\left(l(l + 1) + \dfrac{1}{S}\dfrac{d}{dx}\left((1 - x^2)\dfrac{dS}{dx} \right) \right) = -\dfrac{1}{T}\dfrac{d^2 T}{d\phi^2} = m^2$

where the constant is chosen as m^2, so that the solution for T will be periodic of period 2π. This solution is

$$T = A \cos m\phi + B \sin m\phi$$

where A and B are constant. Then S satisfies

(48) $(1 - x^2)\dfrac{d}{dx}\left((1 - x^2)\dfrac{dS}{dx} \right) + (l(l + 1)(1 - x^2) - m^2) S = 0,$

an equation known as **Legendre's associated equation.** We leave for Exercise 6.1–17, the verification of the fact that the functions

(49) $P^m(x) = (1 - x^2)^{m/2}\dfrac{d^m}{dx^m} P_l(x),$ (m a nonnegative integer),

are solutions of (48). They are called the **associated Legendre functions.** If $m = 0$, we obtain the Legendre polynomials, often called **zonal harmonics** because $P_l(\cos \theta)$ vanishes on parallel circles on the unit sphere. If $m > l$, then $P_l^m(x) = 0$. If $0 < m < l$, the solutions of (45) are

(50) $(A \cos m\phi + B \sin m\phi) \sin^m\theta \dfrac{d^{m+l}}{dx^{m+l}}(x^2 - 1)^l,$

often called **tesseral harmonics** because the locus of points where they vanish on the unit sphere has a curvilinear rectangular pattern. Indeed the first factor vanishes when $\tan m\phi = -A/B$, that is, on great circles through the pole $\theta = 0$, $r = 1$, the second factor vanishes at 0 and π, and the third factor vanishes on $l - m$ parallel circles perpendicular to the axis $\theta = 0$. Finally if $m = l$, the surface harmonics are

$$(A \cos m\phi + B \sin m\phi) \sin^m\theta,$$

vanishing on great circles through the pole $\theta = 0$, $r = 1$, and therefore called **sectorial harmonics.** It can be shown that

(51) $\displaystyle\int_{-1}^{1} P_l^m(x) P_k^m(x)dx = \delta(l, k)\dfrac{2}{2l + 1}\dfrac{(l + m)!}{(l - m)!}$

and so the associated Legendre functions form an orthogonal set over $-1 \le x \le 1$. Moreover (49) are the only solutions of (48) on $-1 \le x \le 1$.

6.1.3   The Hydrogen Atom

The hydrogen atom consists of a positive charge of magnitude e, called the nucleus, together with a negative charge of magnitude $-e$ called the electron. Associated with the electron is an energy E determined by

$$(52) \qquad \nabla^2\psi + k\left(E + \frac{e^2}{r}\right)\psi = 0$$

where r is the distance between the nucleus (considered here as fixed) and the electron, and where $k = \dfrac{8\pi^2 M}{h^2}$, M being the mass of the electron and h being Planck's constant. Let us choose the energy to be zero when the electron is at rest away from the influence of the nucleus, that is, when it is at rest an infinite distance from the nucleus. The more tightly bound the electron is, the less energy it has. Thus E is negative when the electron is connected to the nucleus.

The object is to find values of E for which a solution of (52) exists subject to

$$(53) \qquad \int_{-\infty}^{\infty}\int_{-\infty}^{\infty}\int_{-\infty}^{\infty} \left|\psi(x, y, z)\right|^2 dx\,dy\,dz = 1.$$

Such values of E are the only possible values the energy of the electron may have. As we shall see, (52) has solutions satisfying (53) for only a denumerable set of negative values of E, and for this reason the energy is said to be **quantized.**

Using spherical coordinates, with $\psi = R(r)\,g(\theta, \phi)$, (52) may be written

$$\frac{r^2}{R}\frac{d^2 R}{dr^2} + \frac{2r}{R}\frac{dR}{dr} + k\left(E + \frac{e^2}{r}\right)r^2$$

$$= -\frac{1}{g}\left(\frac{1}{\sin\theta}\frac{\partial}{\partial\theta}\left(\sin\theta\frac{\partial g}{\partial\theta}\right) + \frac{1}{\sin^2\theta}\frac{\partial^2 g}{\partial\phi^2}\right) = c$$

where c is a constant, and thus

$$(54) \qquad \frac{1}{\sin\theta}\frac{\partial}{\partial\theta}\left(\sin\theta\frac{\partial g}{\partial\theta}\right) + \frac{1}{\sin^2\theta}\frac{\partial^2 g}{\partial\phi^2} + cg = 0,$$

$$(55) \qquad r^2\frac{d^2 R}{dr^2} + 2r\frac{dR}{dr} + \left(k\left(E + \frac{e^2}{r}\right)r^2 - c\right)R = 0.$$

Comparing (54) with (45), it is seen that solutions of (54) exist when $c = l(l + 1)$, $l = 0, 1, 2, \ldots$ and it may be shown that these are the only values of c which permit solutions of (54) periodic in θ and ϕ.

Put $c = l(l + 1)$, $x = 2r \sqrt{-kE}$, $R(r) = r^l e^{-x/2} y(x)$, $s = \left(\dfrac{-k\,e^4}{4E}\right)^{1/2}$
$- (l + 1)$, $2l + 1 = \alpha$. Then (55) becomes

(56) $xy'' + (\alpha + 1 - x)y' + sy = 0,$ $0 \le x < \infty,$

which is called **Laguerre's equation**. The only solutions of (56) finite at $x = 0$ are the **associated Laguerre polynomials**, defined by

(57) $L_s^\alpha(x) = \dfrac{x^{-\alpha} e^x}{s!} \dfrac{d^s}{dx^s} (x^{\alpha+s} e^{-x}),$ $s = 0, 1, 2, \ldots .$

It follows that

$$\left(\dfrac{-k\,e^4}{4E}\right)^{1/2} - (l + 1) = s, \qquad s = 0, 1, \ldots,$$

and when we substitute $k = \dfrac{8\pi^2 M}{h^2}$, $n = l + 1 + s$, the possible values of E are given by

(58) $E_n = \dfrac{-2\pi^2 M e^4}{h^2} \dfrac{1}{n^2},$ $n = 1, 2, \ldots .$

These values are subject to experimental verification since the frequency ν of radiation emitted from the atom is restricted by

$$h\nu = E_n - E_m, \qquad n > m.$$

The solution ψ of (52) is of the form

(59) $(A \cos m\phi + B \sin m\phi) \, P_l^m(\cos \theta) \, r^l e^{-r \sqrt{-kE}} \, L_{n-l-1}^{2l+1}(2r \sqrt{-kE}).$

The integers n, l, m are called quantum numbers. How many linearly independent solutions are there for each value of E? Since $\sin m\phi$ and $\cos m\phi$ are linearly independent for $m \ne 0$, there are $2l + 1$ independent solutions for fixed n and l, as m ranges from 0 to l. For each n, l ranges from 0 to $n - 1$ and hence there are $\sum_{l=0}^{n-1} (2l + 1) = n^2$ independent solutions.

When the motion of the nucleus and relativistic effects are taken into account, E is found to depend on other quantum numbers besides n.

For the expansion of functions in terms of solutions of (52) it is also necessary to consider solutions for positive values of E. Solutions exist for all positive values of E. The expansion is composed of an infinite series of solutions (59) together with an integral corresponding to solutions for positive values of E. Such expansions are beyond the scope of this text.

Exercise 6.1

1. Assume that h in (3) has continuous second derivatives on $0 \le x \le L$ with $h(0) = h(L) = 0$, $h''_-(0) = h''(L) = 0$, and that h is extended to be odd and periodic with period $2L$. Show that $h'_-(0) = h'_+(0)$, $h''_-(0) = h''_+(0)$ with similar relations at L. Use the fact that h is odd, h' is even.

2. Consider three dimensional solutions of (18) with spherical symmetry, so that u depends only on r. Using spherical coordinates and $w = ur$, show that u must be of the form

$$u = \frac{1}{r} f(r - ct) + \frac{1}{r} g(r + ct)$$

where f and g are arbitrary.

3. Let (l, m, n) be the direction cosines of a fixed direction. If $u(x, y, z, t)$ has constant values, for fixed t, on each plane perpendicular to the given direction and if these values are propagated with speed $c > 0$ in the given direction, we call u a **plane wave**. Show that a plane wave is of the form

$$u(x, y, z, t) = f(lx + my + nz - ct)$$

and that this function satisfies (18). Show that every solution of (18) which is constant, for fixed t, on planes perpendicular to the direction (l, m, n) is of the form

$$u = f(lx + my + nz - ct) + g(lx + my + nz + ct).$$

4. (a) Applying (22), show that (21) reduces to (23).
    (b) Obtain (23) by use of the invariant definition of divergence,

$$\nabla \cdot \vec{F}(P) = \lim_{|\mathscr{V}| \to 0} \frac{1}{|\mathscr{V}|} \iint_{\mathscr{S}} \vec{F} \cdot \vec{n} \, dS$$

where $|\mathscr{V}|$ is the volume of a region $\mathscr{V}$ with surface $\mathscr{S}$, and the limit is taken as $\mathscr{V}$ shrinks to point P. Here $\vec{n}$ is the unit normal to $\mathscr{S}$ pointing outward. Use $\vec{F} = \nabla u$ and recall that $\nabla u \cdot \vec{n} = \dfrac{\partial u}{\partial n}$ where the derivative $\dfrac{\partial u}{\partial n}$ is taken in the direction of the normal. For $\mathscr{V}$ use a volume element in spherical coordinates, the volume of which is $r^2 \sin\theta \, \Delta r \, \Delta\theta \, \Delta\phi$. *Hint:* The surface integral over the pair of faces corresponding to θ and $\theta + \Delta\theta$ is approximately

$$\frac{\partial u}{\partial \theta}(r, \theta + \Delta\theta, \phi)\frac{1}{r}(r\sin\theta\Delta\phi)\Delta r - \frac{\partial u}{\partial \theta}(r, \theta, \phi)\frac{1}{r}(r\sin\theta\Delta\phi)\Delta r$$

since the derivative in direction of increasing θ is $\dfrac{1}{r}\dfrac{\partial u}{\partial \theta}$. The procedure can be justified by mean value theorems.

5. (a) Using cylindrical coordinates defined by $x = r\cos\phi$, $y = r\sin\phi$, $z = z$, show that

$$\nabla^2 u = \frac{1}{r}\left(\frac{\partial}{\partial u}\left(r\frac{\partial u}{\partial r}\right)\right) + \frac{1}{r}\frac{\partial^2 u}{\partial \phi^2} + r\frac{\partial^2 u}{\partial z^2}\right).$$

    (b) Obtain the same result by the method suggested in Exercise 4(b).

6. (a) Apply the method following equation (15) to the problem of the vibrating string with initial speed $v(x)$. Solve $\dfrac{\partial^2 y}{\partial x^2} = \dfrac{1}{c^2}\dfrac{\partial^2 y}{\partial t^2}$ subject to $y(0, t)$

$= y(L, t) = 0, y(x, 0) = h(x), \dfrac{\partial y}{\partial t}(x, 0) = v(x)$.

Show that the solution is

$$y(x, t) = \tfrac{1}{2}(h(x - ct) + h(x + ct)) + \frac{1}{2c}\int_{x-ct}^{x+ct} v(z)dz.$$

(b) A tightly stretched string with fixed end points at $x = 0$ and $x = 2$ is initially at rest in its equilibrium position. A speed of $\dfrac{\partial y}{\partial t}(x, 0) = 2x - x^2$ is associated with each point. Distances are measured in feet. The string weighs $\tfrac{1}{2}$ lb. and is subjected to a tension of 12 lb. Find the displacement of the midpoint when $t = .01$ sec. Use acceleration of gravity $= 32$ ft./sec².

7. A string stretched between $x = 0$ and $x = L$ is pulled aside at the center to a distance d and then let go. Find the motion.

8. (a) How many zeros does the solution $\sin\dfrac{n\pi}{L}x$ of (7) have on the interval $0 < x < L$?

(b) When $h(x) = D\sin\dfrac{n\pi x}{L}$, D a constant, show that the solution (10) of the problem given by equations (1), (2), (3), (4) reduces to (9). Find the **nodes**, that is, points where the string does not oscillate. Note that the superposition of a wave moving to the right and a wave moving to the left may yield a solution of (1) traveling neither to right nor left. Such a disturbance is called a **standing wave**.

9. Equation (13) suggests a geometrical method for the construction of the solution. Form two graphs of h defined over the entire x axis, and move one to the right, the other to the left with speed c. Then one half the sum of the ordinates for fixed t yields $y(x, t)$. Apply this method to obtain graphs of the motion in Exercise 7 for times $t = \dfrac{nL}{8c}$, $n = 1, 2, \ldots, 8$.

10. Consider the vibration of a gas in a tube of length L, one end at $x = 0$, the other at $x = L$. Let y represent the displacement of a gas particle from its mean position. If the tube is closed at $x = 0$ and open at $x = L$, then y satisfies

$$\frac{\partial^2 y}{\partial x^2} = \frac{1}{c^2}\frac{\partial^2 y}{\partial t^2}, \quad y(0, t) = 0, \quad \frac{\partial y}{\partial x}(L, t) = 0.$$

Obtain standing wave solutions.

11. Consider a rectangular membrane tied down at the edges $x = 0$, $x = a$, $y = 0$, $y = b$. The restrictions satisfied by the displacement $z(x, y, t)$ for small vibrations can be shown to be

$$\nabla^2 z = \frac{1}{c^2}\frac{\partial^2 z}{\partial t^2}, \quad 0 = z(0, y, t) = z(x, 0, t) = z(a, y, t) = z(x, b, t).$$

If the membrane is released from rest, we also have $\dfrac{\partial z}{\partial t}(x, y, 0) = 0$. Show that a periodic solution of the form $z = X(x)\,Y(y)\,T(t)$ must be of the form

$$z = A \sin\frac{m\pi x}{a} \sin\frac{n\pi y}{b} \cos\left(\left(\frac{m^2}{a^2} + \frac{n^2}{b^2}\right)^{1/2} c\pi t \right).$$

Proceeding formally, represent z as a double Fourier Series,

$$z = \sum_{m=1}^{\infty} \sum_{n=1}^{\infty} A_{mn} \sin\frac{n\pi y}{b} \sin\frac{m\pi x}{a} \cos\left(\left(\frac{m^2}{a^2} + \frac{n^2}{b^2}\right)^{1/2} c\pi t \right),$$

and find A_{mn} so that $z(x, y, 0) = f(x, y)$, where f is given.

12. Show that $\nabla^2 \dfrac{1}{r} = 0$, when $r^2 = (x - a)^2 + (y - b)^2 + (z - c)^2 \neq 0$.

13. (a) Let $u(x, y, z)$ satisfy $\nabla^2 u = 0$ in a bounded region $\mathscr{R}$, and be continuous on the closure of $\mathscr{R}$. If $u \leq k$, k constant, on the boundary of $\mathscr{R}$, show that $u \leq k$ within $\mathscr{R}$. *Hint:* $v = u - k$ satisfies $\nabla^2 v = 0$ and is nonpositive on the boundary. Use (40).

   (b) Prove the same result when $\nabla^2 u \geq 0$ in $\mathscr{R}$.

14. Use Exercise 13 to prove the uniqueness for the exterior problem in 6.1.2. That is, if u and v satisfy Laplace's equation outside the sphere $r > a$, are continuous for $r \geq a$, assume the same values on $r = a$, and satisfy $\lim_{P \to \infty} u(P) = 0 = \lim_{P \to \infty} v(P)$, show that u and v are identical for $r \geq a$. *Hint:* For $\epsilon > 0$, take a large sphere on whose surface $|u| \leq \epsilon$, $|v| \leq \epsilon$.

15. (a) Use the results obtained in Section 5.3 (see also Exercise 5.3) to show that the series (36) with A_m determined by (39), and the series obtained by differentiation, converge uniformly in r and θ for $r \leq b < a$. Hence conclude that (36) satisfies Laplace's equation.

   (b) Let $f(\theta)$ have continuous second derivatives. Show that the series (36) is $f(\theta)$ when $r = a$.

16. When $\mathscr{S}$ in (28) is a sphere of radius a about the origin, P is a point on the surface, and σ is a constant, show that $u(P) = M/a$ where $M = 4\pi a^2 \sigma$.

17. Prove that (49) is a solution of (48). *Hint:* If S is a solution of (48) write $S = (1 - x^2)^{m/2} h(x)$ and find a differential equation for h. Show that this is the differential equation obtained by differentiating Legendre's equation m times.

18. Use the method suggested in Exercise 5.3–12 to prove (51). For the case $l = k$, show that $\displaystyle\int_{-1}^{1} (P_l^m(x))^2 dx = (l + m)(l - m + 1)\int_{-1}^{1}(P_l^{m-1}(x))^2 dx$ by integrating $\displaystyle\int_{-1}^{1}(1 - x^2)^m \frac{d^m}{dx^m} P_l(x) \frac{d^m}{dx^m} P_l(x)dx$ by parts and using the differential equation

$$(1 - x^2)\frac{d^{m+1}}{dx^{m+1}} P_l(x) - 2mx\frac{d^m}{dx^m} P_l(x) + (l + m)(l - m + 1)\frac{d^{m-1}}{dx^{m-1}} P_l(x) = 0,$$

obtained by differentiating Legendre's equation $(m - 1)$ times.

19. Show that (57) represents a polynomial of degree s such that the coefficient of x^s is $\dfrac{(-1)^s}{s!}$.

20. For fixed α, let $L_s = L_s^\alpha$ and $D^j = \dfrac{d^j}{dx^j}$. Use Leibnitz's rule on the product $x(x^{\alpha+s-1}e^{-x})$ to show that

(a) $L_s = \dfrac{x^{-\alpha}e^x}{s!} \times D^s(x^{\alpha+s-1}e^{-x}) + L_{s-1}.$

Writing $D^s = D^{s-1} D$ in (57), show that

(b) $L_s = \dfrac{(\alpha + s)}{s} L_{s-1} - \dfrac{x^{-\alpha}e^x}{s!} D^{s-1}(x^{\alpha+s}e^{-x}).$

Differentiating (57) and using (a) above, show that

(c) $xDL_s = (s + 1)L_{s+1} + (x - \alpha - s - 1)L_s.$

Differentiating (b) and using (b) and (c) show that

(d) $xDL_s = sL_s - (\alpha + s)L_{s-1}.$

Replace s in (c) by $s - 1$ and show that

(e) $DL_s = DL_{s-1} - L_{s-1}.$

Use (d) and (e) to prove that L_s satisfies (56).

21. The steady state temperature distribution $u(x, y)$ of a circular plate satisfies $\nabla^2 u = 0$. Show that particular solutions obtained by the method of separation of variables in polar coordinates are

$$A_n r^n \cos n\phi + B_n r^n \sin n\phi, \qquad n = 0, 1, 2, \ldots .$$

22. (a) A rectangular plate is bounded by the lines $x = 0$, $x = a$, $y = 0$, $y = b$. The plate is insulated and the temperature $u(x, y)$ along the edge $y = b$ is held fixed so that $u(x, b) = \begin{cases} x^2 & , \quad 0 \leq x \leq a/2 \\ ax - x^2, & a/2 \leq x \leq a. \end{cases}$
     Along the other edges the temperature is held fixed at zero. At equilibrium, the temperature satisfies $\nabla^2 u = 0$. Determine a formal solution.

(b) Suppose that the temperature along the four edges were fixed so that $u(0, y) = f(y)$, $u(a, y) = g(y)$, $u(x, 0) = h(x)$, $u(x, b) = k(x)$. Show that $u(x, y)$ can be found by first solving four problems of the type given in part (a), each with $u = 0$ along three edges.

23. Assume that a volume $\mathscr{V}$ bounded by a surface $\mathscr{S}$ is of such a type that Gauss' Theorem, $\displaystyle\iint_{\mathscr{S}} \vec{F} \cdot \vec{n}\, dS = \iiint_{\mathscr{V}} \nabla \cdot \vec{F}\, dV$, applies. Put $\vec{F} = u\nabla u$, where u has continuous second derivatives in the closure of $\mathscr{V}$, and obtain $\displaystyle\iint_{\mathscr{S}} u\,\frac{\partial u}{\partial n}\, dS = \iiint_{\mathscr{V}} (\nabla u \cdot \nabla u + u\nabla^2 u)dV.$ Use this result to show that if u has the described continuity properties, satisfies Laplace's equation in $\mathscr{V}$, and vanishes on $\mathscr{S}$, it is uniquely determined.

6.2
SECOND ORDER LINEAR DIFFERENTIAL EQUATIONS

The object of this section is to bring to the attention of the reader some basic facts about second order ordinary differential equations and to indicate that properties of the solutions may be obtained even when explicit expressions for the solutions are not known.

Our attention will be centered on the equation

$$(1) \qquad\qquad f'' + Pf' + Qf = R$$

where P, Q, R are continuous real valued functions of x on the finite interval $a \le x \le b$. A **solution** of (1) is defined to be a function f with continuous second derivatives satisfying

$$f''(x) + P(x)f'(x) + Q(x)f(x) = R(x), \qquad a \le x \le b.$$

It is understood that derivatives at a and b are one-sided derivatives. We call (1) a **linear ordinary differential equation of order two.**

The word "linear" is used because the transformation

$$(2) \qquad\qquad L = \frac{d^2}{dx^2} + P\frac{d}{dx} + Q$$

defined on the linear manifold $\mathscr{M}$ of real functions in $\mathscr{R}\{a, b\}$ with two derivatives on $a \le x \le b$ by

$$(3) \qquad\qquad (Lf)(x) = f''(x) + P(x)f'(x) + Q(x)f(x)$$

is a linear transformation. That is,

$$L(cf + dg) = cLf + dLg$$

whenever f and g are in $\mathscr{M}$ and c and d are scalars.

Equation (1) is equivalent to a system of two first order differential equations. For if we define

$$(4) \qquad\qquad y_1(x) = f(x), \qquad y_2(x) = f'(x),$$

then f is a solution of (1) if and only if y_1 and y_2 satisfy

$$(5) \qquad\qquad \begin{cases} y_1'(x) = y_2(x), \\ y_2'(x) = -Qy_1(x) - Py_2(x) + R. \end{cases}$$

As we shall see, it is extremely useful to have available an existence and uniqueness theorem concerning solutions of (1) and associated boundary conditions.

THEOREM 6.2A   Let $a \le x_0 \le b$ and let c_1 and c_2 be two given real numbers. Then there is one and only one solution of

(6)
$$\begin{cases} f'' + Pf' + Qf = R, \\ f(x_0) = c_1, \quad f'(x_0) = c_2. \end{cases}$$

Proof   A solution f exists for (6) if and only if y_1 and y_2 defined by (4) satisfy

(7)
$$\begin{cases} y_1' = y_2, \\ y_2' = -Qy_1 - Py_2 + R, \\ y_1(x_0) = c_1, \quad y_2(x_0) = c_2. \end{cases}$$

The existence of solutions y_1 and y_2 for the system (7) is, however, equivalent to the existence of continuous solutions of the system of integral equations

(8)
$$\begin{cases} y_1(x) = c_1 + \displaystyle\int_{x_0}^{x} y_2(t)dt, \\ y_2(x) = c_2 + \displaystyle\int_{x_0}^{x} (-Q(t)y_1(t) - P(t)y_2(t) + R(t))dt, \end{cases}$$

and we shall prove that (8) has a unique solution for y_1 and y_2. For this purpose, define

(9)
$$\begin{cases} y_{10}(x) = c_1, \qquad y_{20}(x) = c_2, \\ y_{1n}(x) = c_1 + \displaystyle\int_{x_0}^{x} y_{2,n-1}(t)dt, \\ y_{2n}(x) = c_2 + \displaystyle\int_{x_0}^{x} (-Q(t)y_{1,n-1}(t) - P(t)y_{2,n-1}(t) + R(t))dt. \end{cases}$$

Our aim is to prove that $\{y_{1n}\}$ converges uniformly on $a \le x \le b$ to a function y_1 and $\{y_{2n}\}$ converges uniformly to a function y_2. Then y_1 and y_2 will satisfy (8) as can be readily seen by letting $n \to \infty$ in (9). Equation (9) therefore yields an iterative process for obtaining the solutions of (8). This process, called **Picard's method**, can be applied to more general situations.

The uniform convergence of the sequences defined by (9) will follow if we can show the uniform convergence of the infinite series

(10)
$$\begin{cases} -y_{10}(x) + (y_{11}(x) - y_{10}(x)) + \ldots + (y_{1n}(x) - y_{1,n-1}(x)) + \ldots, \\ y_{20}(x) + (y_{21}(x) - y_{20}(x)) + \ldots + (y_{2n}(x) - y_{2,n-1}(x)) + \ldots, \end{cases}$$

since the partial sums of the first $n + 1$ terms of the series are $y_{1n}(x)$ and $y_{2n}(x)$. To do this, let P_1, Q_1, R_1 be the maximum values of $|P|$, $|Q|$, and $|R|$ respectively on $a \leq x \leq b$, and let

$$M = |c_1| + |c_2| + R_1, \quad N = 1 + P_1 + Q_1.$$

Then

$$|y_{11}(x) - y_{10}(x)| \leq |c_2| \, |x - x_0| \leq M \, |x - x_0| \leq NM \, |x - x_0|,$$

$$|y_{21}(x) - y_{20}(x)| \leq (|c_1| \, Q_1 + |c_2| \, P_1 + R_1)|x - x_0| \leq NM \, |x - x_0|;$$

and, for $n \geq 2$,

$$|y_{1n}(x) - y_{1,n-1}(x)| = \left| \int_{x_0}^{x} (y_{2,n-1}(t) - y_{2,n-2}(t))dt \right|,$$

$$|y_{2n}(x) - y_{2,n-1}(x)| = \left| \int_{x_0}^{x} \Big((y_{1,n-1}(t) - y_{1,n-2}(t))Q(t) + (y_{2,n-1}(t) \right.$$
$$\left. - y_{2,n-2}(t))P(t) \Big)dt \right|.$$

By induction, we establish

$$|y_{1n}(x) - y_{1,n-1}(x)| \leq MN^n \, |x - x_0|^n/n!,$$

$$|y_{2n}(x) - y_{2,n-1}(x)| \leq MN^n \, |x - x_0|^n/n!.$$

Thus each term of the series in (10) is dominated by the corresponding term of the series $M \sum_{n=0}^{\infty} \dfrac{N^n(b - a)^n}{n!} = Me^{N(b-a)}$. By the Weierstrass M test, the series in (10) converge uniformly on $a \leq x \leq b$, and hence converge to continuous functions. In view of the discussion above, the proof of existence of solutions of (8), and hence of (6), is complete.

It remains to prove the uniqueness. Suppose also $z_1(x)$ and $z_2(x)$ satisfy

$$z_1(x) = c_1 + \int_{x_0}^{x} z_2(t)dt,$$

$$z_2(x) = c_2 + \int_{x_0}^{x} \Big(- Q(t) \, z_1(t) - P(t) \, z_2(t) + R(t) \Big)dt.$$

Then $y_1(x) - z_1(x) = \int_{x_0}^{x} \Big(y_2(t) - z_2(t) \Big)dt,$

$$y_2(x) - z_2(x) = \int_{x_0}^{x} \Big(- Q(t) \Big(y_1(t) - z_1(t) \Big) - P(t) \Big(y_2(t) - z_2(t) \Big) \Big) dt;$$

whence

(11) $\quad |y_1(x) - z_1(x)| + |y_2(x) - z_2(x)| \leq N \left| \int_{x_0}^{x} |y_1(t) - z_1(t)| + |y_2(t) \right.$
$$\left. - z_2(t)|dt \right|.$$

With $B = \text{l.u.b.} \left\{ |y_1(x) - z_1(x)| + |y_2(x) - z_2(x)| \,\Big|\, a \le x \le b \right\}$, we obtain from (11),

$$|y_1(x) - z_1(x)| + |y_2(x) - z_2(x)| \le NB \,|x - x_0|$$

and so, by repetition, for any positive integer j,

$$|y_1(x) - z_1(x)| + |y_2(x) - z_2(x)| \le \frac{N^j \, B |x - x_0|^j}{j!},$$

yielding $y_1(x) = z_1(x)$, $\;\; y_2(x) = z_2(x)$.   ★

It is of interest to know that small changes in P, Q, R cause only small changes in the solution of (6), We state this as

Corollary 1

If P, Q, R in (6) are continuous functions of both x and a parameter r on $a \le x \le b$, $r_1 \le r \le r_2$, then the solution f and its derivative f' are continuous functions of x and r.

This follows from the fact that $y_{1n}(x, r)$ and $y_{2n}(x, r)$ defined by (9) are continuous functions of x and r (the proof is by induction on n); and hence, if P_1, Q_1, R_1 are taken to be the least upper bounds of $|P|$, $|Q|$, $|R|$ respectively on $a \le x \le b$, $r_1 \le r \le r_2$, the terms in (10) are continuous functions of x and r and the series converge uniformly to $y_1(x, r) = f(x, r)$ and $y_2(x, r) = \dfrac{\partial f}{\partial x}(x, r)$ on $a \le x \le b$, $r_1 \le r \le r_2$. The limit functions are therefore continuous in x and r.

The equation

$$(12) \qquad\qquad f'' + Pf' + Qf = 0, \qquad a \le x \le b,$$

is called the **homogeneous equation** related to (1). It is clear that any finite linear combination of solutions of (12) is also a solution of (12). We intend to show that the linear manifold of solutions of (12) has dimension two. For this purpose we need the concept of the Wronskian of a pair of functions. Let f and g have first derivatives on $a \le x \le b$. Then the **Wronskian** $W[f, g]$ is defined by

$$(13) \qquad\qquad W[f, g] = \begin{vmatrix} f & g \\ f' & g' \end{vmatrix}.$$

THEOREM 6.2B   If f and g have first derivatives on $a \le x \le b$ and are linearly dependent, their Wronskian is zero.

Proof The vectors f and g being linearly dependent, there exist constants c_1 and c_2, not both zero, such that

$$c_1 f(x) + c_2 g(x) = 0, \qquad a \le x \le b,$$

and hence

$$c_1 f'(x) + c_2 g'(x) = 0, \qquad a \le x \le b.$$

It follows that the determinant of coefficients is zero. ★

The converse of Theorem 6.2B is not true (Exercise 6.2–2). However, it is true if f and g are solutions of (12).

THEOREM 6.2C If f and g are solutions of (12) and if their Wronskian vanishes for one point x_0 in $a \le x \le b$, then it vanishes for all x in $a \le x \le b$ and f and g are linearly dependent.

Proof Consider the equations

$$(14) \qquad \begin{aligned} c_1 f(x_0) + c_2 g(x_0) &= 0, \\ c_1 f'(x_0) + c_2 g'(x_0) &= 0. \end{aligned}$$

The vanishing of $W[f, g]$ at x_0 implies the existence of constants c_1 and c_2, not both zero, satisfying (14). Then

$$(15) \qquad h(x) = c_1 f(x) + c_2 g(x)$$

is a solution of (12) satisfying $h(x_0) = 0$, $h'(x_0) = 0$. The uniqueness property in Theorem 6.2A indicates that h must be identically zero. Equation (15) now shows that f and g are linearly dependent and the Wronskian is zero on $a \le x \le b$ by Theorem 6.2B. ★

THEOREM 6.2D There exist two linearly independent solutions of (12) and every other solution is a linear combination of these two.

Proof Let f and g be solutions of (12) satisfying

$$f(x_0) = 1, \quad f'(x_0) = 0, \quad g(x_0) = 0, \quad g'(x_0) = 1,$$

where $a \le x_0 \le b$. The Wronskian of f and g is not zero, so f and g are linearly independent. If h is any other solution of (12), note that

$$w(x) = h(x) - h(x_0) f(x) - h'(x_0) g(x)$$

is a solution of (12) satisfying $w(x_0) = 0$, $w'(x_0) = 0$; hence $w(x)$ is zero by Theorem 6.2A, and

$$h(x) = h(x_0) f(x) + h'(x_0) g(x). \qquad ★$$

Having found a basis for the linear manifold of solutions of (12), one can solve equation (1) by Lagrange's **method of variation of parameters**, as indicated in the next theorem.

THEOREM 6.2E Let f and g be linearly independent solutions of (12), and let h be any solution of (1). Then every solution of (1) is of the form

$$h + c_1 f + c_2 g$$

for constants c_1 and c_2. As a solution h of (1) we may use

$$(16) \qquad h(x) = \int_{x_0}^x \frac{f(t) g(x) - g(t) f(x)}{W[f(t), g(t)]} R(t)\, dt,$$

where x_0 is any point on $a \le x \le b$.

Proof Let w be a solution of (1). Then $w - h$ is a solution of (12) and is thus of the form

$$w - h = c_1 f + c_2 g$$

in view of Theorem 6.2D.

Let us seek a solution of (1) of the form

$$(17) \qquad h(x) = A(x)f(x) + B(x)g(x)$$

where $A(x)$ and $B(x)$ also satisfy

$$(18) \qquad 0 = A'(x) f(x) + B'(x)g(x).$$

Differentiating (17) we obtain

$$h'(x) = A(x)f'(x) + B(x)g'(x)$$
$$h''(x) = A(x)f''(x) + B(x)g''(x) + A'(x)f'(x) + B'(x)g'(x).$$

Substituting into (1) and remembering that f and g satisfy (12), we find

$$(19) \qquad A'(x)f'(x) + B'(x)g'(x) = R(x).$$

Solving (19) and (18) simultaneously, we obtain

$$A'(x) = \frac{-R(x)g(x)}{W[f, g]}, \qquad B'(x) = \frac{R(x)f(x)}{W[f, g]}.$$

Integrating and substituting into (17) yields (16).   ★

EXAMPLE 1 One solution of Legendre's differential equation

(20) $$(1 - x^2)f'' - 2xf' + n(n + 1)f = 0$$

is $P_n(x)$, the Legendre polynomial of degree n. In any interval not·containing $x = 1$ or $x = -1$, (20) can be put in the form (12) with $P(x) = \dfrac{-2x}{1-x^2}$, $Q(x) = \dfrac{n(n+1)}{1-x^2}$. The following procedure may be used to find a second linearly independent solution. Suppose $f(x)$ is a solution of (12), and

(21) $$g(x) = h(x) f(x)$$

where h is to be determined so that g is a solution of (12). Moreover we desire h to be different from a constant in order that f and g be linearly independent. Differentiating (21) twice and substituting into (12), we obtain

$$fh'' + (2f' + Pf)h' + (f'' + Pf' + Qf)h = 0.$$

The coefficient of h vanishes since f is a solution of (12). Writing $w = h'$, we obtain in turn,

$$\frac{w'}{w} + 2\frac{f'}{f} + P = 0,$$

$$\frac{d}{dx}\left(\log w + 2 \log f + \int_{x_0}^{x} P(t)\,dt \right) = 0,$$

$$\log\left(wf^2\, E\left[\int_{x_0}^{x} P(t)\,dt \right] \right) = c_1 \qquad \text{where } E[z] = e^z,$$

$$h' = w = \frac{c_2}{f^2 E\left[\int_{x_0}^{x} P(t)dt \right]},$$

$$h(x) = c_2 \int_{x_0}^{x} \frac{dz}{f(z)^2 E\left[\int_{x_0}^{z} P(t)dt \right]} + c_3.$$

Then

(22) $$g(x) = f(x) \int_{x_0}^{x} \frac{dz}{f(z)^2 E\left[\int_{x_0}^{z} P(t)dt \right]}$$

is another solution of (12), at least in any interval which contains x_0 and where $f(x)$ is different from zero. Then, evaluation of the Wronskian shows that f and g are linearly independent.

When we apply the above result to equation (20) we find a solution of (20) to be

(23) $$Q_n(x) = P_n(x) \int_{x_0}^{x} \frac{dz}{P_n(z)^2(1 - z^2)}.$$

Now $P_n(z)$ is a polynomial of degree n and $P_n^2(\pm 1) = 1$. Therefore, by the theory of partial fractions,

$$(24) \qquad \frac{1}{(1 - z^2) P_n(z)^2} = \frac{1}{2(1 - z)} + \frac{1}{2(1 + z)} + \sum_{i=1}^{n} \left(\frac{A_i}{z - z_i} + \frac{B_i}{(z - z_i)^2} \right)$$

where $z_1, \ldots, z_n$ are the zeros of $P_n(z)$. We shall show that $A_i = 0$ for each i. Multiply (24) by $(z - z_j)^2$ and define $T_n(z)$ by $P_n(z) = (z - z_j) T_n(z)$. We have, writing T for T_n,

$$\frac{1}{(1 - z^2) T^2} = \frac{(z - z_j)^2}{(1 - z^2)} + A_j(z - z_j) + B_j$$

$$+ (z - z_j)^2 \left(\sum_{i \neq j} \frac{A_i}{z - z_i} + \frac{B_i}{(z - z_i)^2} \right).$$

Hence

$$A_j = \frac{d}{dz} \frac{1}{(1 - z^2) T^2} \bigg|_{z = z_j} = \frac{2 z_j T(z_j) - 2(1 - z_j^2) T'(z_j)}{(1 - z_j^2)^2 T(z_j)^3}.$$

Substituting $(z - z_j) T(z)$ for $P_n(z)$ in Legendre's equation yields

$$(1 - z^2)\left((z - z_j) T'' + 2 T' \right) - 2z\left((z - z_j) T' + T \right) + n(n + 1)(z - z_j) T = 0,$$

and evaluating this equation at z_j gives

$$2(1 - z_j^2) T'(z_j) - 2 z_j T(z_j) = 0,$$

showing that $A_j = 0$.

From (23) and (24), for x and x_0 in an interval containing no zeros of P_n,

$$(25) \qquad Q_n(x) = \tfrac{1}{2} P_n(x) \log \frac{1 + x}{1 - x} - P_n(x) \left(\sum_{i=1}^{n} \frac{B_i}{x - z_i} + K \right),$$

so that

$$(26) \qquad \tfrac{1}{2} P_n(x) \log \frac{1 + x}{1 - x} - P_n(x) \sum_{i=1}^{n} \frac{B_i}{x - z_i}$$

is a solution of (20) valid for $-1 < x < 1$.

The Legendre polynomials are therefore the only solutions of (20) which are finite at $x = \pm 1$.

EXAMPLE 2   Given two functions f and g with two continuous second derivatives on $a \leq x \leq b$ and nonzero Wronskian, find a linear homogeneous differential equation of second order for which f and g are solutions.

If h is a solution of the equation sought, then h is of the form $h = c_1 f + c_2 g$. Differentiating we obtain

$$h' = c_1 f' + c_2 g',$$
$$h'' = c_1 f'' + c_2 g'',$$

and thus

$$\begin{vmatrix} f & g & h \\ f' & g' & h' \\ f'' & g'' & h'' \end{vmatrix} = 0.$$

The required equation is

$$\begin{vmatrix} f & g \\ f' & g' \end{vmatrix} h'' - \begin{vmatrix} f & g \\ f'' & g'' \end{vmatrix} h' + \begin{vmatrix} f' & g' \\ f'' & g'' \end{vmatrix} h = 0.$$

Some of the simpler theorems regarding the zeros of solutions of (12) are of interest. From these theorems we can deduce important properties of the solutions.

THEOREM 6.2F Let f be a nonidentically zero solution of (12). Then the zeros of f are simple, i.e. if $f(z) = 0$, then $f'(z) \neq 0$. On the finite interval $a \leq x \leq b$, f has only a finite number of zeros.

Proof If $f'(z) = 0$ and $f(z) = 0$, f would be identically zero by the uniqueness property given in Theorem 6.2A. Suppose now there exists an infinity of zeros of f on $a \leq x \leq b$. Then there is a sequence $\{z_i\}$ such that $f(z_i) = 0$ and $\lim_{i \to \infty} z_i = z$ where $a \leq z \leq b$ (Theorem 3.1B.) The continuity of f assures that $f(z) = 0$. Moreover, if we let x approach z through the values z_i in the formula $f'(z) = \lim_{x \to z} \dfrac{f(x) - f(z)}{x - z}$, we get $f'(z) = 0$, a contradiction. ★

It is often convenient to write (12) in a different form. Multiply each side of (12) by $E\left[\int_a^x P(y)dy\right]$, where $E[z] = e^z$, to obtain

$$(27) \qquad \frac{d}{dx}\left(E\left[\int_a^x P(y)dy\right]f'(x)\right) + Q(x)E\left[\int_a^x P(y)dy\right]f(x) = 0.$$

The substitution

$$(28) \qquad t = t(x) = \int_a^x E\left[-\int_a^z P(y)dy\right]dz$$

defines t as a strictly monotone increasing function of x with
$\dfrac{dt}{dx} = E\left[-\displaystyle\int_a^x P(y)dy \right]$. Then

$$\frac{df}{dx} = \frac{df}{dt}\frac{dt}{dx}, \qquad \frac{df}{dt} = E\left[\int_a^x P(y)dy\right]\frac{df}{dx},$$

$$\frac{d}{dx}\left(E\left[\int_a^x P(y)dy\right]\frac{df}{dx}\right) = \frac{d}{dt}\left(\frac{df}{dt}\right)\cdot\frac{dt}{dx},$$

and (27) becomes

(29) $$\frac{d^2 f(x(t))}{dt^2} + Q(x(t))\left(E\left[\int_a^{x(t)} P(y)dy\right]\right)^2 f(x(t)) = 0,$$

which, when

(30) $$g(t) = f(x(t)), \qquad q(t) = Q(x(t))\left(E\left[\int_a^{x(t)} P(y)dy\right]\right)^2,$$

may be written as

(31) $$\frac{d^2 g}{dt^2} + q(t)\,g(t) = 0, \qquad 0 \le t \le T = \int_a^b E\left[-\int_a^z P(y)dy\right]dz.$$

Equation (31) is called the **normal form** for (12). We see that $g(t)$ is a solution of (31) if and only if $f(x) = g(t(x))$ is a solution of (12). Furthermore $g(t)$ is zero for $t = t_1$ if and only if $f(x)$ is zero for $x_1 = x(t_1)$, and $g'(t) = f'(x)\,x'(t) = f'(x)E\left[\int_a^x P(y)dy\right]$ is zero for $t = t_1$ if and only if $f'(x)$ is zero for $x = x_1$. Moreover the Wronskian of two solutions $g_1(t)$ and $g_2(t)$ of (31) at $t = t_1$ is $x'(t_1)$ multiplied by the Wronskian of $f_1(x) = g_1(t(x))$ and $f_2(x) = g_2(t(x))$ at $x = x(t_1)$. Hence linearly independent solutions of (31) correspond to linearly independent solutions of (12).

The following theorems illustrate the use of the normal form.

THEOREM 6.2G Let f be a nonidentically zero solution of (12). If $Q(x) < 0$ on $a \le x \le b$, then ff' cannot have more than one zero on the interval.

Proof Assuming the contrary, let z_1 and z_2 be consecutive zeros of ff' on $a \le x \le b$. Then $t_1 = t(z_1)$ and $t_2 = t(z_2)$, where $t(x)$ is given by (28), are consecutive zeros of $g(t)g'(t)$, where $g(t) = f(x(t))$ is a solution of (31). When $Q(x) < 0$, then (30) indicates that $q(t) < 0$, and

(32) $$\int_{t_1}^{t_2} g'(t)^2 dt = gg'\Big|_{t_1}^{t_2} - \int_{t_1}^{t_2} gg''dt = \int_{t_1}^{t_2} q(t)\,g(t)^2 dt < 0.$$

This contradiction proves that we cannot have two zeros z_1 and z_2 on $a \leq x \leq b$.   ★

EXAMPLE 3   Theorem 6.2G indicates that any nonzero solution of Legendre's equation can have at most one zero for $|x| > 1$, since then

$$Q(x) = \frac{n(n + 1)}{1 - x^2} < 0.$$ Indeed, for the Legendre polynomials, the theorem

shows all the zeros lie within $|x| < 1$. We need only consider positive x, the Legendre polynomials being either even or odd. We have $P_n(1) = 1$ and $P_n(x)$ positive for large x. Hence a zero $x_1 > 1$ for $P_n(x)$ would necessitate a zero for $P_n'(x)$ for some value $x_2 > 1$, and thus contradict Theorem 6.2G. Of course this result for Legendre polynomials has already been proved in Theorem 5.3C.

The next theorem is called the **Sturm Comparison Theorem.**

THEOREM 6.2H   Let f and f_1 be not identically zero and satisfy

(33) $$f''(x) + P(x)f'(x) + Q(x)f(x) = 0,$$

(34) $$f_1''(x) + P(x)f_1'(x) + Q_1(x)f_1(x) = 0,$$

respectively on $a \leq x \leq b$. Let z_1 and z_2 be consecutive zeros of f. If $Q_1(x) \geq Q(x)$ on $z_1 \leq x \leq z_2$, then there is a zero of f_1 in this interval. If, on $z_1 \leq x \leq z_2$, Q_1 is not identically Q, the zero of f_1 is within $z_1 < x < z_2$.

Proof   Again use the transformation $t(x)$ given by (28) carrying $f(x)$ into $g(t)$ and $f_1(x)$ into $g_1(t)$ and (33) and (34) respectively into

(35) $$g''(t) + q(t) g(t) = 0,$$

(36) $$g_1''(t) + q_1(t) g_1(t) = 0,$$

where $q_1(t) = Q_1(x(t))\left(E\left[\int_a^{x(t)} P(y)dy\right]\right)^2 \geq Q(x(t))\left(E\left[\int_a^{x(t)} P(y)dy\right]\right)^2 = q(t).$
Then

$$\frac{d}{dt}(gg_1' - g_1g') = gg_1'' - g_1g'' = -(q_1 - q)gg_1,$$

(37) $$gg_1' - g_1g' \Big|_{t_1}^{t_2} = -\int_{t_1}^{t_2}(q_1 - q)gg_1 \, dt,$$

where $t_1 = t(z_1)$ and $t_2 = t(z_2)$ are consecutive zeros of g. We may assume $g(t) > 0$ for $t_1 < t < t_2$ (or else we use $-g$). If $g_1(t)$ is not zero for $t_1 \leq t \leq t_2$, we may assume $g_1(t) > 0$ for $t_1 \leq t \leq t_2$. Then $g'(t_1) > 0$, $g'(t_2) < 0$, the right side of (37) is nonpositive and the left side is positive. This contradiction shows that g_1 has a zero on $t_1 \leq t \leq t_2$.

If q_1 is not identically q, and $g_1(t) > 0$ for $t_1 < t < t_2$, the right side of (37) is negative, whereas the left side is nonnegative. This is again a contradiction. ★

Corollary 1

Let v and w be linearly independent solutions of (12). Between consecutive zeros of v there is one and only one zero of w.

Proof If z_1 and z_2 are consecutive zeros of v then a zero of w occurs on $z_1 \le x \le z_2$. However the zero cannot occur at z_1 or z_2, for then the Wronskian of v and w would be zero, contradicting the linear independence.

There cannot be two zeros of w between z_1 and z_2 for then the same argument would yield a zero of v between the two zeros of w. ★

The equation

$$g''(t) = -q(t)\,g(t)$$

shows that the convexity of g is increased when $q(t)$ is increased. This comment is made more precise by the next theorem.

THEOREM 6.2I Let f and f_1 be not identically zero and satisfy (33) and (34) respectively on $a \le x \le b$. Let $f(a) = f_1(a), f'(a) = f_1'(a)$ and suppose $Q_1(x) > Q(x)$. If $f(x)$ and $f_1(x)$ are positive for $a < x < d \le b$ then $f(x) > f_1(x)$ on this interval. If $f(x)$ and $f_1(x)$ are negative for $a < x < d \le b$ then $f(x) < f_1(x)$ on this interval.

Proof As in the proof of Theorem 6.2H, we obtain, with $t_1 = t(a)$,

$$(38) \qquad g(t)g_1'(t) - g_1(t)g'(t) = gg_1' - g_1g' \Big|_{t_1}^{t} = -\int_{t_1}^{t} (q_1 - q)gg_1 dt.$$

When $t > t_1$, the right side is negative. Therefore

$$\frac{d}{dt}\frac{g_1}{g} = \frac{gg_1' - g_1g'}{g^2} < 0$$

and $\dfrac{g_1}{g}$ is a decreasing function. However $\lim\limits_{t \to t_1} \dfrac{g_1}{g} = 1$, so that $0 < g_1(t) < g(t)$ on $t_1 < t < t(d)$ when g_1 is positive on the interval, and $g(t) < g_1(t) < 0$ when g_1 is negative on the interval. ★

Corollary 1

Under the hypotheses of the theorem, f_1 has at least as many zeros as f on $a \le x \le b$ and the nth zero to the right of a of f_1 is to the left of the nth zero to the right of a of f.

Indeed, taking t in (38) to be the first such zero of g, we find $g_1(t)\,g'(t) > 0$. Assuming g and g_1 positive near t_1, we obtain $g'(t) < 0$, therefore $g_1(t) < 0$, and so the first zero of g_1 occurs to the left of the first zero of g. The same result holds when g and g_1 are negative near t_1. The corollary can then be proved by induction. Suppose the $n - 1^{\text{st}}$ such zero $z_{1,n-1}$ of f_1 is to the left of the $n - 1^{\text{st}}$ zero z_{n-1} of f. By Theorem 6.2H there is a zero of f_1 between z_{n-1} and z_n. Hence the nth zero of f_1 is to the left of z_n.

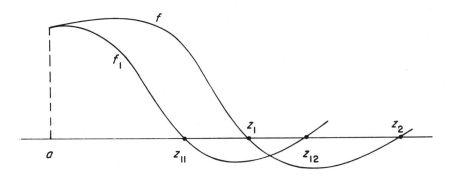

Exercise 6.2

1. (a) By examining the proof of Theorem 6.2A show that the solution f of (6) satisfies $|f(x)| \le Me^{N(b-a)}$ where M and N are defined in the proof of the theorem.

   (b) Now let g be a solution of

   $$g''(x) + Pg'(x) + Qg(x) = R(x), \qquad a \le x \le b,$$
   $$g(x_0) = c_1 + E_1, \qquad g'(x_0) = c_2 + E_2,$$

   where E_1 and E_2 are also constants. Show that

   $$|f - g| \le (|E_1| + |E_2|)e^{N(b-a)}.$$

   This shows that a small change in initial conditions causes only a small change in the solution. *Hint:* What equation does $f - g$ satisfy?

2. (a) Show that the Wronskian of x^3 and $|x|^3$ vanishes identically but that these two functions are not linearly dependent on $-1 \le x \le 1$.

   (b) Why is the example in (a) preferable to a similar example using x and $|x|$?

   (c) Show that if the Wronskian of f and g is zero for all x on $c \le x \le d$ and f (or g) does not vanish on the interval, then f and g are linearly dependent.

3. The Wronskian of a set of $n - 1$ times differentiable functions $f_1, \ldots, f_n$ is defined by

$$W[f_1, \ldots, f_n] = \begin{vmatrix} f_1 & f_2 & \cdots & f_n \\ f_1' & f_2' & \cdots & f_n' \\ & & \cdot & \\ & & \cdot & \\ & & \cdot & \\ f_1^{(n-1)} & f_2^{(n-1)} & \cdots & f_n^{(n-1)} \end{vmatrix}.$$

Show that the Wronskian of any three solutions of (12) is zero.

4. Show that the Wronskian of two solutions f and g of (12) satisfies $W'(x) = -PW$, and hence

$$W(x) = W(x_0)e^{-\int_{x_0}^x P(t)dt}.$$

5. Show that if two solutions f and g of (12) vanish at the same point x_0 or if they have maxima or minima at the same point x_0 interior to $a < x < b$, then they are linearly dependent.

6. Show that $\sin^2 x$ and $\cos^2 x$ are linearly independent solutions of some second order differential equation. Show that the Wronskian is zero at $x = 0$, but not identically zero. Does this contradict Theorem 6.2C?

7. One solution of $f'' = 0$, $-1 \le x \le 1$, is $f(x) = x$. Use equation (22) to find another linearly independent solution, taking first $x_0 = 1$ and then $x_0 = -1$. Hence note that (22) gives different functions on $x > 0$ and $x < 0$, each of which is a solution of $f'' = 0$ on $-1 \le x \le 1$. These functions differ by a multiple of f.

8. Verify that (26) is a solution of (20).

9. Verify that f and g in (22) are linearly independent.

10. By a method similar to that used in Theorem 6.2A, it can be shown that there exists a unique solution of

$$f^{(n)}(x) + P_1(x)f^{(n-1)}(x) + \ldots + P_n(x)f(x) = R(x), \qquad a \le x \le b,$$

such that f and its first $n - 1$ derivatives take on prescribed values at a given point x_0 in $a \le x \le b$. Here $P_1, \ldots P_n$, R are assumed continuous. The Wronskian of n functions is defined in Exercise 3. Prove the following theorems:

(a) If $f_1, \ldots, f_n$ are linearly dependent and have $n - 1$ continuous derivatives, their Wronskian is zero.

(b) If $f_1, \ldots, f_n$ are solutions of
$$(*)\, f^{(n)}(x) + P_1(x)f^{(n-1)}(x) + \ldots + P_n(x)f(x) = 0$$
and if their Wronskian vanishes for one point x_0 in $a \le x \le b$, then it vanishes for all x in $a \le x \le b$ and $f_1, \ldots, f_n$ are linearly dependent.

(c) The linear manifold of solutions of the homogeneous equation (*) has dimension n.

(d) The Wronskian $W[f_1, \ldots, f_n]$ of a set of n solutions of (*) satisfies
$$W(x) = W(x_0)\, e^{-\int_{x_0}^x P_1(t)dt}.$$

11. Show that $f(x) = \sin^2 x$ and $g(x) = \cos^2 x$ are linearly independent solutions of $y''' + 4y' = 0$, but the Wronskian of f and g vanishes at $x = 0$. Does this contradict Exercise 10(b)?

12. Verify that x is a solution of

$$(1 - x)f''(x) + xf'(x) - f(x) = 0, \qquad -1 < x < 1.$$

Then find the general solution.

13. Use the method of variations of parameters to solve
$$4f''(x) - f(x) = e^{-x/2}(x - \cos x/2).$$

14. (a) Verify that x is a solution of

$$x^2 f''(x) - 2xf'(x) + 2f(x) = 0, \qquad x > 0.$$

(b) Find the general solution of

$$x^2 f''(x) - 2xf'(x) + 2f(x) = x^3, \qquad x > 0.$$

15. Solve the equation

$$(x^2 - 2x) f''(x) - (x^2 - 2) f'(x) + 2(x - 1) f(x) = (x^2 - 4x + 2)e^x.$$

16. (a) Let $c_1, \ldots, c_n$ be real and distinct constants. Prove that $e^{c_1 x}, e^{c_2 x}, \ldots, e^{c_n x}$ are linearly independent over any finite interval by showing that they are solutions of an nth order differential equation and that their Wronskian is not zero.

(b) Read *A Wronskian* by D. Zeitlin, *American Mathematical Monthly*, Vol. 65, No. 5, pp. 345–349.

17. Let f and g have power series expansions for some positive interval about the origin. Show that if the Wronskian of f and g is identically zero, then f and g are linearly dependent on that interval. *Hint:* Assume as known that it suffices to prove the result for any subinterval.

18. (a) Show that between every pair of consecutive zeros of $\sin x$ there is one zero of $A \sin x + B \cos x$ for every pair of real numbers A and $B \neq 0$.

(b) Show that between every pair of consecutive zeros of $\sin \log x$ there is a zero of $\cos \log x$.

19. Show that if f and g are linearly independent solutions of (12) then f/g is monotone in every interval where $g \neq 0$.

20. If f and g are solutions of (12) with $f(x_0) = g(x_0) > 0$ and $f'(x_0) > g'(x_0)$, then g will have a zero to the right of x_0 before f does.

21. If f is a solution of (12) and $f(x) > 0$ for $z_1 < x < z_2$ where z_1 and z_2 are consecutive zeros of f, then $f'(z_1) > 0$ and $f'(z_2) < 0$.

22. Use the method of Theorem 6.2G to prove that if $Q(x) \leq 0$ on $a \leq x \leq b$, then a not identically zero solution of (12) has at most one zero. Prove the same result using Theorem 6.2H and $f_1''(x) = 0$.

23. Generalize Theorem 6.2H as follows: If the functions f and g are not identically zero and satisfy

$$\frac{d}{dx}\left\{ p(x) f'(x) \right\} + Q(x) f(x) = 0, \qquad \frac{d}{dx}\left\{ p_1(x) g'(x) \right\} + Q_1(x) g(x) = 0,$$

where $0 \leq p_1(x) \leq p(x)$, $Q_1(x) \geq Q(x)$, and Q_1 and Q are not identical on $z_1 \leq x \leq z_2$, z_1 and z_2 being consecutive zeros of f, then g has a zero on $z_1 < x < z_2$. *Hint:* If $g(x) \neq 0$ on $z_1 < x < z_2$, show that

$$\frac{d}{dx}\left[\frac{f}{g} (pf'g - p_1 g'f) \right] = (Q_1 - Q)f^2 + (p - p_1)(f')^2 + p_1\left(\frac{f'g - g'f}{g} \right)^2.$$

24. Prove Corollary 1 to Theorem 6.2H directly by applying Rolle's Theorem to the function v/w assuming w is not zero between a pair of consecutive zeros of v.

25. Use equation (32) to show that the zeros of E_n, the Hermite functions, and of E_n', are confined to the interval $-\sqrt{2n + 1} < x < \sqrt{2n + 1}$. Compare with Exercise 5.5–11. *Hint:* Let $t_1 > 2n + 1$ be a zero of $E_n E_n'$ and let $t_2 \to \infty$.

26. Show that Corollary 1 of Theorem 6.2H is not valid for complex valued solutions of (12). Consider the solution $\cos x + i \sin x$ of $f'' + f = 0$.

27. Show that a nonidentically zero solution of (12) cannot have an infinite number of maxima or minima in any closed interval where $Q(x)$ is never 0.

28. Show that Theorems 6.2A, B, C, D, E remain valid when the interval is $-\infty < x < \infty$ rather than $a \le x \le b$.

29. (a) Give an example of a nonzero function f satisfying a second order homogeneous differential equation such that f' has an infinity of zeros on a finite interval.

   (b) Show that $x^6 \sin 1/x$ satisfies a second order nonhomogeneous differential equation and has an infinity of zeros on a finite interval.

30. (a) Show that the substitution $f(x) = g(x) E[-\frac{1}{2} \int_0^x P(t)dt]$ transforms (1) into

$$g'' + \left(Q - \frac{P'}{2} - \frac{P^2}{4} \right)g = RE\left[\frac{1}{2} \int_0^x P(t)dt \right].$$

   (b) Using (a), solve

$$f''(x) - 4x f'(x) + (4x^2 - 1) f(x) = -3e^{x^2} \sin 2x.$$

   (c) Using (a), solve

$$f''(x) + 2f'(x) + \left(1 - \frac{2}{x^2} \right) f(x) = 0.$$

31. (a) If u is a solution of $u''(x) + P u'(x) = 0$, show that the change of variable $x = x(u)$ transforms (1) into

$$F''(u) + Q(x(u))(x'(u))^2 F(u) = R(x(u))(x'(u))^2,$$

   where $F(u) = f(x(u))$.

   (b) Using (a), solve

$$f''(x) + \left(1 - \frac{1}{x} \right) f'(x) + 4x^2 e^{-2x} f(x) = 4(x^2 + x^3)e^{-3x}.$$

   (c) Using (a), solve

$$xf''(x) - f'(x) + 4x^3 f(x) = x^5.$$

32. Formulate an equivalent integral equation for the differential equation $y'(x) = x + y(x)$, $y(0) = 0$, and solve by Picard's method.

33. Apply Picard's method to obtain the solution of

$$y'' + (x - 1)y' - xy = 0, \quad y(0) = 1, \quad y'(0) = 1.$$

34. Formulate an equivalent system of integral equations for the differential equation $y''(x) = \left(\frac{x^2}{4} + y'(x) \right)^{1/2} - \frac{x}{2}$, $0 \le x \le b, y(0) = 0, y'(0) = 0$, and solve by Picard's method.

   (b) Show that another solution is $y = -x^3/12$. Does this contradict the uniqueness property in Theorem 6.2A?

   (c) Read Chapters 15 and 16 in *Differential Equations* by R. P. Agnew, 2nd ed., 1960, McGraw-Hill, N.Y.

6.3

A STURM-LIOUVILLE
PROBLEM

The theory of boundary value problems concerns itself with the solution of an equation (ordinary differential equation, partial differential equation, difference equation, integral equation, etc.) where the solution is restricted to satisfy certain conditions on the boundary of the domain of definition of the solution. The central problem is to determine the character of the solution and to indicate how the solution changes when the equation or the boundary conditions change.

We may consider Theorem 6.2A as a theorem about a differential equation with boundary conditions at one point. The corollary to that theorem tells us something about the change in the solution when the equation is changed.

Let us now begin the study of an ordinary second order differential equation with boundary conditions at two points.

The differential equation to be considered will be taken in the form

$$(1) \qquad \frac{d}{dx}\left(P(x)\,\frac{df}{dx}\right) + (r\rho(x) - Q(x))f(x) = 0, \qquad a \le x \le b,$$

where r is a constant, to be considered as a parameter. The functions P, Q, ρ are continuous and P has a continuous derivative on the interval. Moreover $P(x)$ and $\rho(x)$ are positive on $a \le x \le b$.

When we write

$$(2) \qquad\qquad\qquad L = Q - \frac{d}{dx}\left(P\,\frac{d}{dx}\right),$$

equation (1) takes the form

$$(3) \qquad\qquad\qquad Lf = r\rho f,$$

suggesting that we analyze (1) as an eigenvalue problem.

When f and g have continuous first derivatives and piecewise continuous second derivatives on $a \le x \le b$, an integration by parts validates the important identity

$$(4) \qquad\qquad \int_{x_1}^{x_2} ((Lf)g - f(Lg))dx = P(x)\,W\,[f, g]\,\Big|_{x_1}^{x_2},$$

where $W[f, g] = fg' - gf'$ is the Wronskian of f and g.

As a first application of (4), suppose that f and g are solutions of (1) so that

$$Lf = r\rho f, \qquad Lg = r\rho g.$$

Then (4) implies

$$P(x)\, W[f, g]\Big|_{x_1}^{x_2} = 0, \qquad a \le x_1 \le x_2 \le b;$$

or

(5) $$P(x)\, W[f, g] = \text{constant}, \qquad a \le x \le b.$$

In particular, the Wronskian of any two solutions of

$$f'' + hf = 0$$

is a constant, for any continuous function h.

For another application of (4), let f be a solution of (1) and g a solution of (1) when r is replaced by $s \ne r$. Then (4) and

$$Lf = r\rho f, \qquad Lg = s\rho g,$$

yield

$$(r - s) \int_a^b \rho(x)\, f(x)\, g(x)\, dx = P(x)\, [fg' - gf']\Big|_a^b .$$

It follows that f and g will be orthogonal over $a \le x \le b$ with respect to the weight function ρ if and only if f and g satisfy boundary conditions at a and b such that

(6) $$P\, [fg' - gf']\Big|_a^b = 0.$$

We shall confine our study to the following system, called a **Sturm-Liouville system** in honor of the two mathematicians who developed the theory in 1836:

(7) $$Lf = r\rho f, \qquad a \le x \le b,$$

(7a) $$a_1 f(a) + a_2 f'(a) = 0,$$

(7b) $$b_1 f(b) + b_2 f'(b) = 0.$$

Here a_1, a_2, b_1, b_2 are constants with

$$|a_1| + |a_2| \ne 0, \qquad |b_1| + |b_2| \ne 0.$$

Note that if f and g satisfy any one of (7), (7a), (7b), then $cf + dg$ for constants c and d also satisfies the same equation. Let $\mathscr{V}$ be the linear manifold in $\mathscr{R}\{a, b\}$ consisting of functions with continuous second derivatives on $a \le x \le b$ which satisfy (7a) and (7b). L is a linear operator on this linear manifold. A nonzero f satisfying (7), (7a), (7b) for some r will be called an eigenvector corresponding to the eigenvalue r.

It is easily verified that if f and g satisfy (7a) and (7b), then (6) is satisfied. If, for example, $a_2 \neq 0$, then

$$(8) \qquad \begin{vmatrix} f(a) & f'(a) \\ g(a) & g'(a) \end{vmatrix} = \frac{1}{a_2} \begin{vmatrix} f(a) & a_1 f(a) + a_2 f'(a) \\ g(a) & a_1 g(a) + a_2 g'(a) \end{vmatrix} = \begin{vmatrix} f(a) & 0 \\ g(a) & 0 \end{vmatrix} = 0.$$

The same result is valid at b. Hence we have

THEOREM 6.3A   Two solutions of (7), (7a), (7b) corresponding to different values of r are orthogonal over $a \leq x \leq b$ with respect to the weight function ρ.

THEOREM 6.3B   The operator L is a symmetric operator on $\mathscr{V}$.

Proof   This is an immediate consequence of (4), when $x_1 = a$, $x_2 = b$.   ★

THEOREM 6.3C   For each eigenvalue r there is at most one linearly independent eigenvector.

Proof   Equation (8) shows that the Wronskian of any two functions f and g satisfying (7a) vanishes at $x = a$. Hence any two solutions of (7) satisfying (7a) are linearly dependent.   ★

We shall show that the system (7), (7a), (7b) has nonzero solutions only for an increasing sequence of values $r_1, r_2, \ldots$ tending to infinity. The eigenvectors α_n corresponding to r_n can be assumed normalized with respect to the weight function ρ, and so form an orthonormal sequence. For a given function $\beta(x)$, we form the generalized Fourier series

$$\sum_1^\infty (\beta, \alpha_n)_\varrho \, \alpha_n(x), \qquad (\beta, \alpha_n)_\varrho = \int_a^b \rho(t) \, \beta(t) \alpha_n(t) dt,$$

and investigate the conditions which insure that the series converges, in some sense, to the function β.

For example, the system

$$f'' + rf = 0,$$
$$f(0) = 0, \qquad f(\pi) = 0,$$

has nonzero solutions $\alpha_n = \sin nx, n = 1, 2, \ldots$ and these are the eigenvectors leading to an expansion of a function as a Fourier sine series on $0 \leq x \leq \pi$.

It will be convenient to transform (7) into normal form. Equation (7) is

$$f'' + \frac{P'}{P} f' + \frac{1}{P}(r\rho - Q)f = 0.$$

Equation (28) of Section 6.2 indicates that the required transformation is
$$t(x) = \int_a^x \frac{dz}{P(z)} \text{ and the normal form is}$$

(9) $$g''(t) + q(t)\,g(t) = 0, \qquad 0 \le t \le T = \int_a^b \frac{dz}{P(z)},$$

where

(10) $$g(t) = f(x(t)), \qquad q(t) = P(x(t))\Big(r\rho(x(t)) - Q(x(t))\Big).$$

Under this transformation, the boundary conditions are also changed to

(11a) $$c_1 g(0) + c_2 g'(0) = 0,$$

(11b) $$d_1 g\,(T) + d_2 g'(T) = 0,$$

where
$$c_1 = a_1, \quad d_1 = b_1, \quad c_2 = a_2\,P(a), \quad d_2 = b_2\,P(b).$$

We shall consider an equivalent system in the form

(12) $$g''(t) + q(t)\,g(t) = 0, \qquad q(t) \text{ given by (10)}, \qquad 0 \le t \le T,$$

(12a) $$g(0) = c_2, \;\; g'(0) = -\,c_1, \qquad |c_1| + |c_2| \ne 0,$$

(12b) $$d_1 g(T) + d_2 g'(T) = 0, \qquad |d_1| + |d_2| \ne 0.$$

Clearly any solution of (12), (12a), (12b) is a solution of (9), (11a), (11b). Conversely, if g is a nonzero solution of (9), (11a), (11b), and if $c_2 \ne 0$, we must have $g(0) \ne 0$, so that by multiplication of g by a nonzero constant we can obtain a solution g_1 of (12) and (12b) with $g_1(0) = c_2$, whence $g_1'(0) = -\,c_1$ in view of (11a); while if $c_2 = 0$, then $c_1 \ne 0$, $g'(0) \ne 0$, so that by multiplication of g by a nonzero constant we can obtain a solution g_1 of (12) and (12b) with $g_1'(0) = -\,c_1$, whence $g_1(0) = c_2$.

For fixed r there is a unique solution $g(t, r)$ of (12) and (12a). We are interested in obtaining those values of r for which $g(t, r)$ satisfies (12b). For this purpose it is useful to investigate the zeros of $g(t, r)$.

Let $N(r)$ denote the number of zeros of $g(t, r)$ in $0 < t \le T$. For each r, $N(r)$ is an integer. Moreover $N(r)$ is an increasing function of r in view of Corollary 1 of Theorem 6.2I. We shall use this corollary to compare $g(t, r)$, for fixed r, with the solution

$$h(t) = c_2 \cosh kt - \frac{c_1}{k} \sinh kt$$

of

(13) $$\begin{cases} h''(t) - k^2 h(t) = 0, \qquad 0 \le t \le T, \;\; k \text{ a constant}, \;\; k > 0, \\ h(0) = c_2, \qquad h'(0) = -c_1. \end{cases}$$

The function $h(t)$ has no zeros in $0 < t \leq T$ if k is chosen sufficiently large. Then, when r is chosen to be negative and sufficiently large in absolute value we have $q(t) < -k^2$. Corollary 1 of Theorem 6.2I indicates that for such r, $g(t, r)$ has no zeros on $0 < t \leq T$, that is, $N(r) = 0$.

Next, compare $g(t, r)$ with the solution

$$h(t) = c_2 \cos kt - \frac{c_1}{k} \sin kt = \left(c_2^2 + \frac{c_1^2}{k^2}\right)^{1/2} \sin(kt + \gamma)$$

of

$$\begin{cases} h''(t) + k^2 h(t) = 0, & 0 \leq t \leq T, \quad k \text{ a constant}, \quad k > 0, \\ h(0) = c_2, & h'(0) = -c_1. \end{cases}$$

For any fixed integer n, we may choose k so that h has more than n zeros on $0 < t \leq T$. By choosing r sufficiently large we can make $q(t) > k^2$ and so obtain $N(r) > n$.

The discussion above indicates that $N(r)$ is an integer-valued monotone increasing step-function of r with $\lim_{r \to \infty} N(r) = \infty$, $\lim_{r \to -\infty} N(r) = 0$. Thus there is an increasing sequence $r_1 < r_2 < r_3 < \dots$ tending to infinity such that $N(r) = 0$ for $r < r_1$ and $N(r)$ is constant for $r_{j-1} < r < r_j$. The next theorem shows that $N(r) = j$ for $r_j \leq r < r_{j+1}$.

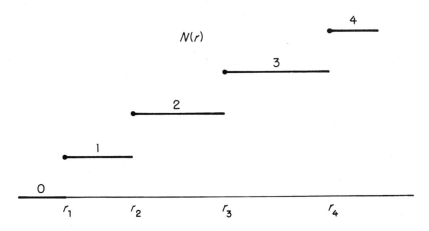

THEOREM 6.3D There is an increasing sequence $r_1 < r_2 < r_3 < \dots$ tending to infinity such that the solution $g(t, r)$ of (12) and (12a) has exactly j zeros in $0 < t \leq T$ for $r_j \leq r < r_{j+1}$. Moreover $g(T, r) = 0$ if and only if $r = r_j$.

Proof We shall show first that when r' is a fixed number, we have

(14) $N(r) \leq N(r')$ for r sufficiently close to r'.

This implies, since $N(r)$ is an increasing function, that $N(r) = N(r')$ for $r \geq r'$ and r sufficiently close to r'.

Consider the zeros of $g(t, r')$ which lie in $0 \leq t \leq T$, and enclose each in an open interval $\mathcal{I}_k$ containing no other zero of $g(t, r')$. (If $g(0, r') = 0$, take the associated interval in the form $0 \leq t < \epsilon$, and if $g(T, r') = 0$, take the associated interval in the form $T - \epsilon < t \leq T$). Then $g(t, r')$ is bounded away from zero on the complement in $0 \leq t \leq T$ of this set of intervals and, therefore, the same is true of $g(t, r)$ for r sufficiently close to r', in view of the uniform continuity of $g(t, r)$ on $0 \leq t \leq T$, $r' - 1 \leq r \leq r' + 1$. It follows that all the zeros of $g(t, r)$ on $0 \leq t \leq T$, for r sufficiently close to r', lie within the intervals $\mathcal{I}_k$. Since $g'(t, r') \neq 0$ at each of the zeros of $g(t, r')$ and since $g'(t, r)$ is continuous in t and r, we may assume that $g'(t, r) \neq 0$ in each of the intervals $\mathcal{I}_k$ for r sufficiently close to r'. Hence no interval $\mathcal{I}_k$ contains more than one zero of $g(t, r)$ for r sufficiently close to r'. This proves (14).

We shall show next that

(15) $N(r) = N(r')$ for r sufficiently close to r', if $g(T, r') \neq 0$.

Indeed, if $c < t < d$ is an interval $\mathcal{I}_k$ in $0 < t < T$ enclosing only one zero of $g(t, r')$, then $g(c, r')$ and $g(d, r')$ have opposite signs, and these signs are preserved for a sufficiently small change in r. Hence there is at least one zero of $g(t, r)$ in $\mathcal{I}_k$ for r sufficiently close to r', that is, $N(r) \geq N(r')$. In view of (14), we obtain (15).

In particular, (15) implies that $g(T, r_j) = 0$ for each j, since $N(r)$ changes as r passes through r_j. That $g(T, r) = 0$ only when $r = r_j$ is left for Exercise 6.3–4.

Our theorem will be proved if we can show that the passage from the interval $r_{j-1} < r < r_j$ to the interval $r_j \leq r < r_{j+1}$ increases $N(r)$ by one.

If $N = N(r_j)$, then $N = N(r)$ for $r_j \leq r < r_{j+1}$ in view of (14). It follows that $N(r)$ for $r_{j-1} < r < r_j$ is at most $N - 1$. Since $g(T, r_j) = 0$, there are $N - 1$ zeros of $g(t, r_j)$ in $0 < t < T$. By the argument which yielded (15), we see there are at least $N - 1$ zeros of $g(t, r)$ for $r < r_j$, r sufficiently close to r_j. It follows that $N(r) = N - 1$ for $r_{j-1} < r < r_j$.   ★

One may summarize the result above by stating that as r increases the zeros of the solution of (12) and (12a) move to the left and new zeros come into the interval only at T.

THEOREM 6.3E   The system (7), (7a), (7b) has nonzero solutions only for an increasing sequence of values $\tilde{r}_0 < \tilde{r}_1 < \tilde{r}_2 \ldots$ tending to infinity. The value $\tilde{r}_0$ is absent if $b_2 = 0$. The solution α_n corresponding to $\tilde{r}_n$ has exactly n zeros in $a < x \leq b$.

Proof   We pass to the normal system given by (12), (12a), (12b). Suppose first d_2 in (12b) is zero. It follows that the functions $g(t, r_j)$ found in the previous theorem are the only solutions of (12) and (12a) satisfying (12b). In this case $\tilde{r}_n = r_n$. However, if $d_2 \neq 0$, we seek the solutions of (12) and (12a) satisfying

(16)
$$\frac{g'(T, r)}{g(T, r)} = -\frac{d_1}{d_2}.$$

Let r' and r'', $r' < r''$, be two values of r in $r_j < r < r_{j+1}$ and let $g(t, r')$, $g(t, r'')$ be corresponding solutions of (12) and (12a). Write (12) as

$$Lg = PQg - g'' = r\rho Pg$$

and apply (4) to obtain

(17) $$\int_{t_1}^{T} (r' - r'')\rho P \, g(t, r') \, g(t, r'')dt = g(t, r') \, g'(t, r'') - g'(t, r') \, g(t, r'') \Big|_{t_1}^{T}$$

where t_1 is chosen as the last zero of $g(t, r')$ on $0 < t \leq T$. Since $g(t, r')$ and $g(t, r'')$ have the same value and the same slope at 0 and have the same number of zeros in $0 < t \leq T$, they have the same sign in $t_1 < t \leq T$. Moreover $g(t_1, r') = 0$ while $g'(t_1, r')$ and $g(t_1, r'')$ have the same sign. Then (17) implies

(18)
$$\frac{g'(T, r'')}{g(T, r'')} < \frac{g'(T, r')}{g(T, r')},$$

that is, $\dfrac{g'(T, r)}{g(T, r)}$ is a decreasing function of r in $r_j < r < r_{j+1}$. The function must decrease from $+\infty$ to $-\infty$, since $g(T, r_j) = g(T, r_{j+1}) = 0$. Hence there is one and only one value of r in the interval $r_j < r < r_{j+1}$ for which (16) is satisfied. For the interval $r < r_1$, use $t_1 = 0$ in (17) to again obtain (18). Hence there is at most one value of r less than r_1 for which (16) is satisfied. That there actually is one will follow if $\lim\limits_{r \to -\infty} \dfrac{g'(T, r)}{g(T, r)} = \infty$. This is actually true (Exercise 6.3–13) but we shall not continue the analysis further.

Note that the eigenvalues $\tilde{r}_n$ and eigenvectors α_n in Theorem 6.3E are the same as the numbers r_n and functions $g(t, r_n)$ given in Theorem 6.3D only in the case $d_2 = 0$.   ★

Exercise 6.3

1. (a) Show that the equation $f''(x) + P(x)f'(x) + Q(x)f(x) = 0$, $a \leq x \leq b$, can be put into the form

(*) $$\frac{d}{dx}\left(p \frac{df}{dx}\right) + qf = 0, \qquad p > 0, \quad a \leq x \leq b,$$

by multiplication by an appropriate factor.

(b)   Prove that a necessary and sufficient condition that the equation (*) in (a) have linearly independent solutions of the form $\sin g(x)$ and $\cos g(x)$ is that $pq = c^2$ where c is a nonzero constant, and then we may take
$$g(x) = \frac{1}{c} \int_{x_0}^{x} q(t)dt.$$
Hint: Use (5) of the text.

2.   Determine the eigenvalues and eigenvectors for each of the following systems. Here r is a constant.

(a) $f'' + rf = 0,$
      $f(0) = 0 = f(1).$

(b) $\frac{d}{dx}\left(x\frac{df}{dx}\right) + \frac{r}{x}f = 0,$
      $f(1) = 0, f(e) = 0.$
      Hint: Try $x = e^t$; also try 1(b).

(c) $\frac{d}{dx}\left(\frac{1}{2x}\frac{df}{dx}\right) + 2xrf = 0,$
      $f(1) = 0, \quad f'(\pi) = 0.$

(d) $(3x + 1)^2 f''(x) + (3x + 1) f' + (r + 1) f = 0,$
      $f(0) = 0, \quad f(\pi) = 0.$

3.   Consider the system

(**) $\begin{cases} \dfrac{d}{dx}\left(P\dfrac{df}{dx}\right) + (r\rho - Q) f = 0, \qquad a \le x \le b, \\ a_1 f(a) + a_2 f(b) + a_3 f'(a) + a_4 f'(b) = 0, \\ b_1 f(a) + b_2 f(b) + b_3 f'(a) + b_4 f'(b) = 0. \end{cases}$

where P, Q, ρ have the properties specified in this section, not all determinants $D_{ij} = \begin{vmatrix} a_i & a_j \\ b_i & b_j \end{vmatrix}$, $i \ne j$, are zero, and $P(a) D_{24} = P(b) D_{13}$.

(a)   Show that the system (7), (7a), (7b) is a special case of (**).
(b)   If matrices
$$[X] = \begin{bmatrix} a_1 & a_3 \\ b_1 & b_3 \end{bmatrix}, \quad [Y] = \begin{bmatrix} a_2 & a_4 \\ b_2 & b_4 \end{bmatrix}$$
are singular, while the matrix $\begin{bmatrix} a_1 & a_2 & a_3 & a_4 \\ b_1 & b_2 & b_3 & b_4 \end{bmatrix}$ has rank 2,
and $[X][C] + [Y][D] = [0]$, for given 2×2 matrices $[C]$ and $[D]$, then $[C]$ and $[D]$ are singular.
Hint: If $[D]$ is nonsingular, multiply the above equation by adj $[X]$ to obtain (adj $[X]$) $[Y] = [0].$
(c)   Show that solutions f and g of (**) satisfy (6). *Hint:* Write the boundary conditions in matrix notation as
$$\begin{bmatrix} a_1 & a_3 \\ b_1 & b_3 \end{bmatrix}\begin{bmatrix} f(a) & g(a) \\ f'(a) & g'(a) \end{bmatrix} + \begin{bmatrix} a_2 & a_4 \\ b_2 & b_4 \end{bmatrix}\begin{bmatrix} f(b) & g(b) \\ f'(b) & g'(b) \end{bmatrix} = [0].$$
If f and g are linearly independent, show that
$$P(a)\begin{vmatrix} f(a) & g(a) \\ f'(a) & g'(a) \end{vmatrix} = P(b)\begin{vmatrix} f(b) & g(b) \\ f'(b) & g'(b) \end{vmatrix}$$
if and only if $P(a) D_{24} = P(b) D_{13}$. (Use part (b) when D_{13} and D_{24} are both zero.)

4. In Theorem 6.3D it was shown that $g(T, r_j) = 0$. Prove that $g(T, r) = 0$ only when $r = r_j$.

5. (a) Keeping P, Q, ρ real and permitting r to be complex, show that if $r = s + it$, s and t real, is an eigenvalue with eigenvector $u(x) + i\,v(x)$ for the system (7), (7a), (7b), then $s - it$ is also an eigenvalue with eigenvector $u - iv$.

  (b) Now use Theorem 6.3A to show that an eigenvalue of the form $s + it$, $t \neq 0$, cannot exist. The eigenvalues are real.

  (c) Show that if $u + iv$ is an eigenvector for real eigenvalue r, then u and v are also eigenvectors for r.

  (d) Hence show that eigenvectors may always be chosen as real valued.

6. (a) Show that the solution f of

$$f'' - (x^3 + ax)f = 0, \quad -\infty < x < \infty,$$
$$f(0) = 1, \quad f'(0) = 0,$$

where a is a fixed constant, has at most a finite number of positive zeros and has an infinity of negative zeros.

7. The one-dimensional Schroedinger equation may be put into the form

$$g'' + (r - q(x))g = 0, \quad -\infty < x < \infty.$$

Let g_1 and g_2 be particular solutions satisfying

$$g_1(0) = 1, \quad g_1'(0) = 0, \quad g_2(0) = 0, \quad g_2'(0) = 1,$$

and define $u(x) = \sqrt{g_1(x)^2 + g_2(x)^2}$, $v(x) = \tan^{-1}\dfrac{g_2(x)}{g_1(x)}$, when $g_1(x) \neq 0$.

  (a) Show that $u(x) > 0$, and $u(x)$ satisfies

$$u'' + (r - q(x))u' = u^{-3},$$
$$u(0) = 1, \quad u'(0) = 0.$$

  (b) Show that $v(0) = 0$ and $v'(x) = u^{-2}$.

  (c) Show that every solution of the Schroedinger equation is of the form

$$g(x) = A\,u(x)\sin(v(x) + B),$$

where A and B are constants.
  Hint: We have $g = ag_1 + bg_2$.

8. Consider the system

$$\frac{d}{dx}\left(P\frac{dg}{dx}\right) + (r\rho(x) - q(x))g(x) = 0, \quad -a \leq x \leq a, \quad g(-a) = g(a) = 0.$$

Assume that $P(x)$, $\rho(x)$, $q(x)$ are even. Show that the eigenvectors are either even or odd. Show that eigenvector g is even if and only if $r = r_j$, j odd.
Hint: Show that $g(-x)$ is an eigenvector when $g(x)$ is. Use Theorem 6.3C and consider the number of zeros.

9. Using the notation of Theorem 6.3D, prove that the kth zero $z_k(r)$ of $g(t, r)$ in $0 < t \leq T$ is a continuous function of r. *Hint:* Let r' be a value of r for which $g(t, r)$ has at least k zeros. Restricting the discussion to an interval $0 < t < T_1$ containing only the first k zeros of $g(t, r')$, and letting $r_1 < r_2 < \ldots$ be the corresponding sequence for $0 < t \leq T_1$ defined in Theorem 6.3D, we have $r_k < r' < r_{k+1}$. Enclose each of the k zeros in an interval $c_i < t < d_i$, $i = 1, \ldots, k$, in $0 < t < T_1$ containing no other zero of $g(t, r')$. Since $g(c_i, r')$ and $g(d_i, r')$ have opposite signs, so do $g(c_i, r)$ and $g(d_i, r)$ for r near r'. Hence, for such r, these intervals each contain a zero of $g(t, r)$ and since $g(t, r)$ has exactly k zeros for $r_k < r < r_{k+1}$, the zero of $g(t, r)$ in $c_k < t < d_k$ must be the kth. Now use the fact that c_k and d_k may be chosen within ϵ of $z_k(r')$. Write this in ϵ, δ notation.

10. Let $Lf = -\dfrac{d}{dx}(1 - x^2)f'$, and consider $Lf = rf$. Show that (4) is satisfied and (6) also, when $a = -1$, $b = 1$. Thus the Legendre polynomials are orthogonal on $-1 \le x \le 1$. Nevertheless, the theory developed in this section is not applicable because $1 - x^2$ vanishes at $x = \pm 1$.

11. (a) Let t_1 and t_2 be consecutive zeros of a solution $g(t, r)$ of (12), (12a), when

$$0 < m < q(T) < M, \quad 0 \le t \le T. \quad \text{Show that} \quad \frac{\pi}{\sqrt{M}} < t_2 - t_1 < \frac{\pi}{\sqrt{m}}.$$

 Hint: By defining $q(t) = q(T)$ for $t > T$, we extend $g(t, r)$ to the interval $0 \le t < \infty$. Compare with the solution of $h'' + mh = 0$, $h(t_1) = g(t_1)$, $h'(t_1) = g'(t_1)$.

(b) Assume that $c_2 = 0$ in (12a) and $r = r_j$ so that $g(t, r)$ vanishes at both 0 and T. Show that the number j of zeros of $g(t, r_j)$ in $0 < t \le T$ satisfies

$$T\frac{\sqrt{m}}{\pi} \le j \le T\frac{\sqrt{M}}{\pi}. \quad \text{Hint: Subdivide the interval } 0 \le t \le T \text{ by points}$$

$$T - \frac{k\pi}{\sqrt{m}}, \quad k = 0, 1, 2, \dots. \text{ If } n \text{ is the number of subintervals of}$$

length $\dfrac{\pi}{\sqrt{m}}$ within $0 \le t \le T$, then $n + 1 \ge T\dfrac{\sqrt{m}}{\pi}$. Each interval

$$T - \frac{k\pi}{\sqrt{m}} < t \le T - (k - 1)\frac{\pi}{\sqrt{m}} \text{ contains at least one zero of } g(t, r_j)$$

while the interval $T - \dfrac{\pi}{\sqrt{m}} < t \le T$ contains two.

(c) Using (b), show that the eigenvalues of

$$g'' + (r - q(x))\, g = 0, \qquad a \le x \le b,$$
$$g(a) = 0 = g(b),$$

satisfy $\dfrac{j^2\pi^2}{(b - a)^2} + q \le r_j \le \dfrac{j^2\pi^2}{(b - a)^2} + Q,$

where $0 < q < q(x) < Q$.

12. Consider the equation $f'' + rf = 0$ under the following boundary conditions. In each case, find the eigenvalues, eigenvectors, and state the number of linearly independent eigenvectors corresponding to each eigenvalue.

(a) $\begin{cases} f(0) = 0 \\ f'(0) = 0 \end{cases}$ (b) $\begin{cases} f(-1) - f(1) = 0 \\ f'(-1) + f'(1) = 0 \end{cases}$ (c) $\begin{cases} f(0) - f(2\pi) = 0 \\ f'(0) - f'(2\pi) = 0 \end{cases}$

13. Let g be a solution of (12) and (12a) for fixed r and let h be a solution of (13), where g and h have no zeros on $0 < t \le T$. Show that $\dfrac{h'(T)}{h(T)}$ approaches ∞ as $k \to \infty$. Show that

$$g(t, r)\, h'(t) - h(t)\, g'(t, r)\Big|_0^T = \int_0^T (k^2 + q(t))\, g(t, r)\, h(t)\, dt$$

and hence, if r is sufficiently negative, $\dfrac{g'(T, r)}{g(T, r)} > \dfrac{h'(T)}{h(T)}$. Hence prove that

$$\lim_{r \to -\infty} \frac{g'(T, r)}{g(T, r)} = \infty.$$

14. Show that, whether $d_2 = 0$ or not, the solution corresponding to the nth of the numbers $\tilde{r}_j$ in Theorem 6.3E (ordered numerically) has $n - 1$ zeros in $a < x < b$.

6.4

THE

INVERSE

OPERATOR

We shall treat the Sturm-Liouville problem from an operational point of view. By considering the inverse of a differential operator, we shall make contact again with the results proved for integral operators. Some results proved in the previous section will be obtained again, and new results and techniques will be introduced.

For simplicity, we consider the problem in the form

(1) $$L\alpha(x) = \left(q(x) - \frac{d^2}{dx^2}\right)\alpha(x) = r\alpha(x), \qquad a \le x \le b,$$

(2) $$c_1\alpha(a) + c_2\alpha'(a) = 0, \qquad |c_1| + |c_2| \ne 0,$$

(3) $$d_1\alpha(b) + d_2\alpha'(b) = 0, \qquad |d_1| + |d_2| \ne 0.$$

Here q is considered as continuous on $a \le x \le b$. The more general case given by equations (7), (7a), (7b) of Section 6.3 can be treated by similar methods. Moreover, in the case when P and ρ in 6.3 (7) have continuous second derivatives, the general case can be reduced to the case here treated by a change of variable (Exercise 6.4–1).

Let $\mathscr{V}$ be the linear manifold in $\mathscr{R}\{a, b\}$ consisting of those functions with continuous second derivatives on $a \le x \le b$ satisfying the boundary conditions (2) and (3).

The operator $L = q - \dfrac{d^2}{dx^2}$ is a linear operator on $\mathscr{V}$. Theorems 6.3A, B, C show that L is a symmetric operator on $\mathscr{V}$, that for each eigenvalue there is exactly one linearly independent eigenvector, and that eigenvectors corresponding to distinct eigenvalues are orthogonal.

Let us investigate the inverse of L. L carries vectors in $\mathscr{V}$ into the class $\mathscr{C}\{a, b\}$ of functions continuous on $a \le x \le b$. Given β in $\mathscr{C}$, we seek to determine α in $\mathscr{V}$ so that

(4) $$L\alpha = \beta.$$

This means we must solve the differential equation (4) for α subject to the boundary conditions (2) and (3).

By Theorem 1.4B, the inverse operator exists if and only if zero is not an eigenvalue of L. Let us then assume that zero is not an eigenvalue. Define two nonzero functions σ_1 and σ_2 with continuous second derivatives by

$$(5) \qquad\qquad L\sigma_1(x) = 0, \qquad c_1\sigma_1(a) + c_2\sigma_1'(a) = 0,$$

$$(6) \qquad\qquad L\sigma_2(x) = 0, \qquad d_1\sigma_2(b) + d_2\sigma_2'(b) = 0.$$

We assert that σ_1 and σ_2 are linearly independent. Indeed if σ_1 were equal to a constant multiple of σ_2, then σ_1 would satisfy both boundary conditions (2) and (3) as well as $L\sigma_1 = 0$ and hence would be an eigenvector of L corresponding to the eigenvalue zero, a contradiction.

We can now obtain a solution of (4) using the method of variation of parameters. Seek f and g so that

$$(7) \qquad\qquad \alpha(x) = f(x)\,\sigma_1(x) + g(x)\,\sigma_2(x)$$

is a solution of (4), and

$$(8) \qquad\qquad f'(x)\,\sigma_1(x) + g'(x)\,\sigma_2(x) = 0.$$

Remembering that σ_1 and σ_2 satisfy $L\sigma = 0$, we find that α satisfies (4) if

$$(9) \qquad\qquad f'(x)\,\sigma_1'(x) + g'(x)\,\sigma_2'(x) = -\,\beta(x).$$

Equations (9) and (8) have solutions

$$(10) \qquad f'(x) = \frac{1}{w}\,\beta(x)\,\sigma_2(x), \qquad g'(x) = -\frac{1}{w}\,\beta(x)\,\sigma_1(x),$$

where $w = W[\sigma_1, \sigma_2]$, the Wronskian of σ_1 and σ_2, is a constant in view of 6.3–(5).

Thus, if we set

$$(11) \qquad f(x) = \int_x^b -\frac{\beta(y)\,\sigma_2(y)dy}{w}, \qquad g(x) = \int_a^x -\frac{\beta(y)\,\sigma_1(y)dy}{w},$$

the function α defined by (7) becomes

$$\alpha(x) = \int_a^x -\frac{\sigma_1(y)\,\sigma_2(x)}{w}\,\beta(y)dy + \int_x^b -\frac{\sigma_2(y)\,\sigma_1(x)}{w}\,\beta(y)dy,$$

or, if we define

$$(12) \qquad G(x, y) = \begin{cases} -\dfrac{1}{w}\,\sigma_1(y)\,\sigma_2(x), & a \le y \le x \le b, \\[2mm] -\dfrac{1}{w}\,\sigma_1(x)\,\sigma_2(y), & a \le x \le y \le b, \end{cases}$$

we have

$$\text{(13)} \qquad \alpha(x) = \int_a^b G(x, y)\, \beta(y)\, dy, \qquad a \le x \le b.$$

The function $G(x, y)$ will be called the **Green's function** corresponding to L and the boundary conditions (2) and (3). An examination of (12) shows that $G(x, y)$ is continuous and symmetric on $a \le x \le b$, $a \le y \le b$. For y fixed, and $x \le y$, $\dfrac{d}{dx} G(x, y) = -\dfrac{1}{w}\, \sigma_1'(x)\, \sigma_2(y)$ is continuous, and for y fixed and $x \ge y$, $\dfrac{d}{dx} G(x, y) = -\dfrac{1}{w}\, \sigma_1(y)\, \sigma_2'(x)$ is continuous. Although $G(x, y)$ has a right derivative and a left derivative at $x = y$, $y \ne a$, $y \ne b$, these derivatives are not equal. Indeed, when

$$\frac{d}{dx} G(y+, y) = \lim_{\substack{t \to y \\ t > y}} \frac{G(t, y) - G(y, y)}{t - y},$$

$$\frac{d}{dx} G(y-, y) = \lim_{\substack{t \to y \\ t < y}} \frac{G(t, y) - G(y, y)}{t - y},$$

then

$$\text{(14)} \quad \frac{d}{dx} G(y+, y) - \frac{d}{dx} G(y-, y) = -\frac{1}{w}\,(\sigma_1(y)\, \sigma_2'(y) - \sigma_2(y)\, \sigma_1'(y)) = -1.$$

Similarly for x fixed, $\dfrac{d}{dy} G(x, y)$ is a continuous function of x and y for $y \ne x$, but

$$\text{(15)} \qquad \frac{d}{dy} G(x, x+) - \frac{d}{dy} G(x, x-) = -1, \qquad x \ne a, \quad x \ne b.$$

Moreover, for fixed y, the Green's function $G(x, y)$ satisfies the boundary conditions (2) and (3). That is

$$\text{(16)} \qquad c_1 G(a, y) + c_2 \frac{dG}{dx}(a, y) = 0, \qquad d_1 G(b, y) + d_2 \frac{dG}{dx}(b, y) = 0.$$

A similar result holds when $G(x, y)$ is considered as a function of y for fixed x.

EXAMPLE 1   Find the Green's function for $L = -\dfrac{d^2}{dx^2}$, with the boundary conditions $\alpha(a) = 0 = \alpha(b)$.

The solution of $L\sigma = 0$ is $\sigma = Ax + B$. σ_1 must satisfy the boundary condition at a and hence $Aa + B = 0$, $\sigma_1(x) = Ax - Aa = A(x - a)$.

σ_2 must satisfy the boundary condition at b, and hence $Ab + B = 0$, $\sigma_2(x) = Ax - Ab = A(x - b)$. The Wronskian of σ_1 and σ_2 is $A^2(b - a)$ and (12) becomes

$$G(x, y) = \begin{cases} -\dfrac{(y - a)(x - b)}{b - a}, & a \le y \le x \le b \\[2ex] -\dfrac{(x - a)(y - b)}{b - a}, & a \le x \le y \le b. \end{cases}$$

We are now in a position to prove

THEOREM 6.4A   If the operator $L = q - \dfrac{d^2}{dx^2}$ on $\mathscr{V}$ does not have zero as an eigenvalue, and $G(x, y)$ is the Green's function associated with L and the boundary conditions (2) and (3), then for every β in $\mathscr{C}\{a, b\}$ the function α defined by

$$\alpha(x) = \int_a^b G(x, y)\, \beta(y)\, dy$$

is in $\mathscr{V}$ and $L\alpha = \beta$.

Proof   First we must verify that α has continuous second derivatives. Write

$$\alpha(x) = \int_a^x G(x, y)\, \beta(y)\, dy + \int_x^b G(x, y)\, \beta(y)\, dy$$

$$= f(x)\, \sigma_1(x) + g(x)\, \sigma_2(x),$$

where $f(x)$ and $g(x)$ are given by (11). Then f' and g' are given by (10), equation (8) is satisfied, and so

$$\alpha'' = f\, \sigma_1'' + f'\, \sigma_1' + g'\, \sigma_2' + g\, \sigma_2'',$$

which is continuous.

From (10) we obtain (9). Then it is easily verified that α given by (7) is a solution of $L\alpha = \beta$ when (8) and (9) are valid.

That α satisfies the boundary conditions, and so is in $\mathscr{V}$, follows from (16).   ★

We have just proved that the integral operator G defined on $\mathscr{R}\{a, b\}$ by

(17) $$G\beta(x) = \int_a^b G(x, y)\, \beta(y)\, dy$$

carries continuous functions into $\mathscr{V}$ and satisfies

(18) $$LG\beta = \beta, \qquad \text{for } \beta \text{ in } \mathscr{C}.$$

We also assert

THEOREM 6.4B

$$GL\alpha = \alpha, \qquad \text{for } \alpha \text{ in } \mathscr{V}.$$

Proof Taking $\beta = L\alpha$ in (18) yields $L(GL\alpha - \alpha) = \theta$, whence $GL\alpha = \alpha$ since α and $GL\alpha$ are in $\mathscr{V}$ and zero is not an eigenvalue.   ★

The two theorems proved above show that the operators L and G are inverse operators. The Green's function is the kernel of the integral operator inverse to L. Indeed we may define the Green's function as the continuous symmetric kernel $G(x, y)$ defining an integral operator G by $G\beta(y) = \int_a^b G(x, y)\, \beta(y)\, dy$ satisfying

(19) $\begin{cases} \beta \text{ in } \mathscr{C} \text{ implies } G\beta \text{ in } \mathscr{V} \text{ and } LG\beta = \beta, \\ \alpha \text{ in } \mathscr{V} \text{ implies } L\alpha \text{ in } \mathscr{C} \text{ and } GL\alpha = \alpha. \end{cases}$

The proof that (19) defines the Green's function uniquely is left for Exercise 6.4–5.

THEOREM 6.4C   The eigenvalues of G are the reciprocals of those of L. The eigenvectors of G are those of L.

Proof First we remark that zero is not an eigenvalue of G. Indeed if $G\beta = \theta$ with $\beta \neq \theta$, then $\theta = L\theta = LG\beta = \beta$, a contradiction. If $L\alpha = r\alpha$ for $\alpha \neq \theta$ in $\mathscr{V}$, then $\alpha = GL\alpha = rG\alpha$ and $G\alpha = \dfrac{1}{r}\,\alpha$. Thus an eigenvector of L corresponding to eigenvalue r is an eigenvector of G corresponding to eigenvalue $1/r$. Conversely, if $G\beta = s\beta$ for β in $\mathscr{R}\{a, b\}$ then $\beta = \dfrac{1}{s}\,G\beta$ is in $\mathscr{C}$, $G\beta$ is in $\mathscr{V}$, β is in $\mathscr{V}$, and $\beta = LG\beta = sL\beta$ yields $L\beta = \dfrac{1}{s}\,\beta$.   ★

We can now apply the results proved for integral operators in Chapter Four. Denote the spectrum of G (the totality of eigenvalues) by s_i, $-\infty \leq -M \leq i \leq N \leq \infty$ where $i \neq 0$, $s_{-j} < s_{-j-1} < 0 < s_{k+1} < s_k$ for positive integers j and k, and where $\lim_{j \to \infty} s_{-j} = 0$ if $M = \infty$, $\lim_{j \to \infty} s_j = 0$ if $N = \infty$.

In view of what we have learned in Section 6.3, M is finite and N is infinite. However, it may be of interest to see how these facts may be obtained without the use of the previous section. At the same time we will develop some useful inequalities.

Let α be in $\mathscr{V}$. Integrating by parts, we have

$$(L\alpha, \alpha) = \int_a^b \alpha(q\alpha - \alpha'')dx = \int_a^b q\alpha^2 dx - \alpha\alpha' \Big|_a^b + \int_a^b (\alpha')^2 dx$$

$$= \int_a^b q\alpha^2 dx + \int_a^b (\alpha')^2 dx + \alpha(a)\,\alpha'(a) - \alpha(b)\,\alpha'(b).$$

Making use of (2) and (3), we see that if $c_2 = 0$ then $\alpha(a)\,\alpha'(a) = 0$, otherwise $\alpha(a)\,\alpha'(a) = -\dfrac{c_1}{c_2}\,\alpha(a)^2$. Hence we obtain

$$(20) \qquad (L\alpha, \alpha) = \int_a^b q\alpha^2 dx + \int_a^b (\alpha')^2 dx - \frac{c_1}{c_2}\,\alpha(a)^2 + \frac{d_1}{d_2}\,\alpha(b)^2,$$

where it is understood that the term $\dfrac{c_1}{c_2}\,\alpha(a)^2 = 0$ when $c_2 = 0$, and $\dfrac{d_1}{d_2}\,\alpha(b)^2 = 0$ when $d_2 = 0$.

There is a value x_0, $a \le x_0 \le b$, such that

$$\|\alpha\|^2 = \int_a^b \alpha^2(x)\,dx = \alpha(x_0)^2 \int_a^b dx = \alpha(x_0)^2\,(b - a).$$

Then

$$\alpha(a)^2 = \alpha(x_0)^2 - \int_a^{x_0} \frac{d}{dx}\,(\alpha^2)dx = \frac{\|\alpha\|^2}{b - a} - \int_a^{x_0} 2\alpha\alpha'dx$$

$$\le \frac{\|\alpha\|^2}{b - a} + 2\Big(\int_a^b \alpha^2 dx \int_a^b (\alpha')^2 dx\Big)^{1/2}$$

or

$$(21) \qquad \alpha(a)^2 \le \frac{\|\alpha\|^2}{b - a} + 2\|\alpha\|\,\|\alpha'\|.$$

A similar result is valid for $\alpha(b)^2$. Putting $z = \|\alpha'\|$, $\|\alpha\| = 1$, $m = $ g.l.b. $\{q(x) \mid a \le x \le b\}$, and inserting the bounds for $\alpha(a)^2$ and $\alpha(b)^2$ in (20), it follows that

$$(22)\ \ (L\alpha, \alpha) \ge \int_a^b q\alpha^2\,dx + z^2 - \left|\frac{c_1}{c_2}\right|\left(\frac{1}{b - a} + 2z\right) - \left|\frac{d_1}{d_2}\right|\left(\frac{1}{b - a} + 2z\right)$$

$$\ge m + z^2 - 2\left(\left|\frac{c_1}{c_2}\right| + \left|\frac{d_1}{d_2}\right|\right)z - (b - a)^{-1}\left(\left|\frac{c_1}{c_2}\right| + \left|\frac{d_1}{d_2}\right|\right).$$

Any quadratic of the form $z^2 + k_1 z + k_2$ is necessarily bounded below. Hence $(L\alpha, \alpha)$ is bounded below when $\|\alpha\| = 1$ and α is in $\mathscr{V}$.

On the other hand, if we denote by σ_j the normalized eigenvectors corresponding to the eigenvalues s_j of G and suppose $M = +\infty$, so that $\lim\limits_{n\to\infty} s_{-n} = 0$, then

$$(L\sigma_{-n},\sigma_{-n}) = s_{-n}^{-1}$$

approaches $-\infty$ as n increases. This contradiction assures that M is finite. If also N were finite we would have $G(x, y) = \sum\limits_{j=-M}^{N} {}' \, s_j \, \sigma_j(x) \, \sigma_j(y)$ in view of Theorem 4.2E, and $G(x, y)$ for fixed y would be a member of $\mathscr{V}$. This cannot be since $\dfrac{\partial}{\partial x} G(x, y)$ is not continuous.

It follows that the spectrum of G may be pictured as

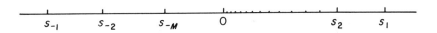

while the eigenvalues of L, the reciprocals of s_n, are represented as

Since there is a first value from the left, it is natural to set

$$r_j = \begin{cases} s_{-M+j-1}{}^{1}, & j = 1, 2, \ldots M \\ s_{-M+j}{}^{-1}, & j = M + 1, M + 2, \ldots . \end{cases}$$

We then represent the normalized eigenvector corresponding to r_j by the symbol α_j. The next theorem shows that the eigenvectors are linearly dense in $\mathscr{R}\{a, b\}$ and so form a basis for that space.

THEOREM 6.4D   If β is in $\mathscr{V}$, and α_j are the normalized eigenvectors of L then

$$\beta(x) = \sum_{j=1}^{\infty} (\beta, \alpha_j) \, \alpha_j(x),$$

the series converging absolutely uniformly for $a \le x \le b$. For every μ in $\mathscr{R}\{a, b\}$, we have

$$\lim_{n\to\infty} \Big\| \mu - \sum_{j=1}^{n} (\mu, \alpha_j) \, \alpha_j \Big\| = 0.$$

Proof   When β is in $\mathscr{V}$, then $\beta = G(L\beta)$ and by Theorem 4.3A every

function of the form $G\sigma$ can be expanded in an absolutely uniformly convergent series of eigenvectors. If μ is in $\mathscr{R}$, we may choose β in $\mathscr{V}$ so that
$\|\mu - \beta\| \le \epsilon/2$. Here we use Theorem 5.2D and note that the theorem permits
us to say that β satisfies the boundary conditions and so is in $\mathscr{V}$. By the
corollary to Theorem 1.3F,

$$\left\|\mu - \sum_{j=1}^{n} (\mu, \alpha_j)\, \alpha_j\right\| \le \left\|\mu - \sum_{j=1}^{n} (\beta, \alpha_j)\, \alpha_j\right\|$$

$$\le \|\mu - \beta\| + \left\|\beta - \sum_{j=1}^{n} (\beta, \alpha_j)\, \alpha_j\right\|.$$

The uniform convergence already obtained in the first part of the proof
permits us to find an integer N such that

$$\left\|\beta - \sum_{j=1}^{n} (\beta, \alpha_j)\, \alpha_j\right\| < \epsilon/2 \quad \text{for } n \ge N.$$

Hence, for $n \ge N$,

$$\left\|\mu - \sum_{j=1}^{n} (\mu, \alpha_j)\, \alpha_j\right\| \le \epsilon. \quad \bigstar$$

It is true that we have assumed zero is not an eigenvalue of L as an
operator over $\mathscr{V}$. Nevertheless, the results of Theorem 6.4D are still true even
when zero is an eigenvalue. To see this, note that the equation

$$q\alpha - \alpha'' = r\alpha$$

may be written

$$(q + c)\alpha - \alpha'' = (r + c)\alpha, \qquad c \text{ constant,}$$

so that the eigenvectors of L are exactly those of the operator

$$L_c = (q + c) - \frac{d^2}{dx^2}$$

and the eigenvalues of L_c are those of L increased by c. Hence we can adjust
c so that zero is not an eigenvalue of L_c. (See Exercise 6.4–10.) Then we need
only apply Theorem 6.4D to the operator L_c.

We shall now show that it is possible to obtain a stronger convergence
theorem than that just given.

THEOREM 6.4E If β is continuous, β' is piecewise continuous on
$a \le x \le b$, $\beta(a) = 0$ when $c_2 = 0$ and $\beta(b) = 0$ when $d_2 = 0$, then

(23) $$\sum_{r_j > 0} (\beta, \alpha_j)^2\, r_j \le k_1 \|\beta\|^2 + k_2 \|\beta'\|^2$$

where k_1 and k_2 are constants independent of β.

Proof Consider first the case when β is in $\mathscr{V}$, so that

$$\beta = \sum_{j=1}^{\infty} a_j \, \alpha_j(x), \qquad a_j = (\beta, \, \alpha_j),$$

the series converging absolutely uniformly for $a \leq x \leq b$. In this case,

$$(L\beta, \, \beta) = (L\beta, \, \sum_{1}^{\infty} a_j \, \alpha_j) = \sum_{1}^{\infty} a_j \, (L\beta, \, \alpha_j)$$

$$= \sum_{1}^{\infty} a_j \, (\beta, \, L\alpha_j) = \sum_{1}^{\infty} a_j^2 \, r_j.$$

Defining

$$M = \text{l.u.b.} \left\{ q(x) \,\middle|\, a \leq x \leq b \right\}$$

and inserting (21), valid at the points a and b, into (20), we have

$$\sum_{1}^{\infty} a_j^2 \, r_j = (L\beta, \, \beta) \leq M \, \|\beta\|^2 + \|\beta'\|^2$$

$$+ \left\{ \left| \frac{c_1}{c_2} \right| + \left| \frac{d_1}{d_2} \right| \right\} \left\{ \frac{\|\beta\|^2}{b-a} + 2\|\beta\| \, \|\beta'\| \right\}.$$

Upon applying the inequality

$$2\|\beta\| \, \|\beta'\| \leq \|\beta\|^2 + \|\beta'\|^2$$

we establish the inequality (23) if all eigenvalues are nonnegative. If, however, $r_j < 0$ for $j = 1, 2, \ldots, m$ while $r_j \geq 0$ for $j \geq m + 1$, then

$$\sum_{r_j > 0}^{\infty} a_j^2 \, r_j = \sum_{1}^{\infty} a_j^2 \, r_j + \sum_{1}^{m} a_j^2 \, | \, r_j \, |$$

$$\leq \sum_{1}^{\infty} a_j^2 \, r_j + |r_1| \sum_{1}^{\infty} a_j^2$$

$$\leq M \, \|\beta\|^2 + \|\beta'\|^2 + \left\{ \left| \frac{c_1}{c_2} \right| + \left| \frac{d_1}{d_2} \right| \right\} \left\{ \frac{\|\beta\|^2}{b-a} + \|\beta\|^2 + \|\beta'\|^2 \right\} + |r_1| \, \|\beta\|^2$$

using Bessel's inequality. This proves (23) for the case when β is in $\mathscr{V}$.

Suppose next that β satisfies the hypotheses of the theorem. We assert that for $\epsilon > 0$ there is a vector μ such that

(24) $\qquad\qquad \mu$ is in $\mathscr{V}, \qquad \mu(a) = \beta(a), \qquad \|\mu' - \beta'\| < \epsilon.$

To preserve the continuity of the argument assume temporarily that this can be shown. We can thus construct a sequence $\mu_n(x)$ in $\mathscr{V}$ such that $\mu_n(a) = \beta(a)$ and

$$\lim_{n \to \infty} \|\mu_n' - \beta'\| = 0.$$

In view of

$$\left| \mu_n(x) - \beta(x) \right| = \left| \int_a^x \mu_n'(x) - \beta'(x)\, dx \right| \leq \|\mu_n' - \beta'\| \, (b - a)^{1/2}$$

we see that $\{\mu_n(x)\}$ converges uniformly to $\beta(x)$. Thus

$$\lim_{n \to \infty} (\mu_n, \alpha_j) = (\beta, \alpha_j) = a_j.$$

If N is a fixed positive integer, we have for each n,

$$\sum_{\substack{r_j > 0}}^{N} (\mu_n, \alpha_j)^2 \, r_j \leq k_1 \|\mu_n\|^2 + k_2 \|\mu_n'\|^2.$$

Letting n approach infinity, we obtain

$$\sum_{\substack{r_j > 0}}^{N} a_j^2 \, r_j \leq k_1 \|\beta\|^2 + k_2 \|\beta'\|^2.$$

Since N is arbitrary, this implies

$$\sum_{\substack{r_j > 0}}^{\infty} a_j^2 \, r_j \leq k_1 \|\beta\|^2 + k_2 \|\beta'\|^2.$$

This is (23).

Here is a method of finding μ to satisfy (24). By Theorem 5.2D there is an α having continuous second derivatives with $\alpha(a) = \alpha(b) = 0$, $|\alpha| \leq |\beta'|$ and $\|\alpha - \beta'\| < \epsilon$. Define

$$\sigma(x) = \int_a^x (\alpha(z) + y)dz + \beta(a)$$

where

$$y = \begin{cases} 0 & \text{if } d_2 \neq 0 \\ -\left(\int_a^b \alpha(x)dx + \beta(a) \right)(b - a)^{-1} & \text{if } d_2 = 0. \end{cases}$$

When $d_2 = 0$, we have $\sigma(b) = 0$, and, since then $\beta(b) = 0$, we have

$$(b - a)|y| = \left| \int_a^b \alpha(x)dx - \Big(\beta(b) - \beta(a) \Big) \right|$$

$$= \left| \int_a^b (\alpha - \beta')dx \right| \leq \|\alpha - \beta'\| \, (b - a)^{1/2} \, .$$

Thus $\|y\| = |y| (b - a)^{1/2} \leq \|\alpha - \beta'\| < \epsilon$. Next choose

$$
\xi(x) = \begin{cases} p(x - a)(x - a - \epsilon)^4 \epsilon^{-4}, & a \leq x \leq a + \epsilon, \\ 0, & a + \epsilon < x < b - \epsilon, \\ q(x - b)(x - b + \epsilon)^4 \epsilon^{-4}, & b - \epsilon \leq x \leq b, \end{cases}
$$

where the constants p and q are determined to satisfy

$$
c_1 \beta(a) + c_2(p + y) = 0,
$$
$$
d_1 \sigma(b) + d_2(q + y) = 0.
$$

Indeed p and q may be chosen in this fashion, since $c_2 = 0$ implies $\beta(a) = 0$ and $d_2 = 0$ implies $\sigma(b) = 0$. Moreover $\xi'(a) = p$, $\xi'(b) = q$, $\xi(a) = 0 = \xi(b)$, and

$$
|\xi'(x)| \leq \begin{cases} 5 |p|, & a \leq x \leq a + \epsilon, \\ 0, & a + \epsilon < x < b - \epsilon, \\ 5 |q|, & b - \epsilon \leq x \leq b. \end{cases}
$$

Thus $\|\xi'\|^2 = \int_a^b \xi'(x)^2 dx \leq 25\epsilon(p^2 + q^2)$.

Finally define $\mu(x) = \xi(x) + \sigma(x)$. It is easily verified that μ has continuous second derivatives and

$$
c_1\mu(a) + c_2\mu'(a) = c_1\beta(a) + c_2(p + y) = 0,
$$
$$
d_1\mu(b) + d_2\mu'(b) = d_1\sigma(b) + d_2(q + y) = 0.
$$

Moreover,

$$
\|\mu' - \beta'\| = \|\xi' + \alpha + y - \beta'\| \leq \|\xi'\| + \|\alpha - \beta'\| + \|y\|
$$
$$
\leq (25\epsilon(p^2 + q^2))^{1/2} + \epsilon + \epsilon.
$$

The quantities p and q are seen by their definition to be bounded independent of ϵ. For example, if $c_2 = 0$ then p may be taken as 0, and if $c_2 \neq 0$,

$$
|p| \leq \left| \frac{c_1}{c_2} \beta(a) \right| + |y| \leq \left| \frac{c_1}{c_2} \beta(a) \right| + (b - a)^{-1} \left(\int_a^b |\beta'| \, dx + |\beta(a)| \right).
$$

It follows that $\|\mu' - \beta'\|$ may be made less than ϵ_1, $\epsilon_1 > 0$, by a proper choice of ϵ. ★

THEOREM 6.4F   If β is continuous, β' is piecewise continuous on $a \leq x \leq b$, $\beta(a) = 0$ when $c_2 = 0$ and $\beta(b) = 0$ when $d_2 = 0$, then

$$(25) \qquad\qquad \beta(x) = \sum_{j=1}^{\infty} (\beta, \alpha_j)\, \alpha_j(x)$$

the series converging absolutely uniformly for $a \leq x \leq b$.

Proof   In view of the comments preceding Theorem 6.4E, we may assume that the eigenvalues r_j of L are all positive. Denoting the eigenvalues by r_j and their reciprocals, the eigenvalues of G, by s_j, we find that

$$\sum_m^n |(\beta, \alpha_j)\, \alpha_j(x)| = \sum_m^n |(\beta, \alpha_j)\, \sqrt{r_j}\, \sqrt{s_j}\, \alpha_j(x)|$$

$$\leq \left(\sum_m^n (\beta, \alpha_j)^2\, r_j \sum_m^n s_j\, \alpha_j(x)^2 \right)^{1/2}.$$

By Theorem 6.4E the series $\sum_1^\infty (\beta, \alpha_j)^2\, r_j < M$ for a constant M. Also Theorem 4.3F implies that the series $\sum_1^\infty s_j\, \alpha_j(x)^2$ converges uniformly to $G(x, x)$ and thus there is an integer N such that if $n > m > N$, then

$$\sum_m^n s_j\, \alpha_j(x)^2 < \frac{\epsilon^2}{M} \quad \text{and hence} \quad \sum_m^n |(\beta, \alpha_j)\, \alpha_j(x)| \leq \epsilon.$$

We have shown that the series in (25) converges absolutely uniformly on $a \leq x \leq b$. This, together with the fact that $\{\alpha_j\}$ is linearly dense, proves that the series converges to β. See Theorem 5.1G.   ★

EXAMPLE 2   For the operator $L = -\dfrac{d^2}{dx^2}$ in the space of functions β with continuous second derivatives satisfying $\beta(0) = 0$, $\beta(\pi) = 0$, the eigenvalues are calculated to be $r_n = n^2$, $n = 1, 2, \ldots$ and the normalized eigenvectors are $\alpha_n(x) = \sqrt{\dfrac{2}{\pi}}\,\sin nx$. The generalized Fourier series in terms of this linearly dense sequence for a function μ is

$$\sum_1^\infty \left(\frac{2}{\pi} \int_0^\pi \mu(t)\, \sin nt \, dt \right) \sin nx.$$

This is exactly the Fourier Sine series on $0 \leq x \leq \pi$ for μ. Theorem 6.4F restated for this case is: If μ is continuous and μ' is piecewise continuous on $0 \leq x \leq \pi$ and if $\mu(0) = 0 = \mu(\pi)$, then the Fourier Sine series for μ converges absolutely uniformly to μ on $0 \leq x \leq \pi$.

EXAMPLE 3   Using the operator $L = -\dfrac{d^2}{dx^2}$ on the space of functions β with continuous second derivatives satisfying $\beta(a) = 0 = \beta(b)$, the eigenvalues are $r_n = \dfrac{n^2\pi^2}{(b-a)^2}$ and the eigenvectors are $\alpha_n(x) = \sqrt{\dfrac{2}{b-a}}\sin\dfrac{n\pi}{b-a}$ $(x-a)$. The generalized Fourier series is

$$\sum_1^\infty \left(\frac{2}{b-a}\int_a^b \beta(t)\sin\frac{n\pi}{b-a}(t-a)\,dt\right)\sin\frac{n\pi}{b-a}(x-a).$$

This is the Fourier Sine series for the interval $a \le x \le b$. We do not obtain the Fourier series with sines and cosines merely by choosing $a = -\pi, b = \pi$.

EXAMPLE 4   For the operator $L = -\dfrac{d^2}{dx^2}$ on the space of functions β with continuous second derivatives satisfying $\beta'(0) = 0$, $\beta'(\pi) = 0$, the eigenvalues are $r_n = n^2$, $n = 0, 1, 2, \ldots$ and the eigenvectors are $\alpha_0 = \dfrac{1}{\sqrt{\pi}}$, $\alpha_n(x) = \sqrt{\dfrac{2}{\pi}}\cos nx$, $n = 1, 2, \ldots$. The generalized Fourier series in terms of this linearly dense sequence for a function σ is

$$\frac{1}{\pi}\int_0^\pi \sigma(t)\,dt + \sum_1^\infty \left(\frac{2}{\pi}\int_0^\pi \sigma(t)\cos nt\,dt\right)\cos nx.$$

This is the Fourier cosine series for σ. Theorem 6.4F in this case is: If σ is continuous and σ' is piecewise continuous on $0 \le x \le \pi$, then the Fourier Cosine series for σ converges absolutely uniformly to σ on $0 \le x \le \pi$.

The results of Examples 2 and 4 lead again to Theorem 5.6C. See Exercise 6.4–6.

The eigenvalues r_n of L may be characterized by extremal properties.

THEOREM 6.4G
a. $r_n = $ g.l.b. $\{(L\alpha, \alpha)\mid \alpha \text{ in } \mathscr{V}, \|\alpha\| = 1, \alpha \perp \alpha_1, \alpha_2, \ldots, \alpha_{n-1}\}$.
b.   If $\sigma_1, \ldots, \sigma_{n-1}$ are arbitrary vectors in $\mathscr{R}$, then

(26) $r_n = \underset{\sigma}{\text{l.u.b.}}\ [\underset{\alpha}{\text{g.l.b.}}\ \{(L\alpha, \alpha)\mid \alpha \text{ in } \mathscr{V}, \|\alpha\| = 1, \alpha \perp \sigma_1, \ldots, \sigma_{n-1}\}].$

(The result is also valid with σ_i restricted to $\mathscr{V}$.)

Proof   With $\sigma_1, \ldots, \sigma_{n-1}$ fixed, choose constants $a_1, \ldots, a_n$ so that the vector

$$\alpha = a_1\,\alpha_1 + \ldots + a_n\,\alpha_n,$$

which is in $\mathscr{V}$, satisfies

$$\|\alpha\| = 1, \qquad \alpha \perp \sigma_1, \ldots, \sigma_{n-1}.$$

We have

$$(L\alpha, \alpha) = \sum_{j=1}^{n} a_j^2 \, r_j \le r_n \sum_{j=1}^{n} a_j^2 = r_n.$$

Thus

(27)   g.l.b. $\{(L\alpha, \alpha) \mid \alpha \text{ in } \mathscr{V}, \qquad \|\alpha\| = 1, \qquad \alpha \perp \sigma_1, \ldots, \sigma_{n-1}\} \le r_n.$

On the other hand, if α is any vector in $\mathscr{V}$ with $\|\alpha\| = 1$, and $\alpha \perp \alpha_1, \ldots,$ α_{n-1}, then

$$\alpha(x) = \sum_{j=n}^{\infty} (\alpha, \alpha_j) \, \alpha_j(x)$$

uniformly for $a \le x \le b$, so that

$$(L\alpha, \alpha) = \int_a^b L\alpha(x) \sum_{j=n}^{\infty} (\alpha, \alpha_j) \, \alpha_j(x) \, dx = \sum_{j=n}^{\infty} (\alpha, \alpha_j)(L\alpha, \alpha_j)$$

$$= \sum_{j=n}^{\infty} (\alpha, \alpha_j)(\alpha, L\alpha_j) = \sum_{j=n}^{\infty} r_j(\alpha, \alpha_j)^2 \ge r_n \sum_{j=n}^{\infty} (\alpha, \alpha_j)^2 = r_n.$$

Hence

(28)   g.l.b. $\{(L\alpha, \alpha) \mid \alpha \text{ in } \mathscr{V}, \qquad \|\alpha\| = 1, \qquad \alpha \perp \alpha_1, \ldots, \alpha_{n-1}\} \ge r_n.$

The inequalities (27) and (28) taken together imply the truth of both parts of the theorem.   ★

At times it is useful to know that we need not restrict the vectors α in Theorem 6.4G (b) to lie in $\mathscr{V}$. Let $\mathscr{V}_1$ be the linear manifold of functions α which are continuous and have piecewise continuous derivatives on $a \le x \le b$, and which satisfy $\alpha(a) = 0$ when $c_2 = 0$, $\alpha(b) = 0$ when $d_2 = 0$. For members of $\mathscr{V}_1$ define

$$D[\alpha] = \int_a^b q\alpha^2 dx + \int_a^b (\alpha')^2 dx - \frac{c_1}{c_2} \alpha(a)^2 + \frac{d_1}{d_2} \alpha(b)^2,$$

where we take $\dfrac{c_1}{c_2} \alpha(a)^2 = 0$ when $c_2 = 0$ and $\dfrac{d_1}{d_2} \alpha(b)^2 = 0$ when $d_2 = 0$. This is $(L\alpha, \alpha)$ when α is in $\mathscr{V}$ by (20). It is then possible to prove

Corollary 1

$$r_n = \underset{\sigma}{\text{l.u.b.}} \, [\underset{\alpha}{\text{g.l.b.}} \, \{ D[\alpha] \mid \alpha \text{ in } \mathscr{V}_1, \|\alpha\| = 1, \alpha \perp \sigma_1, \ldots, \sigma_{n-1} \}].$$

For the proof it suffices to show that if $\sigma_1, \ldots, \sigma_{n-1}$ are fixed, if β is in $\mathscr{V}_1$, $\|\beta\| = 1$, $\beta \perp \sigma_1, \ldots, \sigma_{n-1}$, then for $\epsilon > 0$ there is an α in $\mathscr{V}$, $\|\alpha\| = 1$, $\alpha \perp \sigma_1, \ldots, \sigma_{n-1}$, such that $| D[\alpha] - D[\beta] | < \epsilon$. The construction of such a function is indicated in Exercise 6.4–13.

Corollary 2

Let $r_n^{\#}$ be eigenvalues for the Sturm-Liouville problem

$$
\begin{cases}
q^{\#}(x) - \dfrac{d^2}{dx^2} \, \alpha(x) = r\alpha(x), \\[2mm]
c_1^{\#} \, \alpha(a) + c_2^{\#} \, \alpha'(a) = 0, & |c_1^{\#}| + |c_2^{\#}| \neq 0, \quad c_2^{\#} = 0 \text{ if and only if} \\
& \hspace{4.5cm} c_2 = 0, \\[2mm]
d_1^{\#} \, \alpha(b) + d_2^{\#} \, \alpha'(b) = 0, & |d_1^{\#}| + |d_2^{\#}| \neq 0, \quad d_2^{\#} = 0 \text{ if and only if} \\
& \hspace{4.5cm} d_2 = 0.
\end{cases}
$$

If $q(x) \le q^{\#}(x)$, $-\dfrac{c_1}{c_2} \le -\dfrac{c_1^{\#}}{c_2^{\#}}$, $\dfrac{d_1}{d_2} \le \dfrac{d_1^{\#}}{d_2^{\#}}$, then $r_n \le r_n^{\#}$.

Indeed, if α is in $\mathscr{V}_1$, $\|\alpha\| = 1$, $\alpha \perp \sigma_1, \ldots, \sigma_{n-1}$, then

$$
\int_a^b q\alpha^2 dx + \int_a^b (\alpha')^2 dx - \frac{c_1}{c_2} \alpha(a)^2 + \frac{d_1}{d_2} \alpha(b)^2 \le \int_a^b q^{\#} \alpha^2 dx + \int_a^b (\alpha')^2 dx \\
- \frac{c_1^{\#}}{c_2^{\#}} \alpha(a)^2 + \frac{d_1^{\#}}{d_2^{\#}} \alpha(b)^2,
$$

and since $\mathscr{V}_1 = \mathscr{V}_1^{\#}$, the result follows from Corollary 1.

Extremal properties form the basis for the numerical calculation of bounds for the eigenvalues. We shall describe a method yielding upper bounds, suggested by J. W. Rayleigh and W. Ritz. This **Rayleigh-Ritz method** involves the replacement of the original extremal problem by an extremal problem for a finite dimensional linear manifold.

For fixed integer k, consider the k dimensional linear manifold $\mathscr{V}^{(k)}$ generated by k linearly independent functions $\beta_1, \ldots, \beta_k$ in $\mathscr{V}$. An element of $\mathscr{V}^{(k)}$ is of the form $\alpha = \sum_{i=1}^{k} x_i \beta_i$. In analogy with the values r_n given by (26), we define

$$(29) \quad r_n^{(k)} = \underset{\tilde{\sigma}}{\text{l.u.b.}} \, [\underset{\alpha}{\text{g.l.b.}} \, \{ (L\alpha, \alpha) \mid \alpha \text{ in } \mathscr{V}^{(k)}, \quad \|\alpha\| = 1, \quad \alpha \perp \tilde{\sigma}_1, \ldots, \tilde{\sigma}_{n-1} \}],$$

where $\tilde{\sigma}_i$ are in $\mathscr{V}^{(k)}$. We shall prove in the next theorem that $r_n \le r_n^{(k)}$

so that (29) yields upper bounds for the eigenvalues. But the values $r_n^{(k)}$ can be calculated by matrix methods. To see this, write

$$\alpha = \sum_{i=1}^{k} x_i \beta_i, \qquad L\alpha = \sum_{i=1}^{k} x_i L\beta_i,$$

$$(L\alpha, \alpha) = \sum_{i,j=1}^{k} a_{ij} x_i x_j, \text{ where } a_{ij} = (L\beta_i, \beta_j) = a_{ji},$$

$$\|\alpha\|^2 = \sum_{i,j=1}^{k} b_{ij} x_i x_j, \text{ where } b_{ij} = (\beta_i, \beta_j) = b_{ji},$$

and note that the condition $\alpha \perp \tilde{\sigma}_m, \quad \tilde{\sigma}_m = \sum_{i=1}^{k} c_{im} \beta_i,$ becomes

$$0 = \sum_{i=1}^{k} \left(\sum_{j=1}^{k} b_{ij} x_j \right) c_{im}.$$

Let us now consider real Euclidean vector space $\mathscr{E}_k$ and denote vectors in $\mathscr{E}_k$ by the symbol μ. Define transformations A and B whose representations in the basis

$$\begin{bmatrix} 1 \\ 0 \\ \cdot \\ \cdot \\ \cdot \\ 0 \end{bmatrix}, \quad \begin{bmatrix} 0 \\ 1 \\ 0 \\ \cdot \\ \cdot \\ 0 \end{bmatrix}, \quad \cdots \quad \begin{bmatrix} 0 \\ 0 \\ \cdot \\ \cdot \\ 0 \\ 1 \end{bmatrix},$$

are given by

$$A \leftrightarrow [a_{ij}], \qquad B \leftrightarrow [b_{ij}].$$

In addition to the inner product (μ_1, μ_2), consider also the B inner product defined by

$$(\mu_1, \mu_2)_B = (B\mu_1, \mu_2).$$

Then the results above show that $r_n^{(k)}$ in (29) is also

(30) $\quad r_n^{(k)} = \text{l.u.b.} \underset{\rho}{} [\text{g.l.b.} \underset{\mu}{} \{(A\mu, \mu) \mid \mu \text{ in } \mathscr{E}_k, \|\mu\|_B = 1, (\mu, \rho_m)_B = 0,$

$$m = 1, \dots, n-1\}],$$

where, for fixed m, $\rho_m \leftrightarrow [c_{im}]$ is a vector in $\mathscr{E}_k$.

It will be a good review for the reader to show, using the methods of Sections 2.8 and 2.9, that the values $r_n^{(k)}$ given by (30) are the "eigenvalues" for the equation

$$A\mu = rB\mu$$

ordered as

$$r_1^{(k)} \leq r_2^{(k)} \leq \dots \leq r_k^{(k)}.$$

EXAMPLE 5 Approximate the first two eigenvalues of $L = -\dfrac{d^2}{dx^2}$, $0 \leq x \leq b$, with boundary conditions $\alpha(0) = 0 = \alpha(b)$.

Let $\beta_1 = x(b - x)$, and take $k = 1$. Then $a_{11} = (L\beta_1, \beta_1)$
$= \displaystyle\int_0^b 2x(b - x)dx = b^3/3$. Also $b_{11} = (\beta_1, \beta_1) = \displaystyle\int_0^b x^2(b - x)^2 dx = b^5/30$.
We must find the eigenvalues of $A\mu = rB\mu$, that is, solve $(b^3/3)x = (r\,b^5/30)x$, whence we obtain $r_1^{(1)} = 10/b^2$. As we know, the first eigenvalue of our boundary value problem is $r_1 = \dfrac{\pi^2}{b^2}$, and we see that $r_1 \leq r_1^{(1)}$.

Now let $\beta_1 = x(b - x)$, $\beta_2 = x^2(b - x)$ and take $k = 2$. Then matrices $[a_{ij}] = [(L\beta_i, \beta_j)]$ and $[b_{ij}] = [(\beta_i, \beta_j)]$ are given by

$$[a_{ij}] = \begin{bmatrix} b^3/3 & b^4/6 \\ b^4/6 & (2/15)b^5 \end{bmatrix}, \quad [b_{ij}] = \begin{bmatrix} b^5/30 & b^6/60 \\ b^6/60 & b^7/105 \end{bmatrix}.$$

The eigenvalues are roots of $\det[a_{ij} - r\,b_{ij}] = 0$ and are found to be $10/b^2$ and $42/b^2$. As we know, $r_2 = \dfrac{4\pi^2}{b^2} \leq r_2^{(2)}$. Note also that $r_1 \leq r_1^{(2)}$. Calculations are often simplified if β_i are first orthonormalized.

THEOREM 6.4H With r_n defined by (26) and $r_n^{(k)}$ by (29) we have $r_n \leq r_n^{(k)}$. Moreover $r_n^{(k+1)} \leq r_n^{(k)}$ so that increasing k does not make worse the approximation to the first k eigenvalues.

Proof In comparing (26) and (29), it must be observed that the vectors in (26) lie in $\mathscr{V}$ while those in (29) lie in $\mathscr{V}^{(k)}$. Let $\epsilon_1, \ldots, \epsilon_k$ represent an orthonormal basis for $\mathscr{V}^{(k)}$ and adjoin vectors $\epsilon_{k+1}, \epsilon_{k+2}, \ldots$ in $\mathscr{V}$ so as to obtain a linearly dense orthonormal set in $\mathscr{V}$. (For example, this may be accomplished by adding to $\epsilon_1, \ldots, \epsilon_k$, the eigenvectors of L and applying the Gram-Schmidt process). Choose $\sigma_1, \ldots, \sigma_{n-1}$ in $\mathscr{V}$. If $\sigma_m = \displaystyle\sum_1^\infty d_{im}\,\epsilon_i$, define $\tilde{\sigma}_m = \displaystyle\sum_1^k d_{im}\,\epsilon_i$. Then whenever α is in $\mathscr{V}^{(k)}$, it is clear that $(\alpha, \sigma_m) = (\alpha, \tilde{\sigma}_m)$. Therefore

$$\operatorname*{g.l.b.}_{\alpha} \{(L\alpha, \alpha) \mid \alpha \text{ in } \mathscr{V}, \quad \|\alpha\| = 1, \quad \alpha \perp \sigma_1, \ldots, \sigma_{n-1}\}$$

$$\leq \operatorname*{g.l.b.}_{\alpha} \{(L\alpha, \alpha) \mid \alpha \text{ in } \mathscr{V}^{(k)}, \quad \|\alpha\| = 1, \quad \alpha \perp \tilde{\sigma}_1, \ldots, \tilde{\sigma}_{n-1}\},$$

since $\mathscr{V}^{(k)}$ is only a subset of $\mathscr{V}$. Now permitting σ_m to vary over $\mathscr{V}$, we obtain

$$r_n \leq \operatorname*{l.u.b.}_{\sigma} \left[\operatorname*{g.l.b.}_{\alpha} \{(L\alpha, \alpha) \mid \alpha \text{ in } \mathscr{V}^{(k)}, \quad \|\alpha\| = 1, \quad \alpha \perp \tilde{\sigma}_1, \ldots, \tilde{\sigma}_{n-1}\}\right].$$

The number on the right side of the inequality will be unchanged if we let $\tilde{\sigma}_m$ vary over $\mathscr{V}^{(k)}$. Hence $r_n \leq r_n^{(k)}$.

If, in the above proof we replace $\mathscr{V}$ by $\mathscr{V}^{(k+1)}$, and note that $\mathscr{V}^{(k)}$ is a subset of $\mathscr{V}^{(k+1)}$, we obtain $r_n^{(k+1)} \leq r_n^{(k)}$.   ★

The next theorem should be compared with Theorems 4.4A and B, from which it may also be deduced.

THEOREM 6.4I   When r is not an eigenvalue of L, the equation

$$(31) \qquad\qquad L\alpha = r\alpha + \beta$$

has a unique solution α in $\mathscr{V}$ for every continuous β. When r is an eigenvalue, then a solution in $\mathscr{V}$ of (31) exists if and only if β is orthogonal to the eigenvector ζ corresponding to r. If this condition is satisfied, there will be infinitely many solutions, one and only one being orthogonal to the eigenvector ζ.

Proof $(L - rI)\,\alpha = \beta$ has a solution in $\mathscr{V}$ for every β if and only if 0 is not an eigenvalue of $L - rI$, if and only if r is not an eigenvalue of L.

Now suppose that r is an eigenvalue with associated eigenvector ζ and that α is a solution of (31) in $\mathscr{V}$. Then

$$r(\alpha, \zeta) = (\alpha, r\zeta) = (\alpha, L\zeta) = (L\alpha, \zeta)$$
$$= (r\alpha + \beta, \zeta) = r(\alpha, \zeta) + (\beta, \zeta).$$

It follows that $(\beta, \zeta) = 0$. Conversely, if $(\beta, \zeta) = 0$, we shall exhibit solutions of (31) in $\mathscr{V}$. For this purpose, let σ be a solution of $L\alpha = r\alpha$ which is linearly independent of ζ. Then the general solution of (31) is, according to Theorem 6.2E,

$$\alpha(x) = k_1\zeta(x) + k_2\,\sigma(x) + w^{-1}\int_a^x \Big(\zeta(t)\,\sigma(x) - \zeta(x)\,\sigma(t) \Big)\,\beta(t)\,dt,$$

where w is the Wronskian of ζ and σ, w being constant. The function

$$\mu(x) = \int_a^x \Big(\zeta(t)\,\sigma(x) - \zeta(x)\,\sigma(t) \Big)\,\beta(t)\,dt$$

satisfies

$$\mu'(x) = \int_a^x \Big(\zeta(t)\,\sigma'(x) - \zeta'(x)\,\sigma(t) \Big)\,\beta(t)\,dt$$

and so $\mu(a) = 0$, $\mu'(a) = 0$. Also $d_1\mu(b) + d_2\mu'(b) =$

$$\Big(d_1\,\sigma(b) + d_2\,\sigma'(b) \Big)\int_a^b \zeta(t)\,\beta(t)\,dt - \Big(d_1\zeta(b) + d_2\zeta'(b) \Big)\int_a^b \sigma(t)\,\beta(t)\,dt$$

and this is zero since ζ is in $\mathscr{V}$ and $(\zeta, \beta) = 0$.

Hence, if we take $k_2 = 0$, the function

$$k_1 \zeta + w^{-1}\mu$$

is a solution in $\mathscr{V}$ of (31) for every value of k_1. This solution is orthogonal to ζ if k_1 is chosen to satisfy

$$(k_1 \zeta + w^{-1}\mu, \zeta) = 0.$$

There can be only one solution α in $\mathscr{V}$ of (31) orthogonal to ζ. Indeed, if there were two, their difference $\alpha_1 - \alpha_2$ would satisfy $L(\alpha_1 - \alpha_2) = r(\alpha_1 - \alpha_2)$ and so, if not zero, would be an eigenvector of L for eigenvalue r, linearly independent of ζ, which is impossible.   ★

Exercise 6.4

1. (a) Consider the system

$$(*)\quad \begin{cases} \dfrac{d}{dx}(P(x)\, f'(x)\,) + (r\rho(x) - Q(x))\, f(x) = 0, \quad a \le x \le b, \\ a_1 f(a) + a_2 f'(a) = 0, \quad |a_1| + |a_2| \ne 0, \\ b_1 f(b) + b_2 f'(b) = 0, \quad |b_1| + |b_2| \ne 0, \end{cases}$$

where Q is continuous and P and ρ are positive and have continuous second derivatives on $a \le x \le b$. Make the transformation

$$t(x) = \int_a^x \left(\frac{\rho(y)}{P(y)}\right)^{1/2} dy, \quad \alpha(t) = h(x(t))\, f(x(t)), \text{ where } h(x) = (\rho(x)\, P(x))^{1/4},$$

and obtain the system

$$(**)\quad \begin{cases} \alpha''(t) + \left(r - \dfrac{1}{h(t)}\dfrac{d^2 h}{dt^2} - \dfrac{Q(x(t))}{\rho(x(t))}\right)\alpha(t) = 0, \quad 0 \le t \le T = \int_a^b \left(\frac{\rho}{P}\right)^{1/2} dx, \\ c_1 \alpha(0) + c_2 \alpha'(0) = 0, \quad |c_1| + |c_2| \ne 0, \\ d_1 \alpha(T) + d_2 \alpha'(T) = 0, \quad |d_1| + |d_2| \ne 0. \end{cases}$$

   (b) Show that if α_1 and α_2 are orthogonal on $0 \le t \le T$, and f_1 and f_2 are related to h_1 and h_2 by $\alpha_i(t) = h(x(t))\, f_i(x(t))$, then f_1 and f_2 are orthogonal on $a \le x \le b$ with respect to the weight function ρ.

2. The differential equation in (*) of Exercise 1 can be written

$$Lf = \left(\frac{Q}{\rho} - \frac{1}{\rho}\frac{d}{dx}\left(P\frac{d}{dx}\right)\right)f = rf.$$

Show that L is a symmetric operator on $\mathscr{V}$ when we use the inner product

$$(\alpha, \beta)_\varrho = \int_a^b \rho(x)\, \alpha(x)\, \beta(x)\, dx.$$

3. (a) Carry through the proof for Theorem 6.4A using the operator $L = Q - \dfrac{d}{dx}\left(P\dfrac{d}{dx}\right)$. Show that the Green's function is

$$G(x, y) = \begin{cases} -\dfrac{1}{w\, P(y)}\, \sigma_1(y)\, \sigma_2(x), \quad a \le y \le x \le b \\ -\dfrac{1}{w\, P(y)}\, \sigma_1(x)\, \sigma_2(y), \quad a \le x \le y \le b \end{cases}$$

where $w = W[\sigma_1(y), \sigma_2(y)]$ and wP is a constant, σ_1 and σ_2 being defined by (5) and (6).

(b) Show that $\dfrac{\partial}{\partial x} G(y +, y) - \dfrac{\partial}{\partial x} G(y -, y) = -\dfrac{1}{P(y)}$.

4. Find the Green's function in each of the following cases:

(a) $L = -\dfrac{d^2}{dx^2}$, $\alpha(a) = \alpha'(b) = 0$.

(b) $L = A^2 - \dfrac{d^2}{dx^2}$, $\alpha(a) = \alpha(b) = 0$, $A > 0$.

(c) $L = -A^2 - \dfrac{d^2}{dx^2}$, $\alpha(a) = \alpha(b) = 0$, $A > 0$, $A \neq \dfrac{n\pi}{b-a}$.

(d) $L = \dfrac{A(A-1)}{x^2} - \dfrac{d^2}{dx^2}$, $1 \le x \le 2$, $\alpha(1) = \alpha(2) = 0$, $A \neq \frac{1}{2}$.

5. Let $G_1(x, y)$ be a continuous symmetric kernel on $a \le x \le b$, $a \le y \le b$, defining an integral operator G_1 by $G_1\beta(x) = \displaystyle\int_a^b G_1(x, y)\, \beta(y)\, dy$ satisfying (19) with G replaced by G_1. Show that $G_1(x, y)$ is the Green's function $G(x, y)$. *Hint:* If β is in $\mathscr{C}$, show that $G\beta = G_1\beta$, then use Exercise 4.2–8.

6. Prove Theorem 5.6C by use of the results of Examples 2 and 4. *Hint:* If α satisfies the hypothesis of Theorem 5.6C, write $\alpha = \sigma + \mu$ where σ is even and μ is odd.

7. Using the notation of Theorem 6.4G show that if α is in $\mathscr{V}$, $\|\alpha\| = 1$, $\alpha \perp \alpha_1, \ldots, \alpha_{n-1}$, and $(L\alpha, \alpha) = r_n$, then $\alpha = c\alpha_n$, with $|c| = 1$.

8. Let β be in $\mathscr{V}$. Show that
$$r_i\,(\beta, \alpha_i) = (\beta q, \alpha_i) - (\beta'', \alpha_i)$$
Hence prove that $\displaystyle\sum_1^\infty (\beta, \alpha_i)^2\, r_i^2$ converges.

9. (a) Let β be in $\mathscr{V}$. Suppose that $L\beta$ satisfies the hypothesis given for the function β of Theorem 6.4F. Prove that $L\beta = \sum a_i r_i \alpha_i(x)$, $a_i = (\beta, \alpha_i)$, where the series converges absolutely uniformly on $a \le x \le b$. Show that $(L\beta, L\beta) = \sum a_i^2 r_i^2$.

    (b) Let β be continuous on $a \le x \le b$ and suppose that $\displaystyle\sum_1^\infty a_i r_i \alpha_i$ converges absolutely uniformly, where $a_i = (\beta, \alpha_i)$. Show that β is in $\mathscr{V}$ and that $L\beta = \displaystyle\sum_1^\infty a_i r_i \alpha_i$. *Hint:* Assume first that zero is not an eigenvalue. Show that $\displaystyle\sum_1^\infty a_i \alpha_i$ converges uniformly and $G(\displaystyle\sum_1^\infty a_i r_i \alpha_i) = \beta$. Then apply L to both sides.

10. Using (22) show that if g.l.b. $\{q\,(x) \mid a \le x \le b\}$ is larger than
$$\left(\left|\dfrac{c_1}{c_2}\right| + \left|\dfrac{d_1}{d_2}\right|\right)^2 + (b-a)^{-1}\left(\left|\dfrac{c_1}{c_2}\right| + \left|\dfrac{d_1}{d_2}\right|\right)$$
then zero is not an eigenvalue of L.

11. Let $L_r = (q - r) - \dfrac{d^2}{dx_2}$ be an operator on $\mathscr{V}$ for fixed r. When r is not an eigenvalue of $L = q - \dfrac{d^2}{dx^2}$, we can define the Green's function $G(x, y, r)$ for the operator L_r. Show that
$$G(x, y, r) = \sum_j \frac{1}{r_j - r}\, \alpha_j(x)\, \alpha_j(y),$$

the series converging absolutely uniformly. Here $\alpha_j(x)$ are the eigenvectors of L, and r_j are the eigenvalues of L. See Exercise 4.3–7.
We have

$$H(x, r) = \int_a^b G(x, y, r)\, \beta(y)dy = \sum_j - \frac{(\beta, \alpha_j)}{r - r_j} \alpha_j(x).$$

It can be shown, considering r as a complex variable, and using methods of complex variable theory, that the numbers $(-\beta, \alpha_j)\, \alpha_j(x)$ can be obtained by integrating $H(x, r)$. This suggests that a study of H can lead to the establishment of an expansion theorem $\beta(x) = \Sigma_j (\beta, \alpha_j)\, \alpha_j(x)$. (See Titchmarsh, *Eigenfunction Expansions*.)

12. (a) Assume that r is not an eigenvalue of L. Find the solution α of (31) in $\mathscr{V}$ by use of Exercise 11.
   (b) Deduce Theorem 6.4I from Theorems 4.4A and B.

13. Prove Corollary 1 of Theorem 6.4G as follows:
   (a) Show that it suffices to prove that if $\sigma_1, \ldots, \sigma_{n-1}$ are fixed vectors in $\mathscr{R}\{a, b\}$, β is in $\mathscr{V}_1$, $\|\beta\| = 1$, $\beta \perp \sigma_1, \ldots, \sigma_{n-1}$, then for $\epsilon_1 > 0$, there is an α in $\mathscr{V}$, $\|\alpha\| = 1$, $\alpha \perp \sigma_1, \ldots, \sigma_{n-1}$ such that $|D[\alpha] - D[\beta]| < \epsilon_1$.
   (b) As in the proof of Theorem 6.4E, there is a function μ in $\mathscr{V}$, $\mu(a) = \beta(a)$, $\|\mu' - \beta'\| < \epsilon$. Show that the function μ defined in that theorem satisfies $\mu(b) = 0$ if $d_2 = 0$. Show that $\|\mu - \beta\| \le \epsilon(b - a)$ and hence $|\|\mu\| - 1| \le \epsilon(b - a)$. Also $|(\mu, \sigma_j)| \le \epsilon(b - a)\|\sigma_j\|$.
   (c) Assume that σ_i are ordered so that $\sigma_1, \ldots, \sigma_N$ are linearly independent and $\sigma_{N+1}, \ldots, \sigma_{n-1}$ are linearly dependent on the first N. Let $\psi_m, m = 1, \ldots, N$ be functions with continuous second derivatives, vanishing in neighborhoods of a and b, and satisfying $(\sigma_j, \psi_m) = \delta_{jm}$, $j, m = 1, \ldots, N$. Define $\phi = \mu + \sum_{j=1}^N c_j \psi_j$. Show that we can choose c_j so that $(\phi, \sigma_j) = 0$, $j = 1, \ldots, N$. Note that $c_j = -(\mu, \sigma_j)$, $j = 1, \ldots, N$. Show that $\|\phi - \mu\| \le \epsilon(b - a) \sum_{j=1}^N \|\sigma_j\| \|\psi_j\|$ and $|\|\phi\| - 1| \le \epsilon(b - a)$ $(1 + \sum_{j=1}^N \|\sigma_j\| \|\psi_j\|)$. Hence if ϵ is sufficiently small, $\|\phi\| \ne 0$. Define $\alpha = \phi/\|\phi\|$. Show that this is the desired α. For simplicity, show that $\lim_{\varepsilon \to 0} |D[\phi] - D[\beta]| = 0$, $\lim_{\varepsilon \to 0} \|\phi\| = 1$, then consider $D[\phi]/\|\phi\|^2 = D[\alpha]$.

14. (a) Using Theorem 6.4G (a) and (20) with $c_2 = d_2 = 0$, $q(x) = 0$, prove the following result: If β has continuous second derivatives on $a \le x \le b$ and vanishes at a and b, then

$$\int_a^b \beta(x)^2\, dx \le \frac{(b - a)^2}{\pi^2} \int_a^b \beta'(x)^2\, dx.$$

   (b) Extend the result to the case when β is continuous and has a piecewise continuous derivative on $a \le x \le b$ and vanishes at a and b.
   Hint: Use (24) and note that $\mu(b) = 0$ when $d_2 = 0$.
   (c) Show that (b) follows from Corollary 1 of Theorem 6.4G.

15. (a) As in Exercise 14, with $c_2 = d_1 = 0$, $q(x) = 0$, prove: If β has continuous second derivatives on $a \le x \le b$ and $\beta(a) = \beta'(b) = 0$, then

$$\int_a^b \beta(x)^2\, dx \le \frac{4(b - a)^2}{\pi^2} \int_a^b \beta'(x)^2\, dx.$$

(b) Extend the result to the case when β is continuous and has a piecewise continuous derivative on $a \leq x \leq b$ and $\beta(a) = 0$. *Hint:* Use (24) and note $\mu'(b) = 0$ since $y = 0$ and $\mu'(b) = \xi'(b) + \sigma'(b) = q + \alpha(b) = q$, but q may be chosen to be zero when $d_1 = 0$, $y = 0$.

(c) Show that (b) follows from Corollary 1 of Theorem 6.4B.

16. Show that if σ_1 and σ_2 are linearly independent solutions of $L\alpha = r\alpha$, then a necessary and sufficient condition that r be an eigenvalue is that

$$\begin{vmatrix} c_1\sigma_1(a) + c_2\sigma_1'(a) & c_1\sigma_2(a) + c_2\sigma_2'(a) \\ d_1\sigma_1(b) + d_2\sigma_1'(b) & d_1\sigma_2(b) + d_2\sigma_2'(b) \end{vmatrix} = 0.$$

17. (a) Obtain the value $\dfrac{42}{b^2}$ given in Example 5.

(b) What would be the approximation to r_2 if we chose $\beta_2 = x(b - x)^2$?

(c) Continue Example 5 with $k = 3$, using $\beta_3 = x^2(b - x)^2$.

18. (a) Show that there is no solution for

$$-\alpha(x) - \alpha''(x) = \sin x, \quad \alpha(0) = \alpha(\pi) = 0.$$

(b) What must be the condition on $f(x)$ such that a solution exists for

$$-\alpha(x) - \alpha''(x) = f(x), \quad \alpha(0) = \alpha(\pi) = 0?$$

19. Why is the operator B in (30) positive definite? See Exercise 2.5–5. Show that the Gramian is never negative.

20. Show that

$$r_n = \text{g.l.b.} \left[\text{l.u.b.} \left\{ (L\alpha, \, \alpha) \, \middle| \, \|\alpha\| = 1, \, \alpha = \sum_{i=1}^{n} k_i \, \sigma_i, \, \sigma_i \text{ in } \mathscr{V} \right\} \right].$$

Hint: Fix $\sigma_1, \ldots, \sigma_n$ in $\mathscr{V}$ and pick k_i so that $\alpha = \sum_{i=1}^{n} k_i \, \sigma_i$, $\|\alpha\| = 1$, $\alpha \perp \alpha_1, \ldots,$

α_{n-1}. Then $\alpha = \sum_{n}^{\infty} (\alpha, \, \alpha_j) \, \alpha_j$ and, as in Theorem 6.4G, $(L\alpha, \, \alpha)$

$= \sum_{n}^{\infty} (\alpha, \, \alpha_j)^2 \, r_j \geq r_n$. Conversely, if $\alpha = \sum_{i=1}^{n} k_i \, \alpha_i$, $\|\alpha\| = 1$, then $(L\alpha, \, \alpha) \leq r_n$.

21. Show that if β satisfies the hypothesis of Theorem 6.4F, then $\sum_{j=1}^{\infty} |(\beta, \, \alpha_j)|$ converges.

6.5

GREEN'S

FUNCTION

The solution in $\mathscr{V}$ (the linear manifold of functions with continuous second derivatives satisfying the boundary conditions 6.4–(2) and (3)) of

(1) $$L\alpha(x) = \left(q - \frac{d^2}{dx^2} \right) \alpha(x) = \beta(x), \qquad a \leq x \leq b,$$

where β is continuous, has been shown to be

(2) $$\alpha(x) = \int_a^b G(x, y)\, \beta(y)\, dy$$

when zero is not an eigenvalue of L. Here $G(x, y)$, the Green's function for L and the associated boundary conditions, given by 6.4–(12), satisfies

(3) $$LG(x, y) = 0 \qquad \text{whenever } x \neq y.$$

It is possible to give a physical interpretation to the Green's function as the response of the physical system represented by (1) when β is a point impulse (a Dirac delta function). Such a physical interpretation is often useful in describing and understanding the mathematics.

For fixed y, define the continuous function $\beta_n(x, y)$ so that $\beta_n(x, y) = 0$ outside $|x - y| \leq 1/n$ and $\int_a^b \beta_n(x, y)\, dx = 1$. Such a function may be called a unit pulse. We will also assume $\beta_n(x, y) \geq 0$ and $\beta_n(x, y) = \beta_n(y, x)$. The solution of $L\alpha = \beta_n$ is then by (2),

(4) $$G_n(x, y) = \int_a^b G(x, \mu)\, \beta_n(u, y)\, du.$$

Applying the mean value theorem, we get

$$G_n(x, y) = G(x, z) \int_{y-\frac{1}{n}}^{y+\frac{1}{n}} \beta_n(u, y)\, du = G(x, z),$$

where $y - \dfrac{1}{n} \leq z \leq y + \dfrac{1}{n}$. Letting $n \to \infty$, we have

(5) $$G(x, y) = \lim_{n \to \infty} G_n(x, y),$$

so that $G(x, y)$ is the limit of solutions of (1) when the right side of (1) is a sequence of unit pulses $\beta_n(x, y)$ with $\lim_{n \to \infty} \beta_n(x, y) = 0$ for $x \neq y$.

We can say more. We have, by Theorem 5.2A, for any continuous function μ,

(6) $$\lim_{n \to \infty} \int_a^b LG_n(x, y)\, \mu(x)\, dx = \lim_{n \to \infty} \int_a^b \beta_n(x, y)\, \mu(x)\, dx = \mu(y).$$

We write

(7) $$LG(x, y) = \delta(x, y)$$

where $\delta(x, y)$ is the Dirac delta function introduced in Section 5.2 (there it would have been written $\delta(y, x)$), to indicate there is a sequence G_n satisfying (5) and (6).

Now (2) can be interpreted as the superposition of solutions $G(x, y) \beta(y)$ arising from impulses at y with weight $\beta(y)$.

Continuing this reasoning, note from (4) that

$$|G_n(x, y)| \le B \int_a^b \beta_n(u, y)\, du = B,$$

where $B = $ l.u.b. $\left\{ |G(x, y)| \,\middle|\, a \le x \le b, a \le y \le b \right\}$. Moreover,

$$1 = \int_{y-\frac{1}{n}}^{y+\frac{1}{n}} \beta_n(x, y)dx = \int_{y-\frac{1}{n}}^{y+\frac{1}{n}} LG_n(x, y)dx = \int_{y-\frac{1}{n}}^{y+\frac{1}{n}} [q(x)\, G_n(x, y)$$

$$- \frac{\partial^2}{\partial x^2} G_n(x, y)]dx$$

$$= \int_{y-\frac{1}{n}}^{y+\frac{1}{n}} q(x)\, G_n(x, y)\, dx - \left(\frac{\partial}{\partial x} G_n\!\left(y + \frac{1}{n}, y\right) - \frac{\partial}{\partial x} G_n\!\left(y - \frac{1}{n}, y\right) \right).$$

Letting $n \to \infty$, and noting that the integral on the right side of the last equation approaches zero, we obtain

$$\lim_{n \to \infty} \frac{\partial}{\partial x} G_n\!\left(y + \frac{1}{n}, y\right) - \frac{\partial}{\partial x} G_n\!\left(y - \frac{1}{n}, y\right) = -1.$$

This suggests that we expect

$$\frac{d}{dx} G(y +, y) - \frac{d}{dx} G(y -, y) = -1.$$

EXAMPLE 1   Place a unit force at y, deflecting a tightly stretched string on $a \le x \le b$ into the form of a triangle. Assume that the tension T in the string is so large that it is not appreciably changed by the small deflection. As we shall see, a restriction to small deflections insures that the differential equation characterizing the equilibrium position is linear, implying the

validity of adding effects. (The corresponding physical observation is known
as Hooke's law.) Denote the deflection at x due to the unit force at y by
$D(x, y)$.

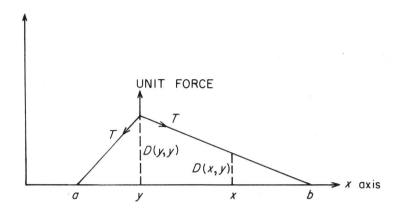

Since $\sin \theta = \tan \theta$ for small angles, taking components of the force along
an axis perpendicular to the x axis yields

$$T \frac{D(y, y)}{y - a} + T \frac{D(y, y)}{b - y} = 1,$$

so that

$$D(y, y) = \frac{(y - a)(b - y)}{T(b - a)}.$$

By similar triangles, it follows that

$$D(x, y) = \begin{cases} \dfrac{(b - x)(y - a)}{T(b - a)}, & y \leq x \\[2mm] \dfrac{(x - a)(b - y)}{T(b - a)}, & x \leq y, \end{cases}$$

so that $D(x, y)$ is continuous and has continuous second derivatives with
respect to x for $x \neq y$. The second derivative is zero for $x \neq y$. The first
derivative has a jump of $-\dfrac{1}{T}$ at $x = y$. Moreover $D(x, y) = D(y, x)$.

The equilibrium position of the string under the action of a distributed
force $\mu(y)$ is given by integration as

$$(8) \qquad \alpha(x) = \int_a^b D(x, y)\, \mu(y)dy = \int_a^x \frac{(b - x)(y - a)}{T(b - a)} \mu(y)dy$$

$$+ \int_x^b \frac{(x - a)(b - y)}{T(b - a)} \mu(y)dy.$$

Differentiation then yields

$$\alpha'(x) = \int_a^x \frac{-(y-a)}{T(b-a)} \mu(y)dy + \frac{(b-x)(x-a)}{T(b-a)} \mu(x)$$

$$+ \int_x^b \frac{b-y}{T(b-a)} \mu(y)dy - \frac{(x-a)(b-x)}{T(b-a)} \mu(x)$$

$$= \frac{1}{T(b-a)}\left(\int_a^x -(y-a)\,\mu(y)dy + \int_x^b (b-y)\,\mu(y)dy \right),$$

(9) $$\alpha''(x) = \frac{1}{T(b-a)}\left(-(x-a)\,\mu(x) - (b-x)\,\mu(x) \right) = -\frac{\mu(x)}{T}.$$

This is the differential equation specifying the equilibrium position. Writing it in the form given by (1), that is,

$$L\alpha = -\alpha''(x) = \frac{\mu(x)}{T} = \beta(x),$$

with solution given by (2), and comparing (2) with (8), we find that

$$G(x, y) = TD(x, y) = \begin{cases} \dfrac{(b-x)(y-a)}{b-a}, & y \le x \\[2ex] \dfrac{(x-a)(b-y)}{b-a}, & x \le y. \end{cases}$$

This can be compared with Example 1 of Section 6.4.

Thus, what essentially has been done above is to obtain the differential equation (9) from the Green's function, instead of obtaining the differential equation first.

The same procedure may be applied in seeking the instantaneous position $\alpha(x, t)$ when the string is not in equilibrium and even when the force $\mu(x, t)$ varies with time. At a fixed time, the position of the string is exactly that which it would have under equilibrium conditions if the applied force were equal to the restoring force. Since the excess of the applied force over the restoring force is equal to the product of mass and acceleration, we may reduce the problem to the equilibrium case by replacing $\mu(x, t)$ by $\mu(x, t) - \rho(x) \dfrac{\partial^2 \alpha}{\partial t^2}$ where ρ is the mass per length of the string. The desired integral equation is then

$$\alpha(x, t) = \int_a^b D(x, y)\left(\mu(y, t) - \rho(y) \frac{\partial^2 \alpha(y, t)}{\partial t^2} \right)dy,$$

and the corresponding differential equation is

$$\frac{\partial^2 \alpha}{\partial x^2} = -\frac{1}{T}\left(\mu(x, t) - \rho(x)\frac{\partial^2 \alpha}{\partial t^2}\right).$$

When μ is independent of t, it is convenient to find the motion relative to the equilibrium position. Let

$$\alpha_0(x) = \int_a^b D(x, y)\,\mu(y)\,dy, \qquad \sigma(x, t) = \alpha(x, t) - \alpha_0(x).$$

Then the integral equation is

$$\sigma(x, t) = -\int_a^b D(x, y)\,\rho(y)\,\frac{\partial^2 \sigma}{\partial t^2}\,dy$$

and the associated differential equation is

$$\frac{\partial^2 \sigma}{\partial x^2} = \frac{\rho}{T}\frac{\partial^2 \sigma}{\partial t^2}.$$

In the above example, we have illustrated the mathematical formulation of a physical problem as an integral equation by the superposition of effects arising from elementary impulses. Very often the integral representation yields a better picture of the physical fact than does the differential relation.

The Green's function is named after G. Green who, in a paper in 1828 entitled "An essay on the application of mathematical analysis to the theories of electricity and magnetism," introduced a function which, in three dimensions, plays a role similar to that performed by the Green's function we have introduced.

The next theorem indicates that we can give a direct characterization of the Green's function as a solution of $LG = \delta$.

The Green's function $G(x, y)$ associated with the equation

$$(10) \qquad\qquad L\alpha(x) = \left(q - \frac{d^2}{dx^2}\right)\alpha(x), \qquad a \le x \le b,$$

and the boundary conditions

$$(11) \qquad\qquad c_1\,\alpha(a) + c_2\,\alpha'(a) = 0, \qquad |c_1| + |c_2| \neq 0,$$

$$(12) \qquad\qquad d_1\,\alpha(b) + d_2\,\alpha'(b) = 0, \qquad |d_1| + |d_2| \neq 0,$$

may be defined by

Definition A

1. $G(x, y)$ is continuous in x and y for $a \le x \le b$, $a \le y \le b$.

2. For fixed y, $a < y < b$, $G(x, y)$ has right and left derivatives with respect to x at $x = y$ satisfying

(13)
$$\frac{\partial}{\partial x} G(y +, y) - \frac{\partial}{\partial x} G(y -, y) = -1.$$

3. For fixed y, $G(x, y)$ has continuous second derivatives with respect to x for $x \ne y$ and these satisfy

(14)
$$LG(x, y) = 0, \qquad x \ne y.$$

4. For fixed y, $a < y < b$, $G(x, y)$ satisfies the boundary conditions (11) and (12).

THEOREM 6.5A If zero is not an eigenvalue of L on $\mathscr{V}$, there exists one and only one function $G(x, y)$ satisfying the conditions of Definition A.

Proof Let $\sigma_1(x)$ and $\sigma_2(x)$ be nonzero functions with two continuous derivatives on $a \le x \le b$ determined as solutions of

(15)
$$L\sigma_1 = 0, \qquad c_1\sigma_1(a) + c_2\sigma_1'(a) = 0,$$

(16)
$$L\sigma_2 = 0, \qquad d_1\sigma_2(b) + d_2\sigma_2'(b) = 0.$$

Then σ_1 and σ_2 are linearly independent and their Wronskian is a nonzero constant w (see the discussion preceding Theorem 6.4A). The most general function satisfying condition **3** of Definition A is, for $a < y < b$,

$$G(x, y) = \begin{cases} A_1(y)\,\sigma_1(x) + B_1(y)\,\sigma_2(x), & a \le x < y, \\ A_2(y)\,\sigma_1(x) + B_2(y)\,\sigma_2(x), & y < x \le b. \end{cases}$$

To satisfy condition **4**, we must have, for $a < y < b$,

$$c_1\Big(A_1(y)\,\sigma_1(a) + B_1(y)\,\sigma_2(a)\Big) + c_2\Big(A_1(y)\,\sigma_1'(a) + B_1(y)\,\sigma_2'(a)\Big) = 0,$$

$$d_1\Big(A_2(y)\,\sigma_1(b) + B_2(y)\,\sigma_2(b)\Big) + d_2\Big(A_2(y)\,\sigma_1'(b) + B_2(y)\,\sigma_2'(b)\Big) = 0,$$

and since σ_1 satisfies the boundary condition at a while σ_2 does not, we obtain $B_1(y) = 0$. Similarly $A_2(y) = 0$. Then

$$G(x, y) = \begin{cases} A_1(y)\,\sigma_1(x), & a \le x < y, \\ B_2(y)\,\sigma_2(x), & y < x \le b. \end{cases}$$

In order that $G(x, y)$ be continuous and condition **2** be satisfied, we must have, for $a < y < b$,

$$A_1(y)\,\sigma_1(y) = B_2(y)\,\sigma_2(y),$$
$$B_2(y)\,\sigma_2'(y) - A_1(y)\,\sigma_1'(y) = -1,$$

so that

$$A_1(y) = -\frac{\sigma_2(y),}{w} \qquad B_2(y) = -\frac{\sigma_1(y)}{w}.$$

Thus, for $a < y < b$,

$$G(x, y) = \begin{cases} -\dfrac{1}{w}\,\sigma_1(x)\,\sigma_2(y), & a \le x < y, \\[2mm] -\dfrac{1}{w}\,\sigma_1(y)\,\sigma_2(x), & y < x \le b, \end{cases}$$

and by continuity, this is the same as 6.4–(12). This proves that definition **A** yields the Green's function. ★

It should be pointed out that when we use the more general operator

$$(17) \qquad\qquad L = Q - \frac{d}{dx}\left(P\frac{d}{dx}\right),$$

then (13) of Definition **A** must be modified to

$$(18) \qquad\qquad \frac{\partial}{\partial x} G(y+, y) - \frac{\partial}{\partial x} G(y-, y) = -\frac{1}{P(y)}.$$

In this case the constant w in 6.4–(12) is $P(z)\,W[\sigma_1(z), \sigma_2(z)]$.

Knowledge of the Green's function permits us to replace a differential boundary value problem by an integral equation. Thus to solve the equation

$$L\alpha = q\alpha - \alpha'' = r\rho\alpha + \beta, \qquad a \le x \le b,$$

for α in $\mathcal{V}$, we conclude from (2) that

$$\alpha(x) = r\int_a^b G(x, y)\rho(y)\,\alpha(y)\,dy + \int_a^b G(x, y)\,\beta(y)\,dy,$$

where we assume zero is not an eigenvalue of L, and $G(x, y)$ is the Green's function for L.

One could also write

$$T\alpha = -\alpha'' = (-q + r\rho)\,\alpha + \beta$$

and so obtain

$$\alpha(x) = \int_a^b G(x, y) \left(- q(y) + rp(y) \right) \alpha(y) \, dy + \int_a^b G(x, y) \, \beta(y) \, dy,$$

where now $G(x, y)$ is the Green's function for $T = -\dfrac{d^2}{dx^2}$, assuming zero is not an eigenvalue of T.

It is possible to handle the situation where zero is an eigenvalue of L. Of course, the Green's function does not exist. But Theorem 6.4I indicates that if zero is an eigenvalue of L with associated eigenvector ζ, $\|\zeta\| = 1$, then there is a one-to-one correspondence between $\mathscr{V}$, that subset of $\mathscr{V}$ whose members are orthogonal to ζ, and $\mathscr{C}$, that subset of $\mathscr{C}$ whose members are orthogonal to ζ. As we shall see, the operator inverse to L over the domain $\mathscr{V}$ is an integral operator H with kernel $H(x, y)$. This kernel is called the **Generalized Green's Function.**

Formal considerations will lead us to the conditions determining a suitable function $H(x, y)$. We cannot have

$$LH(x, y) = \delta(x, y),$$

since then (interpreting as in (5) and (6)), we would have

$$\zeta(y) = (\delta(x, y), \zeta(x)) = (LH(x, y), \zeta(x)) = (H(x, y), L\zeta(x)) = 0.$$

However, if we choose H to satisfy

$$LH(x, y) = \delta(x, y) - \zeta(x)\zeta(y)$$

we would get

$$\zeta(y) = (\delta(x, y), \zeta(x)) = (LH(x, y) + \zeta(x)\zeta(y), \zeta(x)) = \zeta(y),$$

which does not lead to a contradiction. Moreover, if

$$\alpha(x) = \int_a^b H(x, y) \, \beta(y) \, dy$$

and $(\zeta, \beta) = 0$, then formally

$$L\alpha(x) = LH\beta(x) = \int_a^b \left(\delta(x, y) - \zeta(x)\zeta(y) \right) \beta(y) dy = \beta(x),$$

as desired.

Finally, to obtain $(\alpha, \zeta) = 0$ we could demand $(H(x, y), \zeta(x)) = 0$. These considerations suggest

Definition B

Let ζ be the normalized eigenvector corresponding to the eigenvalue zero of L on $\mathscr{V}$. Then the Generalized Green's function $H(x, y)$ associated with L and the boundary conditions $c_1\alpha(a) + c_2\alpha'(a) = 0$, $d_1\alpha(b) + d_2\alpha'(b) = 0$, is defined by the conditions

1. $H(x, y)$ is continuous in x and y for $a \le x \le b$, $a \le y \le b$.
2. For fixed y, $a < y < b$, $H(x, y)$ has right and left derivatives with respect to x at $x = y$ satisfying

(19)
$$\frac{\partial}{\partial x} H(y +, y) - \frac{\partial}{\partial x} H(y -, y) = -1,$$

3. For fixed y, $H(x, y)$ has continuous second derivatives with respect to x for $x \ne y$, and these satisfy

$$LH(x, y) = - \zeta(x)\zeta(y).$$

4. For fixed y, $a < y < b$, $H(x, y)$ satisfies the boundary conditions.

5. $\displaystyle\int_a^b H(x, y)\, \zeta(x)\, dx = 0.$

THEOREM 6.5B There is one and only one function $H(x, y)$ satisfying the conditions of definition B. It is symmetric in x and y.

Proof Let $\sigma_1(x)$ satisfy $L\sigma_1(x) = - \zeta(x)$, $c_1\sigma_1(a) + c_2\sigma_1'(a) = 0$, and $\sigma_2(x)$ satisfy $L\sigma_2(x) = - \zeta(x)$, $d_1\sigma_2(b) + d_2\sigma_2'(b) = 0$. We have $L(\sigma_1 - \sigma_2) = 0$ and therefore the Wronskian of $\sigma_1 - \sigma_2$ and ζ is a constant, which we will now show to be $- 1$. Indeed,

$$1 = (\zeta, \zeta) = \int_a^b - \zeta(x)\, L\sigma_2(x)dx = \int_a^b (\sigma_2 L\zeta - \zeta L\sigma_2)dx$$

$$= \zeta\sigma_2' - \sigma_2\zeta' \Big|_a^b = - \zeta(a)\, \sigma_2'(a) + \sigma_2(a)\zeta'(a),$$

since σ_2 and ζ both satisfy the boundary condition at b. But also the Wronskian of $\sigma_1 - \sigma_2$ and ζ evaluated at a is

$$\begin{vmatrix} \sigma_1(a) - \sigma_2(a) & \zeta(a) \\ \sigma_1'(a) - \sigma_2'(a) & \zeta'(a) \end{vmatrix} = \begin{vmatrix} \sigma_1(a) & \zeta(a) \\ \sigma_1'(a) & \zeta'(a) \end{vmatrix} - \begin{vmatrix} \sigma_2(a) & \zeta(a) \\ \sigma_2'(a) & \zeta'(a) \end{vmatrix},$$

and the first determinant on the right is zero since ζ and σ_1 both satisfy the boundary condition at a. It follows that $W[\sigma_1 - \sigma_2, \zeta] = - 1$.

The function satisfying condition 3 of Definition B must be a particular solution of $L\alpha = -\zeta(x)\zeta(y)$ plus the general solution of $L\alpha = 0$. Thus for fixed y, $a \le x < y$, we must have

$$H(x, y) = \zeta(y)\,\sigma_1(x) + A(y)\,\zeta(x) + A_1(y)\,\mu(x),$$

where μ is a solution of $L\alpha = 0$ independent of ζ. Since H, σ_1, and ζ satisfy the boundary condition at a while μ, being independent of ζ, does not, it follows that $A_1(y) = 0$.

Proceeding similarly for the interval $y < x \le b$, we finally obtain

$$H(x, y) = \begin{cases} \zeta(y)\,\sigma_1(x) + A(y)\zeta(x), & a \le x < y, \\ \zeta(y)\,\sigma_2(x) + B(y)\zeta(x), & y < x \le b. \end{cases}$$

It will be preferable to write $A(y) = \sigma_2(y) + C(y)$, $B(y) = \sigma_1(y) + D(y)$, and so

(20) $\qquad H(x, y) = \begin{cases} \zeta(y)\,\sigma_1(x) + \sigma_2(y)\zeta(x) + C(y)\zeta(x), & a \le x < y, \\ \zeta(y)\,\sigma_2(x) + \sigma_1(y)\zeta(x) + D(y)\zeta(x), & y < x \le b. \end{cases}$

Imposing conditions 1 and 2 of definition B yields, for $a < y < b$,

$$0 = H(y+, y) - H(y-, y) = (D(y) - C(y))\zeta(y),$$
$$-1 = H'(y+, y) - H'(y-, y) = W[\sigma_1 - \sigma_2, \zeta] + (D(y) - C(y))\zeta'(y).$$

Since ζ and ζ' cannot both be zero at y, and the Wronskian is -1, we must have $C(y) = D(y)$, so that (20) becomes

(21) $\qquad H(x, y) = \begin{cases} \zeta(y)\,\sigma_1(x) + \zeta(x)\,\sigma_2(y) + C(y)\zeta(x), & a \le x < y, \\ \zeta(y)\,\sigma_2(x) + \zeta(x)\,\sigma_1(y) + C(y)\zeta(x), & y < x \le b. \end{cases}$

We shall now show $C(y)$ is uniquely determined when condition 5 is satisfied. Indeed we shall obtain

(22) $\quad C(y) = K\zeta(y)$, where

$$K = \int_a^b \left(q(t)\,\sigma_1(t)\,\sigma_2(t) + \sigma_1'(t)\,\sigma_2'(t) \right) dt + \sigma_1(a)\,\sigma_2'(a) - \sigma_2(b)\,\sigma_1'(b).$$

This explicit form proves that $H(x, y)$ is symmetric. We have

(23) $\quad 0 = \int_a^b H(x, y)\,\zeta(x)dx = \zeta(y)\int_a^y \sigma_1(x)\,\zeta(x)dx + \sigma_2(y)\int_a^y \zeta(x)^2 dx$

$$+ C(y)\int_a^y \zeta(x)^2 dx + \zeta(y)\int_y^b \sigma_2(x)\,\zeta(x)dx + \sigma_1(y)\int_y^b \zeta(x)^2 dx$$

$$+ C(y)\int_y^b \zeta(x)^2 dx.$$

Now apply formula 6.3–(4) to get

$$\int_a^y \zeta(x)^2 dx = -\int_a^y \zeta(x) L\sigma_1(x)dx = \int_a^y \Big(\sigma_1(x) L\zeta - \zeta(x) L\sigma_1(x)dx\Big)$$

$$= W[\zeta, \sigma_1]\Big|_a^y = \zeta(y)\,\sigma_1'(y) - \sigma_1(y)\,\zeta'(y).$$

Here we have used the fact that the Wronskian vanishes at a since ζ and σ_1 both satisfy the boundary conditions at a. Similarly,

$$\int_y^b \zeta(x)^2 dx = -\zeta(y)\,\sigma_2'(y) + \sigma_2(y)\,\zeta'(y),$$

$$\int_a^y \sigma_1(x)\,\zeta(x)dx + \int_y^b \sigma_2(x)\,\zeta(x)dx = \int_a^y \sigma_1(x)\zeta(x)dx - \int_a^y \sigma_2(x)\zeta(x)dx$$

$$+ \int_a^b \sigma_2(x)\zeta(x)dx$$

$$= -\int_a^y \sigma_1(x)\,L\sigma_2(x)\,dx + \int_a^y \sigma_2(x)\,L\sigma_1(x)dx - \int_a^b \sigma_2(x)\,L\sigma_1(x)dx$$

$$= W[\sigma_1, \sigma_2]\Big|_a^y - \int_a^b \sigma_2(x)\Big(q\sigma_1(x) - \sigma_1''(x)\Big)dx$$

$$= W[\sigma_1, \sigma_2]\Big|_a^y - \int_a^b \sigma_1\,\sigma_2\,q\,dx + \sigma_2(x)\,\sigma_1'(x)\Big|_a^b - \int_a^b \sigma_1'\,\sigma_2'dx$$

$$= \sigma_1(y)\,\sigma_2'(y) - \sigma_2(y)\,\sigma_1'(y) - \int_a^b \Big(q\sigma_1\,\sigma_2 + \sigma_1'\,\sigma_2'\Big)dx - \sigma_1(a)\,\sigma_2'(a) + \sigma_2(b)\,\sigma_1'(b).$$

Substitution of these results into (23) yields (22). ★

We may now show that the generalized Green's function defines an integral operator inverse to L.

THEOREM 6.5C Let 0 be an eigenvalue of L corresponding to the normalized eigenvector ζ. If β is in $\mathscr{C}$ and $(\beta, \zeta) = 0$, then $\alpha = H\beta = \int_a^b H(x, y)\,\beta(y)dy$ is in $\mathscr{V}$, $(\alpha, \zeta) = 0$, and $L\alpha = \beta$. Conversely if α is in $\mathscr{V}$, $(\alpha, \zeta) = 0$ then $\beta = L\alpha$ is in $\mathscr{C}$, $(\beta, \zeta) = 0$, and $H\beta = \alpha$.

Proof $H(x, y)$ defined by (21) and (22) can be extended so that it and its first two derivatives are continuous on each of the triangles $a \le x \le y \le b$ and $a \le y \le x \le b$. If β is in $\mathscr{C}$, $(\beta, \zeta) = 0$, and

$$\alpha(x) = \int_a^x H(x, y)\,\beta(y)dy + \int_x^b H(x, y)\,\beta(y)dy,$$

then

$$\alpha'(x) = \int_a^x \frac{\partial H(x, y)}{\partial x} \beta(y)dy + H(x, x-) \beta(x)$$

$$+ \int_x^b \frac{\partial H(x, y)}{\partial x} \beta(y)dy - H(x, x+)(x)$$

$$= \int_a^b \frac{\partial H(x, y)}{\partial x} \beta(y)dy.$$

Similarly

$$\alpha''(x) = \int_a^b \frac{\partial^2 H(x, y)}{\partial x^2} \beta(y)dy + \left(\frac{\partial H}{\partial x}(x, x-) - \frac{\partial H}{\partial x}(x, x+)\right) \beta(x)$$

$$= \int_a^b \frac{\partial^2 H(x, y)}{\partial x^2} \beta(y)dy + \left(\frac{\partial H}{\partial x}(x+, x) - \frac{\partial H}{\partial x}(x-, x)\right) \beta(x)$$

$$= \int_a^b \frac{\partial^2 H(x, y)}{\partial x^2} \beta(y)dy - \beta(x).$$

Then

$$L\alpha = q\alpha - \alpha'' = \int_a^b q(x) H(x, y) \beta(y)dy - \int_a^b \frac{\partial^2 H(x, y)}{\partial x^2} \beta(y)dy + \beta(x)$$

$$= \int_a^b LH(x, y) \beta(y)dy + \beta(x) = \int_a^b - \zeta(x) \zeta(y) \beta(y)dx + \beta(x) = \beta(x).$$

That α satisfies the boundary conditions follows from the fact that H does. Moreover

$$(\alpha, \zeta) = \int_a^b \int_a^b H(x, y) \beta(y) \zeta(x)dy \, dx = \int_a^b \beta(y) \int_a^b H(x, y) \zeta(x)dx \, dy = 0$$

by condition 5 of Definition B. Conversely, if α is in $\mathscr{V}$ and $(\alpha, \zeta) = 0$, then $\beta = L\alpha$ is in $\mathscr{C}$, $(\beta, \zeta) = (L\alpha, \zeta) = (\alpha, L\zeta) = 0$, and, by what we have proved above, $H\beta$ is in $\mathscr{V}$ with $LH\beta = \beta$ and $(H\beta, \zeta) = 0$. We therefore have $L(H\beta - \alpha) = \theta$. Either $H\beta = \alpha$ or $H\beta - \alpha$ is an eigenvector of L corresponding to eigenvalue zero and hence a nonzero multiple of ζ. The second possibility cannot hold since $H\beta - \alpha$ is orthogonal to ζ. ★.

The solution in Theorem 6.5C for the equation $L\alpha = \beta$ is not unique. Indeed if α in $\mathscr{V}$ satisfies $L\alpha = \beta$, so does $\alpha + c\zeta$, where ζ is the eigenvector corresponding to eigenvalue zero. However, any two solutions α_1, α_2 in $\mathscr{V}$ differ only by a multiple of ζ, since $\alpha_1 - \alpha_2$ satisfies $L\alpha = 0$.

It is to be noted that for the operator given by (17), (19) must be modified to

$$\frac{\partial}{\partial x} H(y+, y) - \frac{\partial}{\partial x} H(y-, y) = \frac{-1}{P(y)}.$$

Formula (21) remains unchanged, with $C(y) = K\zeta(y)$ where now

$$K = \int_a^b \Big(q(t)\, \sigma_1(t)\, \sigma_2(t) + P(t)\, \sigma_1'(t)\, \sigma_2'(t) \Big) dt$$
$$+ P(a)\, \sigma_1(a)\, \sigma_2'(a) - P(b)\, \sigma_2(b)\, \sigma_1'(b).$$

Exercise 6.5

1. (a) Use Exercise 4.3–7 and obtain an expansion for the Green's function.
    (b) Hence prove that

$$G(x, y) = \begin{cases} \dfrac{x(L - y)}{L}, & 0 \le x \le y \le L, \\[2mm] \dfrac{y(L - x)}{L}, & 0 \le y \le x \le L, \end{cases}$$

    can be expanded in the uniformly convergent series

$$\sum_1^\infty \frac{2L}{n^2\pi^2} \sin\frac{n\pi x}{L} \sin\frac{n\pi y}{L}, \quad 0 \le x \le L, \ 0 \le y \le L.$$

2. (a) Prove directly from definition A, without use of the explicit form of the Green's function, that $G(x, y)$ is symmetric.
    Hint: Suppose that $a < u < v < b$ and consider

$$0 = \left\{ \int_a^{u-} + \int_{u+}^{v-} + \int_{v+}^b \right\} G(x, u)\, LG(x, v)dx.$$

    Substitute $LG = qG - G''$ and integrate by parts twice.
    (b) Prove directly from definition B that $H(x, y)$ is symmetric. *Hint:*

$$0 = - \zeta(v) \int_a^b H(x, u)\, \zeta(x)dx = \int_a^b H(x, u)\, LH(x, v)dx.$$

3. Convert the following problem into an integral equation:

$$a''(x) + x^2\alpha(x) = 0, \quad 0 \le x \le 1, \quad \alpha(0) = \alpha(1) = 0.$$

4. Consider the problem

$$L\alpha = k^2\alpha - \alpha'' = r\alpha, \quad \alpha'(0) = \alpha'(1) = 0, \quad k \text{ constant.}$$

    Find the Green's function, eigenvalues, eigenvectors, when $k > 0$. Find the Generalized Green's function, eigenvalues, and eigenvectors, when $k = 0$.

5. (a) Find the Generalized Green's function for

$$L\alpha = \frac{-\pi^2}{4}\alpha - \alpha'', \quad 0 \le x \le 2, \quad \alpha(0) = \alpha(2) = 0.$$

    (b) Without finding the solution, state why it is true that a solution exists for

$$-\frac{\pi^2}{4}\alpha(x) - \alpha''(x) = \cos\frac{\pi x}{2}, \quad 0 \le x \le 2, \quad \alpha(0) = \alpha(2) = 0.$$

    (c) Find a solution using the results of part (a). What is the general solution?
    (d) Use the method of variation of parameters to find the solution.

6. (a) Show that if we are interested in solving $L\alpha = \beta$ for α in $\mathscr{V}$ by

$$\alpha = \int_a^b H(x, y)\,\beta(y)\,dy \text{ when } (\beta, \zeta) = 0, \text{ we do not need to find } K \text{ in (22).}$$

Hint: Perform the integration to obtain

$$\alpha(x) = \zeta(x)\int_a^x (\sigma_1(t) - \sigma_2(t))\,\beta(t)\,dt + (\sigma_1(x) - \sigma_2(x))\int_x^b \zeta(t)\,\beta(t)\,dt$$
$$+ \zeta(x)\int_a^b \sigma_2(t)\,\beta(t)\,dt.$$

Why is the sum of the first two terms a solution?

(b) Obtain the result in (a) by the method of variation of parameters. Note that ζ and $\sigma_1 - \sigma_2$ are linearly independent solutions of $L\alpha = 0$.

6.6

ASYMPTOTIC

METHODS

The expansion given in Theorem 6.4F was proved by an application of the theory of integral operators, a subject developed in the early part of the twentieth century. However the first expansion theorems were proved by Liouville by use of formulas showing the behavior of the eigenvalues r_n and the eigenvectors α_n as n becomes large. We may refer to such a technique as an **asymptotic method.** This method has proved to be extremely useful in the study of boundary value problems.

It will be convenient to introduce a simple notation which expresses in a concise fashion the behavior, for large n, of a function of an integral variable n. Let $f(n)$ and $g(n) \geq 0$ satisfy

$$|f(n)| \leq Kg(n) \text{ for } n > N \text{ and some constant } K.$$

Then we shall write

$$f = O(g), \qquad n \to \infty.$$

When it is clear that we seek a comparison of f and g for large n, the phrase "$n \to \infty$" may be omitted.

If $f(n)$ and $g(n)$ satisfy

$$\lim_{n \to \infty} \left|\frac{f(n)}{g(n)}\right| = 0,$$

then we write

$$f = o(g), \qquad n \to \infty.$$

EXAMPLE 1

a. If $f(n)$ is bounded for all n, then $f = O(1)$.

b. $1 + \dfrac{1}{2^2} + \dfrac{1}{3^2} + \cdots + \dfrac{1}{n^2} = O(1)$.

c. $\dfrac{1}{3+n} = O\left(\dfrac{1}{n}\right) = o(1)$.

d. $\dfrac{n}{\sqrt{1+n}} = O(\sqrt{n})$.

In a similar fashion we compare two functions of x defined for x near c. Here c may be any real number or ∞ or $-\infty$. Let g be positive. If

$$|f(x)| \leq Kg(x), \text{ for all } x \text{ near } c \text{ and some constant } K,$$

then we write

$$f = O(g), \qquad x \to c,$$

omitting the phrase "$x \to c$" when it is clear from the context that this is implied. The phrase "for x near c" means "for $|x - c| < \delta, \delta > 0$" in case c is a constant, and it means "for $x > x_0$" in case c represents ∞.

Also, if

$$\lim_{x \to c} \left| \frac{f(x)}{g(x)} \right| = 0,$$

we write

$$f = o(g), \qquad x \to c.$$

EXAMPLE 2

a. The relation

$$\frac{1}{1+x} = 1 - x + \frac{x^2}{1+x}, \qquad x > -1,$$

shows that

$$\frac{1}{1+x} = 1 - x + O(x^2), \qquad x \to 0.$$

b. Let A be a positive constant, $B(x)$ a bounded function of x near $x = 0$, $C(x) = O(x^2)$ as $x \to 0$. Then, using part (a), we have

(1)
$$\frac{1}{A + xB(x) + C(x)} = \frac{1}{A} \frac{1}{1 + \dfrac{xB(x)}{A} + \dfrac{C(x)}{A}}$$

$$= \frac{1}{A}\left(1 - \left(\frac{xB(x)}{A} + \frac{C(x)}{A}\right) + O\left(\left[\frac{xB(x)}{A} + \frac{C(x)}{A}\right]^2\right)\right)$$

$$= \frac{1}{A} - \frac{B(x)}{A}x + O(x^2), \qquad x \to 0.$$

c. From the relation

$$(1 + x)^{-1/2} = 1 - \tfrac{1}{2}x + O(x^2), \qquad x \to 0,$$

we obtain, when A, $B(x)$, $C(x)$ are given as in part (b),

$$(2) \qquad \left(A + xB(x) + C(x)\right)^{-1/2} = \frac{1}{A^{1/2}} - \tfrac{1}{2}x \frac{B(x)}{A^{3/2}} + O(x^2), \qquad x \to 0.$$

Relations such as that given for $(1 + x)^{-1/2}$ in Example 2(c) may often be obtained from the mean value theorem or its generalization given by Taylor's formula. Let f and its first $n - 1$ derivatives be continuous for $c \leq x \leq d$ and let $f^{(n)}(x)$ be bounded. Then, for each x in $c < x \leq d$ there is an x_0, $c < x_0 < x$, such that

$$f(x) = f(c) + f'(c)(x - c) + \cdots + \frac{f^{(n-1)}(c)(x - c)^{n-1}}{(n - 1)!} + R_n$$

where $R_n = f^{(n)}(x_0)(x - c)^n/n! = O((x - c)^n), \quad x \to c +$.

EXAMPLE 3

a. With $n = 3$, $c = 0$, $f(x) = \text{Arc tan } x$,

$$(3) \qquad\qquad \text{Arc tan } x = x + O(|x|^3), \qquad x \to 0.$$

b. With $n = 2$, $c = 0$, $f(x) = \sin(A + Bx)$ where A and B are constants, we obtain

$$\sin(A + Bx) = \sin A + (B \cos A)x - \frac{B^2}{2} x^2 \sin(A + Bx_0).$$

It follows from this equality, that even if A and B are functions of x, as long as B is bounded near $x = 0$, we have

$$(4) \qquad \sin(A + Bx) = \sin A + Bx \cos A + O(x^2), \qquad x \to 0.$$

In the same manner

$$(5) \qquad \cos(A + Bx) = \cos A - Bx \sin A + O(x^2), \qquad x \to 0.$$

For notational simplicity, we consider the Sturm-Liouville problem on the interval $0 \leq x \leq \pi$. This is no loss in generality, since the general problem may be reduced to this special case by a linear change of variable. (See Exercise 6.6–4.) Thus we consider

(6)
$$L\alpha = \left(q - \frac{d^2}{dx^2}\right)\alpha = r\alpha, \qquad 0 \le x \le \pi,$$

(7)
$$a_1\,\alpha(0) + a_2\,\alpha'(0) = 0, \qquad |a_1| + |a_2| \ne 0,$$

(8)
$$b_1\,\alpha(\pi) + b_2\,\alpha'(\pi) = 0, \qquad |b_1| + |b_2| \ne 0.$$

The formulas that one can obtain depend upon whether or not a_2 and b_2 are zero or not zero. There are four possible cases. Either $a_2 = b_2 = 0$, or $a_2 \ne 0$, $b_2 \ne 0$, or $a_2 = 0$, $b_2 \ne 0$, or $a_2 \ne 0$, $b_2 = 0$. We shall carry through the details for the case $a_2 = b_2 = 0$. The other cases can be treated in an analogous fashion. Thus we consider in this section

(9)
$$L\alpha = \left(q - \frac{d^2}{dx^2}\right)\alpha = r\alpha, \qquad 0 \le x \le \pi,$$

(10)
$$\alpha(0) = \alpha(\pi) = 0.$$

The eigenvalues and normalized eigenvectors of (9), (10) will be denoted by r_n and $\alpha_n(x)$, $n = 1, 2, 3, \ldots$.

THEOREM 6.6A The normalized eigenvectors α_n are uniformly bounded.

Proof We must verify the existence of a constant c such that $|\alpha_n(x)| \le c$ for all n and $0 \le x \le \pi$. It suffices to show that this is true for n sufficiently large. We may therefore restrict n so that r_n are all positive.

For the moment, keep n fixed, and write α for α_n, r for r_n. It will be convenient to set $r = p^2$.

If μ has continuous second derivatives, the solution of

$$\mu'' + p^2\mu = \beta, \qquad 0 \le x \le \pi,$$

is readily verified by differentiation to be

$$\mu(x) = A \cos px + B \sin px + \frac{1}{p}\int_0^x \beta(u) \sin p(x - u)\, du,$$

where A and B are constants.

Apply this result to the equation

$$\alpha'' + p^2\alpha = q\alpha, \qquad \alpha(0) = 0,$$

to obtain

(11) $$\alpha(x) = B \sin px + \frac{1}{p} \int_0^x q(u)\, \alpha(u) \sin p(x - u)\, du.$$

The constant B cannot be zero, for if it were, we would have

$$\alpha'(x) = \int_0^x q(u)\, \alpha(u) \cos p(x - u)\, du,$$

yielding $\alpha'(0) = 0$ and hence α would be identically zero by Theorem 6.2A. We may therefore assume $B > 0$, by changing the sign of α if necessary.

Let $\sigma(x) = \alpha(x)/B$. Then (11) becomes

(12) $$\sigma(x) = \sin px + \frac{1}{p} \int_0^x q(u)\, \sigma(u) \sin p(x - u)\, du.$$

We shall show that $|\sigma(x)|$ has a bound s which is independent of p. Let $Q = \text{l.u.b.} \left\{ |q(x)| \,\middle|\, 0 \le x \le \pi \right\}$, $s = \text{l.u.b.} \left\{ |\sigma(x)| \,\middle|\, 0 \le x \le \pi \right\}$. Then, from (12),

$$|\sigma(x)| \le 1 + \frac{1}{p} Q s \pi$$

yielding

$$s \le 1 + \frac{1}{p} Q s \pi, \qquad s \le \left(1 - \frac{Q\pi}{p} \right)^{-1} < 2, \quad p \text{ large},$$

since for large p, $1 - \dfrac{Q\pi}{p} > \dfrac{1}{2}$. Equation (12) now yields

$$\sigma(x) = \sin px + O\!\left(\frac{1}{p}\right). \qquad p \to \infty,$$

which, when substituted into (12), gives

(13) $$\sigma(x) = \sin px + \frac{1}{p} \int_0^x q(u) \sin pu \sin p(x - u)\, du + O\!\left(\frac{1}{p^2}\right).$$

We have

$$1 = \int_0^\pi \alpha^2(x)\, dx = B^2 \int_0^\pi \sigma^2(x)\, dx$$

$$= B^2 \left(\int_0^\pi \sin^2 px\, dx + \frac{2}{p} \int_0^\pi \sin px \int_0^x q(u) \sin pu \sin p(x - u)\, du\, dx \right.$$

$$\left. \vphantom{\int_0^\pi} + O\!\left(\frac{1}{p^2}\right) \right)$$

$$= B^2 \left(\frac{\pi}{2} - \frac{\sin 2p\pi}{4p} + \frac{2}{p} M(p) + O\!\left(\frac{1}{p^2}\right) \right),$$

where

(14) $$M(p) = \int_0^\pi \int_0^x q(u) \sin px \sin pu \sin p(x - u) \, du \, dx$$

has a bound $Q\pi^2$ independent of p.

Now use the fact that $\sigma(\pi) = 0$ in (13) to obtain $\sin p\pi = O\left(\frac{1}{p}\right)$, so that

$\sin 2p\pi = 2 \sin p\pi \cos p\pi = O\left(\frac{1}{p}\right)$, and

$$B = \left(\frac{\pi}{2} + \frac{2}{p} M(p) + O\left(\frac{1}{p^2}\right)\right)^{-1/2} = \left(\frac{2}{\pi}\right)^{1/2} - \left(\frac{2}{\pi}\right)^{3/2} \frac{M(p)}{p} + O\left(\frac{1}{p^2}\right)$$

in view of (2).

We now have an asymptotic formula for α.

(15) $$\alpha(x) = B\sigma(x) = \left(\frac{2}{\pi}\right)^{1/2} \sin px - \left(\frac{2}{\pi}\right)^{3/2} \frac{M(p)}{p} \sin px$$
$$+ \left(\frac{2}{\pi}\right)^{1/2} \frac{1}{p} \int_0^x q(u) \sin pu \sin p(x - u) du + O\left(\frac{1}{p^2}\right).$$

The conclusion of the theorem follows directly from this formula.   ★

Later we will need an asymptotic formula giving $\alpha_n(x)$ in terms of n rather than p. For this purpose, let us obtain an asymptotic formula for the eigenvalues in terms of n.

THEOREM 6.6B

(16) $$p = \sqrt{r_n} = n + \frac{A(n)}{n} + O\left(\frac{1}{n^2}\right)$$

where $A(n)$ is bounded.

Proof We will first show that $m \le q(x) \le M$ implies

(17) $$m + n^2 \le r_n \le M + n^2.$$

For the system

$$K\beta - \beta'' = s\beta, \qquad 0 \le x \le \pi, \qquad K \text{ constant,}$$
$$\beta(0) = \beta(\pi) = 0,$$

we readily compute the eigenvalues to be $s_n = K + n^2$. Taking K as m and M in turn and using Corollary 2 of Theorem 6.4G, we obtain (17).

Now (17) implies $r_n = n^2 + G(n)$, where $|G(n)| \leq \max\{|m|, |M|\}$, so that

(18) $\sqrt{r_n} = n\left(1 + \dfrac{G(n)}{n^2}\right)^{1/2} = n\left(1 + \dfrac{1}{2}\dfrac{G(n)}{n^2} + O\left(\dfrac{1}{n^4}\right)\right) = n + O\left(\dfrac{1}{n}\right),$

but this is not sufficient for our purpose, since we desire an explicit expression for $A(n)$ in (16).

For large p, $\cos p\pi$ is bounded away from zero, since $\sin p\pi = O\left(\dfrac{1}{p}\right)$ as we have seen in the proof of Theorem 6.6A. Using $\alpha(\pi) = 0$ in (15) we get

$$\tan p\pi = -\left[\left(\dfrac{2}{\pi}\right)^{1/2} - \left(\dfrac{2}{\pi}\right)^{3/2}\dfrac{M(p)}{p}\right]^{-1}\left(\dfrac{2}{\pi}\right)^{1/2}\dfrac{1}{p}\int_0^\pi \dfrac{q(u)\sin pu \sin p(\pi - u)du}{\cos p\pi}$$

$$+ O\left(\dfrac{1}{p^2}\right) = \dfrac{H(P)}{p} + O\left(\dfrac{1}{p^2}\right),$$

where

(19) $$H(p) = -\int_0^\pi \dfrac{q(u)\sin pu \sin p(\pi - u)du}{\cos p\pi}$$

is bounded, for large p, by a constant independent of p. An application of (3) gives

$$p\pi = \arctan\left(\dfrac{H(p)}{p} + O\left(\dfrac{1}{p^2}\right)\right) = \dfrac{H(p)}{p} + O\left(\dfrac{1}{p^2}\right) + j\pi$$

for some integer j. Comparing this result with (18) shows that $j = n$ for n large, and

(20) $$p = n + \dfrac{H(p)}{p\pi} + O\left(\dfrac{1}{p^2}\right) = n + \dfrac{H(p)}{n\pi} + O\left(\dfrac{1}{n^2}\right).$$

Replace p by $n + O\left(\dfrac{1}{n}\right)$ in (19) and use (4) and (5) to get

$$H(p) = -\int_0^\pi \dfrac{q(u)\sin nu \sin n(\pi - u)}{\cos n\pi}\,du + O\left(\dfrac{1}{n}\right).$$

Now (20) implies

$$p = n + \dfrac{A(n)}{n} + O\left(\dfrac{1}{n^2}\right),$$

where

(21) $$A(n) = \dfrac{(-1)^{n+1}}{\pi}\int_0^\pi q(u)\sin nu \sin n(\pi - u)du. \quad \star$$

It is our intention to show that the study of Sturm-Liouville systems may be reduced to the study of Fourier series, a subject which has been extensively investigated. We therefore examine the difference between the partial sums of the Sturm-Liouville series determined by (9) and (10) and the partial sums of the Fourier Sine series for a given function β. This difference is

$$(22) \qquad \sum_{n=1}^{N} \int_0^\pi \beta(u)\, \alpha_n(u)\, du\, \alpha_n(x) - \sum_{n=1}^{N} \frac{2}{\pi} \int_0^\pi \beta(u) \sin nu\, du \sin nx$$

$$= \int_0^\pi \beta(u)\, Y(N, x, u)\, du$$

where

$$(23) \qquad Y(N, x, u) = \sum_{n=1}^{N} \alpha_n(u)\, \alpha_n(x) - \frac{2}{\pi} \sin nu \sin nx.$$

THEOREM 6.6C   There is a constant C such that

$$|Y(N, x, u)| \leq C, \qquad 0 \leq x \leq \pi, \quad 0 \leq u \leq \pi, \quad N = 1, 2, 3, \cdots$$

Proof   First we obtain an asymptotic formula for $\alpha_n(x)$ in terms of n. Substitute (16) into (15) and use (4) and (5) to get

$$(24) \quad \alpha_n(x) = \left(\frac{2}{\pi}\right)^{1/2} \sin nx + x\left(\frac{2}{\pi}\right)^{1/2} \frac{A(n)}{n} \cos nx - \left(\frac{2}{\pi}\right)^{3/2} \frac{M^*(n)}{n} \sin nx$$

$$+ \left(\frac{2}{\pi}\right)^{1/2} \frac{1}{n} \int_0^x q(u) \sin nu \sin n(x - u)\, du + O\left(\frac{1}{n^2}\right),$$

where

$$(25) \qquad M^*(n) = \int_0^\pi \int_0^x q(u) \sin nx \sin nu \sin n(x - u)\, du\, dx.$$

It is easy to verify, using the trigonometric identities (5), (6), (7) of Section 4.3, that

$$\sin nx \sin nu \sin n(x - u) = -\tfrac{1}{4}(\sin 2nx - \sin 2nu - \sin 2n(x - u)).$$

Thus, interchanging the order of integration in (25), we obtain

$$M^*(n) = -\tfrac{1}{4} \int_0^\pi q(u) \int_u^\pi \left(\sin 2nx - \sin 2\,nu - \sin 2n(x - u) \right) dx\, du$$

$$= \tfrac{1}{4} \int_0^\pi q(u)\, (\pi - u) \sin 2nu\, du + O\left(\frac{1}{n}\right),$$

$$M^*(n) \sin nx = -\frac{1}{8} \int_0^\pi q(u)(\pi - u) \left(\cos n(x + 2u) - \cos n(x - 2u) \right) du$$

$$+ O\left(\frac{1}{n}\right).$$

Similarly,

$$A(n) \cos nx = \frac{(-1)^{n+1}}{\pi} \int_0^\pi q(u) \sin nu \sin n(\pi - u) \cos nx \, du$$

$$= \frac{(-1)^{n+1}}{\pi} \int_0^\pi q(u) \left(\frac{(-1)^{n+1} \cos nx}{2} + \frac{1}{4} \left\{ \cos n(2u - \pi + x) \right. \right.$$

$$\left. \left. + \cos n(2u - \pi - x) \right\} \right) du.$$

Then (24) becomes

(26) $\qquad \alpha_n(x) = \left(\frac{2}{\pi}\right)^{1/2} \sin nx + \frac{x}{2n\pi} \left(\frac{2}{\pi}\right)^{1/2} \int_0^\pi q(u) \, du \cos nx$

$$+ \frac{x}{4n\pi} \left(\frac{2}{\pi}\right)^{1/2} (-1)^{n+1} \int_0^\pi q(u) \left(\cos n(2u - \pi + x) + \cos n(2u - \pi - x) \right) du$$

$$+ \left(\frac{2}{\pi}\right)^{3/2} \frac{1}{8n} \int_0^\pi q(u)(\pi - u) \left(\cos n(x + 2u) - \cos n(x - 2u) \right) du$$

$$- \left(\frac{2}{\pi}\right)^{1/2} \frac{1}{2n} \int_0^x q(u) \left(\cos nx - \cos n(2u - x) \right) du + O\left(\frac{1}{n^2}\right).$$

This is the desired formula. We now note that $\alpha_n(x) \, \alpha_n(u) - \frac{2}{\pi} \sin nx \sin nu$
can be written as the sum of a finite number (independent of n) of terms, one
of which is $O\left(\frac{1}{n^2}\right)$, and the others contain the variable n only in the combination

$$\frac{1}{n} \sin ny \cos nz = \frac{1}{2n} \left(\sin n(y + z) + \sin n(y - z) \right).$$

This, together with the fact that $\sum\limits_{n=1}^N \frac{\sin ny}{n}$ is uniformly bounded in y and N,
proves the theorem. ⋆

The main theorem of this section is the following equiconvergence
theorem, stating conditions assuring that two series converge to the same
value.

THEOREM 6.6D Let β be any function integrable on $0 \le x \le \pi$.
The Sturm-Liouville series for β, corresponding to the Sturm-Liouville
problem given by (9), (10), is $\sum\limits_{n=1}^\infty (\beta, \alpha_n) \alpha_n(x)$. Then this series converges or
diverges at x_0, $0 \le x_0 \le \pi$, according as the Fourier sine series of β on
$0 \le x \le \pi$ converges or diverges. Where both series converge, they have the
same value. The Sturm-Liouville series converges uniformly in any interval
if and only if the Fourier sine series does.

Proof We need only show that the right side of (22) converges to 0 uniformly in x as N approaches infinity. The statement is valid if β has continuous second derivatives and vanishes at $x = 0$ and $x = \pi$. For then the left side of (22) converges uniformly in view of Theorems 5.6C and 6.4D.

Now suppose that β is in $\mathscr{R}$. Then there is an α with continuous second derivatives which vanishes at 0 and π such that $\|\beta - \alpha\| < \epsilon/2C\sqrt{\pi}$, where C is a constant given by Theorem 6.6C such that $|Y(N, x, u)| \leq C$. Write

$$(27) \qquad \int_0^\pi \beta(u)\, Y(N, x, u)du = \int_0^\pi (\beta(u) - \alpha(u))\, Y(N, x, u)du$$

$$+ \int_0^\pi \alpha(u)\, Y(N, x, u)du.$$

The first term on the right is less in absolute value than

$$\left(\int_0^\pi (\beta(u) - \alpha(u))^2\, du \right)^{1/2} \left(\int_0^\pi Y(N, x, u)^2\, du \right)^{1/2} \leq \frac{\epsilon}{2C\sqrt{\pi}}\, \sqrt{\pi} C = \epsilon/2.$$

For N sufficiently large, we can make the second term on the right of (27) less than $\epsilon/2$ in view of the second sentence of this proof. It follows that the right side and hence left side of (27) approaches zero uniformly in x as N approaches infinity. ★

Exercise 6.6

1. Let $f_1 = O(g_1)$, $f_2 = O(g_2)$ as $x \to c$. Show that
   (a) $f_1 + f_2 = O(g_1 + g_2)$ as $x \to c$.
   (b) $f_1 f_2 = O(g_1 g_2)$ as $x \to c$.

2. Let $f_1 = O(g_1)$, $f_2 = o(g_2)$ as $x \to c$. Show that
   (a) $f_1 + f_2 = O(g_1 + g_2)$ as $x \to c$.
   (b) $f_1 f_2 = o(g_1 g_2)$ as $x \to c$.

3. Show that
   (a) $\dfrac{\sin x}{\sqrt{x}} = o(1)$, $x \to 0$,
   (b) $\log x = o(x^k)$, $x \to \infty$, $k > 0$.
   (c) $\sin x - x = o(|x|)$, $x \to 0$.

4. Show that the change of variable $x = \dfrac{\pi}{b - a}(u - a)$ carries the system

$$(*) \qquad \begin{cases} \left(Q(u) - \dfrac{d^2}{du^2} \right) \beta(u) = r\beta(u), & a \leq u \leq b, \\ c_1\beta(a) + c_2\beta'(a) = 0, & |c_1| + |c_2| \neq 0, \\ d_1\beta(b) + d_2\beta'(b) = 0, & |d_1| + |d_2| \neq 0, \end{cases}$$

into the system given by (6), (7), (8). If the eigenvalues and normalized eigen-
vectors of (*) are denoted by r_n^* and β_n, show that $r_n^* = \left(\dfrac{\pi}{b-a}\right)^2 r_n$,

$\beta_n(u) = \sqrt{\dfrac{\pi}{b-a}}\,\alpha_n(x)$, $Q(u) = \left(\dfrac{\pi}{b-a}\right)^2 q(x)$ where r_n, α_n denote the eigenvalues and normalized eigenvectors of (6), (7), (8).

5. (a) Let $f(x) = o(|x - c|^n)$ as $x \to c$. Show that

$$\int_c^x f(t)dt = o(|x - c|^{n+1}), \quad x \to c.$$

(b) Let $f(x)$ have $n - 1$ derivatives in an interval about $x = c$ and have an
nth derivative at $x = c$. Show that

$$f(x) = f(c) + f'(c)(x - c) + \frac{f''(c)}{2!}(x - c)^2$$

$$+ \cdots + \frac{f^{(n)}(c)}{n!}(x - c)^n + o(|x - c|^n).$$

Hint: Since the nth derivative exists, show that

$$f^{(n-1)}(x) - f^{(n-1)}(c) - (x - c)f^{(n)}(c) = o(|x - c|).$$

Now integrate from c to y, using part (a). Repeat the process.

(c) Using (b) show that if f and g have nth derivatives at c and $f^{(m)}(c) = 0$,
$g^{(m)}(c) = 0$, $m = 0, 1, \cdots n - 1$, but $g^{(n)}(c) \neq 0$, then $\lim\limits_{x \to c} \dfrac{f(x)}{g(x)} = \dfrac{f^{(n)}(c)}{g^{(n)}(c)}$

6. Beginning with (11) show that
$$\alpha_n'(x) = \sqrt{\frac{2}{\pi}}\, n \cos nx - \left(\frac{2}{\pi}\right)^{3/2} M^*(n) \cos nx + O\!\left(\frac{1}{n}\right) \text{ where } M^*(n) \text{ is given}$$
by (25).

7. (a) The normalized Hermite functions E_n satisfy

$$E_n'' + 2n E_n = (x^2 - 1) E_n = \alpha.$$

Show that the general solution, for $n \geq 1$, is of the form

$$E_n(x) = E_n(0) \cos \sqrt{2n}\, x + \frac{E_n(0)}{\sqrt{2n}} \sin \sqrt{2n}\, x + \frac{1}{\sqrt{2n}} \int_0^x \alpha(t)\sin \sqrt{2n}\, (x - t)dt.$$

(b) Use Stirling's formula in the form $n! = A_n \sqrt{2\pi n}\, n^n e^{-n}$, where $1 < A_n$
< 2, $\lim\limits_{n \to \infty} A_n = 1$, and Exercise 5.5–4 to show, for $n \geq 1$, that

$$|E_{2n}(0)| = O(n^{-1/4}), \quad |E_{2n+1}'(0)| = O(n^{1/4}).$$

(c) The integral in part (a) is less in absolute value than

$$\left(\int_0^x (t^2 - 1)^2 dt\right)^{1/2} \left(\int_{-\infty}^\infty E_n^2(t)dt\right)^{1/2} \leq |p(x)|^{1/2},$$

where p is a polynomial of fifth degree. Use the above results to show that

$$|E_n(x)| = O((1 + |x|^{5/2})n^{-1/4}).$$

8. Consider the operator $L = q - \dfrac{d^2}{dx^2}$, $0 \le x \le \pi$, defined over the linear
    manifolds $\mathscr{V}'$ and $\mathscr{V}''$ where $\mathscr{V}'$ consists of functions α with continuous second
    derivatives satisfying $a_1\alpha(0) + a_2\alpha'(0) = 0$, $a_2 \ne 0$, and $b_1\alpha(\pi) + b_2\alpha'(\pi) = 0$,
    $b_2 \ne 0$, while $\mathscr{V}''$ consists of functions α with continuous second derivatives
    satisfying $\alpha'(0) = 0$, $\alpha'(\pi) = 0$. Fix $\epsilon > 0$. If $\sigma_1, \ldots, \sigma_{n-1}$ are in $\mathscr{R}$, α is in $\mathscr{V}'$,
    $\|\alpha\| = 1$, $\alpha \perp \sigma_1, \ldots, \sigma_{n-1}$, then there is a β in $\mathscr{V}''$, $\|\beta\| = 1$, $\beta \perp \sigma_1, \ldots,$
    σ_{n-1}, such that $|(L\alpha, \alpha) - (L\beta, \beta)| < \epsilon$. See the proof of Corollary 1 to
    Theorem 6.4G.) In the last sentence, we can interchange $\mathscr{V}'$ and $\mathscr{V}''$. Hence

    $$m - \epsilon + \int_0^\pi (\beta')^2 dx \le -\epsilon + \int_0^\pi q\beta^2 dx + \int_0^\pi (\beta')^2 dx \le (L\alpha, \alpha) \le$$
    $$\int_0^\pi q\beta^2 dx + \int_0^\pi (\beta')^2 dx + \epsilon \le \int_0^\pi (\beta')^2 dx + M + \epsilon,$$

    where $m \le q(x) \le M$. Now use 6.4–(26) to show that

    $$(n - 1)^2 + m \le r_n \le (n - 1)^2 + M, \quad n = 1, 2, \ldots,$$

    where r_n are the eigenvalues of L on $\mathscr{V}'$.

9. (a) Consider the operator L on $\mathscr{V}'$ of Exercise 8. Let α denote an eigenvector
         corresponding to eigenvalue $r = p^2$. As in the proof of Theorem 6.6A,
         show that $\sigma(x) = \alpha(x)/\alpha(0)$ satisfies

         $$\sigma(x) = \cos px + \frac{h}{p} \sin px + \frac{1}{p} \int_0^x q(u)\, \sigma(u) \sin p(x - u) du,$$

         where $h = -a_1 a_2$. Show that

         $$\alpha(0) = \left(\frac{2}{\pi}\right)^{1/2} - \left(\frac{2}{\pi}\right)^{3/2} \frac{N(p)}{p} + O\left(\frac{1}{p^2}\right),$$

         where $N(p) = \int_0^\pi \int_0^x q(u)\, \cos pu \cos px \sin p(x - u) du\, dx$. Now obtain

         an asymptotic formula for $\alpha(x)$ analogous to (15).
    (b) Let $k = b_1/b_2$ and show that

         $$\tan p\pi = \frac{h}{p} + \frac{k}{p} + \frac{1}{p \cos \pi p} \int_0^\pi q(u) \cos pu \cos p(\pi - u) du + O\left(\frac{1}{p^2}\right).$$

         Use this and Exercise 8 (but count n from 0 instead of from 1) to obtain

         $$p_n = n + \frac{h + k + B(n)}{n\pi} + O\left(\frac{1}{n^2}\right), \quad n = 0, 1, 2, \ldots,$$

         where $B(n) = \int_0^\pi q(u) \cos nu \cos n(\pi - u) du/\cos n\pi$.
    (c) Continue, as in the text, to show that if α_n, $n = 0, 1, 2, \ldots$, are the
         eigenvectors of $L = q - \dfrac{d^2}{dx^2}$ on $\mathscr{V}'$, then the series $\sum\limits_{n=0}^{\infty} (\beta, \alpha_n)\, \alpha_n(x)$, for
         β integrable on $0 \le x \le \pi$, is equiconvergent with the Fourier cosine
         series for β.

CHAPTER

7

Fourier Analysis on $-\infty < x < \infty$

7.1

IMPROPER
INTEGRALS

The first section of this chapter is devoted to a review of Riemann integration over an infinite interval.

Let f be a complex valued function of the real variable x defined for $a \leq x < \infty$ and integrable on $a \leq x \leq b$ for every b. We have already defined in Section 3.3,

$$(1) \qquad \int_a^\infty f(x)\, dx = \lim_{b \to \infty} \int_a^b f(x)\, dx,$$

when the limit on the right exists. In this case, we say f is **integrable on** $a \leq x < \infty$. The function f is **absolutely integrable on** $a \leq x < \infty$ if $|f|$ is integrable. When f is integrable, the integral in (1) is said to **converge**, otherwise it is said to **diverge**.

The simplest properties of (1) are given in the following theorem.

THEOREM 7.1A

a. If f is integrable on $a \leq x < \infty$, then f is integrable on $c \leq x < \infty$ for $c > a$, and

$$\int_a^\infty f(x)\, dx = \int_a^c f(x)\, dx + \int_c^\infty f(x)\, dx.$$

b. If f and g are integrable on $a \leq x < \infty$, so is $rf + sg$ for constants r and s, and

$$\int_a^\infty \Big(rf(x) + sg(x) \Big) dx = r \int_a^\infty f(x)\, dx + s \int_a^\infty g(x)\, dx.$$

c. (Cauchy Criterion.) The function f is integrable on $a \leq x < \infty$ if and only if, for $\epsilon > 0$, there is a constant $k(\epsilon)$ such that
$$\left| \int_r^s f(x)\, dx \right| < \epsilon \text{ for } s > r > k(\epsilon).$$

d. If f is absolutely integrable, it is integrable, and

$$\left| \int_a^\infty f(x)\, dx \right| \le \int_a^\infty \left| f(x) \right| dx.$$

Proof   Part **a** is proved by writing

$$\int_a^b f(x)\, dx = \int_a^c f(x)\, dx + \int_c^b f(x)\, dx$$

and letting $b \to \infty$. Part **b** follows similarly from

$$\int_a^b \left(rf(x) + sg(x) \right) dx = r \int_a^b f(x)\, dx + s \int_a^b g(x)\, dx.$$

Suppose now that f is integrable on $a \le x < \infty$. Then there is a number $k(\epsilon)$ such that

$$\left| \int_a^q f(x)\, dx - \int_a^\infty f(x)\, dx \right| < \epsilon/2, \qquad q > k.$$

Choosing q equal to r and s in turn, $s > r > k$, we obtain

$$(2) \quad \left| \int_r^s f(x)\, dx \right| \le \left| \int_a^s f(x)\, dx - \int_a^\infty f(x)\, dx \right| + \left| \int_a^\infty f(x)\, dx - \int_a^r f(x)\, dx \right| < \epsilon.$$

Conversely, if (2) is valid for $s > r > k(\epsilon)$, then the Cauchy criterion for convergence of the sequence

$$\{u_n\} = \left\{ \int_a^n f(x)\, dx \right\}, \qquad n > a, \quad n \text{ integral,}$$

is satisfied, and so there exists $\lim_{n \to \infty} u(n) = L$. That is, there exists $N(\epsilon) > k(\epsilon)$ such that $|u(n) - L| < \epsilon$ for $n > N$. But then for $b > k(\epsilon)$,

$$\left| \int_a^b f(x)\, dx - L \right| \le \left| \int_a^b f(x)\, dx - \int_a^n f(x)\, dx \right| + \left| u_n - L \right| \le 2\epsilon$$

when n is an integer greater than N. This proves part **c**. Part **d** is an immediate consequence of **c** and the inequality

$$\left| \int_r^s f(x)\, dx \right| \le \int_r^s \left| f(x) \right| dx. \quad \star$$

Consider now a function $f(x, y)$ defined on $a \le x < \infty$ for each y in a set $\mathscr{S}$. We say that $\int_a^\infty f(x, y)dx$ **converges uniformly on** $\mathscr{S}$ to $g(y)$ if for each $\epsilon > 0$ there is a $k(\epsilon)$ such that

$$\left| \int_a^b f(x, y)dx - g(y) \right| < \epsilon, \qquad b > k(\epsilon).$$

In view of (1) we have $g(y) = \int_a^\infty f(x, y)dy$. The uniformity arises from the fact that $k(\epsilon)$ is independent of the members of $\mathscr{S}$. The proof of the next theorem, which is analogous to Theorem 7.1A, is left for Exercise 7.1–1.

THEOREM 7.1B

a. If $\int_a^\infty f(x, y)dx$ converges uniformly on $\mathscr{S}$, then so does $\int_c^\infty f(x\ y)dx$ for $c > a$.

b. If $\int_a^\infty f(x, y)dx$ and $\int_a^\infty g(x, y)dx$ converge uniformly on $\mathscr{S}$, so does $\int_a^\infty \left(rf(x, y) + sg(x, y) \right)dx = r \int_a^\infty f(x, y)dx + s \int_a^\infty g(x, y)dx.$

c. (Cauchy Criterion.) $\int_a^\infty f(x, y)dx$ converges uniformly on $\mathscr{S}$ if and only if, for $\epsilon > 0$, there is a constant $k(\epsilon)$ such that $\left| \int_r^s f(x, y)dx \right| < \epsilon$ for $s > r > k(\epsilon)$.

d. If $\int_a^\infty \left| f(x, y) \right| dx$ converges uniformly on $\mathscr{S}$, so does $\int_a^\infty f(x, y)dx$.

The simplest test for absolute-uniform convergence is analogous to the Weierstrass M-test.

THEOREM 7.1C If $|f(x, y| \le g(x)$ for y in $\mathscr{S}$ and $\int_a^\infty g(x)dx$ converges then $\int_a^\infty \left| f(x, y) \right| dx$ converges uniformly on $\mathscr{S}$.

Proof Since g is integrable, the Cauchy criterion in Theorem 7.1A assures the existence of $k(\epsilon)$ such that

$$\left| \int_r^s \left| f(x, y) \right| dx \right| \le \left| \int_r^s g(x)dx \right| < \epsilon, \qquad s > r > k(\epsilon).$$

The theorem is now a consequence of the Cauchy criterion of Theorem 7.1B. ★

Special results are possible when continuity properties are added.

THEOREM 7.1D   Let $h(x)$, $a \le x < \infty$, be integrable on every finite interval $a \le x \le b$, $f(x, y)$ continuous in x and y on $a \le x < \infty$, $c \le y \le d$, and $g(y) = \int_a^\infty h(x) f(x, y)dx$ convergent uniformly for $c \le y \le d$. Then $g(y)$ is continuous on $c \le y \le d$. That is, for $c \le y_0 \le d$,

$$\lim_{y \to y_0} \int_a^\infty h(x) f(x, y)dx = \int_a^\infty h(x) f(x, y_0)dx = \int_a^\infty h(x) \lim_{y \to y_0} f(x, y)dx.$$

Proof   The functions g_n defined, for integral $n > a$, by

$$(3) \qquad\qquad g_n(y) = \int_a^n h(x) f(x, y)dx$$

are continuous for $c \le y \le d$ and converge to $g(y)$ uniformly on $c \le y \le d$. Hence, by Theorem 3.2F, the limit function $g(y)$ is continuous.   ★

THEOREM 7.1E   Assume $h(x)$, $a \le x < \infty$, integrable on every finite interval $a \le x \le b$, $f(x, y)$ and $\dfrac{\partial}{\partial y} f(x, y)$ continuous in x and y on $a \le x < \infty$, $c \le y \le d$, $g(y) = \int_a^\infty h(x) f(x, y)dx$ convergent on $c \le y \le d$, and $\int_a^\infty h(x) \dfrac{\partial}{\partial y} f(x, y)dx$ convergent uniformly on $c \le y \le d$. Then there exists

$$(4) \qquad\qquad g'(y) = \int_a^\infty h(x) \frac{\partial}{\partial y} f(x, y)dx, \qquad c \le y \le d.$$

Proof   The functions $g_n(y)$ defined by (3) are continuous and converge to $g(y)$. The derivatives $g_n'(y) = \int_a^n h(x) \dfrac{\partial}{\partial y} f(x, y)dx$ (see Appendix I) are continuous and converge to $\int_a^\infty h(x) \dfrac{\partial}{\partial y} f(x, y)dx$ uniformly on $c \le y \le d$. By Theorem 3.3M, $g(y)$ has a derivative given by (4).   ★

When the domain of f is $-\infty < x \le a$, we define

$$(5) \qquad\qquad \int_{-\infty}^a f(x)dx = \lim_{b \to -\infty} \int_b^a f(x)dx$$

if the limit exists, and, when the domain is $-\infty < x < \infty$, we define

$$(6) \qquad\qquad \int_{-\infty}^\infty f(x)dx = \int_{-\infty}^a f(x)dx + \int_a^\infty f(x)dx.$$

when both integrals converge.

For integrals given by (5) and (6), theorems are valid analogous to Theorems 7.1A–E. (It is convenient to replace (3) by $g_n(y) = \int_{-n}^{n} h(x) f(x, y) dy$ when considering an integral of type (6).)

Of special importance are theorems permitting interchange of order of integration in iterated integrals.

THEOREM 7.1F Let $\int_{p}^{q} f(x, y) dx$ converge uniformly for $c \leq y \leq d$. Here p may be $-\infty$, q may be ∞, but c and d are both finite. Suppose also that $\int_{c}^{d} \int_{p}^{q} f(x, y) dx\, dy < \infty$ and for every $a, b, (p < a < b < q)$,

$$\int_{a}^{b} \int_{c}^{d} f(x, y) dy\, dx = \int_{c}^{d} \int_{a}^{b} f(x, y) dx\, dy.$$

Then there exists

$$\int_{p}^{q} \int_{c}^{d} f(x, y) dy\, dx = \int_{c}^{d} \int_{p}^{q} f(x, y) dx\, dy.$$

Proof We need only note that

$$\left| \int_{a}^{b} \int_{c}^{d} f(x, y) dy\, dx - \int_{c}^{d} \int_{p}^{q} f(x, y) dx\, dy \right| = \left| \int_{c}^{d} \int_{a}^{b} f(x, y) dx\, dy \right.$$
$$\left. - \int_{c}^{d} \int_{p}^{q} f(x, y) dx\, dy \right| \leq \int_{c}^{d} \left| \int_{a}^{b} f(x, y) dx - \int_{p}^{q} f(x, y) dx \right| dy \leq \epsilon (d - c)$$

whenever b is sufficiently close to q and a is sufficiently close to p.   ★

THEOREM 7.1G Assume (i) $f(x, y)$ is continuous in x and y on $p \leq x \leq q$, $r \leq y \leq s$. (Here p and r may be $-\infty$, q and s may be ∞. Equality signs are dropped for infinite limits); (ii) $\int_{p}^{q} |h(x)| dx < \infty$; (iii) $u(y)$ integrable on every interval $r < c \leq y \leq d < s$; (iv) $\int_{p}^{q} h(x) f(x, y) dx$ convergent uniformly for $r \leq y \leq s$; (v) $\int_{r}^{s} u(y) f(x, y) dy$ convergent uniformly for $p \leq x \leq q$. If $\int_{p}^{q} \int_{r}^{s} h(x) u(y) f(x, y) dy\, dx$ exists, then there exists

$$\int_{r}^{s} \int_{p}^{q} h(x) u(y) f(x, y) dx\, dy = \int_{p}^{q} \int_{r}^{s} h(x) u(y) f(x, y) dy\, dx.$$

Proof In view of Theorem 7.1D, $\int_{p}^{q} h(x) f(x, y) dx$ is continuous on the finite interval $c \leq y \leq d$ and $\int_{c}^{d} \int_{p}^{q} h(x) u(y) f(x, y) dx\, dy$ exists. Since $u(y)$

is bounded on $c \leq y \leq d$ it can be readily seen that $\int_p^q u(y)\, h(x)\, f(x, y)dx$ converges uniformly on $c \leq y \leq d$. Moreover the equality

$$\int_a^b \int_c^d h(x)\, u(y)\, f(x, y)dy\, dx = \int_c^d \int_a^b h(x)\, u(y)\, f(x, y)dx\, dy$$

can be proved as in Exercise 4.1–1. Thus the hypotheses of Theorem 7.1F are satisfied and

$$\int_p^q \int_c^d h(x)\, u(y)\, f(x, y)dy\, dx = \int_c^d \int_p^q h(x)\, u(y)\, f(x, y)dx\, dy.$$

Finally,

$$\left| \int_c^d \int_p^q h(x)\, u(y)\, f(x, y)dx\, dy - \int_p^q \int_r^s h(x)\, u(y)\, f(x, y)dy\, dx \right|$$

$$\leq \int_p^q |h(x)| \left| \int_c^d u(y)\, f(x, y)dy - \int_r^s u(y)\, f(x, y)dy \right| dx \leq \epsilon \int_p^q |h(x)|dx$$

when d is sufficiently close to s and c is sufficiently close to r.   ★

EXAMPLE 1 $\displaystyle \int_0^\infty \frac{\sin ax}{x} = \begin{cases} \pi/2, & a > 0, \\ 0, & a = 0, \\ -\pi/2, & a < 0. \end{cases}$

To obtain this result, we choose $y > 0$, and integrate by parts twice to get

$$\int_0^\infty e^{-yx} \cos tx\, dx = \frac{y}{t^2 + y^2}.$$

Next, integrate over the interval $0 \leq t \leq a$.

$$\int_0^a \int_0^\infty e^{-yx} \cos tx\, dx\, dt = \int_0^a \frac{y}{t^2 + y^2}\, dt = \tan^{-1} \frac{a}{y}.$$

Interchange of order of integration is permitted by Theorem 7.1F since $\int_0^\infty e^{-yx} \cos tx\, dx$ converges uniformly on $0 \leq t \leq a$, being dominated by $\int_0^\infty e^{-yx}\, dx$. Thus

$$\int_0^\infty \int_0^a e^{-yx} \cos tx\, dt\, dx = \tan^{-1} \frac{a}{y}.$$

The inner integral can be evaluated, yielding

(7) $\displaystyle \int_0^\infty e^{-yx} \frac{\sin ax}{x}\, dx = \tan^{-1} \frac{a}{y}.$

It can be shown (Exercise 7.1–4) that the integral on the left converges uniformly on $0 \leq y \leq d$, proving, by Theorem 7.1D, that the integral is continuous at $y = 0$. That is,

$$\int_0^\infty \frac{\sin ax}{x} \, dx = \int_0^\infty \lim_{y \to 0} e^{-yx} \frac{\sin ax}{x} \, dx = \lim_{y \to 0} \int_0^\infty \frac{\sin ax}{x} e^{-yx} \, dx$$

$$= \lim_{y \to 0} \tan^{-1} \frac{a}{y} = \begin{cases} \pi/2, & a > 0 \\ 0, & a = 0 \\ -\pi/2, & a < 0. \end{cases}$$

However, we may also obtain the result as follows: Note that the integral in (7) converges uniformly for all a. We may integrate with respect to a, to get

$$\int_0^z \int_0^\infty e^{-yx} \frac{\sin ax}{x} \, dx \, da = \int_0^z \tan^{-1} \frac{a}{y} \, da = z \tan^{-1} \frac{z}{y} - \frac{y}{2} \log \frac{z^2 + y^2}{y^2},$$

and interchange order of integration to get

(8)
$$\int_0^\infty e^{-yx} \frac{1 - \cos zx}{x^2} \, dx = z \tan^{-1} \frac{z}{y} - \frac{y}{2} \log \frac{z^2 + y^2}{y^2}.$$

The integral in (8) converges uniformly with respect to y, $0 \leq y \leq d$, being dominated by $\int_0^\infty \frac{1 - \cos xz}{x^2} \, dx$. Setting $y = 0$ gives

(9)
$$\int_0^\infty \frac{1 - \cos xz}{x^2} \, dx = |z| \frac{\pi}{2}.$$

Integration by parts reduces (9) to the desired result.

EXAMPLE 2

$$g(y) = \int_0^\infty e^{-x^2} \cos xy \, dx = \frac{\sqrt{\pi}}{2} e^{-y^2/4}.$$

The integral representing $g(y)$ and the integral

$$h(y) = \int_0^\infty -xe^{-x^2} \sin xy \, dx$$

obtained by differentiating the integrand in $g(y)$ both converge uniformly for all y. Hence

$$g'(y) = h(y) = \frac{e^{-x^2}}{2} \sin xy \Big|_0^\infty - \int_0^\infty \frac{e^{-x^2}}{2} y \cos xy \, dx = -\frac{y}{2} g(y).$$

The value $g(y)$ is positive as may be seen by representing the integral as a sum of integrals over the intervals $\left(\dfrac{n\pi}{y}, \dfrac{(n+1)\pi}{y}\right)$, $n = 0, 1, 2, \ldots$, and thus as an alternating series whose first term is positive and whose terms decrease in absolute value. Solving the differential equation, we get $g(y) = ce^{-y^2/4}$ where $c = g(0) = \int_0^\infty e^{-x^2}\, dx$ which is known to be $\sqrt{\pi}/2$ (Exercise 7.1–13).

Exercise 7.1

1. Prove Theorem 7.1B.

2. Assume that f and g are continuous on $a \le x < \infty$, and have piecewise continuous derivatives on every finite interval. Assume also that f' and g' are integrable on $a \le x < \infty$. Show that if $\int_a^\infty f(x)\, g'(x)\, dx$ exists, then there exists
    $$\int_a^\infty g(x)\, f'(x)\, dx = f(x)\, g(x)\Big|_a^\infty - \int_a^\infty f(x)\, g'(x)\, dx.$$
    Hint: Since $\int_a^b f'(x)\, dx = f(b) - f(a)$, $\lim\limits_{b\to\infty} f(b)$ exists.

3. (a) Let $f(x)$ be continuous on $1 \le x < \infty$. If $\left|\int_1^b f(x)\, dx\right| \le M$, a constant independent of b, then $\int_1^\infty \dfrac{f(x)}{x^r}\, dx$ converges for $r > 0$.
    Hint: Integrate $\int_1^b \dfrac{f(x)}{x^r}\, dx$ by parts.
    (b) Hence show that $\int_0^\infty \dfrac{\sin ax}{x}\, dx$ exists for every value of a.

4. (a) Show that if $\int_0^\infty f(x)\, dx < \infty$, then $\int_0^\infty e^{-yx} f(x)\, dx$ converges uniformly for $0 \le y \le d$. Here f is considered continuous. *Hint:* Let $F(x) = \int_a^\infty f(t)\, dt - \int_a^x f(t)\, dt$, choose N so that $|F(x)| < \epsilon$ for $x > N$, and write, for $s > r > N$,
    $$\left|\int_r^s f(x)\, e^{-yx}\, dx\right| = \left|-F(x)\, e^{-yx}\Big|_r^s - y\int_r^s F(x)\, e^{-yx}\, dx\right|.$$
    (b) Give a very simple proof that if $\int_0^\infty |f(x)|\, dx < \infty$, then $\int_0^\infty e^{-yx} f(x)\, dx$ converges uniformly for $0 \le y \le d$.
    (c) Show how Exercise (3b) and (4a) prove that $\int_0^\infty e^{-yx}\, \dfrac{\sin ax}{x}\, dx$ converges uniformly on $0 \le y \le d$. Why can't we use (4b) instead of (4a)?

5. (a) Obtain the formula
    $$1 + 2\cos 2x + \ldots + 2\cos 2nx = \frac{\sin(2n+1)x}{\sin x}, \qquad x \ne n\pi,$$
    and show that
    $$\int_0^{\pi/2} \frac{\sin(2n+1)x}{\sin x}\, dx = \pi/2.$$

(b) Use the Riemann-Lesbesgue theorem to show that

$$\lim_{n \to \infty} \int_0^{\pi/2} (\sin(2n+1)x)\left(\frac{1}{\sin x} - \frac{1}{x}\right) dx = 0.$$

(c) Show that $\int_0^\infty \frac{\sin x}{x} dx$ exists by considering it as an alternating series.

(d) Using (c) we may write $\int_0^\infty \frac{\sin x}{x} dx = \lim_{n \to \infty} \int_0^{n + \frac{1}{2}\pi} \frac{\sin x}{x} dx.$

Thus prove, with help of (a) and (b), that

$$\int_0^\infty \frac{\sin x}{x} dx = \pi/2.$$

(e) From (d) obtain the result of Example 1.

6. (a) Show that $\int_0^\infty \sin x^2 \, dx$ converges.

(b) Is $\lim_{x \to \infty} \sin x^2 = 0$?

7. For $y > 0$, $\int_0^\infty e^{-xy} dx = \frac{1}{y}$. Hence prove, for $y > 0$, that

$$\int_0^\infty x^n e^{-xy} dx = \frac{n!}{y^{n+1}}.$$

8. Show that $\int_0^\infty \frac{x \cos x}{a^2 + x^2} dx$ converges but not absolutely. Here $a > 0$.

9. Prove the following variant of Theorem 7.1F. Let $\int_c^q f(x, y) dx$ converge uniformly for every interval $y_1 \le y \le y_2$ where $c < y_1 < y_2 < d$. Here p may be
$-\infty$, q may be ∞, but c and d are both finite. Suppose that $\int_c^d \int_p^q f(x, y) dx \, dy < \infty$
and, for every a, b, $(p < a < b < q)$,

$$\int_a^b \int_c^d f(x, y) dy \, dx = \int_c^d \int_a^b f(x, y) dx \, dy.$$

Finally, suppose that there are constants a_1 and b_1 such that whenever $a < a_1$,
$b > b_1$, then

$$\left| \int_b^q f(x, y) dx \right| < B(y), \quad \left| \int_p^a f(x, y) dx \right| \le A(y),$$

where $A(y)$, $B(y)$ are integrable on $c \le y \le d$. Then there exists

$$\int_p^q \int_c^d f(x, y) dy \, dx = \int_c^d \int_p^q f(x, y) dx \, dy.$$

Hint: $\left| \int_a^b \int_c^d f(x, y) dy \, dx - \int_c^d \int_p^q f(x, y) dx \, dy \right|$

$= \left| \left\{ \int_c^{y_1} + \int_{y_1}^{y_2} + \int_{y_2}^d \right\} \left(\int_a^b f(x, y) dx - \int_p^q f(x, y) dx \right) dy \right|$

$\le \int_c^{y_1} \left| \int_b^q f(x, y) dx \right| dy + \int_c^{y_1} \left| \int_p^a f(x, y) dx \right| dy$

$+ \int_{y_1}^{y_2} \left| \int_a^b f(x, y) dx - \int_p^q f(x, y) dx \right| dy + \int_{y_2}^d \left| \int_b^q f(x, y) dx \right| dy$

$+ \int_{y_2}^d \left| \int_p^a f(x, y) dx \right| dy.$

10. (a) Show that $\int_0^\infty \frac{\sin xy}{x} dx$ does not converge uniformly for $0 \le y \le t$, but
does converge uniformly for $0 < y_1 \le y \le t$. Hint: For the convergence,
set $z = xy$ and use the Cauchy criterion.

(b) Show that $\left|\int_b^\infty \dfrac{\sin xy}{x}\, dx\right| < B$, a constant independent of y. *Hint:* For

$v > 0$, show that $0 < \int_0^v \dfrac{\sin x}{x}\, dx \le \int_0^\pi \dfrac{\sin x}{x}\, dx < \pi$ by writing the integral

as an alternating series.

(c) Use Exercise 9 to show that $\displaystyle\int_0^\infty \int_0^t \dfrac{\sin xy}{x}\, dy\, dx = \int_0^t \int_0^\infty \dfrac{\sin xy}{x}\, dx\, dy.$

Thus prove that $\displaystyle\int_0^\infty \dfrac{1 - \cos xt}{x^2}\, dx = \dfrac{\pi}{2} t, \quad t > 0.$

(d) Finally, show that $\displaystyle\int_0^\infty \left(\dfrac{\sin xt}{x}\right)^2 dx = \dfrac{\pi}{2}|t|.$

11. Let $f(x, y) = xe^{-x^2}e^{-x^2y^2}$. Use Exercise 9 to show that

$$\int_0^b \int_0^\infty f(x, y)dy\, dx = \int_0^\infty \int_0^b f(x, y)dx\, dy,$$

$$\int_0^d \int_0^\infty f(x, y)dx\, dy = \int_0^\infty \int_0^d f(x, y)dy\, dx.$$

12. Assume that all integrals mentioned exist. Let $f(x, y) \ge 0$ and suppose that

$$\int_c^d \int_a^\infty f(x, y)dx\, dy = \int_a^\infty \int_c^d f(x, y)dy\, dx, \quad \int_c^\infty \int_a^b f(x, y)dx\, dy$$

$$= \int_a^b \int_c^\infty f(x, y)dy\, dx.$$

Then show that $\displaystyle\int_c^\infty \int_a^\infty f(x, y)dx\, dy = \int_a^\infty \int_c^\infty f(x, y)dy\, dx.$

Hint: We have $\displaystyle\int_a^b f(x, y)dx \le \int_a^\infty f(x, y)dx$ so that $\displaystyle\int_c^\infty \int_a^b f(x, y)dx\, dy$

$\le \displaystyle\int_c^\infty \int_a^\infty f(x, y)dx\, dy, \int_a^b \int_c^\infty f(x, y)dy\, dx \le \int_c^\infty \int_a^\infty f(x, y)dx\, dy,$ from which we

deduce $\displaystyle\int_a^\infty \int_c^\infty f(x, y)dy\, dx \le \int_c^\infty \int_a^\infty f(x, y)dx\, dy.$

13. Let $I = \displaystyle\int_0^\infty e^{-x^2}dx$. Show, for $t > 0$, that $I = \int_0^\infty te^{-t^2y^2}dy.$

Then $I^2 = \displaystyle\int_0^\infty e^{-x^2}dx \int_0^\infty xe^{-y^2x^2}dy = \int_0^\infty \int_0^\infty xe^{-x^2}e^{-x^2y^2}dy\, dx.$
Use Exercises (11) and (12) to obtain $I = \sqrt{\pi}/2$.

14. Use the results of Example 1 to show that

$$\int_0^\infty \dfrac{\sin x \cos tx}{x}\, dx = \begin{cases} \pi/2, & |t| < 1 \\ \pi/4, & |t| = 1 \\ 0, & |t| > 1. \end{cases}$$

15. (a) For $y > 0$, $\displaystyle\int_0^\infty e^{-x^2y}dx = \tfrac{1}{2}\sqrt{\dfrac{\pi}{y}}.$

(b) $\displaystyle\int_0^\infty \sin y\, e^{-x^2y}\, dx$ converges uniformly for all $y \ge 0$.

(c) $\displaystyle\int_0^\infty \sin y\, e^{-x^2y}\, dy$ does not converge uniformly for $0 \le x \le b$.

(d) $\displaystyle\int_0^d \int_0^\infty \sin y\, e^{-x^2y}\, dx\, dy = \int_0^\infty \int_0^d \sin y\, e^{-x^2y}\, dy\, dx.$

(e) $\displaystyle\int_0^b \int_0^\infty \sin y\, e^{-x^2y}dy\, dx = \int_0^\infty \int_0^b \sin y\, e^{-x^2y}dx\, dy.$ *Hint:* Exercise 9.

(f) $\int_0^d \dfrac{\sin y}{\sqrt{y}}\,dy = \dfrac{2}{\sqrt{\pi}}\int_0^d\int_0^\infty \sin y\, e^{-x^2 y}dx\,dy = \dfrac{2}{\sqrt{\pi}}\int_0^\infty\int_0^d \sin y\, e^{-x^2 y}dy\,dx$

$\qquad = \dfrac{2}{\sqrt{\pi}}\Big(\int_0^\infty \dfrac{dx}{1+x^4} - \cos d\int_0^\infty \dfrac{e^{-x^2 d}}{1+x^4}dx - \sin d\int_0^\infty \dfrac{x^2 e^{-x^2 d}}{1+x^4}dx\Big).$

(g) $\int_0^\infty \dfrac{\sin y}{\sqrt{y}}\,dy = \sqrt{\dfrac{\pi}{2}}.$

(h) $\int_0^\infty \sin x^2\,dx = \tfrac{1}{2}\sqrt{\dfrac{\pi}{2}}.$

16. As in Exercise 15, prove that $\int_0^\infty \dfrac{\cos y}{\sqrt{y}}\,dy = \sqrt{\dfrac{\pi}{2}}.$

17. (a) Assume that $\int_0^\infty \dfrac{f(x)}{x}\,dx$ converges and $f(x)$ is continuous for $x \geq 0$.

Let $m > 0,\ n > 0,$ and show that $\int_0^\infty \dfrac{f(mx)-f(nx)}{x}\,dx = f(0)\log\dfrac{n}{m}.$

Hint: $\int_0^\infty \dfrac{f(mx)-f(nx)}{x}\,dx = \lim_{a\to 0}\int_a^\infty \dfrac{f(mx)-f(nx)}{x}\,dx = \lim_{a\to 0}\int_{ma}^{na}\dfrac{f(y)}{y}\,dy.$

(b) Find $\int_0^\infty \dfrac{e^{-mx}-e^{-nx}}{x}\,dx.$

7.2

A FOURIER

INTEGRAL THEOREM

Our previous study of differential operators was restricted to the case where the vector space consisted of functions defined on a finite interval. Let us consider the operator $L = -\dfrac{d^2}{dx^2}$ on the vector space $\mathcal{W}$ of real functions α having continuous second derivatives on $0 \leq x < \infty$ and satisfying

(1) $\qquad\qquad\qquad\qquad \alpha(0) = 0,$

(2) $\qquad \displaystyle\int_0^\infty |\alpha(x)|^2\,dx < \infty, \qquad \int_0^\infty |L\alpha|^2\,dx = \int_0^\infty |\alpha''(x)|^2\,dx < \infty.$

$\mathcal{W}$ is a Euclidean vector space when the inner product is defined as

$$(\alpha, \beta) = \int_0^\infty \alpha(x)\,\beta(x)\,dx.$$

The operator L is a symmetric operator on $\mathcal{W}$ in view of

THEOREM 7.2A If $\alpha,\ \beta$ are in $\mathcal{W}$, then $(L\alpha, \beta) = (\alpha, L\beta).$

Proof We have to show that $\int_0^\infty \alpha''(x)\,\beta(x)dx = \int_0^\infty \alpha(x)\,\beta''(x)$. Let $b > 0$ and write

$$\alpha(b)\,\beta'(b) - \alpha(0)\,\beta'(0) = \int_0^b \frac{d}{dx}(\alpha\beta')dx = \int_0^b \alpha\beta'' + \alpha'\beta'\,dx,$$

$$\alpha'(b)\,\beta(b) - \alpha'(0)\,\beta(0) = \int_0^b \frac{d}{dx}(\alpha'\beta)\,dx = \int_0^b \alpha''\beta + \alpha'\beta'\,dx,$$

so that

(3) $$\int_0^b \alpha\beta'' - \alpha''\beta\,dx = \alpha(b)\,\beta'(b) - \alpha'(b)\,\beta(b).$$

When $b \to \infty$, the left side of (3) approaches a limit and therefore the right side does. We shall show that this limit is zero, proving the theorem. Consider

(4) $$\alpha(b)^2 - \alpha(0)^2 = \int_0^b \frac{d}{dx}\,\alpha^2\,dx = \int_0^b 2\alpha\alpha'dx,$$

(5) $$\int_0^b (\alpha')^2\,dx + \int_0^b \alpha\alpha''\,dx = \int_0^b \frac{d}{dx}(\alpha\alpha')dx = \alpha(b)\,\alpha'(b) - \alpha(0)\,\alpha'(0),$$

and let $b \to \infty$ in (5), obtaining the existence of $\lim_{b \to \infty} \alpha(b)\,\alpha'(b)$, possibly $+\infty$. The limit must however be finite for otherwise the right side of (4) would approach ∞ as $b \to \infty$, yielding $\lim_{b \to \infty} \alpha(b)^2 = \infty$ contradicting $\int_0^\infty \alpha(x)^2\,dx < \infty$. It follows from (5) that $\int_0^\infty (\alpha')^2\,dx < \infty$ and hence $\int_0^\infty \alpha(x)\,\alpha'(x)dx < \infty$. Returning to (4), we obtain the existence of $\lim_{b \to \infty} \alpha(b)^2$ and this must be zero, since $\int_0^\infty \alpha^2\,dx < \infty$. The equation

(6) $$\alpha'(b)^2 - \alpha'(0)^2 = \int_0^b \frac{d}{dx}(\alpha')^2dx = \int_0^b 2\alpha'\,\alpha''\,dx$$

indicates that $\lim \alpha'(b)^2$ exists and this limit is zero when $\int_0^\infty \alpha'(x)^2dx < \infty$. We have shown that $\lim_{b \to \infty} \alpha(b) = 0 = \lim_{b \to \infty} \alpha'(b)$. The same results are valid for β. It follows that the right side of (3) approaches zero as b approaches ∞.   ★

When we examine the equation $L\alpha = r\alpha$ for α in $\mathscr{W}$ to obtain the eigenvalues we find immediately that there are no eigenvalues. For the only nonzero solutions of $-\alpha''(x) = r\alpha(x)$ satisfying (1) are Ax when $r = 0$, $A \sin \sqrt{r}x$ when $r > 0$, $A \sinh \sqrt{|r|}\,x$ when $r < 0$, and none of these satisfy $\int_0^\infty \alpha^2(x)dx < \infty$. Nevertheless, as we shall see, it is possible to find, in terms of the solutions $\sin \sqrt{r}\, x\ (r > 0$ and not necessarily an integer) an expansion theorem for functions defined on $0 \leq x < \infty$ which is analogous to the Fourier Sine expansion for functions on a finite interval. Thus, if we desire a general theory embracing the infinite interval as well as the finite interval, we must enlarge our concept of the spectrum. Such a program is left for a more advanced course in spectral theory. Instead, we shall consider the type of expansion theorem one is able to obtain.

It will be convenient to introduce a generalization of the Riemann integral called the Riemann-Stieltjes integral which permits the representation of an infinite series as an integral. This new integral will be used only to motivate our theorems. For this reason an extended discussion will not be undertaken. A readable introduction can be found in *Mathematical Analysis* by T. M. Apostol.

Let P be a partition $a = x_0 < x_1 \ldots < x_n = b$ of $a \leq x \leq b$ augmented by points x_j' in $x_{j-1} \leq x \leq x_j$. We say that the bounded function f, defined on $a \leq x \leq b$, is **Riemann Stieltjes integrable** with respect to the bounded function h, defined on $a \leq x \leq b$, if there is a constant M such that, for every $\epsilon > 0$ there exists a partition $P(\epsilon)$ such that

$$(7) \qquad \left| \sum_{j=1}^{n} f(x_j') \left(h(x_j) - h(x_{j-1}) \right) - M \right| < \epsilon$$

whenever P is an augmented partition containing the partition points of $P(\epsilon)$. The number M is then called the **Riemann-Stieltjes integral** of f with respect to h and is written

$$M = \int_a^b f(x)\, dh(x).$$

Taking $h(x) = x$, condition (7) becomes

$$(8) \qquad \left| \sum_{j=1}^{n} f(x_j') \left(x_j - x_{j-1} \right) - M \right| < \epsilon$$

whenever P is an augmented partition containing the partition points of $P(\epsilon)$. It can be shown (Exercise 7.2–2) that f is Riemann integrable if and only if (8) is valid. Hence the Riemann-Stieltjes integral is a generalization of the Riemann integral. This generalization is due to T. J. Stieltjes (1856–1894).

Here are some of the basic properties.

1. If f is R. S. integrable (i.e., Riemann-Stieltjes integrable) on $a \leq x \leq b$ with respect to h, then h is R. S. integrable with respect to f and

$$\int_a^b f(x)\, dh(x) + \int_a^b h(x)\, df(x) = f(b)\, h(b) - f(a)\, h(a).$$

2. If f is R. S. integrable with respect to h on $a \le x \le b$, and $a < c < b$, then f is R. S. integrable with respect to h on $a \le x \le c$ and on $c \le x \le b$ and

$$\int_a^c f(x) \, dh(x) + \int_c^b f(x) \, dh(x) = \int_a^b f(x) \, dh(x).$$

3. If f is R. S. integrable with respect to h on $a \le x \le c$ and on $c \le x \le b$, for $a < c < b$, then f is R. S. integrable with respect to h on $a \le x \le b$, and the formula in 2 is valid. The restriction $a < c < b$ can be dropped by defining

$$\int_a^a f(x) \, dh(x) = 0, \qquad \int_b^a f(x) \, dh(x) = - \int_a^b f(x) \, dh(x).$$

4. If f is continuous on $a \le x \le b$ and h is monotone increasing (or decreasing) then f is R. S. integrable with respect to h on $a \le x \le b$.

5. If f is R. S. integrable on $a \le x \le b$ with respect to h and also with respect to g then f is R. S. integrable on $a \le x \le b$ with respect to $ph + qg$ for constants p and q. Moreover,

$$\int_a^b f(x) \, d(ph + qg) = p \int_a^b f(x) \, dh(x) + q \int_a^b f(x) \, dg(x).$$

6. If f and g are R. S. integrable on $a \le x \le b$ with respect to h so is $pf + qg$ for constants p and q and

$$\int_a^b (pf + qg) \, dh(x) = p \int_a^b f(x) \, dh(x) + q \int_a^b g(x) \, dh(x).$$

7. If f is R. S. integrable with respect to h on $a \le x \le b$ and h has a continuous derivative, then fh' is Riemann integrable on $a \le x \le b$ and

$$\int_a^b f(x) \, dh(x) = \int_a^b f(x) \, h'(x)dx.$$

8. If f and g are R. S. integrable on $a \le x \le b$ with respect to the monotone increasing function h and if $f(x) \le g(x)$ then $\int_a^b f(x) \, dh(x) \le \int_a^b g(x) \, dh(x)$. Moreover $\int_a^b |f(x)|dh(x)$ exists and

$$\left| \int_a^b f(x) \, dh(x) \right| \le \int_a^b |f(x)|dh(x) \le M\Big(h(b) - h(a)\Big),$$

where $M = $ l.u.b. $\{|f(x)| \,\big|\, a \le x \le b\}$.

Property **7** states that the R. S. integral is just a Riemann integral when h has a continuous derivative and the other properties listed indicate resemblances between the two types of integrals. However, there is an important difference. When h is not continuous, the value of $\int_a^b f(x)\,dh(x)$ can be changed by changing the value of f at a single point.

EXAMPLE 1 Define $h(x) = \begin{cases} p\,, & a \leq x < c \\ q \neq p, & c \leq x \leq d \end{cases}$. For any augmented partition P with partition points $a = x_0 < x_1 < x_2 \cdots < x_n = b$ where c is one of the partition points, $c = x_i$, we have

$$\sum_{j=1}^{n} f(x_j') \left(h(x_j) - h(x_{j-1}) \right) = f(x_i')(q - p),$$

where $x_{i-1} \leq x_i' \leq x_i$. Assuming that $\lim_{x \to c-} f(x) = f(c-)$ exists and is equal to $f(c)$, we obtain

$$(9) \qquad \int_a^b f(x)\,dh(x) = f(c)\,(q - p).$$

Indeed, there exists $\delta(\epsilon)$ such that

$$|f(x_i')(q - p) - f(c)(q - p)| = |q - p|\,|f(c) - f(x_i')| < \epsilon$$

when $|x_i' - c| < \delta$, that is, when P is chosen so that $|x_i - x_{i-1}| < \delta$. However, if f is discontinuous at c from the left, it is not difficult to see that $\int_a^b f(x)\,dh(x)$, with h as specified above, cannot exist.

Equation (9) of the preceding example suggests how we may write a series as an integral. Let $a = x_0 < x_1 \cdots < x_n = b$ and $c_1, c_2, \ldots, c_n$ be constants. Define

$$h(x) = \begin{cases} 0, & x_0 \leq x < x_1, \\ \displaystyle\sum_{j=1}^{k-1} c_j, & x_{k-1} \leq x < x_k, \qquad k = 2, \ldots, n, \\ \displaystyle\sum_{j=1}^{n} c_j, & x = x_n. \end{cases}$$

Thus $h(x)$ has a jump of value c_j at x_j, $j = 1, \ldots, n$. Then, if f is continuous at each x_i, we have

$$(10) \qquad \int_a^b f(x)\,dh(x) = \sum_{j=1}^{n} c_j\,f(x_j).$$

This result can be obtained from (9) after decomposing the integral as a sum of integrals over intervals each of which contains only one of the points $x_1, x_2, \ldots, x_n$.

If $a = x_0 < x_1 < x_2 \ldots$ forms an unbounded sequence of points and $\sum\limits_{j=1}^{\infty} c_j f(x_j)$ is a convergent series, then we obtain from (10) the formula

$$(11) \qquad \int_a^{\infty} f(x)\, dh(x) = \sum_{j=1}^{\infty} c_j f(x_j).$$

To apply this new concept, we recall some results obtained for the operator $L = -\dfrac{d^2}{dx^2}$ defined on the vector space $\mathscr{V}$ of functions α having two continuous derivatives on $0 \le x \le b$ and satisfying $\alpha(0) = 0$, $\alpha(b) = 0$. The orthonormal eigenvectors are

$$(12) \qquad \alpha_n(x) = \sqrt{\frac{2}{b}} \sin \sqrt{r_n}\, x$$

corresponding to eigenvalues $r_n = \dfrac{n^2 \pi^2}{b^2}$. The Parseval equation is

$$(13) \qquad \int_0^b |\beta(x)|^2\, dx = \sum_1^{\infty} |(\beta, \alpha_n)|^2 = \frac{2}{b} \sum_{n=1}^{\infty} |\int_0^b \beta(x) \sin \frac{n\pi x}{b}\, dx|^2,$$

valid for integrable β. Moreover, if β is sufficiently restricted, an expansion theorem is given by

$$(14) \qquad \beta(x) = \sum_{n=1}^{\infty} (\beta, \alpha_n)\, \alpha_n(x) = \sum_{n=1}^{\infty} \left(\frac{2}{b} \int_0^b \beta(y) \sin \frac{n\pi y}{b}\, dy \right) \sin \frac{n\pi x}{b}.$$

Let us rewrite the series appearing in (13) as an integral. Define

$$(15) \qquad \sigma(r) = \int_0^b \beta(x) \sin \sqrt{r}\, x\, dx.$$

Then (13) may be written as

$$(16) \qquad \int_0^b |\beta(x)|^2\, dx = \sum_{n=1}^{\infty} \left| \frac{2}{b} \sigma\left(\frac{n^2 \pi^2}{b^2} \right) \right|^2.$$

The series in (16) may be rewritten as a Riemann-Stieltjes integral by letting $\rho(x, b)$ be a nondecreasing right-continuous step-function vanishing at 0 and constant except for jumps of value $\dfrac{2}{b}$ at the eigenvalues $r_n = \dfrac{n^2\pi^2}{b^2}$.

Now (16) becomes

(17)
$$\int_0^b |\beta(x)|^2\, dx = \int_0^\infty |\sigma(r)|^2\, d\rho(r, b).$$

The points $(r, \rho) = \left(\dfrac{n^2\pi^2}{b^2},\, \rho\!\left(\dfrac{n^2\pi^2}{b^2},\, b\right)\right)$ lie on the curve $\rho = \dfrac{2}{\pi}\sqrt{r}$. Since

$$\left|\frac{2}{\pi}\sqrt{r} - \rho(r, b)\right| < \frac{2}{b}$$

it is clear that $\lim\limits_{b\to\infty} \rho(r, b) = \dfrac{2}{\pi}\sqrt{r} = \rho(r)$.

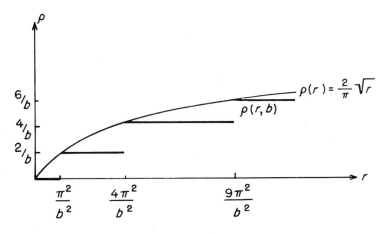

If it were possible to proceed formally, we should obtain from (17), by letting $b \to \infty$,

(18)
$$\int_0^\infty |\beta(x)|^2\, dx = \int_0^\infty |\sigma(r)|^2 d\rho(r) = \int_0^\infty \left|\int_0^\infty \beta(y)\sin\sqrt{r}\, y\, dy\right|^2 \frac{1}{\pi\sqrt{r}}\, dr$$

$$= \int_0^\infty \left|\sqrt{\frac{2}{\pi}}\int_0^\infty \beta(y)\sin xy\, dy\right|^2 dx.$$

Recall also that the Parseval equality (13) is equivalent to

(19)
$$\lim_{k\to\infty}\int_0^b \left|\beta(x) - \sum_{n=1}^k \left(\frac{2}{b}\int_0^b \beta(y)\sin\frac{n\pi y}{b}\, dy\right)\sin\frac{n\pi x}{b}\right|^2 dx = 0.$$

When $0 \leq x \leq c$ is an interval including only the first k eigenvalues, we have

$$\int_0^c \sigma(r) \sin \sqrt{r}\, x\, d\rho(r, b) = \sum_{n=1}^k \sigma\left(\frac{n^2\pi^2}{b^2}\right)\left(\sin \frac{n\pi}{b} x\right)\frac{2}{b}$$

$$= \sum_{n=1}^k \frac{2}{b}\int_0^b \beta(y) \sin\frac{n\pi y}{b}\, dy \sin \frac{n\pi}{b} x = \sum_{n=1}^k (\beta, \alpha_n)\, \alpha_n(x),$$

so that (19) is

(20) $$\lim_{k \to \infty} \int_0^b |\beta(x) - \int_0^c \sigma(r) \sin \sqrt{r}\, x\, d\rho(r, b)|^2\, dx = 0.$$

Again proceeding formally, (20) transforms into

$$\lim_{c \to \infty} \int_0^\infty |\beta(x) - \int_0^c \int_0^\infty \beta(y) \sin \sqrt{r}\, y\, dy\, (\sin \sqrt{r}\, x)\, \frac{1}{\pi\sqrt{r}}\, dr|^2\, dx = 0,$$

or

(21) $$\lim_{c \to \infty} \int_0^\infty |\beta(x) - \frac{2}{\pi}\int_0^c \int_0^\infty \beta(y) \sin ty\, dy \sin tx\, dt|^2\, dx = 0.$$

We see that series (14) is transformed into

(22) $$\beta(x) = \frac{2}{\pi}\int_0^\infty \int_0^\infty \beta(y) \sin ty\, dy \sin xt\, dt.$$

Formulas (18), (21), and (22) are actually valid, when β is sufficiently restricted. Note that (18) may be interpreted as the statement "The square of the norm of β is the square of the norm of the transform $T_s\beta$ of β" if we define $T_s\beta$, the **Fourier Sine Transform**, by

$$T_s\beta = \sqrt{\frac{2}{\pi}} \int_0^\infty \beta(y) \sin xy\, dy.$$

Equation (21) is a statement about convergence in mean square and (22) is an inversion theorem, for it shows that $T_s(T_s\beta) = \beta$. An expansion theorem of type (22) is also called a **Fourier Integral Theorem**.

In a similar fashion we may consider the operator $L = -\dfrac{d^2}{dx^2}$ on the vector space $\mathscr{W}_1$ of real functions having continuous second derivatives on $0 \leq x < \infty$ satisfying (2) but with (1) replaced by $\alpha'(0) = 0$. In this case we obtain formally

(23)
$$\int_0^\infty |\beta(x)|^2\, dx = \int_0^\infty |\sqrt{\frac{2}{\pi}} \int_0^\infty \beta(y) \cos xy\, dy|^2\, dx,$$

(24)
$$\lim_{c \to \infty} \int_0^\infty |\beta(x) - \frac{2}{\pi} \int_0^c \int_0^\infty \beta(y) \cos ty\, dy \cos tx\, dt|^2\, dx = 0,$$

(25)
$$\beta(x) = \frac{2}{\pi} \int_0^\infty \int_0^\infty \beta(y) \cos ty\, dy \cos tx\, dt.$$

The **Fourier Cosine Transform** is defined by

$$T_c\beta = \sqrt{\frac{2}{\pi}} \int_0^\infty \beta(y) \cos xy\, dy.$$

Finally we may consider the operator $L = -\dfrac{d^2}{dx^2}$ on the vector space $\mathcal{W}_2$ of real functions having continuous second derivatives on $-\infty < x < \infty$ and satisfying

(26)
$$\int_{-\infty}^\infty |\alpha(x)|^2\, dx < \infty, \qquad \int_{-\infty}^\infty |L\alpha|^2\, dx = \int_{-\infty}^\infty |\alpha''(x)|^2\, dx < \infty.$$

In this case we obtain formally

(27)
$$\int_{-\infty}^\infty |\beta(x)|^2\, dx = \int_0^\infty \left(|\frac{1}{\sqrt{\pi}} \int_{-\infty}^\infty \beta(y) \sin xy\, dy|^2 \right.$$
$$\left. + |\frac{1}{\sqrt{\pi}} \int_{-\infty}^\infty \beta(y) \cos xy\, dy|^2 \right) dx,$$

(28)
$$\lim_{c \to \infty} \int_{-\infty}^\infty |\beta(x) - \frac{1}{\pi} \int_0^c \int_{-\infty}^\infty \beta(y) \cos t\,(x - y)dy\, dt|^2\, dx = 0,$$

(29)
$$\beta(x) = \frac{1}{\pi} \int_0^\infty \int_{-\infty}^\infty \beta(y) \cos t\,(x - y)dy\, dt.$$

The validity of (27), (28), (29) imply the validity of (18), (21), (22) and (23), (24), (25) and the converse is also true, at least for functions β sufficiently restricted. Suppose, for example, that (27) is valid for functions β such that $|\beta|$ and $|\beta|^2$ are integrable on $-\infty < x < \infty$. Let μ defined on $0 \le x \le \infty$ have the property that $|\mu|$ and $|\mu|^2$ are integrable on $0 \le x < \infty$. Redefine μ to be 0 at $x = 0$ and define μ on $-\infty < x \le 0$ by $\mu(x) = -\mu(-x)$. Then μ is odd and $\int_{-\infty}^\infty \mu(y) \cos xy\, dy = 0$. Thus (27) reduces to (18). If σ defined on $0 \le x < \infty$ has the property that $|\sigma|$ and $|\sigma|^2$ are integrable on $0 \le x < \infty$, define σ on $-\infty < x \leq 0$ by $\sigma(x) = \sigma(-x)$. Then σ is even, $\int_0^\infty \sigma(y) \sin xy \, dy$ $= 0$, and (27) reduces to (23). Conversely, if (18) and (23) are valid for functions β with $|\beta|$ and $|\beta|^2$ integrable on $0 \leq x < \infty$ and α is given with $|\alpha|$ and $|\alpha|^2$ integrable on $-\infty < x < \infty$, write

$$\alpha(x) = \frac{\alpha(x) + \alpha(-x)}{2} + \frac{\alpha(x) - \alpha(-x)}{2} = \sigma(x) + \mu(x)$$

where σ is even, μ is odd. Then, since $\int_{-\infty}^\infty \sigma\mu \, dx = 0$, we have

$$\int_{-\infty}^\infty |\alpha(x)|^2 \, dx = \int_{-\infty}^\infty |\sigma + \mu|^2 \, dx = \int_{-\infty}^\infty |\sigma|^2 \, dx + \int_{-\infty}^\infty |\mu|^2 \, dx$$

$$= 2 \int_0^\infty |\sigma|^2 \, dx + 2 \int_0^\infty |\mu|^2 \, dx = \frac{4}{\pi} \int_0^\infty |\int_0^\infty \sigma(y) \cos xy \, dy|^2 \, dx$$

$$+ \frac{4}{\pi} \int_0^\infty |\int_0^\infty \mu(y) \sin xy \, dy|^2 \, dx$$

$$= \frac{1}{\pi} \int_0^\infty |\int_{-\infty}^\infty \sigma(y) \cos xy \, dy|^2 \, dx + \frac{1}{\pi} \int_0^\infty |\int_{-\infty}^\infty \mu(y) \sin xy \, dy|^2 \, dx$$

$$= \frac{1}{\pi} \int_0^\infty |\int_{-\infty}^\infty \left(\sigma(y) + \mu(y) \right) \cos xy \, dy|^2 \, dx$$

$$+ \frac{1}{\pi} \int_0^\infty |\int_{-\infty}^\infty \left(\sigma(y) + \mu(y) \right) \sin xy \, dy|^2 dx$$

$$= \frac{1}{\pi} \int_0^\infty \left(|\int_{-\infty}^\infty \alpha(y) \cos xy \, dy|^2 + |\int_{-\infty}^\infty \alpha(y) \sin xy \, dy|^2 \right) dx.$$

Here is a simple type of expansion theorem.

THEOREM 7.2B   If β and β' are piecewise continuous on every finite interval, and $\int_{-\infty}^\infty |\beta(x)| dx < \infty$, then there exists

$$\frac{1}{\pi} \int_0^\infty \int_{-\infty}^\infty \beta(y) \cos t \, (x - y) dy \, dt = \tfrac{1}{2} \left(\beta(x +) + \beta(x -) \right).$$

Proof The integral $\int_{-\infty}^\infty \beta(y) \cos t(x - y) dy$ converges uniformly on $0 \leq t \leq b$ to a function continuous in t. It is then possible to interchange the order of integration in

$$I(x, b) = \int_0^b \int_{-\infty}^\infty \beta(y) \cos t(x - y) dy \, dt = \int_{-\infty}^\infty \int_0^b \beta(y) \cos t(x - y) dt \, dy$$

$$= \int_{-\infty}^\infty \beta(y) \frac{\sin b(x - y)}{x - y} \, dy = \int_{-\infty}^\infty \beta(x + z) \frac{\sin bz}{z} \, dz.$$

If we define

$$\alpha(x, z) = \begin{cases} 0, & z = 0, \\ \beta(x + z) + \beta(x - z) - \beta(x +) - \beta(x -), & z > 0, \end{cases}$$

then $\dfrac{\alpha(x, z)}{z}$ is piecewise continuous and

(30) $$I(x, b) - \frac{\pi}{2}\left[\beta(x +) + \beta(x -)\right]$$

$$= \int_0^\infty \left[\beta(x + z) + \beta(x - z)\right] \frac{\sin bz}{z}\, dz$$

$$- \left[\beta(x +) + \beta(x -)\right] \int_0^\infty \frac{\sin bz}{z}\, dz$$

$$= \int_0^\infty \alpha(x, z) \frac{\sin bz}{z}\, dz = \left\{\int_0^c + \int_c^\infty\right\} \frac{\alpha(x, z)}{z} \sin bz\, dz.$$

We must show that the right side of (30) approaches 0 as b approaches infinity. Keep $b > 1$ and $c > 1$ and write

$$\left|\int_c^\infty \frac{\alpha(x, z)}{z} \sin bz\, dz\right| \le \int_c^\infty |\beta(x + z)|\, dz + \int_c^\infty |\beta(x - z)|\, dz$$

$$+ |\beta(x +) + \beta(x -)| \left|\int_c^\infty \frac{\sin bz}{z}\, dz\right|.$$

We may choose c so large that the left side of the inequality is dominated by ϵ. Then, using the Riemann-Lebesgue Theorem (Theorem 5.6B), we can choose B so that $b > B$ implies

$$\left|\int_0^c \frac{\alpha(x, z)}{z} \sin bz\, dz\right| < \epsilon.$$

The right side of (30) is now less than 2ϵ in absolute value for $b > B$.   ★

Corollary 1

If β and β' are piecewise continuous on every finite interval $0 \le x \le b < \infty$ and $\int_0^\infty |\beta(x)|\, dx < \infty$, then there exist

(31) $\dfrac{2}{\pi} \displaystyle\int_0^\infty \int_0^\infty \beta(y) \cos ty\, dy \cos tx\, dt$

(32) $\dfrac{2}{\pi} \displaystyle\int_0^\infty \int_0^\infty \beta(y) \sin ty\, dy \sin tx\, dt$

$\left. \vphantom{\int_0^\infty \int_0^\infty} \right\} = \dfrac{\beta(x +) + \beta(x -)}{2}, \quad x > 0.$

The left side of (31) converges to $\beta(0 +)$ for $x = 0$, and the left side of (32) converges to 0 for $x = 0$.

EXAMPLE 2 $\displaystyle\int_0^\infty \frac{1 - \cos y}{y} \sin xy\, dy = \begin{cases} 0, & x = 0, \\ \dfrac{\pi}{2}, & 0 < x < 1, \\ \dfrac{\pi}{4}, & x = 1, \\ 0, & x > 1. \end{cases}$

The result is obtained from (32) using

$$\beta(y) = \begin{cases} 1, & 0 \le y \le 1, \\ 0, & y > 1. \end{cases} \quad \text{Thus}$$

$$\frac{\beta(x) + \beta(x -)}{2} = \frac{2}{\pi} \int_0^\infty \int_0^1 \sin ty\, dy \sin tx\, dt = \frac{2}{\pi} \int_0^\infty \frac{1 - \cos t}{t} \sin tx\, dt$$

and the desired result follows.

Theorem 7.2B remains true if β is complex valued. The theorem is usually written in complex form. We have

$$\frac{1}{\pi} \int_0^\infty \int_{-\infty}^\infty \beta(y) \cos t(x - y) dy\, dt = \frac{1}{2\pi} \int_0^\infty \int_{-\infty}^\infty \beta(y) \left(e^{it\,(x-y)} + e^{-it\,(x-y)} \right) dy\, dt$$

$$= \lim_{b \to \infty} \frac{1}{2\pi} \left\{ \int_0^b \int_{-\infty}^\infty \beta(y)\, e^{it\,(x-y)} dy\, dt + \int_0^b \int_{-\infty}^\infty \beta(y) e^{-it\,(x-y)} dy\, dt \right\},$$

and so

(33) $\displaystyle \lim_{b \to \infty} \frac{1}{2\pi} \int_{-b}^b \int_{-\infty}^\infty \beta(y)\, e^{it\,(x-y)} dy\, dt = \frac{\beta(x +) + \beta(x -)}{2}.$

The linear operator T defined by

(34) $$T\beta = \frac{1}{\sqrt{2\pi}} \int_{-\infty}^\infty \beta(y)\, e^{-ity} dy$$

is called the **Fourier transform** of β. Replacing t by $-t$ we obtain the **adjoint Fourier transform** T^* defined by

(35) $$T^*\beta = \frac{1}{\sqrt{2\pi}} \int_{-\infty}^\infty \beta(y)\, e^{ity} dy.$$

Theorem 7.2B states that under certain conditions

$$(T^*T\beta)(x) = \tfrac{1}{2}\left(\beta(x +) + \beta(x -) \right).$$

In particular, when β is continuous and $\int_{-\infty}^{\infty} |\beta(x)| \, dx < \infty$ and β' is piecewise continuous, T^* acts as an inverse since

$$T^*T\beta = \beta = TT^*\beta,$$

However, it must be remembered that the inner integral in (33) is not necessarily an absolutely integrable function of t.

The following table lists analogies between Fourier series and Fourier integrals.

$$\frac{a_0}{2} + \sum_{n=1}^{\infty} \left(a_n \cos nx + b_n \sin nx \right)$$

$$= \frac{a_0}{2} + \sum_{n=1}^{\infty} \frac{1}{\pi} \int_{-\pi}^{\pi} \beta(y) \cos n(x - y) dy$$

$$= \sum_{-\infty}^{\infty} c_n e^{inx}$$

$$= \frac{1}{2\pi} \sum_{-\infty}^{\infty} \int_{-\pi}^{\pi} \beta(y) e^{in(x-y)} dy,$$

where

$$a_n = \frac{1}{\pi} \int_{-\pi}^{\pi} \beta(y) \cos ny \, dy,$$

$$b_n = \frac{1}{\pi} \int_{-\pi}^{\pi} \beta(y) \sin ny \, dy,$$

$$c_n = \frac{1}{2\pi} \int_{-\pi}^{\pi} \beta(y) e^{-iny} \, dy,$$

$$c_n = \frac{a_n - ib_n}{2}, \text{ when}$$

$$a_{-n} = a_n, \quad b_{-n} = -b_n.$$

$$\int_0^{\infty} \left(a(t) \cos tx + b(t) \sin tx \right) dt$$

$$= \frac{1}{\pi} \int_0^{\infty} \int_{-\infty}^{\infty} \beta(y) \cos t(x - y) dy \, dt$$

$$= \int_{-\infty}^{\infty} c(t) e^{itx} dt$$

$$= \frac{1}{2\pi} \int_{-\infty}^{\infty} \int_{-\infty}^{\infty} \beta(y) e^{it(x-y)} dy \, dt,$$

where

$$a(t) = \frac{1}{\pi} \int_{-\infty}^{\infty} \beta(y) \cos ty \, dy,$$

$$b(t) = \frac{1}{\pi} \int_{-\infty}^{\infty} \beta(y) \sin ty \, dy,$$

$$c(t) = \frac{1}{2\pi} \int_{-\infty}^{\infty} \beta(y) e^{-ity} \, dy,$$

$$c(t) = \frac{a(t) - ib(t)}{2}.$$

Exercise 7.2

1. (a) Show that it is possible for a nonnegative continuous function α to satisfy $\int_0^{\infty} \alpha(x) dx < \infty$ but not $\lim_{x \to \infty} \alpha(x) = 0$.

   (b) Show that if $\lim_{x \to \infty} \alpha(x) = L$ and $\int_0^{\infty} \alpha(x)^2 dx < \infty$, then $L = 0$.

2. Prove that (8) in the text is a necessary and sufficient condition that f be Riemann integrable.

3. Define $[x]$ to be the greatest integer n such that $n \leq x$.

   (a) Evaluate $\int_0^b x \, d[x]$ for $b = \frac{1}{2}$ and for $b = 3$.

(b)   Evaluate $\int_0^2 [x]\, d\sin x$ in two different ways.

(c)   Evaluate $\int_0^3 x\, d(x - [x])$ in two different ways.

(d)   Evaluate $\int_{-1}^1 x\, d|x|$ in two different ways.

4.   Write $\sum_1^\infty \frac{1}{n^2}$ as a Stieltjes integral.

5.   Consider the operator $L = -\dfrac{d^2}{dx^2}$ on the space of complex valued functions of the real variable x with continuous second derivatives on $0 \le x < \infty$ satisfying (1) and (2). Show that L is symmetric.

6.   (a)   Consider $L = -\dfrac{d^2}{dx^2}$ on the space $\mathscr{W}_1$ (see text preceding (23)) and show that L is symmetric.

   (b)   Obtain (23), (24), (25) formally by considering a boundary problem with $\alpha'(0) = 0$, $\alpha'(b) = 0$ and letting $b \to \infty$.

7.   (a)   Consider $L = -\dfrac{d^2}{dx^2}$ on the space $\mathscr{W}_2$ (see text preceding (26)) and show that L is symmetric.

   (b)   Obtain (27), (28), (29) formally by considering a boundary problem with $\alpha(b) = 0 = \alpha(-b)$ and letting $b \to \infty$. *Hint:* Parseval's equality is

$$\int_{-b}^b |\beta|^2\, dx = \sum_{n=1}^\infty |\int_{-b}^b \beta(x)\, b^{-1/2} \sin\frac{n\pi}{2b}(x - b)dx|^2$$

$$= \sum_{n=1}^\infty \frac{1}{b}\cos^2\frac{n\pi}{2}\sigma(r_n)^2 + \sum_{n=1}^\infty \frac{1}{b}\sin^2\frac{n\pi}{2}\mu(r_n)^2,$$

   where $\sigma(r) = \int_{-b}^b \beta(x) \sin\sqrt{r}\, x\, dx$, $\mu(r) = \int_{-b}^b \beta(x) \cos\sqrt{r}\, x\, dx$.

8.   Use the method of Theorem 7.2A to show that, for α in $\mathscr{W}$, we have $\int_0^\infty \alpha(x)\, \alpha''(x)dx \le 0$, $0 = \int_0^\infty \alpha(x)\, \alpha'(x)dx$, $\int_0^\infty \alpha'(x)\alpha''(x)dx \le 0$.

9.   (a)   Obtain (28) from (21) and (24).
   (b)   Obtain (29) from (22) and (25).

10.   Prove that $\int_0^x \dfrac{\sin at}{t}\, dt \le \int_0^\pi \dfrac{\sin t}{t}\, dt$, $a > 0$, $x > 0$.

11.   (a)   Let $f(x)$ be piecewise continuous on $0 \le x \le b$ and have a right hand derivative at $x = 0$. Show that

$$\lim_{t\to\infty} \int_0^b f(x)\frac{\sin tx}{x}\, dx = \frac{\pi}{2}f(0 +).$$

   Hint: Write the integral as

$$\int_0^b \frac{f(x) - f(0 +)}{x}\sin tx\, dx + f(0 +)\int_0^{bt}\frac{\sin y}{y}\, dy$$

   and apply methods used in Theorem 7.2B.

   (b)   Apply (a) to show that

$$\lim_{t\to\infty} \int_a^b f(x)\frac{\sin t(x - c)}{x - c}\, dx = \frac{\pi}{2}\Big(f(c +) + f(c -)\Big)$$

   whenever $a < c < b$ and $f(x)$ is piecewise continuous on $a \le x \le b$ and has right and left hand derivatives at c.

12. Prove that $\int_0^\infty \dfrac{\cos yx}{1+y^2} dy = \dfrac{\pi}{2} e^{-|x|}$, $-\infty < x < \infty$.

13. Solve the integral equation

$$\int_0^\infty \alpha(y) \cos yx\, dy = \beta(x),$$

where

$$\beta(x) = \begin{cases} 0, & 0 \le x \le \pi/2. \\ 1, & \pi/2 < x < \pi, \\ 0, & x > \pi. \end{cases}$$

14. Use Exercise 11 to find

(a) $\displaystyle\lim_{t\to\infty} \int_0^1 \dfrac{\sin 2\pi x \sin tx}{x^2} dx,$

(b) $\displaystyle\lim_{t\to\infty} \int_0^\pi x(\log x) \sin tx\, dx.$

15. Show that

$$\frac{1}{\pi}\int_{-\infty}^\infty \frac{\sin x}{x} \cos yx\, dx = \begin{cases} 0 & \text{for } |y| > 1, \\ \tfrac{1}{2} & \text{for } |y| = 1, \\ 1 & \text{for } |y| < 1. \end{cases}$$

7.3

THE FOURIER
TRANSFORM

In this section we shall study quantities which correspond to the Fourier coefficients in a Fourier series.

Let $\mathscr{R}^* = \mathscr{R}^*\{-\infty, \infty\}$ denote the vector space of complex valued functions α of a real variable x which are integrable over any finite interval and satisfy $\int_{-\infty}^\infty |\alpha(x)|\, dx < \infty$. The Fourier transform T defined by

(1) $$T\alpha = (T\alpha)(x) = \frac{1}{\sqrt{2\pi}} \int_{-\infty}^\infty \alpha(y)\, e^{-ixy} dy$$

is a linear operator on $\mathscr{R}^*$.

THEOREM 7.3A $T\alpha$ is bounded and uniformly continuous on $-\infty < x < \infty$.

Proof Write

$$\left| T\alpha(x) - T\alpha(x_0) \right| = \left| \frac{1}{\sqrt{2\pi}} \int_{-\infty}^\infty \alpha(y)\, (e^{-ixy} - e^{-ix_0y})dy \right|$$

$$= \left| \frac{1}{\sqrt{2\pi}} \int_{-\infty}^\infty \alpha(y)\, e^{-ix_0y}(e^{i(x_0-x)y} - 1)dy \right|.$$

Now

$$\left| e^{iy\,(x_0-x)} - 1 \right| = \left| e^{iy\,(x_0-x)} - 1 \right| \left| e^{-iy\,(x_0-x)/2} \right|$$

$$= \left| e^{iy\,(x_0-x)/2} - e^{-iy\,(x_0-x)/2} \right| = 2 \left| \sin y \, \frac{(x_0-x)}{2} \right|.$$

Hence

$$\left| T\alpha(x) - T\alpha(x_0) \right| \le \frac{2}{\sqrt{2\pi}} \left\{ \int_{-\infty}^{-N} + \int_{-N}^{N} + \int_{N}^{\infty} \right\} |\alpha(y)| \left| \sin y \, \frac{x_0-x}{2} \right| dy.$$

Choose N so large that the first and third integrals are each less than $\epsilon/3$. Then, since $|\sin u| < |u|$, there is a $\delta(\epsilon) = \epsilon \left(3N \int_{-\infty}^{\infty} |\alpha(y)| dy \right)^{-1}$ such that whenever $|x - x_0| < \delta$, we have

$$\int_{-N}^{N} |\alpha(y)| \, |\sin y \, \frac{x_0-x}{2}| \, dy \le \int_{-N}^{N} |\alpha(y)| \, \frac{N|x_0-x|}{2} \, dy$$

$$\le \frac{\delta}{2} N \int_{-\infty}^{\infty} |\alpha(y)| dy < \epsilon/3.$$

We have shown that there exists $\delta(\epsilon)$ such that

$$|T\alpha(x) - T\alpha(x_0)| < \epsilon \text{ for } |x - x_0| < \delta.$$

This proves the uniform continuity. That $T\alpha(x)$ is bounded follows from

(2) $$|T\alpha(x)| \le \frac{1}{\sqrt{2\pi}} \int_{-\infty}^{\infty} |\alpha(y)| \, dy.$$

The next theorem is the analogue of the Riemann-Lebesgue Theorem for Fourier series.

THEOREM 7.3B

$$\lim_{|x| \to \infty} T\alpha(x) = 0.$$

Proof We already know that

$$\lim_{x \to \infty} \int_{a}^{b} \alpha(y) \cos xy \, dy = 0 = \lim_{x \to \infty} \int_{a}^{b} \alpha(y) \sin xy \, dy$$

for any finite interval $a \le y \le b$. It is necessary to show that we can replace a by $-\infty$, b by ∞. Write

$$\int_{-\infty}^{\infty} \alpha(y) \cos xy \, dy = \left\{ \int_{-\infty}^{a} + \int_{a}^{b} + \int_{b}^{\infty} \right\} \alpha(y) \cos xy \, dy.$$

Since the integral on the left converges uniformly with respect to x on $-\infty < x < \infty$, we may choose a so small and b so large that the first and third integrals on the right are each less in absolute value than $\dfrac{\epsilon}{3}$. Then choose x so large that the second integral on the right is less in absolute value than $\dfrac{\epsilon}{3}$, using the Riemann-Lebesgue Theorem. We have proved that

$$\left| \int_{-\infty}^{\infty} \alpha(y) \cos xy \, dy \right| < \epsilon \text{ for } x > N(\epsilon).$$

That is, $\lim\limits_{x \to \infty} \int_{-\infty}^{\infty} \alpha(y) \cos xy \, dy = 0.$ ★

Let us now consider formal operations with this transform.

THEOREM 7.3C

Let a be a real number.

1. If $\beta(y) = \alpha(ay)$, $a \neq 0$, then $(T\beta)(x) = \dfrac{1}{|a|} (T\alpha)\left(\dfrac{x}{a}\right)$.

2. If $\beta(y) = \overline{\alpha(y)}$, then $(T\beta)(x) = \overline{(T\alpha)(-x)}$.

3. If $\beta(y) = e^{iya}\alpha(y)$, then $(T\beta)(x) = (T\alpha)(x - a)$.

4. If $\beta(y) = \alpha(y - a)$, then $(T\beta)(x) = e^{-ixa}(T\alpha)(x)$.

Proof We shall prove only the first relationship, leaving the others for the exercises. If $a \neq 0$,

$$T(\alpha(ay))(x) = \frac{1}{\sqrt{2\pi}} \int_{-\infty}^{\infty} \alpha(ay) \, e^{-ixy} dy$$

$$= \frac{1}{|a|\sqrt{2\pi}} \int_{-\infty}^{\infty} \alpha(t) \, e^{-ixt/a} \, dt = \frac{1}{|a|} (T\alpha)(x/a). \quad ★$$

THEOREM 7.3D

1. If α, α' are in $\mathscr{R}^*$, then $T(\alpha')(x) = ix(T\alpha)(x)$ and $\lim\limits_{|x| \to \infty} \alpha(x) = 0$.

2. If $\alpha(x)$ and $x\alpha(x)$ are in $\mathscr{R}^*$, then there exists

$$\frac{d}{dx}(T\alpha)(x) = T(-iy\alpha(y))(x).$$

Proof By writing

$$\alpha(b) - \alpha(a) = \int_{a}^{b} \alpha'(t) dt$$

and letting b approach ∞, we see that $\lim\limits_{x \to \infty} \alpha(x)$ exists. Then, since $\int_{-\infty}^{\infty} |\alpha(x)| \, dx < \infty$, we must have $\lim\limits_{x \to \infty} \alpha(x) = 0$. By letting a approach $-\infty$, we also obtain $\lim\limits_{x \to -\infty} \alpha(x) = 0$. Integrating by parts, for $x \neq 0$, we get

$$\sqrt{2\pi}\,(T\alpha)(x) = \int_{-\infty}^{\infty} \alpha(y)\, e^{-ixy} dy = \int_{-\infty}^{\infty} \alpha'(y)\, \frac{e^{-ixy}}{ix}\, dy,$$

so that

$$(T\alpha')(x) = ix(T\alpha)(x),$$

a result valid even when $x = 0$.

The integral

$$\int_{-\infty}^{\infty} \alpha(y) \frac{\partial}{\partial x}\, e^{-ixy}\, dy = \int_{-\infty}^{\infty} -\, iy\alpha(y)\, e^{-ixy}\, dy$$

converges uniformly on $-\infty < x < \infty$ since $x\alpha(x)$ is in $\mathscr{R}^*$. Theorem 7.1E now indicates that there exists

$$\frac{d}{dx}\,(T\alpha)(x) = -\, i \int_{-\infty}^{\infty} y\alpha(y)\, e^{-ixy}\, dy = -\, iT(y\alpha(y))\,(x). \quad \star$$

We have called T^* the adjoint transform when

$$(T^*\alpha)(x) = \frac{1}{\sqrt{2\pi}} \int_{-\infty}^{\infty} \alpha(y)\, e^{ixy}\, dy.$$

It satisfies the equation characteristic for the adjoint.

THEOREM 7.3E   For α and β in $\mathscr{R}^*$,

$$\int_{-\infty}^{\infty} (T\alpha)(x)\, \overline{\beta(x)} dx = \int_{-\infty}^{\infty} \alpha(x)\, \overline{(T^*\beta)(x)}\, dx.$$

Proof   The integrals exist since α and β are in $\mathscr{R}^*$, while the transforms are continuous and bounded. The theorem states that

$$\frac{1}{\sqrt{2\pi}} \int_{-\infty}^{\infty} \int_{-\infty}^{\infty} \alpha(y)\, e^{-ixy}\, dy\, \bar\beta(x) dx = \frac{1}{\sqrt{2\pi}} \int_{-\infty}^{\infty} \alpha(y) \int_{-\infty}^{\infty} \bar\beta(x)\, e^{-ixy}\, dx\, dy.$$

Thus the validity of the theorem depends upon the validity of an interchange of order of integration. For this we need only apply Theorem 7.1G. $\star$

Corollary 1

If α and σ are in $\mathcal{R}^*$, then

$$\int_{-\infty}^{\infty} (T\alpha)(x)\, \sigma(x)dx = \int_{-\infty}^{\infty} \alpha(x)\, (T\sigma)(x)dx.$$

Indeed, choosing $\bar{\beta}(x) = \sigma(x)$ in the theorem, and noting that $\overline{T^*\bar{\sigma}} = T\sigma$, we obtain the corollary.

In a sense, the Fourier transform of a function determines the function uniquely.

THEOREM 7.3F   If α and β are in $\mathcal{R}^*$, and $T\alpha = T\beta$, then α and β coincide at all points x where α and β are simultaneously continuous.

Proof   It suffices to show that if α is in $\mathcal{R}^*$ and $(T\alpha)(x) = 0$ for all x, then $\alpha(x) = 0$ at every point of continuity. For this purpose, define $\sigma(x, c, \epsilon)$ by

$$\sigma(x) = \begin{cases} 0 & , \quad x \le -c - \epsilon \ \text{ or } \ x \ge c + \epsilon, \\[2mm] \dfrac{c - x + \epsilon}{\epsilon}, & \quad c < x < c + \epsilon, \\[2mm] 1 & , \quad -c \le x \le c, \\[2mm] \dfrac{c + x + \epsilon}{\epsilon}, & \quad -c - \epsilon < x < -c. \end{cases}$$

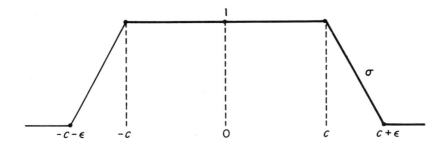

We shall show that $T\sigma$ is in $\mathcal{R}^*$. Since σ is an even function, for $x \ne 0$, we have

$$\sqrt{2\pi}\, T\sigma(x) = \int_{-\infty}^{\infty} \sigma(y)\, e^{-ixy}\, dy = \int_{-\infty}^{\infty} \sigma(y) \cos xy\, dy$$

$$= 2 \int_0^{c+\varepsilon} \sigma(y) \cos xy\, dy = 2\sigma(y) \frac{\sin xy}{x} \Big|_0^{c+\varepsilon} - 2 \int_c^{c+\varepsilon} \frac{\sin xy}{x} \left(-\frac{1}{\epsilon} \right) dy$$

$$= \frac{-2}{\epsilon x^2} \cos xy \Big|_c^{c+\varepsilon} = O\left(\frac{1}{x^2} \right),$$

Therefore

$$\int_{-\infty}^{\infty} |T\sigma(x)| \, dx < \infty.$$

By Theorem 7.2B,

$$\sigma(x) = \frac{1}{2\pi} \int_{-\infty}^{\infty} \int_{-\infty}^{\infty} \sigma(y) \, e^{it(x-y)} \, dy \, dt = \frac{1}{\sqrt{2\pi}} \int_{-\infty}^{\infty} (T\sigma)(t) \, e^{itx} \, dt$$

$$= \frac{1}{\sqrt{2\pi}} \int_{-\infty}^{\infty} (T\sigma)(-t) \, e^{-itx} \, dt = \frac{1}{\sqrt{2\pi}} \int_{-\infty}^{\infty} (T\sigma)(t) \, e^{-itx} \, dt,$$

the last equality being a consequence of the fact that the transform of an even function is an even function (Exercise 7.3–4).

It follows that $\sigma(x) = (T\mu)(x)$, where $\mu(x) = (T\sigma)(x)$. Applying part (4) of Theorem 7.3C and the corollary to Theorem 7.3E, we get

$$\int_{-\infty}^{\infty} \alpha(x - a) \, \sigma(x)dx = \int_{-\infty}^{\infty} \alpha(x - a) \, (T\mu)(x)dx = \int_{-\infty}^{\infty} \mu(x) \, T(\alpha(y - a)) \, (x) \, dx$$

$$= \int_{-\infty}^{\infty} \mu(x) \, e^{-ixa} \, (T\alpha) \, (x)dx = 0,$$

since we are assuming $(T\alpha) \, (x) = 0$. That is,

$$\int_{-c-\varepsilon}^{-c} \alpha(x - a) \, \sigma(x)dx + \int_{-c}^{c} \alpha(x - a)dx + \int_{c}^{c+\varepsilon} \alpha(x - a) \, \sigma(x)dx = 0.$$

Letting $\epsilon \to 0$ gives

$$\int_{-c}^{c} \alpha(x - a)dx = 0,$$

or, for all $c > 0$, all a,

$$\int_{-c-a}^{c-a} \alpha(y)dy = 0.$$

This implies that

$$\int_{r}^{s} \alpha(y)dy = 0$$

for arbitrary $r, s > r$, since we can always find $c > 0$, and a to satisfy $c - a = s$, $-c - a = r$. The final equation implies that $\alpha(x) = 0$ at every continuity point of α.

EXAMPLE 1   Consider the differential equation

(3)
$$\frac{d^2\beta}{dx^2} + 2\frac{d\beta}{dx} + x\beta = 0, \qquad -\infty < x < \infty.$$

Let us assume that the solution β is the Fourier transform of a function α in $\mathscr{R}^*$ with continuous derivative (See Exercise 7.3-3). The fact that β satisfies (3) imposes a restriction on α which we shall now seek.

We have

$$\beta = T\alpha, \quad \frac{d\beta}{dx} = \frac{d}{dx}\, T\alpha = T(-ix\alpha), \quad \frac{d^2\beta}{dx^2} = \frac{d}{dx}\, T(-ix\alpha) = T(-ix(-ix\alpha))$$
$$= T(-x^2\alpha),$$

where we assume that α, α', $x\alpha$, $x^2\alpha$ are in $\mathscr{R}^*$. Then (3) becomes

(4)
$$T(-x^2\alpha) + 2T(-ix\alpha) + xT\alpha = 0.$$

Again applying Theorem 7.3D, we obtain $xT\alpha = -iT\alpha'$, so that (4) becomes

(5)
$$T(-x^2\alpha - 2ix\alpha - i\alpha') = 0$$

and the uniqueness theorem yields

$$x^2\alpha + 2ix\alpha + i\alpha' = 0,$$

the solution of which may be verified to be

$$\alpha = c\, e^{\frac{ix^3}{3} - x^2}.$$

Then

$$\beta(x) = (T\alpha)(x) = \frac{c}{\sqrt{2\pi}} \int_{-\infty}^{\infty} e^{(iy^3/3) - y^2}\, e^{-ixy}\, dy = \frac{c}{\sqrt{2\pi}} \int_{-\infty}^{\infty} e^{-y^2}\, e^{i[(y^3/3) - xy]}dy$$

$$= \frac{c}{\sqrt{2\pi}} \int_{-\infty}^{\infty} \cos\left(\frac{y^3}{3} - xy\right)e^{-y^2}dy + \frac{ci}{\sqrt{2\pi}} \int_{-\infty}^{\infty} \sin\left(\frac{y^3}{3} - xy\right) e^{-y^2}\, dy.$$

(6)
$$\beta(x) = \frac{c}{\sqrt{2\pi}} \int_{-\infty}^{\infty} \cos\left(\frac{y^3}{3} - xy\right) e^{-y^2}\, dy.$$

Equation (3) has two linearly independent solutions. We have here obtained only one as a Fourier transform. We leave to the reader the verification that (6) is actually a solution.

EXAMPLE 2   Consider again the differential equation of Example 1 and assume β, β', β'' and $x\beta$ in $\mathscr{R}^*$. Let $\sigma = T\beta$ and note that

$$T\beta' = ixT\beta = ix\sigma, \quad T\beta'' = ixT\beta' = -x^2\sigma, \quad T(x\beta) = i\frac{d}{dx}T\beta = i\sigma'.$$

Thus, if we take the transform of both sides of (3), we get

$$- x^2\sigma + 2ix\sigma + i\sigma' = 0,$$

leading to $\sigma = c\,e^{(-ix^3/3)-x^2}$.
Then, by Theorem 7.2B,

$$\beta = \frac{c}{\sqrt{2\pi}}\int_{-\infty}^{\infty} e^{(-iy^3/3)-y^2}\,e^{ixy}\,dy$$

yielding (6).

EXAMPLE 3 Consider the difference differential equation

$$(7) \qquad \frac{d\alpha}{dx} + \alpha(x) + \alpha(x+2) = \frac{1}{x^2+1}, \qquad -\infty < x < \infty.$$

Assume α and α' in $\mathscr{R}^*$. When $\beta = T\alpha$, then $T\alpha' = ix\beta$ and $T(\alpha(x+2)) = e^{2ix}\beta$. Taking the transforms of both sides of (7), we get

$$ix\beta + \beta + e^{2ix}\beta = T\!\left(\frac{1}{x^2+1}\right) = \sqrt{\frac{\pi}{2}}\,e^{-|x|}$$

by Exercise 7.2–12. Thus

$$\beta(x) = \sqrt{\frac{\pi}{2}}\,\frac{e^{-|x|}}{1 + ix + e^{2ix}},$$

$$\alpha(x) = \frac{1}{\sqrt{2\pi}}\int_{-\infty}^{\infty} \beta(y)\,e^{ixy}\,dy = \tfrac{1}{2}\left\{\int_{-\infty}^{0} + \int_{0}^{\infty}\right\}\frac{e^{-|y|}\,e^{ixy}}{1 + iy + e^{2iy}}\,dy$$

$$= \tfrac{1}{2}\left(\int_{0}^{\infty}\frac{e^{-z}\,e^{-ixz}}{1 - iz + e^{-2iz}}\,dz + \int_{0}^{\infty}\frac{e^{-y}\,e^{ixy}}{1 + iy + e^{2iy}}\,dy\right)$$

$$= \int_{0}^{\infty} e^{-y}\left(\frac{\cos xy + y\sin yx + \cos(yx - 2y)}{2 + 2\cos 2y + 2y\sin 2y + y^2}\right)dy.$$

EXAMPLE 4 The temperature $\alpha(x, t)$ of an infinite homogeneous cylinder with insulated lateral surface satisfies the partial differential equation

$$(8) \qquad \frac{\partial\alpha}{\partial t} = k\,\frac{\partial^2\alpha}{\partial x^2}, \qquad -\infty < x < \infty, \qquad t > 0, \quad k > 0.$$

when the axis of the cylinder is taken to be the x-axis. We seek a solution assuming that we know the initial temperature $\alpha(x, 0) = \sigma(x)$. Let α be a solution in $\mathscr{R}^*$ for each t, and denote the Fourier transform of α by

$$\beta(x, t) = \frac{1}{\sqrt{2\pi}}\int_{-\infty}^{\infty} \alpha(y, t)\,e^{-ixy}\,dy.$$

Proceeding formally, we obtain

$$\frac{\partial \beta}{\partial t} = \frac{1}{\sqrt{2\pi}} \int_{-\infty}^{\infty} \frac{\partial \alpha}{\partial t}(y, t) \, e^{-ixy} \, dy = \frac{k}{\sqrt{2\pi}} \int_{-\infty}^{\infty} \frac{\partial^2 \alpha}{\partial x^2} e^{-ixy} \, dy.$$

When α and α' vanish at $x = \pm \infty$, integration by parts yields

$$\frac{\partial \beta}{\partial t} = -\frac{kx^2}{\sqrt{2\pi}} \int_{-\infty}^{\infty} \alpha(y, t) \, e^{-ixy} \, dy = -kx^2 \beta,$$

so that

$$\beta = c(x) \, e^{-kx^2 t}.$$

When $t = 0$, $c(x) = \beta(x, 0) = \dfrac{1}{\sqrt{2\pi}} \displaystyle\int_{-\infty}^{\infty} \sigma(y) \, e^{-ixy} \, dy = T\sigma.$

Hence

$$T\alpha = T\sigma \, e^{-kx^2 t},$$

$$\alpha = \frac{1}{2\pi} \int_{-\infty}^{\infty} \int_{-\infty}^{\infty} \alpha(u, t) \, e^{-iuy} \, du \, e^{iyx} \, dy = \frac{1}{\sqrt{2\pi}} \int_{-\infty}^{\infty} \beta(y, t) \, e^{iyx} \, dy$$

$$= \frac{1}{2\pi} \int_{-\infty}^{\infty} \int_{-\infty}^{\infty} \sigma(u) \, e^{-iyu} \, du \, e^{-ky^2 t} \, e^{iyx} \, dy$$

$$= \frac{1}{2\pi} \int_{-\infty}^{\infty} \int_{-\infty}^{\infty} \sigma(u) \, e^{-ky^2 t} \, e^{-iy(u-x)} \, du \, dy.$$

The solution may also be written as

(9) $$\alpha(x, t) = \frac{1}{\pi} \int_{0}^{\infty} \int_{-\infty}^{\infty} \sigma(u) \, e^{-ky^2 t} \cos y(u - x) \, du \, dy.$$

Assuming interchange of order of integration is permissible and using the fact that the Fourier cosine transform of $e^{-x^2/2}$ is $e^{-x^2/2}$ (Exercise 7.3–6), we can write equation (9) as

(10) $$\alpha(x, t) = \frac{1}{2\sqrt{\pi kt}} \int_{-\infty}^{\infty} \sigma(u) e^{-(x-u)^2/4kt} \, du, \qquad t > 0.$$

(See Exercise 7.3–8.)

Exercise 7.3
1. Show that the vector space $\mathscr{R}^*$ is not a Euclidean vector space with inner product $(\alpha, \beta) = \displaystyle\int_{-\infty}^{\infty} \alpha(x) \, \overline{\beta}(x) dx$.
2. Prove (2), (3), (4) of Theorem 7.3C.

3. (a) Show that if α, α', α'' are in $\mathscr{R}^*$, then $T\alpha$ is also in $\mathscr{R}^*$. *Hint:* Use the method indicated in Theorem 7.3D to show that $\lim\limits_{|x|\to\infty} \alpha(x) = 0$

$$= \lim_{|x|\to\infty} \alpha'(x).$$ Integrate by parts twice to get $(T\alpha)(x) = O(|x|^{-2})$ as $x \to \infty$.

    (b) Hence show that α is the Fourier transform of some function in $\mathscr{R}^*$.

4. Show that the Fourier transform of an even function is an even function.

5. Verify that (6) is a solution of (3).

6. (a) Use Example 2 of Section 7.1 to show that the Fourier cosine transform of $e^{-x^2/2}$ is $e^{-x^2/2}$.

    (b) Obtain the result in (a) as follows: Use the uniform convergence of

$$\cos xy = \sum_{n=0}^{\infty} \frac{(-1)^n (xy)^{2n}}{(2n)!} \quad \text{to get} \quad \sqrt{\frac{2}{\pi}} \int_0^\infty e^{-y^2/2} \cos xy \, dy$$

$$= \sqrt{\frac{2}{\pi}} \int_0^\infty e^{-y^2/2} dy + \sqrt{\frac{2}{\pi}} \sum_{n=1}^{\infty} \frac{x^{2n}(-1)^n}{(2n)!} \int_0^\infty y^{2n} e^{-y^2/2} dy.$$

The Gamma function $\Gamma(p) = \int_0^\infty x^{p-1} e^{-x} dx$, $p > 0$, satisfies $\Gamma(\tfrac{1}{2}) = \sqrt{\pi}$,

$\Gamma(p+1) = p\Gamma(p)$. When $x = y^2/2$, $\Gamma(p) = \int_0^\infty \frac{y^{2p-1}}{2p-1} e^{-y^2/2} dy$. Put

$2p - 1 = 2n$ and calculate the infinite sum. Hence show that the Fourier transform of $e^{-x^2/2}$ is $e^{-x^2/2}$.

7. Show that $x\, e^{-x^2/2}$ is its own Fourier Sine transform.

8. (a) Obtain (10) from (9).

    (b) Assuming $\sigma(x)$ is uniformly bounded and integrable over finite intervals, show that (10) is a solution of (8) for $t > 0$.

    (c) Show that $\lim\limits_{t\to 0} \alpha(x, t) = \sigma(x)$ when σ is continuous.

    (d) Show that (9) may be interpreted as an integral of solutions obtained from (8) by separating the variables, that is, by assuming $\alpha(x, t) = f(x) g(t)$, where the integral is adjusted so that it yields $\sigma(x)$ when $t = 0$.

9. In determining the plane flow through a slit in a rigid plane body, take the slit to be the segment $-a \le x \le a$. Assume an irrotational two-dimension perfect fluid flow entering the upper half plane through the slit, moving parallel to the y axis when $y = 0$. The equation determining the flow is $\dfrac{\partial^2 \phi}{\partial x^2} + \dfrac{\partial^2 \phi}{\partial y^2} = 0$ where $\phi(x, y)$ is called the scalar potential and has the property that the components of velocity along the x and y axes respectively are given by

$$u(x, y) = -\frac{\partial \phi}{\partial x}, \qquad v(x, y) = -\frac{\partial \phi}{\partial y}.$$

The boundary conditions at the slit are

$$v(x, 0) = \sigma(x), \text{ where } \sigma(x) = 0 \text{ for } |x| > a,$$

$$\phi(x, 0) = c, \text{ a constant, } |x| \le a.$$

The second boundary condition follows from the fact that the orthogonal trajectories of the stream lines $\left(\text{the latter given by } \dfrac{dx}{u} = \dfrac{dy}{v}\right)$ are surfaces along which ϕ is constant, and the streamlines at $y = 0$ are parallel to the y axis. Let

$$\alpha(x, y) = \frac{1}{\sqrt{2\pi}} \int_{-\infty}^{\infty} \phi(w, y)\, e^{-ixw}dw, \quad \beta(x) = \frac{1}{\sqrt{2\pi}} \int_{-\infty}^{\infty} \sigma(w)\, e^{-ixw}dw,$$

assume $\phi, \dfrac{\partial\phi}{\partial x}, \dfrac{\partial^2\phi}{\partial x^2}$ are in $\mathscr{R}^*$ for fixed y (see Exercise 3) and show that

$\dfrac{\partial^2\alpha}{\partial y^2} = x^2\alpha, \quad \dfrac{\partial\alpha}{\partial y}(x, 0) = -\beta(x)$. Obtain

$$\phi(x, y) = \frac{1}{\sqrt{2\pi}} \int_{-\infty}^{\infty} \frac{\beta(w)}{|w|}\, e^{-|w|y}\, e^{ixw}dw, \quad y > 0,$$

as a solution bounded in y.

10. Show that if $\alpha(x)$, $\alpha'(x)$, $x\alpha(x)$, $x^2\alpha(x)$ are in $\mathscr{R}^*$ and α satisfies $\alpha''(x) - x^2\alpha(x)$ $= r\alpha(x)$ for constant r, then $T\alpha$ satisfies the same equation.

11. Consider $\dfrac{\partial^4\alpha}{\partial x^4} + \dfrac{\partial^2\alpha}{\partial y^2} = 0$, $-\infty < x < \infty$, $y \geq 0$ where $\alpha(x, y)$ and its first 4 derivatives with respect to x are in $\mathscr{R}^*$ for each y and tend to 0 as $|x| \to \infty$. Let $\alpha(x, 0) = \sigma(x)$, $\dfrac{\partial\alpha}{\partial y}(x, 0) = 0$. For fixed y, let $\beta(x, y)$ be the Fourier transform of α. Assuming repeated differentiation under integral sign permissible, show that $\dfrac{\partial^2\beta}{\partial y^2} + x^4\beta = 0$. Show that $\beta = T\sigma(x)\cos x^2y$. Using an inversion theorem, show that

$$\alpha(x, y) = \frac{1}{\sqrt{2\pi}} \int_{-\infty}^{\infty} T\sigma(w)\, (\cos w^2y)\, e^{ixw}dw.$$

12. (a) Consider $\dfrac{\partial\alpha}{\partial t} = k\dfrac{\partial^2\alpha}{\partial x^2}$, $0 \leq x < \infty$, $t > 0$, $k > 0$, $\alpha(0, t) = 0$ for $t > 0$, $\alpha(x, 0) = \mu(x)$. Show how to obtain a formal solution from (10) by extending μ to be odd.

   (b) How would you obtain the solution if $\alpha(0, t) = c$, a constant, for $t > 0$, $c \neq 0$?

13. Show that $T\!\left(\dfrac{1}{x^2 + 1}\right) = \sqrt{\dfrac{\pi}{2}}\, e^{-|x|}$. Use Exercise 7.2–12.

14. The equation

$$\frac{d^2\alpha}{dx^2} - \frac{\alpha}{a^2} = \frac{-b}{a^2}\beta(x), \quad a \text{ and } b \text{ positive constants,}$$

arises in the one-dimensional case of neutron diffusion. Let $T\alpha$ and $T\beta$ be the Fourier transforms of α and β. Show that the differential equation formally becomes

$$T\alpha = b\,\frac{T\beta}{a^2x^2 + 1}.$$

Then

$$\alpha(x) = \frac{b}{\sqrt{2\pi}} \int_{-\infty}^{\infty} T\beta(y)\, \frac{1}{a^2y^2 + 1}\, e^{ixy}dy.$$

Use Exercise 13 to find $T\!\left(\dfrac{e^{ixy}}{a^2y^2 + 1}\right)$, and Corollary 1 of Theorem 7.3E to get

$$\alpha(x) = \frac{b}{2a} \int_{-\infty}^{\infty} \beta(y)\, e^{-|y-x|/a}dy.$$

7.4

THE

CONVOLUTION THEOREM AND

PARSEVAL'S FORMULA

Consider the integral

(1) $$\sigma(x) = \frac{1}{\sqrt{2\pi}} \int_{-\infty}^{\infty} \alpha(x - t)\, \beta(t)dt = \alpha * \beta$$

called the **convolution** of α and β. If α and β are members of $\mathscr{R}^*\{-\infty, \infty\}$, the space of functions σ having $\int_{-\infty}^{\infty} |\sigma(x)|dx < \infty$, the convolution of α and β may not exist for some values of x. Suppose, for example, that $\alpha(t) = \beta(-t)$, where $\int_{-\infty}^{\infty} |\alpha(x)|\, dx < \infty$ but $\int_{-\infty}^{\infty} |\alpha(x)|^2\, dx$ does not exist. Then $(\alpha * \alpha)(x)$ does not exist for $x = 0$. Nevertheless, the integral (1) exists for enough values of x to enable one to develop a theory for (1) when α and β are absolutely integrable in the Lebesgue sense. We shall not do this here. Instead we consider (1) only for functions α and β which are in $\mathscr{R}^*\{-\infty, \infty\}$ and also in $\mathscr{R}_2^*\{-\infty, \infty\}$, the class of functions σ with $\int_{-\infty}^{\infty} |\sigma(x)|^2\, dx < \infty$. Such functions will be said to belong to $\mathscr{R}^* \cap \mathscr{R}_2^*$. For α and β in $\mathscr{R}^* \cap \mathscr{R}_2^*$, the integral (1) exists for all x, since $\mathscr{R}_2^*$ is a Euclidean vector space with inner product

$$(\alpha, \beta) = \int_{-\infty}^{\infty} \alpha(x)\, \bar{\beta}(x)dx.$$

By Schwarz's inequality, we have

$$2\pi\, |\sigma(x)|^2 \leq \int_{-\infty}^{\infty} |\alpha(x - t)|^2\, dt \int_{-\infty}^{\infty} |\beta(t)|^2\, dt = \int_{-\infty}^{\infty} |\alpha(t)|^2\, dt \int_{-\infty}^{\infty} |\beta(t)|^2\, dt,$$

so that $\sigma(x)$ is bounded uniformly in x.

By a change of variable $y = x - t$ we obtain

$$(\alpha * \beta)(x) = \frac{1}{\sqrt{2\pi}} \int_{-\infty}^{\infty} \alpha(y)\, \beta(x - y)\, dy = (\beta * \alpha)(x)$$

showing that the convolution product is commutative.

THEOREM 7.4A   The convolution $\sigma(x) = \alpha * \beta$, for α and β in $\mathscr{R}^* \cap \mathscr{R}_2^*$, is uniformly bounded, continuous, and in $\mathscr{R}^* \cap \mathscr{R}_2^*$.

Proof We have already seen that σ is uniformly bounded. To prove the continuity consider first the case where α is continuous so that $\alpha(x - t)$ is continuous in both variables. The continuity of σ will be assured by Theorem 7.1D if the integral (1) converges uniformly. The uniform convergence is obtained by an application of the Cauchy criterion to the inequality

$$\left| \int_m^n \alpha(x - t)\,\beta(t)dt \right|^2 \leq \int_m^n |\alpha(t)|^2\,dt \int_m^n |\beta(x - t)|^2\,dt$$

$$\leq \int_m^n |\alpha(t)|^2\,dt \int_{-\infty}^\infty |\beta(t)|^2\,dt,$$

for the right side can be made less than ϵ when m, $n > m$ have the same sign and $|m|$, $|n|$ are sufficiently large.

Since $\alpha*\beta = \beta*\alpha$, we see that the convolution is continuous whenever one of α or β is continuous.

Suppose now that α and β are in $\mathscr{R}^* \cap \mathscr{R}_2^*$. Choose μ continuous, vanishing outside of a finite interval, and satisfying $\int_{-\infty}^\infty |\beta - \mu|^2\,dt < \epsilon^2 \left(16 \int_{-\infty}^\infty |\alpha(t)|^2\,dt \right)^{-1}$. Write

$$\sqrt{2\pi}\,\sigma(x) = \int_{-\infty}^\infty \alpha(x - t)(\beta(t) - \mu(t))dt + \int_{-\infty}^\infty \alpha(x - t)\,\mu(t)dt = I(x) + J(x).$$

Then

$$\sqrt{2\pi}\,|\sigma(x + h) - \sigma(x)| \leq |I(x + h) - I(x)| + |J(x + h) - J(x)|$$

which can be made less than ϵ for h sufficiently small, since $J(x)$ is continuous and

$$|I(x + h) - I(x)| \leq |I(x + h)| + |I(x)| \leq \left(\int_{-\infty}^\infty |\alpha(x + h - t)|^2\,dt \right.$$

$$\left. \int_{-\infty}^\infty |\beta(t) - \mu(t)|^2\,dt \right)^{1/2} + \left(\int_{-\infty}^\infty |\alpha(x - t)|^2\,dt \int_{-\infty}^\infty |\beta(t) - \mu(t)|^2\,dt \right)^{1/2}$$

$$= 2 \left(\int_{-\infty}^\infty |\alpha(t)|^2\,dt \int_{-\infty}^\infty |\beta - \mu|^2\,dt \right)^{1/2} < \epsilon/2.$$

This proves the continuity.

We have

$$\sqrt{2\pi} \int_c^d |\sigma(x)|\,dx \leq \int_c^d \int_{-\infty}^\infty |\alpha(x - t)|\,|\beta(t)|\,dt\,dx$$

$$= \int_{-\infty}^\infty \int_c^d |\alpha(x - t)|\,|\beta(t)|\,dx\,dt$$

the interchange being justified by Theorem 7.1F since $\int_{-\infty}^{\infty} |\alpha(x - t)||\beta(t)| \, dt$ converges uniformly in x. Therefore,

$$\sqrt{2\pi} \int_{c}^{d} |\sigma(x)| \, dx \leq \int_{-\infty}^{\infty} |\beta(t)| \int_{-\infty}^{\infty} |\alpha(x - t)| dx \, dt = \int_{-\infty}^{\infty} |\beta(t)| \int_{-\infty}^{\infty} |\alpha(x)| \, dx \, dt$$

$$= \int_{-\infty}^{\infty} |\beta(t)| dt \int_{-\infty}^{\infty} |\alpha(t)| \, dt.$$

Letting $d \to \infty$, $c \to -\infty$, yields

$$\sqrt{2\pi} \int_{-\infty}^{\infty} |\sigma(x)| \, dx \leq \int_{-\infty}^{\infty} |\alpha(t)| \, dt \int_{-\infty}^{\infty} |\beta(t)| \, dt.$$

Since we have proved that σ is in $\mathscr{R}^*$ and that it is uniformly bounded, it follows at once that σ is in $\mathscr{R}_2^*$, for $|\sigma(x)| \leq M$ implies

$$\int_{-\infty}^{\infty} |\sigma(x)|^2 \, dx \leq M \int_{-\infty}^{\infty} |\sigma(x)| \, dx. \quad \star$$

One of the most important properties of the convolution relates to its Fourier transform.

THEOREM 7.4B

$$T(\alpha * \beta) = T\alpha \cdot T\beta$$

Proof

$$T(\alpha * \beta) = \frac{1}{\sqrt{2\pi}} \int_{-\infty}^{\infty} \sigma(y) \, e^{-ixy} \, dy = \frac{1}{2\pi} \int_{-\infty}^{\infty} \int_{-\infty}^{\infty} \alpha(y - t) \, \beta(t) \, e^{-ixy} \, dt \, dy.$$

If we could interchange the order of integration we would have

$$T(\alpha * \beta) = \frac{1}{2\pi} \int_{-\infty}^{\infty} \beta(t) \, e^{-itx} \int_{-\infty}^{\infty} \alpha(y - t) \, e^{-i(y-t)x} \, dy \, dt$$

$$= \frac{1}{2\pi} \int_{-\infty}^{\infty} \beta(t) \, e^{-itx} \int_{-\infty}^{\infty} \alpha(w) \, e^{-iwx} \, dw \, dt$$

$$= \frac{T\alpha}{\sqrt{2\pi}} \int_{-\infty}^{\infty} \beta(t) \, e^{-itx} \, dt = T\alpha \cdot T\beta$$

The interchange is justified by Theorem 7.1G (Exercise 7.4–3). $\star$

EXAMPLE 1   Consider the integral equation

$$\int_{-\infty}^{\infty} \alpha(x - t) \, \alpha(t) dt + 3 \, \alpha(t) = \beta(t)$$

Taking the transform of both sides, we obtain

$$\sqrt{2\pi}\, T(\alpha*\alpha) + 3\, T\alpha = T\beta,$$

$$\sqrt{2\pi}\, (T\alpha)^2 + 3\, T\alpha - T\beta = 0,$$

$$T\alpha = \frac{-3 \pm \sqrt{9 + 4\sqrt{2\pi}\, T\beta}}{2\sqrt{2\pi}}.$$

For each x, we may choose either the $+$ sign or the $-$ sign. Finally an infinity of solutions is represented by

$$\alpha(x) = \frac{1}{4\pi} \int_{-\infty}^{\infty} \left(-3 \pm \left(9 + 4 \int_{-\infty}^{\infty} \beta(y)\, e^{-iyw}\, dy \right)^{1/2} \right) e^{iwx}\, dw.$$

The next results are related to Parseval's equality in the theory of Fourier series.

THEOREM 7.4C Let α and β be in $\mathscr{R}^* \cap \mathscr{R}_2^*$. Then $T\alpha$ and $T\beta$ are in $\mathscr{R}_2^*$ and

$$(2) \qquad \int_{-\infty}^{\infty} T\alpha(x)\, \overline{T\beta}(x)\, dx = \int_{-\infty}^{\infty} \alpha(x)\, \bar\beta(x)\, dx.$$

In particular,

$$(3) \qquad \int_{-\infty}^{\infty} |T\alpha(x)|^2\, dx = \int_{-\infty}^{\infty} |\alpha(x)|^2\, dx.$$

Proof Consider first the case when α and β have three continuous derivatives and vanish outside a finite interval. By Exercise 7.3–3, $T\alpha$ and $T\beta$ are in $\mathscr{R}^*$. We have

$$\alpha(x) = \frac{1}{2\pi} \int_{-\infty}^{\infty} \int_{-\infty}^{\infty} \alpha(y)\, e^{-iyt}\, e^{itx}\, dy\, dt = \frac{1}{\sqrt{2\pi}} \int_{-\infty}^{\infty} T\alpha(t)\, e^{itx}\, dt,$$

so that

$$\int_{-\infty}^{\infty} \alpha(x)\, \bar\beta(x)\, dx = \frac{1}{\sqrt{2\pi}} \int_{-\infty}^{\infty} \int_{-\infty}^{\infty} T\alpha(t)\, e^{itx}\, \bar\beta(x)\, dt\, dx.$$

An interchange of order of integration is permissible by Theorem 7.1G. Then

$$\int_{-\infty}^{\infty} \alpha(x)\, \bar\beta(x)\, dx = \int_{-\infty}^{\infty} \frac{1}{\sqrt{2\pi}} \int_{-\infty}^{\infty} \bar\beta(x)\, e^{itx}\, dx\, T\alpha(t)\, dt = \int_{-\infty}^{\infty} T\alpha(t)\, \overline{T\beta}(t)\, dt.$$

This proves (2) and (3) when α and β have the properties assigned above.

Next we shall prove that $T\alpha$ is in $\mathscr{R}_2^*$ when α is in $\mathscr{R}^* \cap \mathscr{R}_2^*$. We may select a sequence of infinitely differentiable functions α_n with $|\alpha_n(x)| \leq |\alpha(x)|$ such that α_n vanish outside a finite interval and satisfy $\int_{-\infty}^{\infty} |\alpha_n(x) - \alpha(x)| dx < \frac{1}{n}$. Then

$$|T\alpha_n(x) - (T\alpha)(x)| \leq \frac{1}{\sqrt{2\pi}} \int_{-\infty}^{\infty} |\alpha_n(y) - \alpha(y)| dy$$

indicates that $T\alpha_n$ converge uniformly to $T\alpha$.

By what we have already proved,

$$\int_a^b |T\alpha_n|^2 \, dx \leq \int_{-\infty}^{\infty} |T\alpha_n|^2 \, dx = \int_{-\infty}^{\infty} |\alpha_n|^2 \, dx \leq \int_{-\infty}^{\infty} |\alpha|^2 \, dx.$$

Letting $n \to \infty$,

$$\int_a^b |T\alpha|^2 \, dx \leq \int_{-\infty}^{\infty} |\alpha|^2 \, dx.$$

Finally letting $a \to -\infty$, $b \to \infty$, we obtain

(4) $$\int_{-\infty}^{\infty} |T\alpha|^2 \, dx \leq \int_{-\infty}^{\infty} |\alpha|^2 \, dx,$$

so that $T\alpha$ is in $\mathscr{R}_2^*$.

Here is a proof of (3). Let $\beta(n)$ be a sequence of infinitely differentiable functions with $|\beta_n| \leq |\alpha|$, β_n vanishing outside a finite interval, and satisfying $\int_{-\infty}^{\infty} |\beta_n(x) - \alpha(x)|^2 \, dx < \frac{1}{n}$. The inequality

(5) $$\left| \|\beta_n\| - \|\alpha\| \right| \leq \|\beta_n - \alpha\|$$

shows that

(6) $$\lim_{n \to \infty} \int_{-\infty}^{\infty} |\beta_n(x)|^2 \, dx = \int_{-\infty}^{\infty} |\alpha(x)|^2 \, dx.$$

Replace α in (4) by $\beta_n - \alpha$ to get

$$\left| \|T\beta_n\| - \|T\alpha\| \right|^2 \leq \|T\beta_n - T\alpha\|^2 = \int_{-\infty}^{\infty} |T(\beta_n - \alpha)|^2 \, dx$$

$$\leq \int_{-\infty}^{\infty} |\beta_n - \alpha|^2 \, dx,$$

and hence

(7) $$\lim_{n \to \infty} \int_{-\infty}^{\infty} |T\beta_n|^2 \, dx = \int_{-\infty}^{\infty} |T\alpha|^2 \, dx.$$

However, we have already seen that

$$\int_{-\infty}^{\infty} |T\beta_n|^2 \, dx = \int_{-\infty}^{\infty} |\beta_n|^2 \, dx.$$

If we let $n \to \infty$, and use (6) and (7) we derive (3).

We can now obtain (2) from (3). Indeed by (3) we have

(8) $(\alpha + \beta, \alpha + \beta) = (T(\alpha + \beta), T(\alpha + \beta))$

and if we expand both sides and use (3) again, we find that the real parts of (α, β) and $(T\alpha, T\beta)$ are equal. Replacing $\alpha + \beta$ in (8) by $\alpha + i\beta$ leads to equality of the imaginary parts of (α, β) and $(T\alpha, T\beta)$.   ★

Corollary 1
If α and β are in $\mathscr{R}^* \cap \mathscr{R}_2^*$, so is $T(\alpha*\beta)$.

Corollary 2
If α and β are in $\mathscr{R}^* \cap \mathscr{R}_2^*$, then $\alpha*\beta = T^*T(\alpha*\beta)$.

Proof   Let $\sigma(x, t) = \overline{\beta(x - t)}$. Then the theorem implies

$$\int_{-\infty}^{\infty} \alpha(t) \, \beta(x - t) dt = \int_{-\infty}^{\infty} \alpha(t) \, \bar{\sigma}(x, t) dt = \int_{-\infty}^{\infty} T\alpha \, \overline{T\sigma} \, dt$$

$$= \int_{-\infty}^{\infty} T\alpha(t) \, \overline{T\bar{\beta}(x - t)} dt = \int_{-\infty}^{\infty} T\alpha(t) \, T\beta(x + t) dt = \int_{-\infty}^{\infty} T\alpha(t) \, T\beta(t) \, e^{ixt} \, dt$$

$$= \int_{-\infty}^{\infty} T(\alpha*\beta) \, e^{ixt} \, dt = T^*T(\alpha*\beta)\sqrt{2\pi}.   ★$$

Corollary 3
Let α and β be real functions in $\mathscr{R}\{0, \infty\}$ and $\mathscr{R}_2\{0, \infty\}$. Then $T_c\alpha, T_s\alpha,$ $T_c\beta, T_s\beta$ are also members of these sets and

$$\int_0^{\infty} T_c\alpha(x) \, T_c\beta(x) dx = \int_0^{\infty} \alpha(x) \, \beta(x) dx.$$

$$\int_0^{\infty} T_s\alpha(x) \, T_s\beta(x) dx = \int_0^{\infty} \alpha(x) \, \beta(x) dx.$$

For, if α and β are extended to be even on $-\infty < x < \infty$, we obtain $T\alpha = T_c\alpha, T\beta = T_c\beta$, with $T\alpha$ and $T\beta$ even. Then the theorem yields the first desired result. If α and β are odd, $T\alpha = -i \, T_s\alpha, \overline{T\beta} = i \, T_s\beta.$

EXAMPLE 2   Show that

$$\int_0^\infty \frac{dx}{(a^2 + x^2)(b^2 + x^2)} = \frac{\pi}{2ab(a + b)}, \quad a > 0, b > 0.$$

We have, from Example 1, Section 7.1,

$$T_c(e^{-ax}) = \sqrt{\frac{2}{\pi}} \frac{a}{a^2 + x^2}.$$

Hence, if $\alpha(x) = e^{-ax}$, $\beta(x) = e^{-bx}$, Corollary 3 states that

$$\int_0^\infty T_c\alpha\, T_c\beta\, dx = \int_0^\infty e^{-(a+b)x}\, dx = \frac{1}{a + b}.$$

This is the desired result.

There is a certain aspect of symmetry in many of these formulas. For example, Corollary 2 of the last theorem indicates that the inverse Fourier transform of $T(\alpha*\beta)$ returns $\alpha*\beta$. There is, however, an element of asymmetry. If α is in $\mathscr{R}^* \cap \mathscr{R}_2^*$, its Fourier transform is in $\mathscr{R}_2^*$ but not necessarily in $\mathscr{R}^*$. Thus the Fourier transform does not carry a set of functions into itself. A theory has been developed for Fourier transforms of functions restricted only to lie in $\mathscr{R}_2^*$. For this purpose it is necessary to define what is meant by the Fourier transform of a function in $\mathscr{R}_2^*$. Let

$$(9) \qquad T_n\alpha(x) = \frac{1}{\sqrt{2\pi}} \int_{-n}^n \alpha(t)\, e^{-ixt}\, dt, \qquad n > 0, \quad -\infty < x < \infty.$$

If α_n are defined by

$$\alpha_n(x) = \begin{cases} \alpha(x) & -n \le x \le n, \\ 0 & |x| > n, \end{cases}$$

then $T_n\alpha(x)$ may also be defined by

$$(10) \qquad\qquad T_n\alpha(x) = T\alpha_n(x) = \frac{1}{\sqrt{2\pi}} \int_{-\infty}^\infty \alpha_n(t)\, e^{-ixt}\, dt.$$

Therefore, $T_n\alpha$ is uniformly bounded, continuous, and in $\mathscr{R}_2^*$ in view of Theorems 7.3A and 7.4C.

If there is a function β in $\mathscr{R}_2^*$ such that

$$\lim_{n\to\infty} \|T\alpha_n - \beta\| = 0,$$

that is,

$$\lim_{n\to\infty} \int_{-\infty}^\infty |T\alpha_n(x) - \beta(x)|^2\, dx = 0,$$

then we say β is the **Fourier-Plancherel transform** of α, and write $\beta = T\alpha$. The adjoint transform $T^*\alpha$ is similarly defined by replacing $-i$ by i in (9).

If α is also in $\mathscr{R}^*$, then the Fourier transform $T\alpha$ will serve as β. For, in this case, we may use Theorem 7.4C to write

$$\int_{-\infty}^{\infty} |T\alpha_n(x) - T\alpha(x)|^2 \, dx = \int_{-\infty}^{\infty} |T(\alpha_n - \alpha)(x)|^2 \, dx = \int_{-\infty}^{\infty} |\alpha_n - \alpha|^2 \, dx$$

$$= \int_{|x|>n} |\alpha(x)|^2 \, dx < \epsilon, \qquad \text{when } n > N(\epsilon).$$

It may be proved that if α has a Fourier-Plancherel transform $T\alpha$, then

(a) $\|T\alpha\| = \|\alpha\|$,

(b) $T^*T\alpha = \alpha$ (as vectors in $\mathscr{R}_2^*$).

For proofs using only Riemann integration, the reader is referred to the article *The Fourier Transform and Mean Convergence* by E. J. McShane, *American Mathematical Monthly*, March 1961, Vol. 68, #3.

Exercise 7.4

1. Show that if, for every $\epsilon > 0$, there is a decomposition of $\sigma(x)$ into two functions, $\sigma(x) = \alpha(x) + \beta(x)$ (which may depend on ϵ), such that $|\beta(x)| < \epsilon$ for all x in an interval about x_0, and such that $\alpha(x)$ is continuous at x_0, then $\sigma(x)$ is continuous at x_0. Note how this method is used in Theorem 7.4A.

2. (a) Let α, β, σ be in $\mathscr{R}^* \cap \mathscr{R}_2^*$. Show that, for constants a and b, $\sigma*(a\alpha + b\beta) = a\sigma*\alpha + b\sigma*\beta$.
    (b) Show that $\alpha*(\beta*\sigma) = (\alpha*\beta)*\sigma$.
    Hint: There is a question of interchange of order of integration. Show that both sides exist. Show that $\int_c^d \alpha(x - t) \int_{-\infty}^{\infty} \beta(t - y) \, \sigma(y) \, dy \, dt = \int_{-\infty}^{\infty} \int_c^d \alpha(x - t) \, \beta(t - y) \, \sigma(y) \, dt \, dy$, and finally (b).
    (c) Prove the result in (b) by applying Theorem 7.4B to $T(\alpha*(\beta*\sigma))$ and then using Theorem 7.3F.

3. Justify the interchange of order of integration in Theorem 7.4B. Begin by writing
$$\int_{-\infty}^{\infty} \int_{-\infty}^{\infty} \beta(t) \, \alpha(y - t) \, e^{-ixy} dy \, dt = \int_{-\infty}^{\infty} \int_{-\infty}^{\infty} \beta(t) \, \alpha(v) \, e^{-ix(v+t)} dv \, dt.$$

4. Let $\alpha(x) = \begin{cases} 1, & 0 < x < y, \\ 0, & x > y, \end{cases} \qquad \beta(x) = \begin{cases} 1, & 0 < x < u, \\ 0, & x > u. \end{cases}$

Show that $T_c\alpha = \sqrt{\dfrac{2}{\pi}} \dfrac{\sin yx}{x}$, $T_c\beta = \sqrt{\dfrac{2}{\pi}} \dfrac{\sin ux}{x}$, and
$$\int_0^{\infty} \frac{\sin xy \sin ux}{x^2} \, dx = \frac{\pi}{2} \min(y, u).$$

Note that $T_c\alpha$ and $T_c\beta$ are not in $\mathscr{R}^*$.

5. Take $\alpha(x) = e^{-ax}$, $a > 0$, $\beta(x)$ as in Exercise 4 and show that
$$\int_0^\infty \frac{\sin xu}{x(a^2 + x^2)}\, dx = \frac{\pi}{2} \frac{1 - e^{-au}}{a^2}.$$

6. If $\beta = \alpha * \alpha * \alpha * \ldots * \alpha$, α being repeated n times, show that $T\beta = (T\alpha)^n$.

7. Show that a formal solution of
$$\alpha(x) + \int_0^\infty \alpha(x - t)\, e^{-t} dt = \frac{1}{x^2 + 1}$$

is

$$\alpha(x) = \tfrac{1}{2} \int_{-\infty}^\infty e^{itx} \frac{1 + it}{2 + it} e^{-|t|}\, dt.$$

Hint: Replace e^{-t} by
$$\beta(t) = \begin{cases} e^{-t}, & t > 0 \\ 0, & t \le 0. \end{cases}$$

8. Find the Fourier transform of
$$\beta(x) = \begin{cases} e^{-x}, & x > 0 \\ 0, & x \le 0. \end{cases}$$

Is it in $\mathcal{R}*$?

9. (a) In this problem, let α and β be defined in $-\infty < x < \infty$ and equal 0 for $-\infty < x < 0$. If $s = x + iy$, x and y real, the function

$$(L\alpha)(s) = \int_0^\infty e^{-st} \alpha(t) dt$$

is called the **Laplace transform** of α, and is defined for those values of s for which the integral converges. In the study of Laplace transforms, the function

$$(\alpha \star \beta)(x) = \int_0^x \alpha(t)\, \beta(x - t) dt$$

is called the convolution of α and β. Show that

$$(L\alpha)(s) = T\left(\sqrt{2\pi}\, e^{-xt}\, \alpha(t) \right)(y), \quad (\alpha * \beta)(x) = \frac{1}{\sqrt{2\pi}} (\alpha \star \beta)(x).$$

(b) Show that, if $e^{-xt}\alpha(t)$ and $e^{-xt}\beta(t)$ are in $\mathcal{R}* \cap \mathcal{R}_2^*$, then $L(\alpha \star \beta) = L\alpha \cdot L\beta$.

(c) If also α and β are continuous on $0 \le x < \infty$, and $L\alpha = L\beta$ along the line $s = x + iy$, x fixed, then $\alpha(t) = \beta(t)$ for all t.

APPENDIX

The following theorem on the differentiation of an integral with respect to a parameter contained in the integrand and in the limits of integration is frequently used.

THEOREM Let $f(t)$ and $g(t)$ be continuous on $a \le t \le b$, and $K(t, u)$ and $K_t(t, u)$ be continuous on the closed set $\mathscr{S}$ defined by $a \le t \le b$, $\min [f(t),\ g(t)] \le u(t) \le \max [f(t),\ g(t)]$. Here the statement regarding $K_t(t, u)$ means K_t exists in the interior of $\mathscr{S}$ and has continuous limits on the boundary. Let $h(u)$ be bounded and integrable on g.l.b.$\{\min [f(t), g(t)] \mid a \leq t \leq b\} \leq u \leq$ l.u.b. $\{\max [f(t), g(t)] \mid a \leq t \leq b\}$ and let $\phi(t) = \int_{f(t)}^{g(t)} K(t, u) h(u) du$. If f and g have derivatives at $t = c$, and h is continuous at $u = f(c)$ and $u = g(c)$, then there exists

$$\phi'(c) = \int_{f(c)}^{g(c)} K_t(c, u) h(u) du + K(c, g(c)) h(g(c)) g'(c) - K(c, f(c)) h(f(c)) f'(c).$$

(At $c = a$ or b we consider right or left hand derivatives respectively.)

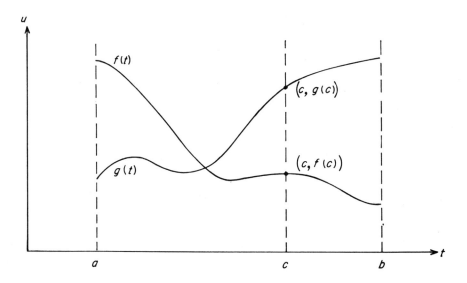

Proof Consider first the case when $f(c) < g(c)$. By continuity, there is a $\delta > 0$ such that for all points t in the interval

$$\mathcal{T} = \left\{ t \,\middle|\, |t - c| \leq \delta, \quad a \leq t \leq b \right\}$$

we have

$$f(c) + \alpha + |t - c| < g(c) - \beta - |t - c|,$$

where

$$\alpha(t) = \begin{cases} f(t) - f(c), & \text{if } f(t) - f(c) > 0, \\ 0 & , \text{if } f(t) - f(c) \leq 0 \end{cases} \qquad \beta(t) = \begin{cases} g(c) - g(t), & \text{if } g(c) - g(t) > 0, \\ 0 & , \text{if } g(c) - g(t) \leq 0. \end{cases}$$

For t in $\mathcal{T}$, write

$$\phi(t) - \phi(c) = \int_{f(t)}^{g(t)} K(t, u)\, h(u)\, du - \int_{f(c)}^{g(c)} K(c, u)\, h(u)\, du$$

$$= \left\{ \int_{f(t)}^{f(c)+\alpha+|t-c|} + \int_{f(c)+\alpha+|t-c|}^{g(c)-\beta-|t-c|} + \int_{g(c)-\beta-|t-c|}^{g(t)} \right\} K(t, u)\, h(u)\, du$$

$$- \left\{ \int_{f(c)}^{f(c)+\alpha+|t-c|} + \int_{f(c)+\alpha+|t-c|}^{g(c)-\beta-|t-c|} + \int_{g(c)-\beta-|t-c|}^{g(c)} \right\} K(c, u)\, h(u)\, du$$

$$= \int_{f(t)}^{f(c)+\alpha+|t-c|} K(t, u)\, h(u)\, du + \int_{g(c)-\beta-|t-c|}^{g(t)} K(t, u)\, h(u)\, du$$

$$- \int_{f(c)}^{f(c)+\alpha+|t-c|} K(c, u)\, h(u)\, du - \int_{g(c)-\beta-|t-c|}^{g(c)} K(c, u)\, h(u)\, du$$

$$+ \int_{f(c)+\alpha+|t-c|}^{g(c)-\beta-|t-c|} h(u)\Big(K(t, u) - K(c, u) \Big)\, du.$$

Using the mean value theorem of integral calculus on the first four integrals and the mean value theorem of differential calculus on the integrand of the last integral, we obtain for t in $\mathcal{T}$, $t \neq c$,

$$\frac{\phi(t) - \phi(c)}{t - c} = L_1(t)\left(\frac{f(c) - f(t)}{t - c} + \frac{\alpha}{t - c} + \frac{|t - c|}{t - c} \right)$$

$$+ L_2(t)\left(\frac{g(t) - g(c)}{t - c} + \frac{\beta}{t - c} + \frac{|t - c|}{t - c} \right)$$

$$- L_3(t)\left(\frac{\alpha}{t - c} + \frac{|t - c|}{t - c} \right) - L_4(t)\left(\frac{\beta}{t - c} + \frac{|t - c|}{t - c} \right)$$

$$+ \int_{f(c)+\alpha+|t-c|}^{g(c)-\beta-|t-c|} K_t(c + \theta(t - c), u)\, h(u)\, du,$$

where $L_1(t)$ and $L_2(t)$ lie between the g.l.b. and l.u.b. of $h(u)\, K(t, u)$ on the respective intervals $f(t) \leq u \leq f(c) + \alpha + |t - c|$, $g(c) - \beta - |t - c|$ $\leq u \leq g(t)$; $L_3(t)$ and $L_4(t)$ lie between the g.l.b. and l.u.b. of $h(u)\, K(c, u)$ on the respective intervals $f(c) \leq u \leq f(c) + \alpha + |t - c|$, $g(c) - \beta - |t - c|$ $\leq u \leq g(c)$; and $0 \leq \theta(t) \leq 1$. As $t \to c$, the sum of the first four terms approaches $K(c, g(c))\, h(g(c))\, g'(c) - K(c, f(c))\, h(f(c))\, f'(c)$. It remains to verify that the last term approaches $\int_{f(c)}^{g(c)} K_t(c, u)\, h(u)\, du$. In view of the uniform continuity over $\mathcal{S}$, there is a $\delta_1(\epsilon) > 0$ such that

$$|K_t(t, u) - K_t(c, u)| < \epsilon \text{ for } |t - c| < \delta_1, \qquad (t, u) \text{ in } \mathcal{S}.$$

We may also take δ_1 so small that

$$\left| \left\{ \int_{f(c)}^{g(c)} - \int_{f(c)+\alpha+|t-c|}^{g(c)-\beta-|t-c|} \right\} h(u)\, K_t(c, u)du \right| < \epsilon \text{ for } |t - c| < \delta_1.$$

Therefore, whenever t is in $\mathcal{T}$, and $|t - c| < \delta_1$, we have

$$\left| \int_{f(c)}^{g(c)} K_t(c, u)\, h(u)du - \int_{f(c)+\alpha+|t-c|}^{g(c)-\beta-|t-c|} h(u)\, K_t(c + \delta(t - c), u)\, du \right| \le$$

$$\left| \left\{ \int_{f(c)}^{g(c)} - \int_{f(c)+\alpha+|t-c|}^{g(c)-\beta-|t-c|} \right\} K_t(c, u)\, h(u)du \right| + \left| \int_{f(c)+\alpha+|t-c|}^{g(c)-\beta-|t-c|} h(u)\Big(K_t(c, u) \right.$$

$$\left. - K_t(c + \theta(t - c), u)\, du \right| \le \epsilon + \epsilon \int_{f(c)}^{g(c)} |h(u)|\, du.$$

This proves the theorem if $f(c) < g(c)$. In case $f(c) > g(c)$, we consider $-\phi = \int_{g(t)}^{f(t)} K(t, u)\, h(u)du$. Finally, if $f(c) = g(c)$, we need only show there exists

$$\phi'(c) = K(c, f(c))\, h(f(c))\Big(g'(c) - f'(c) \Big).$$

In this case, we obtain

$$\frac{\phi(t) - \phi(c)}{t - c} = \int_{f(t)}^{g(t)} \frac{K(t, u)}{t - c} h(u)du = L(t)\left(\frac{g(t) - f(t)}{t - c} \right)$$

$$= L(t)\left(\frac{g(t) - g(c)}{t - c} - \frac{f(t) - f(c)}{t - c} \right)$$

where $L(t)$ lies between the g.l.b. and l.u.b. of $h(u)\, K(t, u)$ on the interval $\min\,[f(t), g(t)] \le u \le \max\,[f(t),\, g(t)]$. From this the desired result follows. ★

BIBLIOGRAPHY

Chapters 1 and 2

1. Birkhoff, G. and MacLane, S., *A Survey of Modern Algebra*, 2nd Ed., Macmillan, New York, 1953.
2. Gelfond, I. M., *Lectures on Linear Algebra*, Interscience, New York, 1961.
3. Halmos, P. R., *Finite Dimensional Vector Spaces*, 2nd Ed., Van Nostrand, Princeton, N.J., 1958.
4. Hoffman, K. and Kunze, R., *Linear Algebra*, Prentice Hall, Englewood Cliffs, N.J., 1961.
5. Thrall, R. M. and Thornheim, L., *Vector Spaces and Matrices*, Wiley, New York, 1957.

Chapter 3

1. Graves, L. M., *The Theory of Functions of Real Variables*, 2nd Ed., McGraw-Hill, New York, 1956.
2. Mendelson, B., *Introduction to Topology*, Allyn and Bacon, Boston, 1962.

Chapter 4

1. Courant, R. and Hilbert, D., *Methods of Mathematical Physics*, Vol. 1, Interscience, New York, 1953.
2. Lovitt, S. V., *Linear Integral Equations*, McGraw-Hill, New York, 1924.
3. Smithies, F., *Integral Equations*, Cambridge, London, 1958.
4. Tricomi, F., *Integral Equations*, Interscience, New York, 1957.
5. Yosida, K., *Lectures on Differential and Integral Equations*, Interscience, New York, 1960.

Chapter 5

1. Berberian, S. K., *Introduction to Hilbert Space*, Oxford, New York, 1961.
2. Erdelyi, A., *Operational Calculus and Generalized Functions*, Holt, Rinehart, and Winston, New York, 1962.
3. Jackson, D., *Fourier Series and Orthogonal Polynomials*, Carus Monograph No. 6, Collegiate Press, Menasha, Wisc., 1941.
4. Lighthill, M. J., *Introduction to Fourier Analysis and Generalized Functions*, Cambridge, London, 1958.
5. Sansone, G., *Orthogonal Functions*, Interscience, New York, 1959.
6. Schwartz, G., *Theorie des distributions*, 2 vols. Hermann and Cie, Paris, 1950–51.
7. Stone, M. H., *Developments in Legendre Polynomials*, Annals of Math., 2nd series, Vol. 27, Princeton, N.J., 1926, pp. 315–329.
    Developments in Hermite Polynomials, Annals of Math., 2nd series, Vol. 29, 1928, pp. 1–13.
8. Szego, G., *Orthogonal Polynomials*, Colloquium Publication, V 23 a, American Mathematical Society, New York, 1959.

Chapter 6

1. Coddington, E. A. and Levinson, N., *Theory of Ordinary Differential Equations*, McGraw-Hill, New York, 1955.
2. Ince, E. L., *Ordinary Differential Equations*, Dover, New York, 1926.
3. Titchmarsh, E. C., *Eigenfunction Expansions*, Part 1, 2nd Ed., Clarendon, Oxford, Eng., 1962.

Chapter 7

1. Apostol, Y. M., *Mathematical Analysis*, Addison-Wesley, Reading, Mass., 1957.
2. Bochner, S. and Chandrasekharan, K., *Fourier Transforms*, Princeton, N.J., 1949.
3. Titchmarsh, E. C., *Introduction to Theory of Fourier Integrals*, Clarendon, Oxford, Eng., 1937.

Index